CARBONATITES

OLDOINYO LENGAI

CARBONATITES

Edited by

O. F. TUTTLE Professor of Geochemistry, Department of Geology,
Stanford University, U.S.A.

J. GITTINS Associate Professor of Geology, Department of
Geology, University of Toronto, Canada

INTERSCIENCE PUBLISHERS
a division of John Wiley & Sons   New York   London   Sydney

First published 1966 by John Wiley & Sons Ltd.

Library of Congress catalog card No.: 66-30188

Made and printed in Great Britain by
Richard Clay (The Chaucer Press), Ltd, Bungay, Suffolk

Contributing Authors

D. K. BAILEY — Department of Geology, University of Reading, England

T. F. W. BARTH — Mineralogisk-Geologisk Museum, University of Oslo, Norway

J. B. DAWSON — Department of Geology, University of St. Andrews, Scotland

T. DEANS — Overseas Division, Institute of Geological Sciences, London, England

H. v. ECKERMANN — Edeby, Ripsa, Sweden

H. W. FAIRBAIRN — Department of Geology and Geophysics, Massachusetts Institute of Technology, Cambridge, Mass., U.S.A.

M. S. GARSON — Malawi Geological Survey, Zomba, Malawi

J. GITTINS — Department of Geology, University of Toronto, Canada

P. M. HURLEY — Department of Geology and Geophysics, Massachusetts Institute of Technology, Cambridge, Mass., U.S.A.

R. L. JOHNSON — Mining Geology Division, Department of Mineral Resources, Saskatchewan, Canada

B. C. KING — Department of Geology, Bedford College, London, England

F. J. KUELLMER — New Mexico Institute of Mining and Technology, Socorro, New Mexico, U.S.A.

D. McKIE — Department of Mineralogy and Petrology, University of Cambridge, England

G. C. MELCHER — Departamento de Geologia e Paleontologia, Universidade de São Paulo, Brazil

J. L. POWELL — Department of Geology, Oberlin College, Ohio, U.S.A.

I. B. RAMBERG — Mineralogisk-Geologisk Museum, University of Oslo, Norway

DIANE S. SUTHERLAND — Department of Geology, University of Leicester, England

O. F. TUTTLE — Department of Geology, Stanford University, U.S.A.

W. J. VERWOERD — Geological Survey, Pretoria, Republic of South Africa

A. P. VISOCKY — Bureau of Mines and Mineral Resources, Socorro, New Mexico, U.S.A.

W. WIMMENAUER — Geologisches Landesamt in Baden—Württemberg, Freiburg i. Breisgau, Germany

P. J. WYLLIE — Department of the Geophysical Sciences, University of Chicago, U.S.A.

Preface

N. L. Bowen's criticism of W. C. Brögger's work on the Fen area in Norway began a controversy which has persisted for forty years in the petrological literature. During this period a large number of papers have appeared dealing with carbonatites and their associated rocks, but no comprehensive treatment has been published. It is the purpose of the present volume to fill this gap in the literature by bringing together a series of articles dealing with field and laboratory studies of carbonatites and associated rocks, and providing a catalogue and comprehensive bibliography of carbonatite occurences.

The book is divided into five sections: (1) descriptions of carbonatite complexes, (2) fenitization, (3) experimental studies, (4) economic aspects and (5) summaries and bibliography of all known carbonatites.

A new and exciting aspect of the carbonatites has recently been introduced by the papers dealing with volcanic carbonatites and the existence of lava flows of unusual compositions. This has confirmed the experimental work which has demonstrated the stability of low-melting liquids at low pressures over a considerable range of compositions.

The growing interest in carbonatites and their genesis was recently emphasized by the simultaneous publication during 1956 of review articles in three countries by Agard, Smith and Pecora. The reviewers discussed the problems posed by the carbonatites and suggested that there are four distinct controversial aspects of their genesis: (1) physical nature of the emplacement process, (2) source of the carbon dioxide, (3) nature of the differentiation which produces the nepheline syenite–carbonatite association, and (4) chemical reactions of the fenitization process.

Recognition of the association of carbonatites with the nepheline-bearing volcanic suites represents a major contribution to the petrology of these unusual rock types. These field discoveries, coupled with the laboratory findings of recent years that simplified carbonatite compositions could exist at low temperatures with water vapour and carbon dioxide as the principal volatiles, mark a milestone in the understanding of these rocks. These complementary investigations, the field studies and the laboratory studies, have convinced even the most stubborn geologists that a magmatic origin for these unusual rocks is not unlikely.

Limitations on space have dictated the number of contributors to this volume, and it cannot be claimed that by any means all aspects of the carbonatites are represented. We hope, however, that the papers presented will be of interest to the field geologist and the laboratory men alike and will stimulate even more fruitful work on carbonatites in the future.

The authors were selected on the basis of recent contributions in the field of carbonatites with some effort to select authors who are familiar with a specific aspect. We have also included current experimental work on carbonatites, much of which appears here for the first time. The bibliography and possibly even the catalogue of known carbonatites may not be completely up to date when this is published but we hope even so that a useful purpose will be served. The section dealing with the Soviet Union is the least satisfactory owing to the difficulty of obtaining detailed locations of specific complexes in that country. Similarly it has not been possible to ascertain if there are any carbonatites in China. It seems unlikely that such a huge country would be without them but our attempts to gather information in Peking and Taipei have led only to the suggestion that they do exist but have not been described in print. It is also odd that none have been found so far in Australia but this may well be a question of the incomplete exploration of the country.

No attempt has been made to deal with the subject of nomenclature. Even if sufficient accord could be found to formulate majority recommendations it seems likely that individual geologists would continue to exercise their own preferences. It will be noted that within this volume the term 'carbonatite' is used both as a synonym for 'carbonatite complex' and to describe the carbonate rock which characterizes these complexes. Heier (1961) has taken issue with the use of sövite as a general name for calcite carbonatite preferring to retain it for the variety at Söve in the Fen complex which contains niobium and rare earths. Most carbonatites do of course contain niobium and rare earths. Other examples could be cited but natural selection does appear to be leading to a rather simpler nomenclature judging by the publications of recent years.

We shall be very grateful for having our attention drawn to new carbonatite complexes and to subsequent work on carbonatite problems.

Finally we should like to express our appreciation to the many individuals and Geological Surveys who have contributed information and answered our queries. They are, unfortunately, too numerous to list. Our thanks are also due for permission to reproduce or modify maps of many carbonatite occurences.

O. F. TUTTLE
J. GITTINS

Contents

O. F. TUTTLE and J. GITTINS

Introduction

The carbonatites pose a number of unusual problems in petrogenesis of which the foremost are the physical nature of carbonate emplacement and the ultimate origin of the carbonate. Have they been emplaced as magmatic melts corresponding to rhyolites and basalts of the silicate rocks, or by hydrothermal solutions, solid flow, or by gaseous transfer? The magmatic origin has been strongly advocated by Högbom (1895), Brögger (1921), Daly (1925), v. Eckermann (1928, 1948d) and recently by a larger number of petrologists, especially those who have worked in the now-famous localities of Africa. The carbonatites are rarely homogeneous like the granitic rocks, but tend to be heterogeneous with layering and banding as a general feature. This inhomogeneity has suggested to some field workers that the carbonatites were intruded as a crystal mush or as completely crystalline material. Shand has advocated solid flow as a mechanism for carbonatite emplacement and his thoughts on the origin of the carbonate rock have been described in detail in the final edition of his textbook (Shand, 1950, p. 326). On the other hand, the heterogeneous nature of the carbonatites has suggested hydrothermal solutions to some workers including Bowen (1924, 1926a,b), and many later investigators. Finally, transfer of material by a gaseous phase has been advocated by Pecora (1956). Transport by solid solubility in a gaseous phase differs from the hydrothermal hypothesis only in the density and viscosity of the transporting medium.

A problem equally as puzzling as the physical conditions of carbonate emplacement is the source of the carbonate; is it a primary magma, or is it derived from sedimentary limestone? Many carbonatites occur in shield areas where there is no known limestone, but, of course, it is always possible to postulate limestone at depth. Carbon dioxide is a common gas associated with active volcanoes, and there seems to be no *a priori* reason why carbon dioxide could not at times become concentrated by differentiation of silicate magmas resulting in a carbonate-rich fraction.

Experimental studies in the system CO_2–H_2O–K_2O–SiO_2 by Morey and Fleischer (1940) indicate that alkali-rich liquids carrying appreciable amounts of silica can dissolve up to 20 per cent carbon dioxide; presumably carbon dioxide is also soluble in alkali-silicate melts. On the other hand, Wyllie and Tuttle (1960) demonstrated that carbon dioxide has a negligible solubility in albite melts and in granite melts. It seems reasonable to expect that despite this insolubility of carbon dioxide in melts that are saturated or over-saturated with silica, alkali-rich silica undersaturated melts (alkaline rock magmas) can dissolve appreciable quantities of carbon dioxide and, therefore, can produce carbonate liquids by fractional crystallization.

Whether the carbonate is primary as v. Eckermann (1948d) and Holmes (1950) would have it, or a differentiate of more siliceous magma as Saether (1957), Strauss and Truter (1951) and Dawson (1962a,b) suggest is a much-debated question.

Recent studies of the isotopic composition of the carbonate have attempted to show that the carbonate could not be derived from sedimentary limestone, but rather that it originates in the upper mantle or lower crust.

In carbonatite complexes there appears to be a succession from ijolitic rocks through nephelinites and faugasites to carbonatite liquids. There can be no doubt about the carbonatite-alkaline rock association; rather the question is, do the carbonatite liquids produce the alkaline rocks or are the alkaline magmas the parents of the carbonatites?

REVIEW OF CARBONATITE STUDIES

The idea of carbonate crystallizing from a melt together with silicate minerals that are normally regarded as primary igneous minerals was put forward nearly three-quarters of a century ago by Högbom (1895), who described dikes of igneous rocks containing considerable amounts of carbonate on Alnö Island near Sundsvall, Sweden. In his guide book to Alnö Island (Högbom, 1909) he stated, 'Other evidence also proves that the calcite and limestone have really formed part of a magma and have consolidated together with the silicate and silicate rocks. Fluidal structures are common in the limestone.' Although Högbom regarded the carbonate as having crystallized from a magma with the silicate minerals, he was uncertain of its ultimate origin and was inclined to consider it as due to assimilation of limestone by a silicate magma. Between 1895 and the appearance of Brögger's classic Fen Memoir in 1921, few papers appeared dealing with the magmatic aspects of carbonate. It was during this period, however, that the controversy over the origin of the alkalic rocks developed. In 1910 Daly published his *Origin of The Alkaline Rocks* in which he attributed the nepheline rocks to desilication of basaltic magma by limestone assimilation and subsequent differentiation. In his list of 155 alkalic rock localities, limestone is present in 107. It is interesting to note that some of Daly's examples of limestone assimilation are in fact carbonatites in which the carbonate is primary and magmatic. Such localities include Alnö and Fen in which no sedimentary limestone is believed to have been involved in the genesis of the alkalic rocks. Daly was aware that some of these localities may not have limestone and he wrote, 'These exceptional cases suggest the hypothesis that it is the presence of carbon dioxide rather than of dissolved carbonate in sub-alkaline magma which is the principal condition for differentiation of fractions high in alkalies.' Again, on page 108, he writes, '. . . finally, it is possible that Cripple Creek, Red Hill and some other alkaline magmas have nowhere made contact with carbonate rocks, though those magmas were for some special reason unusually rich in juvenile carbon dioxide.' Three years later C. H. Smyth (1913) also maintained that the dominant agent in the formation of alkaline rocks was their high content of volatile constituents or 'mineralizers' and some rare elements. Unlike Daly, however, Smyth thought limestone assimilation unnecessary and that the alkaline rocks were differentiation products of a primary sub-alkaline magma. In other words, he believed the volatiles associated with the alkaline rocks to be juvenile volatiles and not the result of limestone assimilation, although he was quite willing to have assimilation in some cases.

During this period the influence of stable and unstable regions in the production of alkaline rocks came under discussion. Harker (1909) noted that the alkaline rocks tend to occur in the plateau regions, whereas the sub-alkaline igneous rocks were more apt to be found in the folded mountain belts. Smyth (1913) believed that differentiation of alkaline rocks took place in relatively stable regions during long periods of crystallization practically free from tectonic disturbance when slow cooling would favour complete separation of the alkaline fraction, while at the same time retention of the volatile constituents would promote fluidity and favour crystal settling. Many geologists have subsequently noted the association of the alkaline rocks with tectonically stable periods of the earth's history.

It was in this setting of general discussion of the alkaline rocks that Brögger wrote the now classic Fen Memoir, published in 1921, in which a carbonate magma was proposed for the first time. He still did not go so far as to suggest that the magma was a primary one, but rather considered its source as the Telemark limestone melted at depth by ijolitic magma. He postulated that the carbonate magma floated on the silicate magma and that mixing at the junction gave rise to the silicate-carbonate rocks. Extensive metasomatic activity around the intrusion was attributed to both magmas.

While Högbom did not attach new names to the carbonate-bearing rock types that he described, Brögger on the other hand introduced a host of new names, many of which have found their way into the subsequent literature.

In 1924 Bowen criticized Brögger's interpretation and with this criticism the carbonatite controversy can be said to have started in earnest. Bowen investigated the region during 1923 and concluded from his brief visit and collection there that the carbonate rocks owed their origin to metasomatic hydrothermal replacement. He also pointed out that the experimental work of Smyth and Adams (1923) presented insurmountable difficulties to the acceptance of a calcium carbonate magma because of the very high melting temperature of calcite—about 1200°C—a temperature high enough to melt the surrounding granitic gneisses. It is surprising indeed that Bowen did not entertain the possibility that volatile constituents such as water would depress the liquidus of calcite to a petrologically reasonable value, for he was certainly aware of the effect of water on the liquidus of granitic rocks and the silicates in general.

In Africa, meanwhile, Shand's work gave qualified support to Daly's views. Addressing the Geological Society of South Africa in 1922 he said, 'In a nutshell, my conception of the alkaline rocks as a whole is that they are developed where a magma is, or for any reason becomes, abnormally rich in volatile constituents. In one respect, however, I venture to differ from Professor Daly, for I am disposed to throw the main weight both of the preliminary concentration of the alkaline fraction and of the subsequent reaction of limestone on magmatic gases.' Thus Smyth, Daly and Shand all more or less agreed on the importance of volatiles in the genesis of the alkaline rocks.

In 1925 Daly described in some detail the carbonate dikes in the kimberlite of the Premier Diamond Mine in the Transvaal and concluded that they represented intrusion of carbonate magma formed by dissociation of dolomite heated at great depth by the kimberlite magma. Daly appealed to Dr. F. H. Smyth of the Geophysical Laboratory to investigate the possible melting of the carbonate dikes. Smyth apparently was the first to consider that water might be a very important ingredient, and the finely powdered carbonate dikes were heated by him with various amounts of water at 750°C, 850°C, 900°C, and 1030°C. Daly was quite prepared to read melting into the results despite the fact that Smyth was unwilling to commit himself on the existence of a liquid. Later experimental work on related compositions has shown that Smyth probably melted carbonate with water at temperatures as low as 850°C. He was not able to establish melting because the calcite did not quench to a glass or to a recognizable quench product. The following year Brauns (1926) joined the controversy in Germany by supporting Brögger's magmatic theories for the origin of the calcium carbonate dikes. Despite this support of the magmatic origin of carbonatites, many petrologists remained sceptical of carbonate magmas, and the general opinion among experimentalists and most North American geologists was that carbonatites were probably the result of low temperature metasomatic replacement.

The scepticism with which petrologists looked upon Brögger's magmatic carbonate rocks is illustrated by the absence of any mention of such rocks in many of the petrology and petrography textbooks that appeared during the period 1930–1950. For example, in Johannsen's volume 1 (1931) under the definition of rock types, the names of carbonate rocks from the Fen Area such as sövite and rauhaugite are not found, while silicate rocks such as fenite and melteigite do appear and are accepted as magmatic rocks. Even in the final edition of his Eruptive Rocks, Shand (1950) still gives a hypothetical section of the Spitskop complex (Fig. 50, p. 322) showing the carbonatite core as a mass of Transvaal dolomite that has floated up in the foyaite magma, and when presented with the detailed re-study of the complex by Strauss and Truter (1950) in which there was strong evidence for intrusion of an outer ring of alvikite and an inner ring dike of beforsite, he preferred to consider the carbonate as remobilized dolomite, thus not really conceding much to the magmatists. His views are summarized in this quotation (Shand, 1950, p. 326) which is unchanged in essence from the first edition of his book:

'Nobody can doubt the facts so clearly set forth by v. Eckermann and Dixey. Some limestone is intrusive; that has long been known. Plastic deformation of limestone is no new thing to Alpine geologists, who have described it again and again. The conversion of normal sedimentary limestone into intrusive carbonatite is clearly demonstrated in Ontario. It is certainly astonishing to find it intruded on such a large scale as in Nyasaland, Kenya and Uganda, where it seems to have come up like great salt domes; but if one admits the existence of small intrusions of mobilized limestone, it is not difficult to accept the evidence of larger ones. To admit that limestone may be mobilized and intruded in a plastic condition is a very different thing from believing in a carbonate magma, or a silicate-carbonate magma, so charged with carbon dioxide that it could give rise in crystallizing to the hollaite and the kasenite of the Fen area. Can a silicate magma dissolve a quarter of its own weight of carbon dioxide? We have no reason to suppose that it can. If it could, what sort of pressure would be necessary to keep the gas in solution? Something tremendous, we may be quite sure. Yet the carbonatites of East Africa and the limestone of the Kaiserstuhl, which are associated with lavas and breccias, must have been pushed up nearly or quite to the surface. . . .

   'The writer finds it easier to accept the evidence presented to his senses at Bancroft, Lock Borolan and Sekukuniland, and to regard all so-called "carbonatites" as mobilized or hydrothermally redistributed sedimentary limestones. To the argument that no limestone is known in the basement rocks of Fen and Alnö, and only a few thin dolomites in Nyasaland, he can only reply that between imagining a deep-seated mass of limestone in the Archæn, which would be no such strange thing, and imagining a carbonate magma of unknown origin, which would be a very strange thing indeed, he prefers the solution that puts the smaller strain on the imagination.'

v. Eckermann joined the discussion in 1928 with a description of the dikes of the Alnö region. He found the dikes concentrically arranged about Alnö Island and he believed that they represented differentiates of the carbonatite magma which had as its centre the Alnö Island Complex. He rejected any hydrothermal origin of 'mysterious circumlating solutions, carrying away or adding molecules so as to suit every rock coming under discussion'.
   At this stage a new and impressive field of alkaline rocks was discovered in the Zambesi basin in Africa. In 1929 Dr. F. Dixey, Director of the Geological Survey of Malawi (formerly Nyasaland), recognized the Chilwa Igneous Complex with well-developed volcanic vents, and dominating the main centre was Chilwa Mountain, a great mass of crystalline limestone. Dr. W. Campbell Smith of the British Museum (Natural History) undertook the petrographic examination of these rocks, and in 1933 recognized their close similarity with the intrusive carbonatites of Fen, and when Dixey returned to Chilwa Island in 1934 he found Campbell Smith's suggestions amply confirmed. The limestone proved to be an intrusive core, and Chilwa Island was thus the first carbonatite complex to be recognized in Africa. The combined work of Dixey and Campbell Smith led to the publication in 1937 of Bulletin 5 of the Geological Survey of Nyasaland (Dixey, Smith and Bisset, 1937) dealing with all the known members of the Chilwa Series and advocating a magmatic origin for the carbonatites. There was still, however, reluctance to consider the carbonate magma as comparable to ordinary silicate magmas, as indicated by the italicized part (our italics) of the following passage: '*Without claiming for these limestones a mode of emplacement similar*

to that of ordinary intrusions, one may confidently regard them as of magmatic origin and comparable to the magmatic limestones or carbonatites of Alnö in Sweden, and of the Fen District in Norway, but developed on a scale far larger than at either of these localities.'

In 1942 Larsen published his account of the Iron Hill carbonatite complex in Colorado based on work that began in 1912. Larsen considered a carbonate magma among other modes of origin and, rather half-heartedly, decided in favour of hydrothermal solutions. It is difficult to believe that Larsen totally rejected a magmatic origin and the preface to his paper suggests that he might have been under some editorial pressure to conform to a less radical point of view.

In 1948 Harry v. Eckermann published his Alnö Memoir, the most detailed in chemistry, petrology and structure of any paper since Brögger, and presenting the results of twenty years' work. v. Eckermann had no hesitation in calling these rocks magmatic and assuming normal differentiation in the production of the magmas. He deduced in great detail the depth at which the complex must have been buried at the time of the explosion which produced the Alnö eruptive centre together with its radial and concentric dikes, and considered the magma to have had a very high vapour pressure, a reasonably low temperature (400–600°C), and to be rich in volatile constituents as proposed by earlier authors. In addition to outlining the events which led up to the emplacement of the dike rocks and the central carbonatite, v. Eckermann described the associated fenitization in great detail and noted that it followed the same general process described by Brögger. One very notable difference between v. Eckermann's work and other writings on carbonatite genesis was his postulation of a potassium-rich carbonate magma. This was in strong contrast to the calcium–magnesium carbonate magma that has generally been assumed by other workers, but the recent discovery of alkali-rich carbonate lavas at Oldoinyo Lengai appears to justify his ideas.

Recognition of the Malawi carbonatites had provided a key to the understanding of certain puzzling hills of crystalline limestone which were striking scenic features near the alkaline volcanic regions of Eastern Uganda. Here Davies (1947) discovered prominent ring structures in deeply eroded volcanic centres cored with carbonatite and fringed with vast reserves of apatite and magnetite, and King elucidated the structure of the Napak nephelinite tuff volcano with its ijolite core and central carbonatite plug. This was the first carbonatite to be revealed in direct association with an overlying volcanic pile.

The economic significance of the Uganda apatite discoveries prompted Deans of the Mineral Resources Division of the Imperial Institute in London (now Overseas Geological Surveys), to suggest in 1948 that the African carbonatites deserved investigation for other economic deposits, especially for niobium. This stemmed from German work on the koppite of the Kaiserstuhl and Norwegian proposals to develop the sövites of Fen as niobium ores. Following the discovery of the Sukulu apatite-pyrochlore deposits in Uganda (this volume, p. 392), Deans sampled the Malawi carbonatites in 1951 and found pyrochlore at Chilwa Island and Tundulu, and monazite in unexpected abundance at

Kangankunde Hill. These events greatly stimulated the search for carbonatites in Africa, and over the next few years many more were found, and several proved to contain niobium minerals or rare earths, as well as apatite and other ores.

Publication of Dr. Campbell Smith's work on the Malawi carbonatites had been intended to follow the Bulletin by Dixey, Smith and Bisset (1937), but this was delayed by war service and subsequent reorganization of the collections at the Natural History Museum, and his 'Carbonatites of the Chilwa Series of Southern Nyasaland' did not appear until 1953, but the delay afforded an opportunity to include his studies of the material collected by Deans.

The search for niobium deposits had meanwhile led to a re-examination of every known carbonatite and the discovery of several more in widely scattered parts of the world such as Canada, Brazil and the United States. It is of interest that at least two previously classical occurrences of feldspathoidal rocks that had figured prominently in such early petrology textbooks as Rosenbusch (e.g. Magnet Cove in Arkansas and Jacupiranga in Brazil) were now found to be carbonatite complexes.

After the exhaustive work of v. Eckermann, the most thorough field and laboratory study of carbonatites is that of M. S. Garson undertaken for the Geological Survey of Malawi (formerly Nyasaland) in a programme lasting from 1952 to 1963. This has resulted in the publication of a wealth of petrological, mineralogical and structural data contained in four memoirs (Garson and Smith, 1958; Garson, 1962, 1965b,c).

As a result of this intensive post-war study, three reviews of carbonatite problems appeared almost simultaneously in different parts of the world: Pecora (1956), Smith (1956) and Agard (1956). None was prepared to accept a carbonatite magma *in toto*. Pecora insisted on, '. . . carbonate-rich solutions which at elevated temperature and pressure can have a higher concentration of dissolved ingredients than normally believed for hydrothermal solutions.' Campbell Smith wrote, 'The carbonatites are believed to owe their origin to concentration of carbon dioxide or of carbonatitic fluid of magmatic origin. . . .'

This reluctance to accept a 'normal' magmatic origin for carbonatites presumably reflects the lack of experimental support for the existence of such a magma. The work of Smyth and Adams (1923) suggested prohibitively high temperatures for a calcite melt while field evidence clearly indicates a moderate to low crystallization temperature for carbonatites. Evidence for the existence of such a low temperature melt was experimentally demonstrated by Tuttle and Wyllie in 1958 and published in detail in 1960 (Wyllie and Tuttle, 1960). Although a much simplified system (CaO–CO_2–H_2O) was used to demonstrate the general principles, the compositions used were not far removed from mixtures of calcite and water and such liquids would crystallize sövite over a range of temperatures. and pressures although complete crystallization would require that portlandite also crystallize from the liquid. Portlandite is unstable in the presence of a vapour rich in carbon dioxide and reacts to form calcite. It is suggested that carbonatite liquids which crystallize to a mixture of calcite and portlandite would react with the vapour phase leaving a monomineralic rock—a sövite. Furthermore, the experimental evidence was strongly against an origin by gas transfer. Detailed experimental studies of the ratio of water to carbon dioxide in the vapour phase were carried out, but no determinations of the CaO content of the vapour were made; however, it is unlikely that the maximum CaO content of the vapour exceeds a few wt per cent. Studies of the composition of the vapour phase in the system $MgO-CO_2-H_2O$ have been made at pressures up to 4000b and the solubilities are less than 1.0 wt per cent (Walter, Wyllie and Tuttle, 1956).

The pressure required to prevent the liquids from dissociating was found to be very low, less than 27b, and it was suggested (Wyllie and Tuttle, 1962) that carbonatite magmas bearing sodium carbonate could well be expected to reach the surface as lava flows. This is, in fact, found to be the case in parts of Africa where lava flows containing various amounts of carbonate from carbonate-rich to pure carbonate have been found. Incontrovertible proof of carbonatite lavas came in 1960 when J. B. Dawson descended into the crater of Oldoinyo Lengai, a neighbouring volcano to Kerimasi, and witnessed molten carbonatite lava in eruption. The eruptions continued for many months and several geologists were able to visit this crater and collect carbonatite lavas as soon as they were cool enough to handle and before rainfall altered their composition. Descriptions of these lavas can be found in Dawson (1962a,b), DuBois *et al.* (1963), Guest (1963) and this volume p. 163. A carbonate-rich lava flow in Uganda also has been described by von Knorring and DuBois (1961). Subsequently Dawson (1964b,c) has described carbonatite tuffs, agglomerates and ashes that form cones and surficial blankets that previously were mistaken for ordinary limestone deposits. The volume of evidence for the emergence on surface of carbonatite magma is now considerable.

The experimental study of carbonate systems begun in the late 1950's was concerned initially with the physical conditions of carbonatite emplacement and whether carbonatite magmas are possible. This, however, tells little about the ultimate origin of carbonatite magmas which remains the outstanding problem in carbonatite studies. The most recent investigations by Wyllie and his students (this volume, pp. 311–352) in which silicate minerals are introduced as additional components and in which assemblages very similar to those found in some carbonatite complexes are found, may be considered the second phase of these studies and can be expected to yield a great deal of information about this ultimate problem of petrogenesis. This is one of the most fruitful approaches that is being explored today.

Isotopic studies are of three kinds: carbon, oxygen and strontium. One of the earliest carbon isotope studies was reported by v. Eckermann, Ubisch and Wickman (1952). Both carbon and oxygen isotope studies appear in Kukharenko and Dontsova (1963) and Gonfiantini and Tongiorgi (1964). Strontium isotope studies are associated principally with Powell, Fairbairn and Hurley and are reviewed in this volume (p. 365–378). In all cases the fundamental thesis is that significant differences exist between the isotopic abundance ratios of carbonatites and sedimentary limestones and that these rule out the possibility of carbonatites being xenoliths or melted limestones.

Field studies of carbonatites are entering an interesting stage with the discovery of complexes that do not have the classic ring structure or association with alkaline rocks. Examples recently described are Sangu and Songwe Scarp in Tanganyika. These are elongate, dike-like bodies 12 to 16 miles in length and although there are no alkalic igneous rocks there is the associated fenitization and enrichment in strontium, niobium and rare earths so characteristic of carbonatites. Another example would be Kaluwe in Zambia. Additional variants are provided by the rare earth bearing carbonate veins of Ravalli County, Montana, U.S.A. which may or may not be related to carbonatites. The difficulty with this kind of body is that rare earth mineralization associated with granitic and syenitic pegmatities is common in a number of highly metamorphosed terrains such as the Grenville Province of Ontario and Quebec in Canada where there is also an abundance of sedimentary limestone which in places has been mechanically intruded into dike- and vein-like bodies. It is not difficult to imagine that under such metamorphic conditions carbonate bodies containing rare earth minerals could be generated which would bear no genetic relation to carbonatite-alkaline complexes.

It does appear that the classic ring structure is not the only type of carbonatite complex and that there may be variants that are as yet unrecognized, representing either stages in the complex formational history or different branches of the processes involved. It is also clear, however, that a number of false alarms are being raised in reporting carbonatite occurrences and that each case will have to be examined critically.

It is rather interesting that no example of a regionally metamorphosed carbonatite complex has yet been described. Of course the tendency for emplacement in stable crustal regions probably makes it unlikely that carbonatites complexes will be subsequently involved in orogenies but it is also not entirely certain that a regionally metamorphosed complex would be readily recognized.

Stuart and Ramsay (1965) have recently described carbonatite associated with nepheline syenite on Sørøy, Norway and it seems that both this and the Stjernøy occurence have been emplaced during the closing stages of the Caledonian orogeny and therefore suffered some degree of metamorphism. The general form of these two occurrences is rather unusual, however, and they certainly do not conform to the general pattern of carbonatites.

The relation of carbonatites to kimberlites is receiving increased emphasis today. This was reflected in the 'Symposium on Carbonatites, Kimberlites and Their Minerals' held at the 1964 meeting of the International Mineralogical Association. The general concensus appears to be that both have their ultimate origin in the upper mantle.

Part I

Descriptions of Carbonatite Complexes

H. v. ECKERMANN

Progress of Research on the Alnö Carbonatite

The Alnö syenitic rocks and associated carbonatites are situated on the Swedish NE coast. They occupy the north east part of Alnö Island as well as part of the mainland north of the island. The central area of comparatively coarse-grained carbonatites, the so-called sövites, comprises an area of about 4 sq km and is surrounded by about 21 sq km of syenites and fenites. About 65 per cent of the total area is submerged under the Baltic, but has been partly explored by drill holes (Fig. 1).

The surrounding country rocks are migmatitic Archaean gneiss-granites, intersected by pegmatites and Jotnian porphyry and dolerite dikes enclosing more or less metamorphosed relics of graywackes, mostly altered into mica schists. Up to a distance of about 12 km from the sövite centre cone sheet dikes occur, varying in composition from pure carbonatites to kimberlites and melilite basalts, while radial dikes of the same or similar compositions may be found at distances as far as 2–25 km.

The originally suggested genesis and manner of emplacement of the alkaline rocks, and especially of the carbonatites have been subject to repeated modifications and even drastic changes. In 1895 the eminent Swedish geologist A. G. Högbom described the carbonates of Alnö Island as segregations of calcite within an intrusion of nepheline syenitic magma and rejected the suggestion of their being metamorphosed sedimentary limestones (Högbom, 1895). Daly and Shand, on the other hand, looked upon Alnö as an excellent example of limestone syntexis, and Daly (1914), redrew Högbom's map to fit this suggestion. Possibly influenced by this hypothesis, Högbom later accepted the possibility of the alkaline magma being genetically connected with an earlier absorption of limestone at unknown depths and from unknown sources, but maintained that the visible sövite bodies were all products of late magmatic differentiation.

Geijer (1922) pointed out that limestones could not have been stoped down from above for, in such a case, they could not have furnished the gas necessary for the opening of the diatreme. He also emphasized the improbability of a funnel being blown through kilometres of overlying acid rocks and only limestones falling back into the magma, or of the rising magma encountering limestones in sufficient quantities in this region which, at the surface, consists exclusively of granitic rocks extending for hundreds of kilometres in every direction.

These early conflicting views are understandable when looking at Högbom's map which pictures the sövite as isolated patches. The alkaline area of the island, as well as the mainland to the north, is mostly covered by overburden. Outcrops were at the time scarce or absent within large critical areas. The emplacement of the sövite, partly as a big central 'plug' and partly as brecciating cone sheets and radial dikes, was therefore unknown until the rock surface was

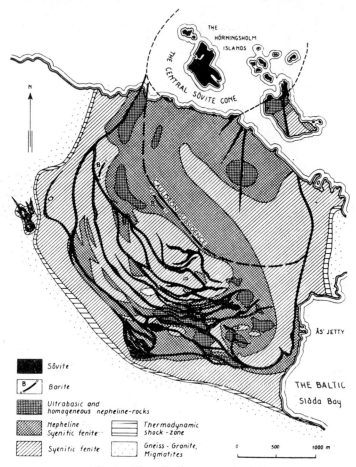

Fig. 1. The alkaline area of Alnö.

extensively exposed during road building in the years between the two world wars, and by the digging of trenches and drilling of scores of holes in 1937–1939 during my survey of Alnö Island (Fig. 2). Högbom's conception of the sövite as a magmatic end-product was thereby confirmed, and on an enormous scale, when compared with his isolated patchy segregations. On the other hand, his suggestion of a parental nepheline syenitic magmatic intrusion proved untenable.

Subsequent study of the enormous scientific material collected at the time disclosed the metasomatic origin of all the syenitic rocks, the main part being fenitized country rocks *in situ* and a smaller part either rheomorphic fenites or hybrid products of the originally intruded carbonatitic magmatic liquid and the substances withdrawn from the wall rocks during the process of fenitization. The fenitization was found to have progressed at rising temperature and pressure as follows:

(1) thermodynamic shattering of the micro-fabric of the surrounding country rocks;

(2) introduction of CO_2, F, and H_2O, producing carbonate and fluorite pseudomorphs after the feldspars, hydrating the sillimanite and the alkali feldspar components and raising the oxidation ratio;

(3) introduction of Ca and some P and Ti in exchange for Si and some Na, replacement of biotite and hydrated minerals by aegirine augite and soda-orthoclase;

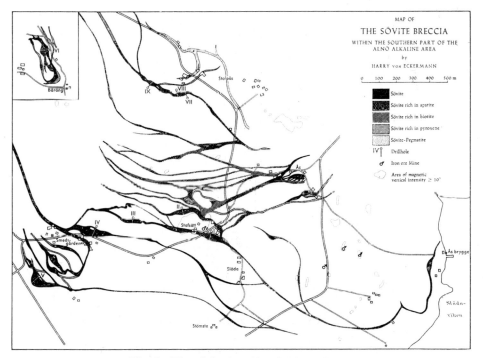

Fig. 2. The sövite breccia of Alnö Island.

(4) dehydration and further loss of Si resulting in the crystallization of potash-rich nepheline;

(5) release of the leucocratic components of the fenite leaving a pyroxen-itic 'rest-fenite' rich in melanite formed by the break-up of the aegirine molecule;

(6) accumulation of rheomorphic 'fenite-magmas' subjected to agpaitic crystal differentiation leading to the formation of juvites, foyaites, urtites, ijolites, melteigites, malignites and jacupirangites.

Since this sequence was worked out (v. Eckermann, 1948b,c,d), later investigations have not disclosed any evidence to invalidate it. However, the depth of 9000 m to which the process was assumed to have operated continuously has been found to be far too great (v. Eckermann, 1948d, Fig. 50, p. 148). As further discussed below, continued study of the dikes has shown that the existence of rheomorphic nepheline magmas is improbable below the fracturing centre of the sövite, viz. about 3200 m below the actual rock surface at the time of the opening of the diatreme. Consequently the earlier schematic diagram of the PTX-

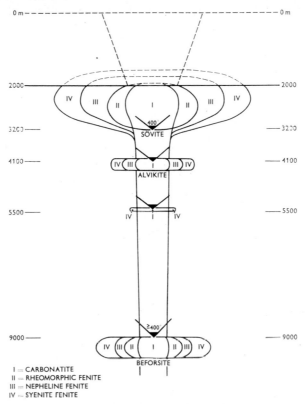

I = CARBONATITE
II = RHEOMORPHIC FENITE
III = NEPHELINE FENITE
IV = SYENITE FENITE

Fig. 3. Schematic *TP*-diagram of the Alnö intrusion.

conditions of the Alnö intrusions (v. Eckermann, 1948d, p. 148) has been redrawn as shown in Fig. 3 and is discussed further below. It is now thought that the accumulated carbonatite at the top of the volcanic funnel, and not the parental magma itself, is responsible for the extensive fenitization and birth of rheomorphic magmas, laterally encircling the carbonatite. For this reason, fenitization of the wall rocks is no longer considered to be continuous in a vertical direction.

The shallow spread of fenitization was confirmed when breccia boulders were pushed up by the ice from the sea floor on to the rocky Sälskär shoals north of Alnö Island (v. Eckermann, 1960b). The breccia contains no fenite but consists of more or less rounded chips and fragments of sövite, boulder-like inclusions of kimberlites, melilitites and olivine aggregates, surrounded by melilitic reaction rims, embedded in a matrix of apatite, calcite and mica. Numerous small crystals of a pyrochlore-like mineral in the matrix are responsible for the strong radioactivity of the breccia.

The sövite fragments are quite different in composition and general appearance from those at the erosion surface or in the two deep drill holes described in the Alnö Memoir (v. Eckermann, 1948d, p. 59). While the latter contain practically no strontium but occasionally much barium as barite, the former have only 0.15 per cent BaO; but about 1 per cent SrO. Thus the deep-seated part of the sövite body has an inverted Sr:Ba ratio (v. Eckermann, 1948a, 1951). At the bottom of the body, apatite may also be concentrated, as it makes up about 40–45 per cent of the matrix. The most noteworthy feature of the breccia, however, is the absence of all rocks intermediate between sövite and kimberlite. This suggests a kimberlitic or melilitic magma immediately below the sövite and excludes the presence of any rheomorphic fenite magmas.

The comparatively shallow depth of the fenitized rocks both *in situ* and as rheomorphic magmas, is also emphasized by the patches of unaffected country rocks still found within the fenitized area and by fenitized fragments of the collapsed roof occurring in diminishing amounts downward within the central sövite plug as shown by the drill cores. The incomplete fenitization of some of these fragments suggests engulfing by the sövite at the time of the explosive opening of the diatreme, when the sudden drop in pressure must have led to rapid congealing of the sövite. This in turn indicates a fairly long period before the explosion, during which the sövite remained fluid and brought about extensive, more or less lateral, fenitization and liquefaction of part of the fenites.

During the formation of the diatreme the rheomorphic, more or less siliceous magmas of foyaitic and ijolitic composition were probably less sensitive to the drop in pressure than the carbonatite and remained fluid even after solidification of the sövite. This should explain why some nepheline syenitic dikes intersect sövite cone sheets.

At the time of fenitization the migmatitic gneiss-granite of the region was probably covered by several thousand metres of Jotnian sediments. A small relic of the basal conglomerate of these sediments is preserved at Barsevik north east of Alnö. Another proof of their existence is given by a brecciating alnöite dike at Hovid (v. Eckermann, 1948d, p. 100), outside the fenitized area which contains fragments of Jotnian sandstones, sövite pegmatite and rounded boulders of Jotnian diabase but which is free of inclusions where exposed at a level about 40 m lower, close to the sea shore. Other breccias of tuffitic character on the mainland contain fragments of gneiss-granite, quartzite sediments and kimberlites in a matrix of quartz and feldspar grains, cemented by fluorite and secondary calcite. Sövite and syenitic rocks are wanting. No analyses of these breccias are available yet but the kimberlite resembles that in the Sälskär breccia, and the sediments resemble the Jotnian sandstone.

From which part of the breccia the kimberlite-bearing boulders derive is not known. As the breccia is probably associated with the big fault to the west of the island, a location at the north end of the sound, well outside the fenitized area, may be assumed. This implies the occurrence of kimberlite to the west of the site of the volcanic funnel (Fig. 5) or a displacement of the latter towards the west, in which case the breccia must reach a greater depth than that indicated by the dikes, viz. below 10 km. In any case the kimberlite fragments, some of which measure up to 25 cm, must have been carried up by the gas stream from already consolidated rock not directly associated with carbonatite.

The magmatic liquid of the Alnö intrusion was earlier defined (v. Eckermann, 1948d), as having high vapour pressure and low temperature (400–600°C), with lime, magnesia, potassium, alumina, iron, titanium and phosphorus as essential additional components, as well as carbon dioxide, much fluorine and

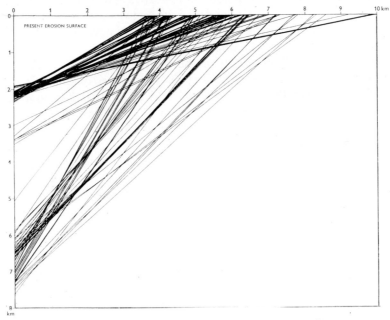

Fig. 4. Projection of the cone sheets of the Bergeforsen–Östrand region
on a vertical plane.

comparatively little water. Later investigations have now somewhat modified this definition and also restricted its application to the strongly carbonatitic fraction responsible for the fenitization and for the rheomorphic magmas. The main primary intrusive is now believed to have been kimberlitic. The present conception of the genesis and emplacement of the sövite, as well as of the calcitic and dolomitic carbonatites is based on the intimate study of a series of dikes uncovered during the blasting of tunnels and underground installations for the Bergeforsen hydro-electric power station north west of Alnö. These tunnels are about 2–5 m below sea level and now cover a radial distance of 6400 m. They start well outside the fenitization area about 3.6 km from the alkaline intrusion centre. Altogether 305 dikes were mapped and preliminarily classified. Of these, 30 have so far been analysed and investigated in detail. The location of the earlier-deduced pressure foci was confirmed by adding the projection of the dips of the new cone sheets to those previously measured on the erosion surface, and plotting them on the same vertical plane (Fig. 4). These projected depths, however, are minimum values; the true ones may be deeper owing to downward curving of the cone sheets. This applies especially to the lowest focus.

Besides the two earlier known pressure centres, Fig. 4 indicates a third, less accentuated centre 3.5 km below the erosion surface. The deepest centre is that of the dolomitic carbonatites (the so-called beforsites), the next highest that of magnesia-rich calcitic carbonatites and the highest that with dominantly calcitic carbonatites (so-called alvikites). But the dikes at the different centres are not all

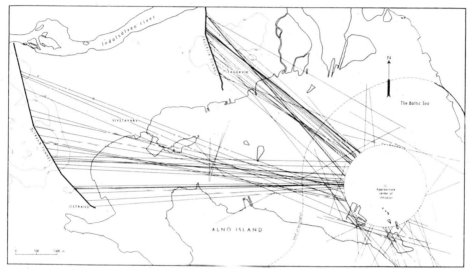

Fig. 5. Horizontal projection of the radial dikes of the Alnö intrusion.

carbonatitic. Most of them are kimberlitic. Of the three foci, the highest one seems to have produced by far the greatest number of cone sheets as well as intermediate rocks grading into kimberlites, melilitites and ouachitites. The numbers, however, are misleading, as will be further explained below.

A most interesting feature brought out by the new projection is that the focus of the projection lines is about 0.8–1 km from the central axis. As the volcanic intrusion must have had a feeding pipe of some size, and the dikes may be assumed to start from the walls of the pipe, this distance seems to indicate half the width of the crater funnel at the respective depth. Another method of locating the site of the central intrusion was previously tried by a similar projection of the strike of the radial vertical dikes in the above-mentioned tunnels (v. Eckermann, 1958, Fig. 8, p. 20). This projection has now been added to by remeasuring and projecting all other known radial dikes on the islands and the mainland outside the central sövite area and within 10 km of the eruptive centre. The result, given in Fig. 5, seems to confirm the earlier, somewhat hazardous and one-sided location of the site and dimension of the volcanic conduit, but shows also that many dikes may not be radial to the centre but tangential to crater walls. An interesting feature is the focusing of a few dikes on the sea bottom to the west of the main centre and north of the north west point of Alnö Island. This might signify an outcrop of kimberlite (all the dikes are kimberlitic), which might be connected with the previously mentioned volcanic breccia rich in kimberlite fragments. Unfortunately, the depth of the sea is here about 15 m and prevents any further investigation.

Each set of cone sheets is accompanied by a set of vertical radial dikes, representing intrusions into tension cracks (Fig. 6). Difficulties were encountered in trying to assign each dike to a pressure focus. On the present erosion surface few intersections of cone sheets and radial dikes were previously observed because of their deep weathering. This led to an erroneous statement (v. Eckermann, 1961b, p. 26), that the absence of intersections of deep-seated cone sheets

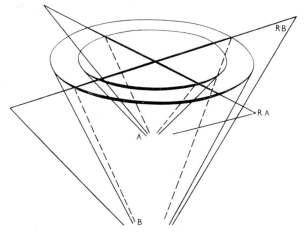

Fig. 6. Diagram of the dike systems, A representing the alvikites, B the beforsites and RA and RB the contemporaneous radial dikes, respectively.

with nepheline-bearing tinguaites and borengites (v. Eckermann, 1960a) was evidence of the shallow *mise-en-place* of the rheomorphic fenite-syenites. As this did not agree with the previously established age relations between the different fracturing pressure centres, previously known intersections on the erosion surface were dug up and re-examined along with all the material collected from the intersections in the Bergeforsen tunnels. New localities where intersections could be expected were looked for and several were discovered. Altogether nine cases were found where foyaitic dikes of rheomorphic origin are unquestionably intersected by beforsitic cone sheets. They are also in most cases intersected by the alvikitic dikes, e.g. the radial dike no. 34 at the Bergeforsen power station, labelled alkorthosite biotite alvikite (v. Eckermann, 1958, anal. 4, p. 34 and Pl. I, Fig. 2), which is intersected by cone sheets no. 23, 24 and 25 (v. Eckermann, 1958, Fig. 4, p. 9). On the other hand, a few foyaitic dikes are intersected by small dikes of calcitic composition with generally rather small and irregular dips. An example is the foyaite-porphyrite (v. Eckermann, 1948d, anal. 58, p. 91. Disregarding their tectonic emplacement, these carbonatites are quite similar to the alvikite carbonatites. Genetically, however, they are probably differentiates of either the foyaites or the sövites.

An important criterion of the consanguinity of cone sheets and radial dikes is the composition of the carbonates. Chemical analyses and staining methods show that the carbonates of cone sheet dikes from the deepest pressure centre contain appreciable amounts of ankerite, while those from the alvikite centre occasionally contain very small amounts, and those from the sövite centre none. Application of this characteristic to the radial dike rocks made it possible to allot each of them to an appropriate centre of fracture with a fairly high degree of probability. The only uncertainty concerns those dikes at a great distance from the volcanic centre, where auto-metamorphic alteration obscures the primary mineralogy. Such a case has just been described from recent underground blasting at Sundsvall, about 15 km south west of the Alnö eruption centre (v. Eckermann, 1961b). A vertical radial composite dike 3 m wide is composed of an early carbonatite and a later, more normal kimberlite, which occupies the centre of the dike, and borders on the carbonatite with fine-grained chilled margins. The carbonate of the latter is now pure calcite, but the great number of small magnetite grains, amounting to about 12 per cent by weight of the rock, can hardly be explained other than by oxidation of ankerite. The mineralogy of the carbonatite is quite simple, being limited to calcite, remarkably fresh forsteritic olivine, some apatite and perovskite and the ore minerals. Without the ore minerals one would expect a very light-coloured rock, but the ore-pigmentation turns it almost black. Another case of similar decomposition of the ankeritic carbonate has recently been described (v. Eckermann, 1963a, pp. 265–266) from a steeply dipping kimberlitic cone sheet, listed as no. 16 (v. Eckermann, 1958, p. 11, Pl. XIX), where a carbonate of almost dolomitic composition, viz. $cc_{55}mgt_{45}$, must have originally contained ankerite since the crystals, especially around vesicles, are pigmented by 'ore-dust' and are almost opaque.

The first-mentioned composite dike at Sundsvall embodies the solution to the problem of the genesis of the carbonatites. In order to explain this a short description of the kimberlitic part of the dike must first be given. The dominant mineral components are phlogopitic mica, partly serpentinized olivine in a matrix of probably dolomitic carbonate, serpentine, perovskite, apatite and ore minerals. This is a normal composition for micaceous kimberlite, but embedded in the fabric are a few round 'globules', which at first glance may be taken as vesicles filled by secondary carbonate and fluorite (Fig. 8). The refractive indices as well as the brownish weathering colour of this carbonatite suggest a dolomitic composition fairly rich in ankerite.

The first-intruded carbonatite part of the dike, however, contains no similar globules, although it must have contained an excess of carbon dioxide as evidenced by the montmorillonitization and carbonatization of the plagioclases in the gneiss-granite at the contacts. This makes it rather improbable that during intrusion of the succeeding kimberlite, the PT-conditions were such as to allow bubbles of carbon dioxide to form. I have, therefore, recently suggested

(v. Eckermann 1961b), these globules represent a fluid phase of carbon and fluorine compounds, ascending through liquefied melilite basalt (Holmes' olivine melilitite) and on the way being saturated with alkalies (preferably

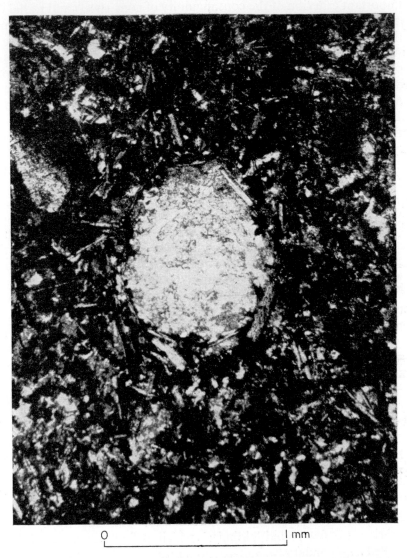

O ⊢_____⊣ 1 mm

Fig. 7. 'Globule' of calcite (white) and ankeritic dolomite (light grey) in ouachititic kimberlite. The melilite of the groundmass is altered to hydrogarnet, clay minerals and carbonate. It appears black with irregular light patches of carbonate. The phlogopitic mica is grey or white. Ordinary light with blue filter.

potassium), lime, magnesia and iron, thereby turning the composition of the basal parts of the melilite basalt into kimberlite but passing when saturated through the upper part without interaction (Figs. 7–9). The concentration of the globules at the top, it is suggested, forms a cap of carbonates which, under favourable circumstances, such as the presence of faults in the overlying acid rocks, may attack them and work its way upwards. Its penetrating ability

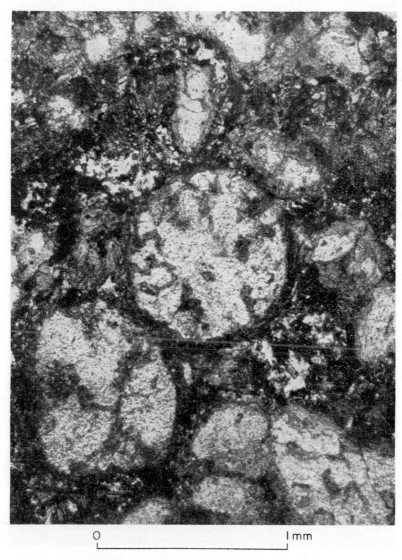

O _____ I mm

Fig. 8. 'Globules' of calcite (mottled white) and ankeritic dolomite (grey) surrounded by rims of small melilite-pseudomorphs containing no secondary calcite. Above and to the right of the central globule are rounded serpentinized olivines. Ordinary light with light blue filter.

will, of course, depend upon the maintenance of temperature by convective currents and the supply of new globules to replace the losses arising through Ca–Si exchange at the zone of penetration. By this action the magma becomes

B

increasingly siliceous, carbon dioxide is liberated, and an increased internal gas pressure follows. When the accumulated alkaline carbonate magma reaches a level where the internal pressure exceeds the lithostatic load, the roof fractures.

During the continued ascent fenitization was probably directed mainly

Fig. 9. 'Globule' in melilitic kimberlite, surrounded by phlogopite and partly altered melilite crystals. Ordinary light with blue filter.

upwards with little or no fenitization of the wall-rocks in the wake of the carbonatite. So far, the volcanic breccias and dikes have not been found to include any fenite, except in connection with carbonatites at the pressure centres. The first fracturing of the roof at Alnö occurred when the sövite accumulation had reached slightly above the present erosion level.[1] But, as already stated, the sövite must have remained for quite some time at this level before the internal pressure overcame the lithostatic load. This is shown by the extensive lateral spread of the fenitization as well as by the abyssal character of both the sövite and the rheomorphic syenite-fenites. There may have been a variety of causes for this pause in the ascent, but a reasonable one seems to be high permeability of both the probably weathered surface part of the gneiss-granite and of the possibly not quite consolidated and recrystallized overlying Jotnian sediments. This must have led to a leakage of gases at a rate which, for some time, matched the supply of gas liberated from the carbonate-fluorine 'globules' below and prevented the further rise of internal pressure.

The ever-spreading fenitization of the surrounding migmatitic country rocks, their recrystallization and gradual homogenization as well as rheomorphic liquefaction, it is suggested, may have finally lowered the permeability around the sövite to such an extent that the internal pressure rose to fracturing point. The opening up of the diatreme was either preceded or accompanied by the sövite cone sheet brecciation around the volcanic centre, and succeeded by a cauldron subsidence of about 100 m, including part of the fenite area south of the volcanic funnel (Fig. 1).

The sövite as now known is probably not of the same composition as the one which first started the grand scale fenitization. The accumulation of 'globules' may first have had the character of a gas-phase or fluid as suggested by Bailey (this vol., p. 149), with the difference, however, that chlorine seems to have been wanting at Alnö. During the absorption of silica from the wall rocks in return for essentially Ca, CO_2 and F, the fenitization process led to de-dolomitization and to the formation of the typical main silicate minerals of the sövites, namely biotite and diopsidic pyroxene.

In certain cases, such as in the so-called sövite pegmatites (v. Eckermann, 1948d, p. 80) aegirine-augite and nepheline were formed; in the apatite sövites (v. Eckermann, 1948d, Pl. 35) olivine was formed; and in sövites rich in radioactive pyrochlore, phlogopite and magnetite were formed. Consequently the sövite, at the time of the opening of the diatreme, was not a homogeneous body. This is further emphasized by the concentration of Ba, F and S in its upper part represented by barite, fluorite and pyrite, and Sr and apatite in its lower part. The rare elements, U, Th, Ta, Nb, Ce, however, occur throughout the whole body, although the crystals of pyrochlore, dysanalyte and perovskite are larger in deep-seated cone sheets. The amount of apatite in the sövite cone sheets in a dike at Stolpås (Fig. 2) locally reaches a maximum of 23 per cent which, however, is lower than the 40–45 per cent in the matrix of the breccia boulders at Sälskär.

As previously emphasized in my Alnö Memoir the sövite shows distinct flow structures but without many signs of crystal fracturing that might indicate

---

[1] I take this opportunity to correct an error in my description of the Alnö alkaline region in the guide to excursion No. C 27 of the 21st International Geological Congress where, through a mistake during the final rewriting of the manuscript, the sequence of fracturing is stated to proceed from lower centres towards higher instead of the reverse.

lubrication of the crystal mush by intergranular fluid as suggested for the Ru-funsa Valley carbonatites by Bailey (this vol., p. 141). Even if such textures are observed occasionally, the main part of the sövite in the cone sheet breccia

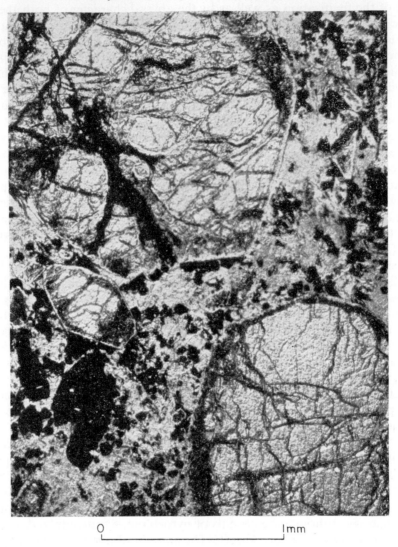

O |mm

Fig. 10. Carbonatitic kimberlite from Sundsvall. Two large olivine crystals and a small one are seen. One of the crystals is rounded due to abrasion in a moving mush of carbonate crystals. White matrix is carbonate, black spots are ore minerals and ilmenite pseudomorphs after perovskite. Ordinary light.

was undoubtedly quite fluid at the time of intrusion, a state which I have earlier suggested may be due to the astounding amount of fluorine associated with the Alnö occurrence and the possibility of its reducing the melting temperature of carbonate magmas at even moderate CO_2-pressure. Actually, the fenitized migmatitic wall contacts of the larger sövite cone sheets are 'soaked' to a depth of several feet with fluorite and the margins of the barite dikes (v. Eckermann, 1948d, p. 83) consist to a depth of one to two decimetres of about 20–25 per cent fluorite. More recently Wyllie and Raynor have experimentally confirmed the existence of even simplified hydrous carbonate melts down to pressures of 10 b (Wyllie and Tuttle, 1962).

Fracturing textures have, however, been observed in some carbonatitic dikes from the deeper pressure centres, as for instance, the dike mentioned above at Sundsvall, in which case the carbon dioxide liberated on the decomposition of the ankerite may have supplied the intergranular fluid that made possible the extension of the intrusion to such a distance from the volcanic centre (Fig. 10).

As already mentioned, there is no proof of the existence of any primary rocks intermediate between sövites and kimberlites. Neither are there any basaltic or kimberlitic cone sheets which may be directly associated with the sövite.

Normally, in my opinion, the sövites should have been followed by intrusions of kimberlites and melilitites or melilite basalts (Holmes' olivine melilitites), but it seems as if the collapse of pressure led to a congealing of the less fluorine-rich bottom part of the sövite and to an effective shutting off of the volcanic conduit, barring the way to any magma rising in the wake of the sövite. The caving in of comparatively colder rocks through the already mentioned cauldron subsidence may also have contributed to the sealing up of the crater.

The rather sudden change of temperature distribution in the whole complex of fluid lava in the conduit, the remaining frozen sövite and the surrounding country rocks after the opening up of the diatreme, may be supposed to have led to tension stresses around the volcanic funnel. This may explain the occurrence of radial cracks younger than those of the sövite cone sheets and filled by intrusive melilite basalts and even melilitites, viz. the so-called alnöites.

The age of their intrusion is definitely limited by their intersection of the sövites as well as of all *in situ* or rheomorphic fenites on the one hand, and its own intersection by dikes from the alvikite and deeper pressure centres on the other. Take, for instance, the previously mentioned upper brecciating alnöite at Hovid. It was earlier known to be intersected by a beforsite carbonatite rich in apatite, assumed to represent some 'late solutions' (v. Eckermann, 1948d, p. 100). Since then, further blasting at the locality has uncovered another intersecting calcitic cone sheet dike dipping towards the alvikite centre. Another example is given by dike no. 100 of the Fagervik tunnel at Bergeforsen (v. Eckermann, 1958, Pl. XIX): an almost pure calcitic carbonatite (alvikite) which, according to the mapping, crossed a vertical alnöite dike, no. 99, somewhere outside the tunnel. The intersection was not observable, but the outcrop of the carbonatite on the top of the hill contains inclusions of alnöitic fragments. Another alnöite dike intersected by two alvikitic cone sheets is located at Stavreviken, about 8 km to the north of Alnö on the mainland. The map (v. Eckermann, 1948d, Pl. 58) shows one intersection; the second one, by a dike to the east of the first alvikite, was uncovered later. Finally, the classic locality of about 600 m north west of Stornäset (v. Eckermann, 1948d, Pl. 60), where alnöite was first discovered during the nineteenth century, may be mentioned.

The occurrence was beautifully exposed during the building of a new road but is, unfortunately, now covered up again. Representative samples were, however, collected. It showed the alnöite intersecting a sövite cone sheet but intersected itself by an alvikitic dike.

These examples suggest that the magma underlying the sövite and above the alvikite pressure centre at the time of the opening up of the diatreme was alnöitic and separated from the sövite by a certain degree of immiscibility. The composition of the alnöite, however, is not quite homogeneous. The dike at Stavreviken, for instance, contains no melilite but a calcitic carbonate, probably derived from an alteration of the former. Most other alnöites, on the other hand, are fairly rich in melilite. The previously mentioned Hovid rock (v. Eckermann, 1948d, anal. 71, p. 105) contains 18.3 per cent melilite, and a long alnöite dike analysed at two localities 2 km from each other (v. Eckermann, 1948d, Pl. LVIII and anal. 70, p. 101 and 74, p. 106) as much as 23.3 per cent. The calcitic alnöite mentioned above may be presumed to derive from the contact zone towards the base of the sövite, where the silicification of the sövite and the increased internal pressure may have induced an instability of the melilite and led to its carbonatization. The normal melilite-bearing alnöites, on the other hand, may be taken to represent the primary melilite basalts derived from very great depths through which the immiscible fluid globules passed to form the carbonatitic accumulation on top. It must, however, be admitted that thin sections of alnöites, show no such globules, but additional slides will be made especially from recently collected samples of a new alnöite dike outcropping at the bottom of the sea west of Alnö. This dike was discovered when putting down the foundations for a new road bridge to Alnö.

According to my hypothesis, the alnöitic magma should grade into a kimberlitic one through the decomposition of melilite, and loss of lime and alkalies to the fluid globules, but there is no evidence of this having taken place during the first two kilometres below the sövite 'plug', where the lava may have only been partly kimberlitic. To this depth the volcanic funnel seems to have frozen solid at a time when the supply and accumulation of new globules, as well as the heat of convective currents, were able to stop the retreat and to restart the building up of a new pressure centre. If we could expose a cross-section through this carbonate-fluorite concentration or what remains of it today, we should probably find it surrounded by another girdle of fenitization, although on a much smaller scale than that produced by the sövite. Probably only comparatively small amounts of rheomorphic fenite magmas were formed, the only evidence of their existence being two orthositic, extremely potassic cone sheet dikes (v. Eckermann, 1948d, anal. 101 and 102, p. 128) and a less potassic radial one (v. Eckermann, 1958, anal. 4, p. 34). From this, one may conclude that the accumulation of carbonate and gases lasted for a shorter time than during the formation of the sövite, and that an internal pressure exceeding the lithostatic load was reached more quickly. This could obviously be the sequel to a weakening of the overlying rocks by the preceding brecciation at the time the diatreme was opened. A more dubious contributory factor may also have been the removal of some of the Jotnian sediments by weathering.

However, even if the time between emplacement and fragmentation were in this case shorter, the period must nevertheless have been long enough to allow for an almost complete silicification of the magnesia, leaving almost pure calcite carbonatite to solidify. The mica of this carbonatite is mostly phlogopitic and the olivine forsteritic. There are also dikes derived from the alvikite centre and which were previously classified in the Alnö Memoir (v. Eckermann, 1948d, pp. 128–136) as alnöitic alvikites, biotite picrite alvikites, melilite biotite alvikites, chlorite alvikites, etc., which must now be regarded as metamorphically altered alnöites in which the melilite has turned into hydro-garnet, melanite, calcite, clay minerals and/or phlogopitic mica and chlorite; and the olivine occasionally into serpentine and calcite, indicating a former monticellite. This confirms the previously suggested filling of the volcanic funnel by alnöitic magma down to the new pressure centre. It seems reasonable to assume that the alnöite immediately above the new accumulation of fluid carbonate was still fairly hot at the time and it may even still have been a crystal mush. It may, therefore, have been subject to both carbonatization of the silicate minerals and even to total liquefaction and recrystallization into new mineral assemblages in equilibrium with the new PTX-conditions. On fracturing, however, these assemblages may have changed into unstable associations.

This may explain the bewildering variation of alvikite dikes. Especially should be mentioned those extremely rich in fluorite, apatite and silicophosphate, wollastonite and corundum (v. Eckermann, 1948d, pp. 130, 133–137). On inspection however, all disclose chemical or textural features indicative of their primary alnöitic origin. An item of special interest, common to alvikite dikes of both alnöitic and carbonatitic origin, but mostly of the latter, is the presence of carbon dioxide in minute vesicles in several of the minerals, principally in the calcite and the apatite (v. Eckermann, 1948d, anal. 120, p. 137). Probably, the CO_2-percentage is even higher than that given by the analyses owing to losses during crushing and grinding of the samples for analysis. Generally, the CO_2 is concentrated towards the chilled margins of the dikes, suggesting a very rapid congealing at the contacts. These parts of the dikes are quickly decomposed by percolating water (v. Eckermann, 1961a). The interior of the same dikes may be CO_2 free. The CO_2 content of the apatites of the sövite, which are also responsible for the quick weathering of the sövites, is worthy of special consideration. Generally, the apatite of magmatic rocks is supposed to be one of the first minerals to crystallize, but in the case of the carbonatites this is not always true, and those containing CO_2 inclusions must have crystallized almost simultaneously with the calcite.

At this second pressure centre the fracturing of the surrounding wall rocks and the drop in pressure does not seem to have led to congealing of the basal parts of the carbonatite and to blocking of the volcanic funnel. Deep-seated magma could therefore have followed in the wake of the carbonatites, the rheomorphic fenites and the rheomorphic metamorphosed alnöites. The rheomorphic alnöites probably settled at the bottom of the carbonates before intrusion, where the majority of the hybrid rocks may have formed, and they may also have influenced the composition of the adjoining kimberlitic magma farther down the

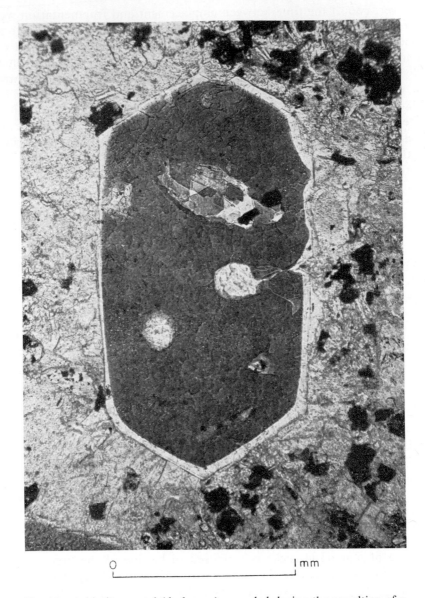

O   I mm

Fig. 11. A biotite crystal (dark grey) corroded during the remelting of a more or less congealed magma of alnöitic composition. It is surrounded by a secondary growth of phlogopitic mica (light grey). The original biotite has crystallized around two small carbonate globules. The apparent 'inclusion' within the upper part of the biotite is an accidental shattering of the mica during the preparation of the thin section.

The carbonate immediately surrounding the composite mica crystal is calcitic, having lost its magnesia to the phlogopite. Ordinary light.

funnel. It seems as if the carbonatites were the first to intrude the tension cracks. The evidence for this is the composite dikes and is discussed in greater detail below in connection with the similar case of the beforsites. There is no evidence to suggest the order in which the few rheomorphic fenite dikes were intruded; it is difficult to distinguish between the rheomorphic alnöites derived from above the carbonatite accumulation, and the kimberlitic and alnöitic dike magmas derived from below. One characteristic feature, however, is the occurrence of two generations of mica in the rheomorphic basic rocks, while those which have not undergone remelting contain only one generation (Fig. 11). Another difficulty, when deciding which is which, is the alteration of the original mineral assemblage by autometamorphism due to the percolation of CO_2, H_2O and F, and in this case by a slower fall in pressure than that which accompanied the blowing up of the diatreme at the sövite centre. Nevertheless, a few dikes have been found, which may be taken as typical representatives of the more deep-seated magma of the funnel, as for instance a melilite-bearing kimberlitic rock (previously termed alnöitic-biotite-picrite-alvikite) south of Bergeforsen (v. Eckermann, 1948d, anal. 107, p. 131) and several from the power station tunnels, such as an olivine-melilitite (v. Eckermann, 1958, anal. 14, p. 44) and two kimberlites (v. Eckermann, 1958, anal. 15, p. 45 and 1960c, anal. 1, p. 540). In some cases the original texture of the melilite-bearing alnöite is still visible, although the melilite is completely altered. In others, where the hydrogarnet formed during the metamorphism has begun to recrystallize into larger garnet crystals, it is in most cases impossible to tell the difference between metamorphic remelting and autometamorphism, especially as the latter may have also affected the remelted alnöites. In any case, it may be taken as proved that some melilitic and kimberlitic magma followed the carbonatitic intrusion and that this in turn was followed by a small amount of a more melilitic and alnöitic one before the magma in the volcanic conduit congealed again.

The retreating carbonate accumulation made its next 'stand' at about 3.5–4 km below the present erosion level, but it must have been one of comparatively short duration to judge by the few, all strongly carbonatitic carbonatite cone sheet dikes originating from this pressure centre. The congealing of the lava in the conduit then continued downwards till it reached a depth of 9–10 km which at the time, however, may not have been equal to 12 km below the erosion surface, as we do not know how much time had elapsed or how much of the Jotnian sediments overlying the gneiss-granite still remained. If we could observe a section of the volcanic neck, a stream of 'frozen' carbonate globules would probably also be present. The evidence for the presence of such globules exists in a few of the late kimberlitic dikes of the alvikite centre. The phenomenon will be further discussed, however, in connection with the beforsitic dikes.

The dikes from the beforsite centre are also of a bewildering variety, and differ in many respects from those of the alvikite centre. As further discussed below, the internal pressure needed to overcome the lithostatic load at the moment of fracturing may also have been greater at this centre and the PTX-conditions under which the different mineral assemblages originated correspondingly different. In this case too, when trying to classify the different dikes as to

their geneses, one has to consider the possibility of the carbonatization and remelting of part of the earlier consolidated crater magma. The time needed to
bring this about must have been considerably longer than that at the alvikite
centre, and the extent of fenitization also noticeably larger, as indicated by the
greater number of rheomorphic fenite dikes. Probably the total number of all
kinds of dikes derived from the beforsite centre is far greater than that from the
alvikite centre, though many of them congealed before they reached the present
erosion surface. Even within the comparatively short distance of 200–400 m
from the Östrand water-tunnel to the surface of the hill above, several of the
beforsite dikes taper off and disappear.

As is the case for the alvikite dikes, the carbonatitic beforsites were the first
to intrude the tension cracks. Ample evidence is offered by a large number of
composite dikes. These show in every case that the first intrusive was a very
pure carbonatite of dolomitic-ankeritic composition, generally containing small

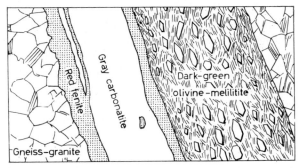

Fig. 12. Composite beforsite-melilite dike at Bergeforsen hydro-electric
power station. Scale 1 : 4.

percentages of silicate minerals, mainly phlogopite, as well as fluorite, apatite,
perovskite and radioactive minerals of the dysanalyte–pyrochlore series. Following the carbonatite, more siliceous magmas were intruded into fissures formed
either within the already frozen carbonatite or along one of the previous wall
contacts. In the latter cases, screens of reddish fenitized wall-rock have occasionally remained as dividing slabs between the earlier and later intrusion, thus helping to elucidate the sequence of intrusions, as shown by Fig. 12. A striking confirmation was obtained during a recent survey of the hill north west of the Östrand
pulp mill when trying to find the outcrops of the previously mapped dikes in the
Östrand water-tunnel (v. Eckermann, 1958, Pl. XX). The kimberlite dike No. 36
(v. Eckermann, 1958, p. 15) in the tunnel is a composite one with a 5 cm wide
carbonatite occupying the north side of the dike. The dike outcrops on the hill
about 200 m from the tunnel. Five centimetres of carbonatite persists while the
width of the kimberlite has dwindled from 35 to 5 cm.

While the alvikite-carbonatites are only slightly radioactive, many beforsite-
carbonatites are strongly so and even match the radioactivity of most pyrochlore-
bearing sövites. This may also be taken as a confirmation of the comparatively
shorter duration of the accumulation of carbonate magma at the alvikite centre.

The most radioactive dikes also show an intimate relation to the rheomorphic fenites by containing soda-orthoclase (v. Eckermann, 1960c, anal. 3, p. 547) and therefore represent a rather late period in the accumulation of fluid carbonatite at the pressure centre, viz. a time when the fenitization had already given rise to rheomorphic magmas. Among the beforsite-carbonatites much more extreme mineral assemblages are found than in the alvikites. For instance, the extremely fluorite-rich carbonatite, intersecting blocks north east of Alnö and earlier classified as an alvikite has, on re-examination of its carbonate, been found to be a beforsite (v. Eckermann, 1948d, anal. 116, p. 135).

A megascopically similar dike in the Fagervik tunnel has recently been analysed (v. Eckermann, 1963a, anal. 8, p. 267). Dikes, very rich in either barite (v. Eckermann, 1960c, anal. 3, p. 547) or strontianite (v. Eckermann, 1948d, anal. 97, p. 121) have no equivalent at the alvikite centre, but show a separate concentration of Ba and Sr similar to that previously mentioned in the case of the sövite.

Even if the fenitization of the wall-rocks has a greater extension than at the alvikite centre, it probably cannot compare with that of the sövites. The liquefaction of the fenites seems to be restricted to rather short distances from the contacts, if one may judge from the evidence of the dikes. Nor is there appreciable proof of secondary crystal differentiation comparable to that of the nepheline syenite rocks around the sövites. Consequently, the dikes of rheomorphic fenites, even if they are fairly numerous, mostly contain, besides carbonate, soda-orthoclase, aegirine-augite and occasionally nepheline. In other words, they represent the fenitization stage around the sövite centre, which in my Alnö Memoir was characterized as the beginning of the fourth stage when the biotite, hornblende, and part of the hydrated feldspars were replaced by aegirine-augite and soda-orthoclase and when the crystallization of nepheline from the remaining mixture of natrolite and sericite began (v. Eckermann, 1948d, p. 161).

The problem of distinguishing the rheomorphic dike rocks of remelted overlying melilite-basalt from similar primary kimberlitic and alnöitic rocks which may have followed as the last intrusives in the tension cracks is just as difficult in this case as at the alvikite centre. However, the two-fold generation of mica seems to be a fairly reliable indication of rheomorphism. Another is the complete absence of any primary textural features. On the other hand, a conclusive indication of the dike being primary, is the presence of the round globules of dolomitic–sideritic carbonate occasionally containing minute octahedral crystals of perovskite or maybe Nb-minerals and spots of fluorite (Fig. 8). It was the observation of such globules within the serpentinized groundmass of a kimberlite, poor in calcite, which first suggested that they were not blow-holes or vesicles filled with secondary carbonate. There was no reason why they should not, in such a case, have been filled with serpentine, too. In both carbonatitic and kimberlitic dikes vesicles occur occasionally at the present erosion level, but they are all characterized by more or less irregular shapes and by crystal faces of the secondary minerals which have 'grown' into the previously gas-filled space. Such a case is the above-mentioned kimberlite where the surrounding, originally dolomitic–ankeritic carbonate through oxidation, has turned into an opaque calcite with iron oxides. This carbonate shows nicely developed crystal faces, creating the picture of old-fashioned fortifications with salient bastion lines, and the centres of the vesicles are filled with colourless serpentine (Fig. 13). The

0   0.25 mm

Fig. 13. Vesicle in kimberlite. The white angular fringes separating the serpentine of the vesicle from the surrounding dolomite consist of calcite. Dolomite crystals rendered almost opaque by precipitated ore dust are seen at the top and both sides of the vesicle. Ordinary light.

globules, on the contrary, are characterized by their almost perfect spherical shape and by a concentric texture. They also show, figuratively speaking, complete indifference to the minerals and texture of the surrounding rock. They are mostly found in the dikes which contain or have contained melilite (for instance most ouachitites) and rarely in typical kimberlites. This is in confor-mity with my hypothesis that the kimberlites are the end product resulting from the removal essentially of alkalies, lime and magnesia from the melilite-basalt by the low melting carbonate 'globules'.

One very well preserved kimberlitic cone sheet dike from the beforsite centre occurs at Norrvik on the mainland north of Alnö. It is mentioned in my Alnö Memoir but is wrongly termed 'alnöite' (v. Eckermann, 1948d, anal. 73, p. 106), the pyroxene on re-examination, being aegirine-augite. Two other previously described dikes, an olivine-melilitite (v. Eckermann, 1958, dike No. 7, p. 15 and anal. 12, p. 42) and an ouachitite (v. Eckermann, 1958, anal. 13, p. 43) are autometamorphosed but still recognizable as primary melilite-basalt and kimberlite respectively. The same applies to a recently analysed dike from the Fagervik tunnel (v. Eckermann, 1958, dike No. 16, pp. 11 and 21, anal. 7, p. 263) and to composite dike No. 60 of the Östrand tunnel (v. Eckermann, 1958, anal. 8, p. 38 and anal. 16, p. 46), which consists of a primary intrusion of a more calcitic kimberlite and a later intrusion of a less calcitic one. But the dikes, which so far have been analysed and examined in detail and found to represent the last intrusions from the beforsite centre, are few. As far as can be judged from the evidence available today, the volcanic conduit froze shortly after the intrusion of the preceding rheomorphic and kimberlitic magmas. An interesting feature of the former, as well as of the primary magma, is the presence of aegirine-augitic pyroxene in contrast to the augite of the alnöites. This indicates a higher oxida-tion ratio as well as an addition of soda. Almost all the beforsites, except the carbonatites analysed and classified under different names in the Alnö Memoir (v. Eckermann, 1948d, pp. 113–120), are rheomorphic rocks of one kind or another. Noticeable is the presence of quartz in several of them. This is partly due to included minute fragments of the country rocks and partly to auto-metamorphic alterations far from the intrusion point. Liquefaction of partly fenitized wall-rocks may also have played a part. Another item of interest is the frequency of free carbon dioxide in the analyses, which far surpasses that of the alvikites. The reason for this might be a greater solidity of the overlying and surrounding country rocks, caused by the sealing of older fissures, slip joints and cracks by previous intrusions. As in the case of the alvikite carbonatites, the carbon dioxide is concentrated in the marginal chilled parts of the dikes. It is generally far greater than shown by the analyses which, as a rule, represent the average of samples covering the whole width of the dikes.

The part played by CO_2 in fenitization is, of course, paramount, but in 1951 (v. Eckermann, 1951) I was still of the same opinion as in 1948 (v. Eckermann, 1948d, Fig. 50, p. 148), namely that the intensity of fenitization gradually decreased with depth and ceased at a depth far below the lowest fracturing level. From what has been said above this is an erroneous interpretation. Fenitization is mainly located at the four levels of carbonate and fluorine accumulation, as schematically shown by Fig. 3. Between these the chemical interchange at the wall-rocks between melilite-basalt magma and country rocks was probably rather limited and still more so when kimberlite magma filled the feeding channel. Although the three deep-seated fenitization centres are not accessible for research, a study of the fenitization along the dike contacts gives valuable information confirming the low fenitization power of the kimberlite magmas. A measurement of the depths to which fenitization has penetrated at the carbonatite contacts has previously disclosed an almost linear equal relationship between width and depth (v. Eckermann, 1958, Fig. 23, p. 50), for both alvikite and beforsite carbonatites. At first glance this suggests an equal temperature at the two foci, presupposing an equal internal pressure too. The occurrence of alvikite and beforsite dikes with quite different mineralogy but almost identical chemical composition calls for cautious conclusions. As is well known, comparatively slight chemical differences as well as local variations in the gas phases may radically rearrange equilibria, as may also small variations in temperature and pressure. It seems reasonable to suppose that the temperature could have been higher at the lowest fracturing centre than at the sövite one owing to its deeper geothermal level. On the other hand, this factor must have been very subordinate as compared with the heat supply delivered by the fluid globules and convection currents. Continued investigation of the dikes at Bergeforsen (v. Eckermann, 1958, p. 50) suggests that the previous estimate (v. Eckermann, 1948d) of about 400°C at the sövite focus at the time of the explosive opening of the diatreme is correct. For the beforsite focus, the temperature of 600°C previously suggested was based on the supposed energy loss during a continuous fenitization between the two foci and on the geothermal increase in temperature. The validity of this earlier suggestion is now challenged by the equality of fenitization displayed by alvikite and beforsite carbonatites Also suggesting a lower temperature, is the presence of occasional periclase crystals and pectolitic wollastonite in the carbonatites, while brucite is totally absent. If the newly proposed genetic emplacement of the carbonatite accumulations is the true one, it may be assumed that the heat transfer by the globules was about the same for at least the three major foci. This implies that the temperature may also have been about equal at the time of fracturing and that, consequently, the temperature at the beforsite focus was closer to 400° than 600°C.

On the other hand, the temperature of the olivine-melilititic and kimberlite magmas following in the wake of the carbonatite may not have been of the same temperature as the latter. Those magmas have one feature in common when congealing as cone sheets: they come from either the alvikite or the beforsite pressure centre. In the survey at Bergeforsen a concentration of olivine crystals towards the lower part of the cone sheets was observed. It was noticeable even in dikes of only a few decimetres in width and was found more frequently in dikes from the upper pressure centres, probably on account of their generally lower dips. Very large dikes of 2–3 m in width containing a fair amount of carbonate 'globules', occasionally even grade into carbonatitic biotite alvikites and phlogopite alvikites, with beforsites at the top while the percentage of olivine at the bottom may reach 70–80 per cent. Even in the case of fairly steep dips there is a marked increase, as for instance dike no. 7 in the Östrand tunnel (v. Eckermann, 1958, p. 42) which averages 57.4 per cent olivine (including pseudomorphs) with a bottom concentration of about 66 per cent. In the case of the vertical dikes there is no similar massing of the olivine crystals towards one of the boundaries. The only reasonable conclusion to be drawn from these observations is the occurrence of a gravitational settling of the olivine during the period of congealing. This could hardly have taken place in dikes of a few decimetres width unless the magma was kept fluid for an appreciable time by high temperature or other factors. Fluorine could not have contributed very much to a lowering of the temperature in this case as most analyses of olivine-rich kimberlites do not contain much more fluorine than is bound in the apatite. Fluorine is also seldom found in the wall-rock contacts, and the number of 'globules' in the narrow dikes is limited. A higher temperature of the primary magma flowing through the beforsite centre in the wake of the previously covering carbonate-accumulation might be explained by loss of heat from the carbonate through fenitization and percolation of gas into the wall-rocks. At present, however, there are no data permitting evaluation of a temperature difference. Perhaps a detailed investigation of the dike minerals might give an indication of their temperature of crystallization and, in turn, lead to a better understanding of the temperatures prevailing at the beforsite pressure centre and in the dikes.

The internal pressure at the beforsite focus at the time of fracturing, had to overcome a lithostatic load of at least 8–9 km of gneiss-granite, not to mention the Jotnian sediments. This is about three times as much as the sövite explosion had to overcome. However, the difference may have been smaller, as the sövite had to shatter solid rock, while the rocks opposing the 'beforsite-pressure' to a depth of at least 3–4 km were already badly fractured. Even so, the conclusion seems inevitable that a higher pressure existed at the beforsite centre.

This is also supported by the observed brecciating capacity of the beforsitic carbonatites, which far exceeds that of the alvikitic ones, and is illustrated by numerous inclusions of wall-rock fragments and earlier dike rocks. Another evidence of the considerably greater gas charge carried by the beforsite carbonatites is the extensive alteration of plagioclase in the wall-rocks to montmorillonite.

This alteration starts at a point where the energy level of the intruding carbonatite sinks below that necessary for Ca–Si interchange at the wall contacts. From this point on, only carbon dioxide and fluorine seem to enter the wall-rocks.

From this point too, the extra contribution to the dike magma of CO_2 from the carbonate dissociated during the fenitization process, ceases. This means a stagnation followed by a drop in internal pressure and a decline in the brecciating power of the carbonatite as verified by numerous observations in outcrops. In the case of the alvikite carbonatites the montmorillonite alteration is not noticeable until fenitization ends but the two processes, as a rule, overlap in the case of the beforsite carbonatites, sometimes by distances of up to several metres. In such cases the higher initial pressure of the beforsite carbonatite has forced still active gases through the thin fenite zone. The phenomenon is beautifully exposed at many localities in the Bergeforsen tunnels, where the bright red fenitization is followed by the white colour of the calcite-montmorillonite pseudomorphs of the plagioclases. The TP-range within which the energy level lies, and which draws the line between the two metamorphic processes, is so far unknown but will no doubt be elucidated both theoretically and experimentally within the near future. A starting point, supplied by field observations and confirmed by analyses, is the waning of the oxidation power of the carbon dioxide when fenitization ceases and formation of montmorillonite begins.

The higher pressure at an almost equal temperature may be responsible for the differences in mineralogy of the alvikite and beforsite dikes. For instance, wollastonite, anatase and corundum have so far been found only in alvikites, while pectolite, rutile and aegirine-augite occur only in beforsites. Monticellitic olivine seems to be more common in beforsites, and forsteritic olivine in alvikites. The average content of fluorine is considerably higher in the case of the beforsites, and reaches concentrations comparable to those of the sövite-centre. Statistically, however, the number of thoroughly investigated dikes is far too small to allow any definite comparison yet. Besides, the paragenesis of each dike at the outcrop on the erosion surface or in the Bergeforsen tunnels depends largely on the distance from its pressure apex. As 6000–10,000 m separate the innermost and outermost cone sheets the autometamorphic alterations within the dikes will depend on the length of paths they have travelled to reach the present outcrops. The dikes, in consequence, show us today consecutive stages of their composition, theoretically starting from a point where they have travelled the vertical distance from the apex, but in practice from a later point on account of the volcanic feeding channel and the vertical outcrops being covered by the sea. The more dikes investigated, the easier it will be to determine the trend of the autometamorphic alterations and to make a reasonable interpolation of the compositions right down to the very pressure centre. The radial dikes may also furnish important information if systematically sampled. Unfortunately, they are largely inaccessible on account of the overburden, but as some of them extend as far as 15–20 km from the eruption centre intermediate outcrops could certainly be exposed by digging. So far, very little has been done in this direction. Investigation of the large number of samples collected at Bergeforsen is still going on, and the data will eventually give a more satisfactory statistical basis for speculation. Valuable information about the tangential extensions and compositions of the cone sheets may also be obtained from a railway tunnel through the rocky hills north west of Östrand at right angles to the previously mapped soft-water tunnel (v. Eckermann, 1958). Preliminary drill-core soundings have already started.

Extensive house building, however, is making the collection of material difficult. Already many scientifically important localities have disappeared, but at the same time blasting for foundations occasionally temporarily exposes new outcrops. As scientific evidence accumulates the conception presented in this paper of the carbonatites being a series of derivates, with melilite-basaltic magma the primary derivative, may have to be modified again. Many questions remain. Why did such a great difference exist between the internal pressure at the opening up of the diatreme and the fracturing at the beforsite centre? Why did the sövite not accumulate at a deeper level? Is it, perhaps, possible that the earlier estimate of the 'sövite-overburden', viz. 200 m of gneiss-granite and 1800 m of Jotnian sediments is wrong, and that the sediment was far thicker and even included early Cambrian sediments? Possibly these sediments had been largely removed by erosion at the time of the last beforsite fracturing. In other words, could the internal pressures in spite of contrary evidence, have been about equal, presuming that the varying strengths of the overlying rocks were taken into consideration? Suggestive in this connection are the steep dips and brecciating power of the conical fractures of the sövites and beforsites as compared to the gentle dips of the alvikites.

If a removal of sediments did occur between the two major 'explosions', a considerable time interval must have separated the two events, maybe a whole geological epoch. The last fracturing could, in such a case, even have been a re-birth of an already extinct volcanism, and perhaps of Silurian or even Permian age. The age of the sövite is known to be the same as at Fen in Norway, viz. about 550×10^6 years or early Cambrian (v. Eckermann and Wickman, 1956). Such a long period, comprising at least the better part of an epoch, should be traceable by age determination of suitable minerals. A research programme has been started which, it is expected, will shortly give an answer to this question.

Research at Alnö during the last fifteen years has been concentrated on the tectonics and compositions of the dikes. Even if our knowledge of the main sövite area and its girdle of rheomorphic magmas and fenites remains at the stage arrived at in 1948, much material has since been collected for further research, and the chemistry and optical characters of the minerals have been determined and will shortly be published. This improved knowledge of the minerals will then facilitate a critical scrutiny of previous conclusions as will also the results derived from examination of the dikes. Preparations have been made for a similar series of analyses of the dike minerals. Finally, an investigation of the radioactivity of the sövite minerals may be mentioned as well as a survey of the radioactivity of the alkaline area on Alnö Island. A map showing the distribution of the radioactivity has been published recently, the most interesting feature of which is the very strong radioactivity of the central part of the sövite area as well as of some steeply dipping sövite dikes (v. Eckermann, 1964a). Analyses show that this radioactivity is due to pyrochlore and dysanalyte crystals which contain up to 3 per cent ThO_2 and 0.03–0.05 per cent U_2O_5.

These minerals were already crystallized at the time of the accumulation of the sövite and when metasomatic action on the surrounding country rocks was in progress. The general level of radioactivity of the latter can be entirely explained by their content of the potassium isotope K^{40}. Only within a short distance from the sövite contacts occurs a small increase in radioactivity, bound to minerals of comparatively high fluorine content.

Autoradiographs of the kimberlite dikes show a conspicuous concentration of radioactivity to pyrochlore minerals within the above-mentioned carbonate globules, and a few minute radioactive nuclei in the rest of the rock coinciding with perovskite-like minerals. This confirms the transportation to the top of the lava column of already crystallized radioactive minerals, while the still free radioactive molecules within the sövite, responsible for the formation of the radioactive minerals at the contacts of the metasomatic rock sequence, seem to have been associated with fluid or gaseous fluorine compounds.

A similar survey of the radioactivity of the carbonatite, kimberlite and alnöite dikes within the region surrounding the now mapped central Alnö area has been started. A comparison between the radioactivity of the sövite and the two later alvikitic and beforsitic carbonatites may possibly indicate the relative time during which the accumulation of carbonatite took place before eruptions.

REFERENCES

Daly, R. A., 1914, *Igneous rocks and their origin:* New York, McGraw-Hill.

v. Eckermann, H., 1928, Dikes belonging to the Alnö formation in the cuttings of the East Coast Railway: *Geol. Fören. Förh.*, v. **50**, pp. 381–412.

v. Eckermann, H., 1939, De alkalina bergarternas genesis i belysning av nya forskningsrön från Alnön: *Geol. Fören. Förh.*, v. **61**, pp. 142–151.

v. Eckermann, H., 1942, Ett preliminärt meddelande om nya forskningsrön inom Alnö alkalina område: *Geol. Fören. Förh.*, v. **64**, pp. 399–415.

v. Eckermann, H., 1946, Alnö alkalina intrusionsteknik och genesis i belysning av dess gång-bergarter: *Geol. Fören. Förh.*, v. **68**, pp. 115–119.

v. Eckermann, H., 1948a, The distribution of barium in the alkaline rocks and fenites of Alnö Island: *Internat. Geol. Congr.*, *18th Sess.*, Pt. **2**, pp. 46–48.

v. Eckermann, H., 1948b, The process of nephelinization: *Internat. Geol. Congr.*, *18th Sess.*, Pt. **3**, pp. 90–93.

v. Eckermann, H., 1948c, The genesis of the Alnö alkaline rocks: *Internat. Geol. Congr.*, *18th Sess.*, Pt. **3**, pp. 94–101.

v. Eckermann, H., 1948d, The alkaline district of Alnö Island: *Sveriges. Geol. Undersokning*, ser. Ca. No. **36**.

v. Eckermann, H., 1951, The distribution of barium and strontium in the rocks and minerals of the syenetic and alkaline rocks of Alnö Island: *Arkiv. f. Mineral. Geol.*, v. **1**, No. 13, pp. 367–375.

v. Eckermann, H., 1958, The alkaline and carbonatitic dikes of the Alnö formation on the mainland north west of Alnö Island: *Kungl. Vetenskap. Akademiens Handl.*, *Fjärde serien*, v. **7**, No. 2.

v. Eckermann, H., 1960a, Borengite. A new ultra-potassic rock from Alnö Island: *Arkiv. f. Mineral. Geol.*, v. **2**, pp. 519–528.

v. Eckermann, H., 1960b, Boulders of volcanic breccia at the Sälskär shoals north of Alnö Island: *Arkiv. f. Mineral. Geol.*, v. **2**, pp. 529–537.

v. Eckermann, H., 1960c, Contributions to the knowledge of the alkaline dikes of the Alnö region. I–III: *Arkiv. f. Mineral. Geol.*, v. **2**, pp. 539–550.

v. Eckermann, H., 1960d, The Alnö alkaline region: *Internat. Geol. Congr.*, *21st Sess.*, Guide to excursion No. C 27, pp. 18–25.

v. Eckermann, H., 1961a, Contributions to the knowledge of the alkaline dikes of the Alnö region. IV: *Arkiv. f. Mineral. Geol.*, v. **3**, pp. 65–68.

v. Eckermann, H., 1961b, The petrogenesis of the Alnö alkaline rocks: *Bull. Geol. Inst. Uppsala*, v. **40**, pp. 25–36.

v. Eckermann, H., 1961c, The decomposition of the Alnö alkaline dikes by percolating water: *Comptes Rendus de la Soc. de Finlande*, No. 33, pp. 244–254.

v. Eckermann, H., 1962, Contributions to the knowledge of the alkaline dikes of the Alnö region. V–VIII: *Arkiv. f. Mineral. Geol.*, v. **3**, pp. 259–275.

v. Eckermann, H., 1963a, Contributions to the knowledge of the alkaline dikes of the Alnö region. IX: *Arkiv. f. Mineral. Geol.*, v. **3**, pp. 397–402.

v. Eckermann, H., 1963b, Contributions to the knowledge of the alkaline dikes of the Alnö region. X: *Arkiv. f. Mineral. Geol.*, v. **3**, pp. 403–406.

v. Eckermann, H., 1964a, Distribution of radioactivity in minerals and rocks of the Alnö alkaline area: *Arkiv. f. Mineral. Geol.*, v. **3**, pp. 479–488.

v. Eckermann, H., 1964b, Contributions to the knowledge of the alkaline dikes of the Alnö region. XI–XII: *Arkiv. f. Mineral. Geol.*, v. **3**, pp. 521–535.

v. Eckermann, H., and Wickman, F. E., 1956, A preliminary determination of the maximum age of the Alnö rocks: *Geol. Fören. Förh.*, v. **78**, pp. 122–124.

Geijer, P., 1922, Problems suggested by the igneous rocks of the Jotnian and sub-Jotnian age: *Geol. Fören. Förh.*, v. **44**, pp. 438–439.

Högbom, A. G., 1895, Uber das nephelinsyenitgebiet auf der Insel Alnö: *Geol. Fören. Förh.* v. **17**, pp. 100–160, 214–256.

Wyllie, P. J., and Tuttle, O. F., 1962, Carbonatitic lavas: *Nature*, v. **194**, p. 1269.

M. S. GARSON

Carbonatites in Malawi

INTRODUCTION

The carbonatites in Malawi, the first intrusive limestones in Africa to be recognized as such (Dixey *et al.* 1937), occur as vents and dikes in the Southern Region and in the southern parts of the Central Region. They form a late stage of the Chilwa Alkaline Province, the rocks of which were previously known as the Chilwa Series, a dominantly alkalic group of igneous intrusions of Upper Jurassic to Lower Cretaceous age, which post-date the Stormberg basic volcanic episode at the close of Karroo times. These rocks are typically developed in the Lake Chilwa area but carbonatites and other rocks which probably also belong to the Chilwa Alkaline Province are found in the adjacent parts of Mozambique (Dias, 1961) and at the south east corner of Zambia in the Feira District (Bailey, this volume, p. 127). The Chilwa Alkaline Province rocks comprise mainly plugs of syenite and pulaskite; volcanic vents and necks infilled by carbonatite, feldspathic breccia and agglomerate, nepheline-syenite and ijolite; and dikes of sölvsbergite, trachyte, microfoyaite, phonolite and nephelinite.

The carbonatitic centres occur in two main belts (Fig. 1). The eastern belt comprises an irregular chain of vents near the eastern border of southern Malawi with Mozambique. These vents and associated alkaline plugs and dike-swarms occur within a zone of depression which passes to the NNE into a down-faulted zone through Lake Chiuta. The western belt of carbonatitic intrusions is found within the Shire Rift Valley and in association with lines of rifting in this area. It is noteworthy that these carbonatites fall within a portion of the main rift valley of Malawi which trends nearly parallel to the zone of weakness extending through Lake Chiuta. This structural evidence that the carbonatite vents in Malawi are related to deep-seated tectonic movements is important in understanding the petrogenesis of the carbonatites and associated alkaline intrusions.

Intense denudation since Cretaceous times has removed most of the effusive equivalents of the rocks now exposed, and has produced spectacular inselberg-like features which stand boldly out of the surrounding plains. In general the early syenitic and pulaskitic plugs form imposing steep-sided mountain masses while the carbonatite vents, which originally must have resembled the large volcanic structures of Elgon and Kerimasi in East Africa, are now weathered down into craggy, deeply dissected necks and ring-structures, often bounded by smooth slopes or discontinuous arcuate foothills composed of fenites.

Detailed mapping of the carbonatite complexes in Malawi in recent years has

33

disclosed that many of these form ring structures which rival in their complexity, and yet orderly structural arrangement, the well known Tertiary ring structures in Scotland (Richey, 1948). Features in common with these Scottish intrusive complexes include occasional cauldron subsidences, arcuate structural forms

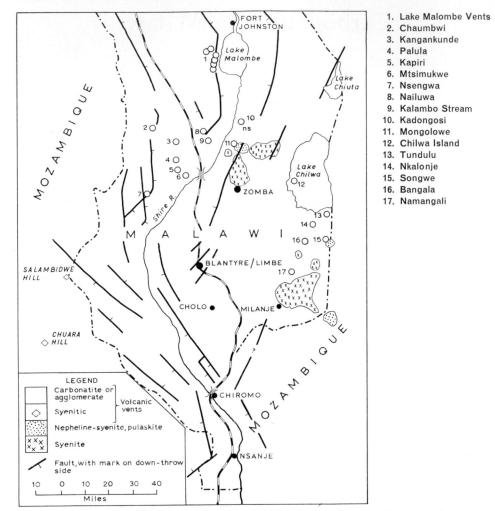

1. Lake Malombe Vents
2. Chaumbwi
3. Kangankunde
4. Palula
5. Kapiri
6. Mtsimukwe
7. Nsengwa
8. Nailuwa
9. Kalambo Stream
10. Kadongosi
11. Mongolowe
12. Chilwa Island
13. Tundulu
14. Nkalonje
15. Songwe
16. Bangala
17. Namangali

Fig. 1. Distribution of intrusives of the Chilwa Alkaline Province in southern Malawi.

such as ring dikes and cone sheets, and linear features such as radial and tangential dike swarms. Also, younger intrusions are generally found successively inwards towards intrusion centres, while the shifting of centres of intrusion invariably has occurred along the longer axis of the normally oval shaped ring complex. In Malawi it has been found possible by a close study of the stress analysis to determine the relationships between the various structural patterns. A summary of the structural evolution of the carbonatite ring complexes is as follows:

1. A dome-like zone of contact breccia is formed above a carbonatite pluton owing to the intensity of stress (Fig. 2). Shear cracks surrounding this fragmental zone are infilled with fenitic material while the contact breccia is itself recrystallized, and ramified and partly replaced by carbonatite magma.

2. Renewed magmatic pressure on this reinforced zone, consisting now of fenite, breccia, carbonatite-agglomerate and consolidated upper portions of carbonatite, leads to the formation of a symmetrical pattern of related shear and tension cracks. The shear cracks occur as two families of orthogonal

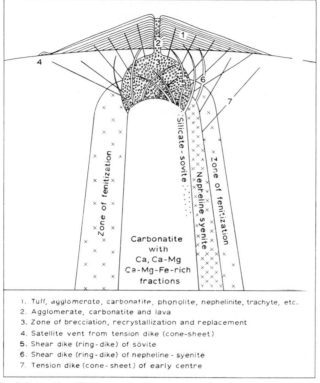

1. Tuff, agglomerate, carbonatite, phonolite, nephelinite, trachyte, etc.
2. Agglomerate, carbonatite and lava
3. Zone of brecciation, recrystallization and replacement
4. Satellite vent from tension dike (cone-sheet)
5. Shear dike (ring-dike) of sövite
6. Shear dike (ring-dike) of nepheline-syenite
7. Tension dike (cone-sheet) of early centre

Fig. 2. Schematic diagram of the structural pattern in a carbonatite complex.

systems of spirals at roughly 45° to tension cracks which radiate approximately from the focus of igneous pressure. An outward pressure from the pipe-like pluton produces a pattern of radial or spiral cracks.

3. Carbonatite and associated magmatic material is injected into the shear cracks to form ring dikes and sill-like bodies, into the tension cracks to form cone sheets and into the radial and spiral cracks to form radial and spiral dikes.

4. Cauldron subsidences may occur within steeply inclined zones of shear cracks, lubricated by magma, with the resultant widening of these ring dikes, and at times the formation of composite ring dikes.

5. Following on the consolidation of these rocks, renewed pressure from the active underlying part of the carbonatite pluton repeats the cycle at a different level or centre. Effusive activity takes place finally and a volcanic cone of ejectamenta and lava is formed.

A schematic diagram of part of the structural pattern described above is shown in Fig. 2. The structural pattern related to each intrusion centre is exceptionally orderly owing to the tremendous magmatic pressure involved. This may have amounted to over 60,000 lb/in² (4 kb) so that the effects of overburden pressure and friction were relatively negligible.

In all, seventeen occurrences of carbonatite intrusion have been located in Malawi, eleven in the form of vents or ring structures and the remainder as dike-like bodies or groups of these infilling fissures. In order of size the vents and ring-structures with their respective diameters (or greatest dimensions in the case of oval-shaped structures) are as follows: Chilwa Island, 2 miles by 1.5 miles; Tundulu, 1 mile; Songwe, 0.8 mile by 0.5 mile; Kangankunde, 0.5 mile by 0.4 mile; Nkalonje, 0.5 mile; and Namangali, 0.5 mile by 0.33 mile. In addition to these occurrences there is definite evidence of sub-surface carbonatite at eleven other localities which exhibit fenites and agglomerates of feldspathized fenites often with a slightly carbonatized matrix. At seven other localities including several of the large syenite, pulaskite and foyaite ring structures there are strong petrogenetic indications of deep-seated carbonatite. The Chilwa Alkaline Province therefore contains one of the most remarkable concentrations of carbonatites and related alkaline rocks in the whole of Africa.

Three of the largest occurrences of carbonatite, Tundulu, Chilwa Island and Kangankunde, have been the subject of close examination mainly because of their economic interest. These are described separately in some detail.

I. DESCRIPTION OF THE CARBONATITE COMPLEXES

Tundulu carbonatite ring complex

Three igneous centres have been recognized within the Tundulu ring complex (Figs. 3, 4 and 5). The three ring structures developed around these centres are the most perfectly developed of any within the Chilwa Alkaline Province, and are comprised of a wide variety of rock types derived from a range of levels beneath the present erosion centre (Garson, 1962).

Centre 1

Updoming and fenitization

The country rocks around the first igneous centre are variably fenitized up to a distance of about 7500 ft from the margin of the early vent of carbonatite and associated breccias. The shape of this aureole of fenitization is nearly circular with a small lobe to the south. The country rocks involved comprise mainly Basement Complex granulites, quartz syenite and granite, and also dolerite dikes belonging to a dike swarm of Karroo (Stormberg) age. The Basement

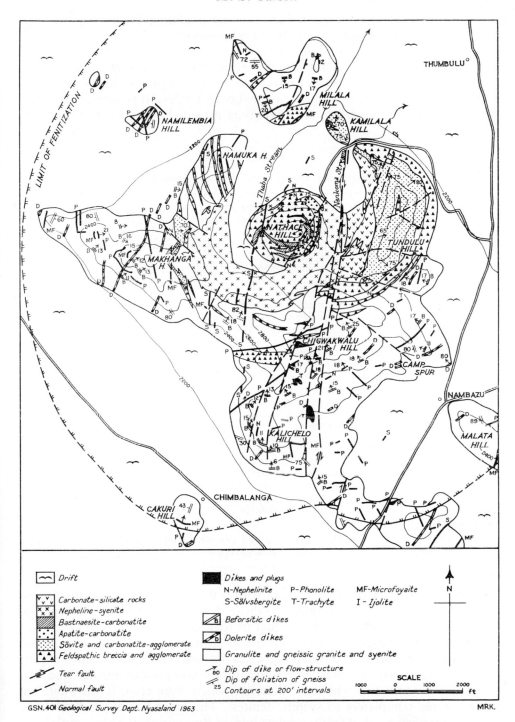

GSN.401 *Geological Survey Dept. Nyasaland* 1963   MRK.

Fig. 3. Geology of the Tundulu carbonatite ring complex.

Complex rocks form an ancient ring structure predating the younger igneous centre but perhaps influencing its structural position.

A deviation of the fenitized dolerite dikes from original near-vertical inclinations shows that the updoming above the underlying pluton of carbonatite is more than 1500 ft. This pre-volcanic dome extended practically as far as the limit of fenitization with a diameter of well over 3 miles. It is considered that a pattern of joints produced by the updoming provided access for the fenitizing solutions.

TABLE I

Summary of the geological history of the Tundulu carbonatite ring complex

	Centre 3	Intrusion of sheets of beforsite into shear cracks and partial replacement of lamprophyres and melanephelinites by ankeritic carbonates.
		Intrusion of sheets of alnöite, monchiquite and ouachitite into shear cracks.
		Intrusion of sheets and plugs of melanephelinite and ankaratrite.
		Tear-faulting
Chilwa Alkaline Province U. Jurassic to L. Cretaceous	Centre 2	Formation of quartz-barite veins.
		Intrusion of vertical dikes of coarse white sövite.
		Cauldron-subsidence of Nathace area (?).
		Emplacement of main foyaitic ring dike and associated alkaline and ijolitic dikes. Reaction with fenites to form pulaskitic fenites and with sövites to form silicate-sövites and calcite-silicate rocks.
		Intrusion of ring dikes of sideritic bastnaesite carbonatite.
		Intrusion of dikes of apatite rock and apatite sövite.
		Formation of agglomerates, tuffsites and trachytic rocks.
	Centre 1	Intrusion of dikes of sövite and sövite agglomerate, mainly into shear cracks.
		Feldspathization of the contact breccia and rheomorphism to leucotrachytic rocks.
		Intrusion of nephelinite and melanephelinite dikes.
		Intrusion of carbonatite in depth producing updoming and aureole of fenitization.
Stormberg Early Jurassic		Intrusion of dolerite dike-swarm associated with early rifting.
U. Precambrian to L. Cambrian		Quartz syenite and granite intruded into Basement Complex granulites and gneisses.

Owing to the variety of rock types within the aureole it is not possible to delimit zones of fenitization similar to those described at Alnö (v. Eckermann, 1948, pp. 27–28). The ultimate product of fenitization, however, in each rock group is a syenitic rock, consisting mainly of aegirine, orthoclase-microperthite or anorthoclase, and albite. The process has operated such that the most alkalic rocks, viz. the quartz syenites, attain this syenitic composition farther from the margin of the vent than the basic dolerites which, even close to the vent, are rarely altered completely to syenitic fenites. The outer fenites of shock-zone type are ramified by thin fenite veinlets infilled by aegirine or sodic amphibole, albite and orthoclase with accessory anatase, barite, calcite and apatite. Nearer the intrusion centre permeation type fenites predominate in which quartz is completely replaced by aegirine and albite, while the original feldspar is altered to microperthite, with a characteristic zebra-striped appearance, and finally to anorthoclase.

Chemical analyses show that SiO_2 was removed and that much K_2O and Fe_2O_3 and a little Na_2O, BaO, CaO, CO_2 and P_2O_5 were added to the country rocks during fenitization, while trace element analyses indicate that there were also significant increases in the amounts of La, Y and possibly of V. Compared with other areas the fenitization at Tundulu is believed to be of high level type where potash metasomatism was dominant, while at lower levels soda metasomatism was more important.

Brecciation and feldspathization

The feldspathic rocks of the first ring structure were derived from brecciated fenites by a process of feldspathization attributed to potassic emanations from the intrusive carbonatites. The end product of this metasomatism was the localized development of rheomorphic leucotrachytes consisting dominantly of sanidine.

The central body of feldspathic breccia, prior to sövitic intrusion and faulting, originally occupied a nearly circular area about a mile in diameter. Arcuate belts of breccia and agglomerate occur up to several thousand feet from the igneous centre. These outer belts, which consist of a contact breccia of fenite fragments, pass laterally at times into zones of *in situ* brecciation. Recognizable belts of contact breccia become increasingly feldspathized inwards towards the carbonatite-rich igneous centre, such that the fenite fragments with cracks infilled with green aegirine, are altered to pale pinkish rocks consisting of orthoclase, microcline and iron oxides. Accessory minerals are brownish green anatase, turbid zircon and infrequent pyrochlore. More advanced feldspathization has resulted in considerable recrystallization and the development of orthoclase-microperthite and sanidine in a trachytic felt of potash feldspar. In the mobilized leucotrachytic product the principal feldspar is tabular sanidine with an optic axial angle of 52–54°. These rheomorphic rocks in places intrude the feldspathic breccias.

Partly feldspathized agglomerates occur in various parts of the vent and as outer belts. These comprise angular to rounded fragments of varieties of fenitized rock, dolerite and nephelinite in a comminuted feldspathic matrix which rarely is calcareous. The thorough mixing of close-packed fragments is analogous to that in the Bull-Domingo breccia pipe in Colorado, regarded by Reynolds (1954) as a typical example of the process of fluidization in which a large volume of gas is the agent of transport of rock materials.

Chemical analyses indicate that the principal changes in the formation of feldspathic rocks from fenites comprise increases in K_2O and Al_2O_3 and corresponding decreases in Na_2O, MgO and $FeO + Fe_2O_3$. The ferrous iron of the fenites is completely oxidized to ferric iron. Relative changes indicated in trace element distribution associated with feldspathization include increases in Ba and Sr, and locally in Mo, Nb, Zr, Y and La.

Sövite agglomerate and sövite

Sövite agglomerates are the products of the saturation with carbonates of arcuate stretches within the central body of breccia. This rock type comprises fragments and schlieren of all shapes and sizes in a matrix of sövite and sideritic sövite. Later thin dikes of sideritic sövite, intruded in a concentric ring pattern, were followed by thick dikes of calcite-rich sövite, and by large scale impregnations of sövitic material accompanied by variable amounts of rare earth carbonate minerals. The dip of these dikes varies from about 60° outwards from the

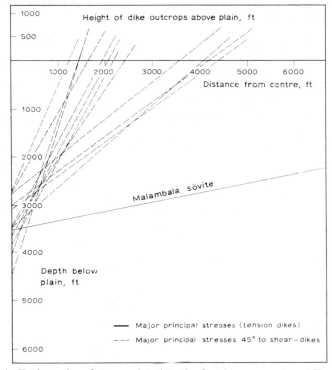

Fig. 4. Trajectories of stress related to the first igneous centre at Tundulu.

igneous centre, at points on the western slopes of Tundulu, to dips of over 75° outwards, at points near the outer edge of the ring structure. Locally there are thin sheets of sövite with shallow inward dips; these are connected in an orthogonal pattern with larger steeply-dipping sövitic dikes. The analysis of the stress pattern of these dikes and sheets indicates an igneous centre at between 3000 and 4000 ft below the plain around the Tundulu Complex (Fig. 4).

All stages in the production of sövite agglomerate from feldspathic breccia can be observed on the eastern slopes of Tundulu Hill. The first stage, near the foot of the hill, comprises the impregnation and veining of the matrix of the breccia by white to brownish carbonates. Increasing saturation with carbonates of belts higher up the hill results in the formation of agglomeratic rocks consisting of angular, partly carbonatized blocks of breccia in a sövitic matrix. Closer to the igneous centre there is a rough orientation of elongated fragments parallel to streaming effects in the matrix; these effects consist of parallel dark- and light-coloured sövitic bands rich in trails of broken fragments of feldspars. Calcite replacing original feldspar is often rimmed by dusty iron oxides derived from the latter. In late stages of replacement sanidine is converted to microcline and zeolite.

In places siderite sövites have sharp intrusive contacts with sövite agglomerate, and elsewhere feldspar-rich types merge with agglomerate. Most dikes of siderite sövite consist mainly of medium-grained calcite and brownish-zoned siderite or its pseudomorphs. On Kamilala Hill and the north eastern half of Tundulu Hill many of the siderite sövites contain numerous tiny flakes and tufts and sheaves of synchysite and parisite, associated with the incoming of clear calcite. Other minerals in these partly replaced sideritic sövites comprise turbid orthoclase, quartz, skeletal plates of barite, and dark blue anatase.

The replacement of siderite sövites by calcite results in the formation of sövites with only small amounts of relict siderite. These rocks are the most characteristic and widespread of the sövites developed in the first ring structures of Tundulu, and also of Chilwa Island (Garson and Campbell Smith, 1958). At an early stage the sideritic rhombohedra develop pale yellow zones, often wavy and sometimes mamillary, against the invading calcite. The pseudomorphic siderite is partly replaced, broken up and pushed to the sides of the growing calcite crystals to form the characteristic 'rim' texture. The ultimate product of the replacement of siderite by calcite is the formation of almost pure white, marble-like sövites which contain only very small amounts of accessory apatite, barite and rare earth minerals.

Other types of sövite developed in the first ring structure include apatite sövite and silicate sövite.

Apatite sövite takes the form of schlieren-like bodies, a few feet long by a few inches wide, oriented parallel to the strike of white sövitic host rock. These schlieren are composed of fine-grained calcite, occasional pale yellow-grey pyrochlore, and bands and patches of aggregates of subhedral fluor-apatite. Accessory minerals are cubes of pyrite, turbid fibres of synchysite, a little clear quartz and purple fluorite.

Silicate sövites containing either aegirine or biotite or both occur on the inner slopes of Tundulu Hill and on Makhanga Hill. These comprise the outer parts of an extensive aureole of metasomatism around the foyaitic ring dike (Fig. 4). Uniform varieties contain much disseminated biotite, magnetite, aegirine and apatite; there are occasional thin bands of richer concentrations of these minerals adjacent to carbonate-silicate rocks of the aureole. On the north western slopes of Tundulu an irregular stretch of banded silicate sövite, about 400 ft wide, displays spectacular flow phenomena due to remobilization within the aureole. The fold structures vary from simple anticlinal and synclinal folds to complicated crumpled folds and overfolds. Bands of magnetite-biotite rock of the metasomatic 'front' of the aureole, have been broken into boudins, often displaying rotation effects. Other bands and pods of this rock have been invaded and partly digested by silicate sövite and there is an occasional segregation of calcite-rich material as patches and veins.

Analyses of varieties of sövite agglomerate and sövite in the first ring structure are given in Table II.

TABLE II

Chemical analyses of sövitic rocks of the first ring structure

	1	2	3	4	5
SiO_2	41.89	4.29	3.99	0.88	4.65
TiO_2	0.91	0.23	0.06	0.18	0.59
Al_2O_3	8.69	1.32	0.57	0.37	1.42[a]
Fe_2O_3	9.82	9.28	3.36	2.62	17.10
FeO	nil	nil	tr	nil	1.90
MnO	1.00	0.96	1.40	0.39	0.68
MgO	0.22	0.25	1.35	0.31	0.50[b]
CaO	13.36	45.62	48.54	53.60	40.06
Na_2O	0.31	0.06	0.21	0.09	1.00
K_2O	7.59	0.22	0.13	0.03	0.16
H_2O+	1.85	1.20	nil	nil	0.05
H_2O-	0.40	0.35	0.09	0.06	0.11
P_2O_5	0.08	0.03	0.07	3.18	1.60
CO_2	11.03	34.88	40.22	38.38	28.43
F	0.04	nil	—	0.06	0.69
ZrO_2	0.04	tr	—	tr	—
Nb_2O_5	0.25	0.30	—	0.04	—
Ta_2O_3	tr	tr	—	tr	—
Cl	0.02	0.01	—	tr	—
SO_3	0.22	0.22	—	—	—
$(Ce,Y)_2O_3$	0.20	0.40	—	0.05	—
BaO	0.20	0.40	—	0.08	—
SrO	0.06	0.11	—	0.23	—
available O	0.13	0.07	—	0.013	—
less O for F	—	—	—	—	0.03
Total	98.31	100.20	99.99	100.56	98.97

[a] Includes rare earth oxides.
[b] Determined spectrographically by Miss J. M. Rooke.
1. Sövite agglomerate (N1185) collected by Dr. F. Dixey from Tundulu Hill. M. H. Hey, anal.
2. Brown carbonatite (N1380) collected by Dr. F. Dixey from a dike on Chigwakwalu Hill. M. H. Hey, anal.
3. Siderite sövite (G1377) from the upper northern slopes of Tundulu Hill. Miss J. R. Baldwin, anal.
4. Pale-coloured sövite (N1377) collected by Dr. F. Dixey from a dike on Chigwakwalu Hill. M. H. Hey, anal.
5. Aegirine magnetite sövite (G1368) from a dike on the north western spur of Tundulu Ridge. Mrs. M. H. Kerr, anal.

Centre 2

The second ring structure was centred on Nathace Hill, 1800 ft SW of the first igneous centre. The concentric series of igneous intrusions around the Nathace centre invaded sövite and breccia of the first ring structure, and fragments of these rocks are included in the Nathace agglomerates.

Nathace agglomerate and breccia

Most of the upper slopes of Nathace Hill are formed of reddish craggy agglomerate while the lower slopes consist of feldspathic breccia of the first ring structure. Fragments in the agglomerate comprise leucotrachyte-porphyry, feldspathized fenite, varieties of sövite, dolerite, massive magnetite, and also occasional fragments of tuffsite similar to material in the Rufunsa Valley vents of Zambia (Bailey, this volume, pp. 127–154). The matrix is mainly feldspathic with a trachytic texture, and is partly replaced by fine-grained quartz and barite. Locally there are purplish black veins of manganese oxides. Accessory minerals in the matrix include calcite, siderite, aegirine, anatase and pyrochlore.

The general appearance of the agglomerate is that of high-level pyroclastic vent material, and it is postulated that the Nathace rocks have been brought into their present position by some form of cauldron subsidence possibly during the intrusion of the foyaite into a ring structure.

Apatite rock and apatite sövite

Apatite rock and associated apatite sövite form an arcuate zone, measuring from 300 ft to less than 100 ft wide, around the north, east and south east edges of the Nathace agglomerate. Smaller bodies occur at other points on the hill.

The apatite rock is a pearly white to pale pinkish, sugary rock which is often massive or has 'streaming' effects, and occasional oriented 'eyes' of dark brown siderite. Thin, interbanded, pink apatite-rich layers and greyish-pink carbonate-rich layers impart a characteristic crinkled or wavy appearance. This variety of apatite rock grades through varieties with numerous oriented crystals of siderite into greyish apatite sövite containing streaks and patches of pink apatite in a matrix of calcite, barite, strontianite and bastnaesite.

The apatite in these rocks averages about 0.1 mm across, and occurs as pink ovate grains with turbid cores and clear rims. Refractive indices range from $\omega = 1.632 - 1.634$ and $\epsilon = 1.627 - 1.629$, indicating a fairly pure fluorapatite. Some very turbid grains of apatite have cores with $\epsilon = 1.636$, probably indicating some content of hydroxylapatite, and there are also some sector twinned crystals which are possibly dahllite. Chalk-like weathered patches in some apatite rocks consist of staffelite similar to that in apatite sövites at Bukusu in Uganda (Davies, 1956).

Analyses and modes of typical apatite-rich rocks are given in Table III.

Bastnaesite carbonatite

Dikes of bastnaesite carbonatite are mainly confined to the Nathace Hill area where they take the form of arcuate ring dikes varying in thickness from a few feet to over a hundred feet wide. There are three main discontinuous ring dikes which dip outwards from the igneous centre at angles of 75° to 85°. Xenolithic schlieren of apatite-rich rock and feldspathic rock are caught up in several parts of these ring dikes.

Both apatite-rich and apatite-poor bastnaesite carbonatites are represented at Nathace Hill, the former predominating in the inner ring dike and the latter dominant in the outer ring dikes, which also contain more abundant patches of drusy rare earth minerals and clear carbonate minerals.

The apatite-rich bastnaesite carbonatites contain much brownish siderite or its pseudomorphs with coarse, zoned or mamillary form, and leucocratic streaks

TABLE III

Chemical analyses and modes of apatite-rich rocks at Nathace Hill

	1	2	3
SiO_2	3.40	14.88	17.30
TiO_2	0.08	0.24	0.49
Al_2O_3	0.59	2.56	2.65
Fe_2O_3	0.28	8.24	14.10
FeO	0.09	—	—
MnO	0.04	1.46	2.52
MgO	tr	0.36	0.40
CaO	52.78	36.12	28.65
Na_2O	0.36	0.17	0.60
K_2O	0.09	0.66	1.05
SrO	—	0.67	0.33
BaO	—	0.42	0.41
Rare-earth oxides	—	1.84	2.43
Nb_2O_5	—	0.29	0.91
H_2O+	0.10	1.30	2.85
H_2O-	0.04	0.90	0.82
P_2O_5	38.94	24.58	20.80
CO_2	0.87	3.60	1.90
F	3.70	2.44	2.27
$SO_3{}^a$	tr	nd	0.22
	101.36	100.73	100.70
Less O for F	1.56	1.03	0.95
Total	99.80	99.70	99.75

a Total S as SO_3

	1 per cent	2 per cent	3 per cent
Apatite	93.20	58.20	48.91
Quartz	1.30	11.31	9.36
Iron and manganese oxides and goethite	0.37	11.05	19.50
Feldspar	3.07	5.48	11.91
Calcite	1.98	6.21	2.34
Strontianite	—	0.90	0.44
Bastnaesite	—	2.66	3.29
Barite	—	0.70	0.70
Fluorite	—	0.80	0.70
Pyrochlore	—	0.45	1.36
Anatase	0.08	0.24	0.49
Clay minerals	—	1.00	1.00

1. Apatite rock (G578) from south eastern slopes of Nathace Hill. M. H. Kerr, anal.
2. Chip sample of apatite rock (G499) from eastern slopes of Nathace Hill. R. Pickup, anal.
3. Chip sample of apatite rock (G1472) from north eastern slopes of Nathace Hill. R. Pickup, anal.

consisting of patches of granular apatite and quartz into which there has been a later introduction of clear calcite carrying tiny plates of barite, rhombs of dolomite, small pyrochlore octahedra and brown sheaves and fibres of bastnaesite. In some varieties calcite plates are mottled due to fine-grained vermicular strontianite and ankerite. Strontian florencite ($\omega = 1.666$, $\epsilon = 1.672$) is a rare accessory mineral as lozenge-shaped crystals, and there are also small amounts of purple fluorite, green aegirine, amber-yellow monazite and tiny cubes of pyrite.

In the apatite-poor bastnaesite carbonatites the rare earth minerals are mainly concentrated in druse-like or tooth-shaped, leucocratic areas, often oriented perpendicular to the strike. These areas consist of pools of clear calcite, ankerite and strontianite, studded with rods of colourless synchysite and radiating fibres and plates of pale yellow bastnaesite. Accessory minerals are pale yellow pyrochlore, acicular pyrolusite, green aegirine and euhedral plates of barite. In one specimen pinkish grains of hyalophane occur in association with barite, parisite and lustrous black crystals of brookite.

The bastnaesite has the refractive indices $\omega = 1.719$ and $\epsilon = 1.820$. It occurs often in lamellar intergrowths with both parisite ($\omega = 1.672$, $\epsilon = 1.771$) and synchysite ($\omega = 1.645–1.648$, $\epsilon = 1.733–1.735$). An associated uniaxial negative mineral with pronounced yellow zoning in vertical sections is possibly cordylite.

Chemical analyses and modes of bastnaesite carbonatites from Nathace Hill are given in Table IV.

Foyaitic ring dike and ijolite

The foyaitic ring dike centred on Nathace Hill measures up to 1800 ft in width; its outer edge is roughly elliptical with a longer NE–SW axis of about 1 mile and a shorter axis of about 4000 ft. The main rock type is foyaite and foyaite porphyry with local variations to microfoyaite porphyry and pulaskitic foyaite, especially in areas adjacent to the peripheries of the ring dike. The mafic minerals in these rocks are aegirine-augite and orange-brown biotite while the felsic minerals are nepheline, potash feldspar and subordinate albite. Accessory minerals are zircon, sphene, apatite, melanite, magnetite and calcite.

A thin dike of ijolite intrudes foyaite near Nathace Hill. This has urtitic bands but is mainly composed of nepheline, sphene and aegirine-augite partly replaced by biotite.

In the series of nepheline-bearing rocks from pulaskitic foyaite to ijolite the biotites exhibit increasing FeO/MgO ratios, and there is a soda-enrichment of feldspars and nephelines concomitant with an actual decrease in feldspar content.

Aureole of nephelinized fenites and carbonate-silicate rocks

The ring dike of foyaite is bordered by an aureole within which a narrow zone of fenitized rocks has been nephelinized, and an extensive stretch of sövite and sövite agglomerate has been altered to carbonate-silicate rocks.

The nephelinization at Tundulu is found in a narrow zone, rarely exceeding 100 ft wide, around the outer parts of the foyaitic ring dike. The first indications of nephelinization are found in the rapid change over a few feet from red fenite to resistant white or greyish rock similar to pulaskitic fenite at Spitskop (Strauss and Truter, 1951). The original bluish green, aegirine-rich veins are altered to dark green aegirine-augite accompanied by sphene and biotite, while the orthoclase-microperthite and anorthoclase are recrystallized to orthoclase and albite in microperthite. Occasionally nepheline develops as square turbid

C

TABLE IV

Chemical analyses and modes of bastnaesite carbonatites from Nathace Hill

	1	2	3	4
SiO_2	30.44	4.34	6.44	6.01
CO_2	10.48	20.56	27.96	26.99
TiO_2	0.27	0.56	0.50	0.10
Nb_2O_5	0.24	0.32	0.15	0.20
Al_2O_3	1.44	0.77	1.93	2.67
Fe_2O_3	11.90	11.80	14.80	13.00
MnO	1.38	2.54	2.72	3.06
MgO	0.76	0.53	2.19	5.76
CaO	25.21	39.64	33.32	25.53
SrO	1.32	1.21	1.64	5.95
BaO	0.58	0.51	0.51	0.44
Rare-earth oxides	1.52	2.40	2.63	3.74
Na_2O	0.40	0.53	0.35	0.40
K_2O	2.08	0.18	0.93	0.20
P_2O_5	9.04	10.65	1.91	3.25
F	0.95	1.06	0.67	0.81
SO_3[a]	0.38	0.34	0.45	1.41
H_2O+[b]	1.39	1.97	1.05	1.09
H_2O-	0.43	0.42	0.53	0.28
	100.21	100.33	100.68	100.89
Less O for F	0.40	0.45	0.28	0.34
	99.81	99.88	100.40	100.55

	1 (G1468)	2 (G1469)	3 (G1473)	4 (G1471)
Quartz	20.34	1.26	0.30	0.96
Orthoclase	12.23	1.11	5.56[c]	1.11[c]
Albite	3.14	1.57	3.14	1.05
Kaolinite	—	0.65	0.72	5.67
Aegirine	—	1.85	—	1.85
Apatite	21.18	25.22	4.52	7.71
Calcite	19.50	44.24	48.30	18.90
Dolomite	3.50	1.39	9.94	—
Siderite	—	—	0.81	—
Ankerite	—	—	—	32.27
Strontianite	1.92	1.77	2.21	8.41
Bastnaesite	2.01	3.07	{ 3.98	{ 5.46[d]
Synchisite	—	—		
Barite	0.96	0.93	0.82	0.70
Pyrochlore	0.40	0.48	0.23	0.30
Fluorite	tr	tr	0.43	1.48
Anatase	0.27	0.56	0.50	0.10[e]
Iron and manganese oxides	1.38	2.54	8.92	8.21
Goethite	13.17	12.36	9.26	3.92
Pyrite	—	—	0.36	1.80

[a] SO_3 Total S as SO_3.
[b] Difference figure. Loss on ignition less (H_2O- and CO_2).
[c] Includes hyalophane.
[d] Includes a little parisite.
[e] Includes brookite and knopite (?)

1. Silicified bastnaesite apatite carbonatite (G1468). Chip sample collected from strike-width of 100 ft in Trench No. 13, west foot of Nathace Hill. R. Pickup, anal.

2. Bastnaesite apatite carbonatite (G1469). Chip sample collected from strike-width of
   80 ft on western slopes of Nathace Hill. R. Pickup, anal.
3. Bastnaesite carbonatite (G1473). Chip sample collected from strike-width 170 ft on
   southern slopes of Nathace Hill. R. Pickup, anal.
4. Bastnaesite carbonatite (G1471). Chip sample collected from strike-width of 88 ft in
   Trench No. 3, eastern slopes of Nathace Hill. R. Pickup, anal.

cores in feldspar in a similar fashion to early nepheline at Alnö (v. Eckermann, 1948). Close to the intrusive foyaite there is a large-scale introduction of melanite as veinlets, patches and aggregates of euhedral crystals, which replace aegirine-augite, sphene, ilmenite and biotite, and are themselves bordered by calcite, sodalite, nepheline and cancrinite. Associated minerals are scapolite and wollastonite. Pyroxene-rich rocks occur locally which are analagous to the melanocratic pyroxenites at the boundary between the fenites and the inner rheomorphic rocks at Alnö (v. Eckermann, 1948). These rocks consist of nepheline, sphene and aegirine-augite and very subordinate feldspar. In some areas pulaskitic fenites are partly mobilized and vein *in situ* nephelinized rocks.

Chemical analyses indicate that the formation of pulaskitic fenites and mobilized alkaline rocks at Tundulu was similar to that at Alnö (v. Eckermann, 1948). At both localities there was an early loss in SiO_2 and Na_2O and a slight increase in K_2O, followed by a sharp increase in Na_2O towards the intrusive rocks, while a marked increase in iron, calcium and titanium locally resulted in concentrations of sphene, titano-magnetite and melanite in association with sodic pyroxene, wollastonite and apatite.

In the carbonatite areas silicate sövites were developed within the aureole (see p. 41). The products of the reaction of foyaite with silicate sövite were a broad inner zone of hybrid feldspathoidal carbonate-silicate rock similar to busorite, and an outer zone of biotite-magnetite rock which also formed metasomatic 'fronts' in silicate sövites at the edge of the aureole.

The feldspathoidal carbonate-silicate rocks are dark olive-grey with a fine-grained granulitic texture. All transitions from foyaite to this rock type occur east of Nathace Hill. Typically the carbonate-silicate rock consists of an orthoclase–nepheline–cancrinite mixture, with individual grains from microns to 0.1 mm in diameter, peppered by tiny crystals of biotite, titano-magnetite, aegirine and calcite. Accessory minerals are apatite, wollastonite, pyrite and sphene.

The biotite-magnetite rocks are typically medium- to coarse-grained and consist mainly of crystals of black biotite and titaniferous magnetite up to 1 cm across, and variable amounts of platy feldspar in a matrix of calcite. Locally there are segregations of aegirine and apatite; accessory minerals are melanite, anatase and apatite.

Chemical analyses show that there has apparently been a metasomatic introduction of Fe_2O_3, P_2O_5, TiO_2 and Na_2O into sövite to form silicate sövite, and an introduction of $FeO + Fe_2O_3$, P_2O_5, MgO, TiO_2 and H_2O but apparently not of Na_2O to form the hybridized carbonate-silicate rocks.

Both in the process of nephelinization of the fenites and in the formation of carbonate-silicate rocks there has been an enrichment in MgO, total iron, TiO_2,

P_2O_5 and H_2O within the aureole. That this aureole is more extensive in the carbonate-rich areas may be partly due to the relative availability of large pore spaces and channels in sövites and sövite agglomerates as compared with the resistant fenites.

Coarse white sövite and quartz-barite mineralization

After the intrusion of the foyaite ring dike a few thin vertical dikes of coarse-grained white sövite were intruded in arcuate fashion near the inner contact of the foyaite. These rocks are composed mainly of anhedral calcite and a few grains of orthoclase-microperthite, apatite and anatase. Pyrochlore is locally abundant as pale amber to black crystals in association with laths of niobian rutile crowded with inclusions of blue anatase.

The quartz-barite veins and disseminations are probably a late hydrothermal phase of carbonatite activity at the second igneous centre. Massive quartz-barite rock forms a series of lenses up to 8 ft wide on the southern parts of Nathace Hill while other parts of the hill have been impregnated with numerous quartz-barite veins and more siliceous material.

Alkaline dikes

Associated with the foyaitic ring dike there is a series of radial, arcuate and semi-arcuate dikes of alkaline type ranging from porphyritic and non-porphyritic varieties of phonolite and microfoyaite to leucite- and analcite-rich varieties. These dikes, which occur up to 5.5 miles from the igneous centre, emphasize the striking ring-like structure of the Tundulu Complex. It is probable that a pattern of arcuate, semi-arcuate and radial cracks was infilled during a fairly short period of time, but in a slightly different order at various points, by related alkaline magma types, which originated from the same alkalic reservoir as foyaitic ring dike.

A few NNE–SSW trending dikes of sölvsbergite belong to a late dike-swarm which cuts across the other intrusive rocks of the complex and which is probably associated with rift faulting.

Several of the arcuate alkaline dikes which are up to 3 ft thick, are of cone sheet type with inward dips of between 20° and 30° to the Nathace igneous centre, at 1500 ft to 2000 ft below the level of the plain around Nathace Hill (see Fig. 5).

In many of the phonolites natrolite replaces the analcite and occasionally the nepheline in the groundmass. Minerals of interest in the alkaline dikes include melanite, pectolite, lamprophyllite, astrophyllite, eudialyte, låvenite and aenigmatite.

Centre 3

Prior to the formation of the third ring structure tear-faulting occurred along roughly N–S directions, with subsidiary NE–SW and NW–SE trends. Along the major Nankoma Fault the west half of the first ring structure was moved about 800 ft to the north. Late faulting of normal or hinge type, often along the same fracture lines, took place after the intrusion of sheets, dikes and plugs of the third ring structure.

Melanephelinite, olivine melanephelinite and ankaratrite

Intrusions of these rocks are generally small in extent, plugs seldom exceeding 50 ft across and dikes generally less than 2 ft in thickness. They are typically crowded with xenoliths consisting of rounded fragments of fenite, foyaite, ijolite, silicate sövite, trachyte and feldspathic breccia. Hand specimens are medium to dark greyish green, fine-grained rocks with phenocrysts of mica, pyroxene and nepheline. Accessory minerals include sphene, perovskite, melanite, melilite and pyrite.

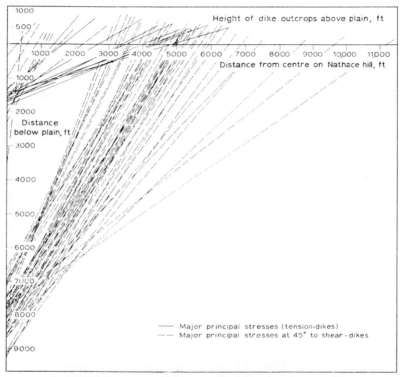

Fig. 5. Trajectories of stress related to the second and third igneous centres at Tundulu.

Of particular interest in these intrusions are xenoliths of feldspathic rocks with leucitic rims, and fenitic xenoliths exhibiting nephelinization effects similar to those in the foyaitic aureole.

A chemical analysis of a biotite olivine melanephelinite (ankaratrite) from Nathace Hill shows the resemblance of this rock to katungite and olivine melilite.

Beforsites and beforsitic lamprophyres

The final manifestation of igneous activity at Tundulu took the form of the intrusion of numerous thin sheets and veins of beforsitic rocks. These intrusions, which vary in thickness from less than an inch to rarely over one foot across, comprise a series of beforsitic lamprophyres, apatite beforsites with silicate minerals, aegirine beforsites, analcite beforsites and almost pure beforsites with a little sphalerite and galena. There are also a few sheets of beforsitic breccia consisting of abundant xenoliths of rounded to sub-rounded fragments of fenite and feldspar rock in a matrix of ankeritic carbonate. It is clear that the beforsitic lamprophyres were produced by the partial replacement by ankeritic carbonate of the groundmass of a series of lamprophyres, including alnöite, ouachitite and monchiquite. A gradual transition between beforsitic lamprophyre and apatite beforsite, due to more intense carbonatization, has been observed at several localities. However, it seems likely that many of the pure beforsites (ankeritic sövites) were not the result of the complete replacement of other rocks but were formed from intrusive beforsitic magma, similar to that on Chilwa Island (Garson and Campbell Smith, 1958).

TABLE V

Chemical analyses of beforsitic alnöite and beforsite at Tundulu

	1	2
SiO_2	23.54	1.03
TiO_2	4.18	0.01
Al_2O_3	8.54	1.17
Fe_2O_3	9.31	1.02
FeO	5.70	11.61
MnO	0.51	3.21
MgO	5.91	10.37
CaO	19.29	28.47
Na_2O	3.01	0.20
K_2O	2.21	0.11
H_2O+	1.55	0.00
H_2O-	0.49	0.10
CO_2	12.87	41.80
P_2O_5	—	0.02
S	—	0.63
	99.83	99.75
Less O for S		0.24
		99.51

1. Carbonatized alnöite (G750), Tundulu. Miss J. R. Baldwin, anal.
2. Beforsite (G672), Makhanga Hill, Tundulu. Miss J. R. Baldwin, anal.

The beforsitic sheets and the melanephelinite sheet at Kalicelo Hill, although shallow-dipping, have been shown to be associated with an igneous centre about 8000 ft below the plain at Nathace Hill. These arcuate sheets dip at angles of between 0° and 25° towards the Nathace igneous centre such that the closer to this centre the steeper the dip of the sheet. Some of the most distant sheets dip away from the igneous centre at from 5° to 10°. This phenomenon which is an integral part of the stress pattern has also been observed on Chilwa Island (Garson and Campbell Smith, 1958, p. 102 and Plate V, Fig. 1). The association of melanephelinite, ankaratrite, alnöite, ouachitite, monchiquite and beforsite in the same stress pattern connected with a deep igneous centre probably signifies a close petrochemical relationship between these types in a deep-seated magma chamber.

The early carbonatization of the beforsitic lamprophyres was firstly by calcite-rich material followed later by ankeritic carbonates. Melilite generally occurs as very pale yellow, partly carbonatized laths, and carbonatization has also resulted in the replacement of perovskite centrally by carbonate while the crystal boundaries are outlined by ilmenite, as noted in biotite-beforsites at Alnö (v. Eckermann, 1948, Pl. L, Fig. 3).

The ankerite in the beforsites is normally fine-grained with an average grain-size of about 0.04–0.05 mm, and shows no twinning. The refractive index ω measured on ankerites from several beforsites ranges from about 1.695 to 1.718 indicating ankerites of the composition 45–80 per cent $CaMg(CO_3)_2$ and 20–25 per cent of $CaFe(CO_3)_2 + CaMn(CO_3)_2$.

Analyses of beforsitic alnöite and beforsite carrying anorthoclase, magnetite, anatase and sphalerite are given in Table V.

Chilwa Island carbonatite ring complex (Fig. 6)

Chilwa Island (Garson and Campbell Smith, 1958) is the largest and most ortherly carbonatite centre of the east belt of vents. Four igneous centres are present on a vertical axis extending from a depth of over 8000 ft to above the present lake-level (2050 ft). Each focus of igneous pressure is about half a mile above the previous one, and lies within the brecciated region where the shear

TABLE VI

Summary of the Geological History of the Chilwa Island carbonatite ring complex

		Faulting and minor overthrusting.
		Intrusion of lamprophyric plug into Summit Plateau sövite.
		Intrusion of radial dikes of sölvsbergite, olivine nephelinite and dolerite.
	Centre 4	Hydrothermal introduction of BaO, ThO_2, Ce_2O_3, PbS, F and late quartz and calcite.
		Intrusion of manganiferous and sideritic carbonatites.
		Intrusion of ankeritic carbonatite and partial replacement of sövite by ankeritic carbonates.
		Apatite-veining of pressure cracks.
Chilwa Alkaline Province U. Jurassic to L. Cretaceous	Centre 3	Intrusion of dikes of foyaite, juvite, phonolite and ijolite, and formation of silicate-sövites.
		Intrusion of sövite with siderite.
		Intrusion of 'alkorthosites' and trachytes (mobilized feldspathic breccia?). Brecciation.
	Centre 2	Intrusion of olivine nephelinite, alnöite and pyrochlore-sövite into shear planes.
		Intrusion of cone sheets of phonolite.
		Intrusion of aegirine biotite sövite into shear planes.
		Brecciation.
	Centre 1	Intrusion of Marongwe acmite sövite.
		Feldspathization of contact breccia.
		Brecciation above carbonatite pluton.
		Intrusion of carbonatite in depth producing aureole of fenitization.
U. Precambrian to L. Cambrian		Quartz syenite and granite intruded into Basement Complex granulite, gneisses and limestones.

stress of the previous centre was virtually at a maximum. The complex was therefore formed in progressive stages, carbonatite advancing each time into the shattered dome of stress above its previous position.

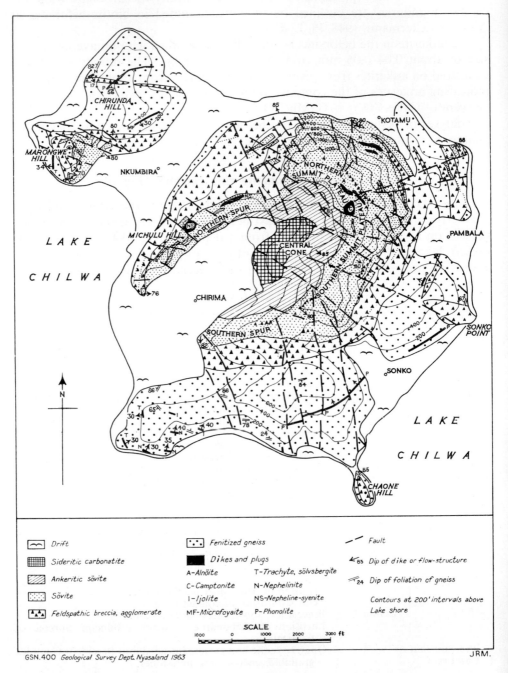

Fig. 6. Geology of the Chilwa Island carbonatite ring complex.

Fenitization, agglomerate and feldspathic breccia

The oldest rocks on Chilwa Island comprise various Basement Complex granulites, gneisses and marbles which have been invaded in a ring-like fashion by gneissic quartz syenite and granite. Owing to the limited size of the Island these rocks, which in general form the lower slopes, fall within the aureole of fenitization. These fenites are similar to those at Tundulu and there are analagous, highly fenitized, equivalents of the alkalic quartz syenites.

Agglomerate similar to that at Tundulu forms vents at Sonko and on Marongwe Hill, and also forms screens in various stages of replacement by carbonatite.

Unaltered stretches of contact breccia occur in several outer parts of the complex. These consist of close-packed fragments of fenitized gneiss and syenite in a very sparse matrix of finely divided material of the same rocks. Stretches of contact breccia closer to the vent are considerably feldspathized. The Chilwa Island complex is at a lower level of erosion than the Tundulu complex so that, in addition to 'Tundulu-type' feldspathic breccias and rheomorphic leucotrachytic rocks, there are revealed medium- to coarse-grained feldspathic rocks which have been considerably recrystallized. These consist mainly of stout to platy, Carlsbad-twinned crystals of orthoclase-cryptoperthite and microcline and small amounts of interstitial dark greyish brown pseudomorphs after pyroxene. Accessory minerals are zircon and iron oxides. Near Kotamu Village some bands of feldspathic breccia are crowded with cubes of pyrite up to 1 cm across, now mainly altered to iron oxides. Intrusive dikes of 'alkorthosite' are local rheomorphic equivalents of these feldspathic breccias.

Carbonatites

Carbonatites of various types are well represented on Chilwa Island and occupy an area greater than all the other vent rocks put together. Prior to faulting the central body of carbonatite was originally oval shaped with a long NE–SW axis of 9000 ft and a short axis of 4000–5000 ft. Erosion over a long period has produced an alluvial-filled area which obscures the south west portion of the carbonatite body.

Feldspathic breccia forms a collar around the carbonatites and this outlines the ring structure of the inner rocks. Further emphasis to this ring complex is provided by the pattern of outer arcuate dikes of steeply inclined sövite. Inwards from the reddish feldspathic breccia the first ring belt comprises coarse white sövite with abundant xenoliths of feldspathic breccia. This sövitic ring reaches a maximum width of over 2400 ft west of Kotamu Village. The contact between the sövite and the next innermost 'ring belt' of ankeritic carbonatite is sharp and readily apparent in the field owing to the contrast between the dark brown weathering crust of the ankeritic carbonatite and the greyish white weathering crust of the sövite. As the ankeritic carbonatite belt is traversed towards the centre of the complex, although the colour of the weathering surface is fairly constant, the fresh rock gradually changes from bluish white and creamy shades to brownish drab colours. The dark brown ankeritic carbonatites appear to grade over a few score of feet into the manganiferous sideritic carbonatites of the central core which contain black segregations rich in iron and manganese oxides.

The evidence that the carbonatites have acted as intrusive rocks is provided by the manner in which outer dikes of sövite cut cleanly through fenites and breccia. Convincing flow structures, displayed by most of the various types of carbonatite, include linear parallelism of minerals such as acmite, apatite, magnetite and rutile, and the orientation of xenolithic boulders and streaks of feldspathic breccia (Garson, 1955).

Sövite

The sövite was probably intruded originally as a series of steeply inclined dikes separated by narrow screens of feldspathic breccia which were saturated by sövite and largely replaced. Evidence of the existence of some inner screens is confined to the presence of broken and dragged-out belts rich in carbonatized relics of feldspar. The dips of outward dipping flow structures increases towards the margins of the central complex until they are nearly vertical, and dips of dikes in the fenites are inclined steeply inwards towards the igneous centre. Strong faulting and erosion in some areas has revealed deep sections which indicate that the inclination of outward dipping sövite steepens in depth, and is eventually inclined inwards.

On the basis of the mineral composition the sövites are sub-divided into four groups.

(1) Pyroxene sövite and pyroxene mica sövites. In general these sövites occur towards the margins of the sövitic ring belt or as outer sövitic dikes.

The pyroxene mica sövite at Marongwe Hill is associated with the oldest igneous centre of the complex. It is a fine-grained buff rock with abundant crystals of acmite, up to 1.5 cm long and 0.8 mm across, and dark brown biotite in crystals up to 1 cm across. Accessory minerals, abundant in some bands, are niobian rutile, rounded apatite and cubo-octahedra of pyrochlore and magnetite.

Similar pyroxene mica sövites of the second igneous centre occur on the margins of the central complex. In some of these rocks the pyroxene is pale green aegirine or aegirine-augite and the mica is a phlogopite with pleochroism $X =$ light buff and $Z =$ light green. Biotite sövites without pyroxene occur on the Southern Spur.

(2) Sövites with only small amounts of constituents other than calcite. These rocks occur at the inner margins of the feldspathic breccia and consist of white anhedral calcite up to 1.5 cm across and occasional small amounts of magnetite and apatite.

(3) Sövites with small amounts of siderite or its pseudomorphs. The bulk of the Chilwa Island sövite, as also at the Tundulu Complex, is composed of this rock type. These sövites are greyish, fawn and pale brown, even-grained rocks. In thin section small rhombs and patches of siderite are disposed along intercrystal boundaries of the calcite. Other minerals

noted in small amounts in these siderite sövites include pyrochlore, quartz, synchysite, pyrite, apatite and barite.

(4) Apatite sövites. Streaky apatite-rich sövites of the fourth igneous centre occur mainly on the Northern Spur where they are inclined at angles of between 45° and 60° inwards towards the centre of the complex. They consist of calcite with many thin, flat, long lenticles of close-packed apatite prisms, averaging 0.04 mm in breadth, which lie in roughly parallel bands.

TABLE VII
Chemical analyses of ankeritic and sideritic carbonatites from Chilwa Island

	1	2	3	4	5
CaO	46.37	36.73	29.04	}28.68	29.07
SrO	nd	0.37	0.12		nd
MgO	7.60	14.91	15.31	13.62	12.00
FeO	} 1.46	} 1.65	8.18	8.62	nil
Fe_2O_3			nil	nil	11.1
MnO	nd	0.75	1.53	3.47	6.7 (MnO_2)
Al_2O_3	nd	nd	0.24	0.14	—
P_2O_5	nd	0.43	0.10	0.04	—
$H_2O+110°$	nd	—	nil	0.12	0.30
Loss on ignition	nd	nd	43.34	42.74	38.90
Insol. (HCl)	—	0.19	0.77	1.32	0.90
			98.63	98.75	98.97

Calculated as Carbonates and Apatite

	1	2	3	4
$Ca_3(PO_4)_2$	nd	1.01	0.23	0.10
$CaCO_3$	83	64.59	51.63	} 51.12
$SrCO_3$	nd	0.53	0.18	
$MgCO_3$	16	31.06	31.89	28.37
$FeCO_3$	2	2.67	13.20	13.92
$MnCO_3$	nd	1.22	2.48	5.62
Al_2O_3	—	—	0.24	0.14
Insol.	—	0.19	0.77	1.32
	101	101.27	100.62	100.59

1. Ankeritic sövite, upper western slopes of Northern Summit Plateau. D. I. Bothwell, anal.
2. Ankeritic sövite, upper western slopes of Northern Summit Plateau. A. A. Moss, anal.
3. Ankeritic sövite, dike cutting Western Summit sövite. A. A. Moss, anal.
4. Ankeritic sövite, Northern Spur. A. A. Moss, anal.
5. Sideritic carbonatite, central core of complex. A. A. Moss, anal.

Ankeritic carbonatite

Apart from the main intrusion of ankeritic carbonatite within the sövitic ring belt there are numerous thin, steeply inclined dikes and related sheets of ankeritic carbonatite which intrude and replace the older sövite. The outer part of the ankeritic carbonatite ring belt comprises white, cream and grey, fine-grained rocks, often carrying tiny cubes of fresh pyrite up to 0.5 mm across.

The dark brown ankeritic carbonatite nearer the complex centre consists of oxidized equivalents of these leucocratic rocks. Accessory minerals are occasional pyrochlore, euhedral microcline, magnetite, florencite, synchysite and apatite.

Chemical analyses of several ankeritic carbonatites are given in Table VII.

Sideritic carbonatite

The central core of the complex consists of sideritic carbonatite and stretches of coarse-grained feldspathic breccia intimately mixed with, and saturated by, sideritic carbonatite. Manganiferous segregations occur as dike-like bands from inches to several feet across within these rocks.

The sideritic carbonatites are typically medium- to coarse-grained and mainly comprise brown to black rhombohedral to anhedral crystals of siderite up to 1 cm across, and irregular drusy areas lined or filled with calcite, pink florencite and very fine-grained white or yellow bastnaesite. The siderite is generally replaced by iron oxides and is quite opaque except for fragments of translucent brown limonite or goethite; the cleavages are frequently blackened by a coating of manganese oxides.

Pyrochlore-rich carbonatite

Belts of greyish, pyrochlore-rich carbonatite, several feet in width, occur within the outer sövitic ring belt on the Northern and Southern Summit Plateaux and on parts of the Northern and Southern Spurs. The field occurrence of these rocks is extraordinary. In some areas they apparently form dikes intrusive into sövite while in other parts of the same belts pyrochlore carbonatites have been 'dragged-out' and partly digested (carbonatized) by sövite. This conflicting evidence can be explained by a later local mobilization of the host rock into which the pyrochlore carbonatites were intruded. In the relatively undisturbed areas the dip of these rocks is from 70° to 80° outwards from the igneous centre.

The pyrochlore carbonatites are flanked on the north east and eastern edges of the Summit Plateaux by acmite sövite. Several lenticular bodies, apparently barren of pyrochlore occur within these carbonatites and also as a sort of buffer zone against sövite.

The pyrochlore-rich rocks comprise assemblages of pyrochlore, apatite, amphibole and fine-grained turbid ankerite. In addition there are scattered crystals of phlogopite. The pyrochlore is well crystallized and varies in size from 0.05 mm up to 2 or 3 mm across, and in colour from pale yellow to dark reddish brown or black. Zoned and broken crystals are common and some specimens have black inclusions and veins of columbite. Apatite occurs as colourless, stout, close-packed prisms averaging 0.2 mm across. The amphibole is probably a soda-tremolite in the form of very pale green to colourless prisms, or composites of these, up to 2 mm across, with $\gamma:c = 19°-23°$, $2V\alpha = 82°$ and the refractive indices $\alpha = 1.621$ and $\gamma = 1.635$. Most crystals are considerably altered to carbonate. Accessory minerals include feldspar, fluorite, spinel and pyrite.

The phlogopite rocks are greenish grey in colour and consist mainly of phlogopite with some very pale soda tremolite and yellow acmite (α:c $= 5.5°$). The phlogopite averages about 0.5 mm across and has the pleochroism scheme: $X =$ colourless, $Z =$ yellow. Some patches within colourless crystals have the abnormal pleochroism scheme: $X =$ ochraceous buff, $Z =$ light buff.

Nepheline syenite and ijolite

Arcuate dike-like intrusions of nepheline syenite and ijolite occur on the Northern Spur; these are elongated approximately parallel to the breccia-sövite margin.

The nepheline syenite bodies comprise varieties of foyaite, microfoyaite and juvitic foyaite similar to those at the Tundulu Complex. The principal mafic mineral is aegirine-augite often with a rim of aegirine. Biotite occurs in some of these rocks, and niobian sphene is locally abundant. Accessory minerals are zircon, apatite and calcite.

A thin dike of wollastonite ijolite, similar to rocks at Homa Bay (Pulfrey, 1950), intrudes fenitized syenite. The leucocratic minerals are pale pink nepheline and long silky prisms of pale green wollastonite. The dark minerals are aegirine-augite and dark brown melanite. Apatite is an abundant accessory mineral and calcite fills interstices.

Carbonate-silicate rocks

These rocks are found in an aureole around an arcuate foyaite body on the Northern Spur, and also adjacent to a dike of olivine nephelinite south of Kotamu Village.

The aureole rocks on the Northern Spur consist of melanite pyroxene sövite and also, adjacent to the foyaite, of feldspathoidal carbonate-silicate rock, similar to that at Tundulu. The melanite-rich sövites are fine-grained, speckled grey and black rocks with dark veinlets consisting of dodecahedra of melanite. The grain size of the calcite is about 0.5 mm, and that of the melanite about 0.25 mm. Associated minerals include dark green aegirine, dark brown biotite, titano-magnetite, apatite and pyrochlore. In pyroxene-rich varieties there are remarkable dendritic groups of aegirine-augite and magnetite.

The carbonate-silicate rocks south of Kotamu Village comprise diopside, biotite, calcite, accessory sphene and apatite and turbid pseudomorphs after nepheline. Biotite-sphene veinlets traverse ilmenite (?) patches. These rocks possibly represent partly carbonatized relics of olivine nephelinite.

Alkaline and lamprophyric dikes and plugs

These comprise varieties of nephelinite, olivine nephelinite, phonolite, microfoyaite, ijolite porphyry, porphyritic trachyte, sölvsbergite, alnöite and camptonite. The dikes occur as cone sheets and related sheets associated with igneous centres 2 and 3, and there are also some late radial dikes associated with centre 4.

The nephelinites and olivine nephelinites include extensively carbonatized types near Kotamu with augite, biotite, olivine and dark green spinel, apatite-rich types cutting fenitized syenite, and a radial dike of olivine nephelinite with abundant serpentinized olivine, large phenocrysts of augite, and nepheline altered to sheaf-like bundles of cancrinite.

The phonolites, microfoyaites, trachytes and a radial sölvsbergite are similar to varieties at the Tundulu Complex. The trachytes are probably rheomorphosed feldspathic fenites but the evidence is not so convincing here as at Tundulu.

The alnöite on the Northern Summit Plateau occurs as an irregular tapering body about 1000 ft long and 100 ft across at its widest part. The 'contact' between the sövite and alnöite is a zone of replacement by sövite in which there are xenoliths of alnöite in all stages of carbonatization. The alnöite, which is itself crowded with rounded xenoliths of sövite and xenocrysts of mica, magnetite, pyroxene and hornblende, closely resembles the alnöite breccia at Hovid on Alnö Island (v. Eckermann, 1948, Figs. 1 and 2). The matrix is an intimate mixture of carbonate, lath-shaped carbonate pseudomorphs after melilite, pale brown mica, magnetite and many small prisms of pyroxene. Micro-insets include olivine pseudomorphs, broken apatite, brown mica and colourless pyroxene.

The largest of the camptonitic intrusions is an oval-shaped plug, about 440 ft long by 340 ft across, in the saddle between the Northern and Southern Plateaux. This rock contains insets of olivine and augite in a groundmass of brown barke-vikite prisms, laths of plagioclase, small augite prisms, minute cubes of magnetite and a turbid analcite base carrying tiny apatite needles. Similar finer-grained camptonites occur as dikes on the southern part of the complex.

Hydrothermal quartz-fluorite rocks and radioactive rocks

The final manifestation of waning carbonatitic activity took the form of the introduction of hydrothermal solutions. The principal hydrothermal minerals are fluorite, quartz and barite in vein assemblages. Several radioactive rocks on the Southern Spur and central part of the complex are probably also related to this phase.

The quartz-fluorite rocks occur as lens-shaped bodies, up to several feet across and a few hundred feet long, on the Northern Summit Plateau and in association with faults at Marongwe Hill. The fluorite is in pale green or purple cubes up to 0.5 mm across within a matrix of granular to drusy quartz. Associated minerals are barite, dickite, apatite and pyrochlore.

The radioactive 'dikes' vary in thickness from a few feet to more than 30 ft. They consist mainly of brecciated siderite altered to yellowish brown goethite with interstitial quartz, fluorite, barite and opaque oxides. The radioactivity is due to thoria associated with goethite; chemical analyses indicate over 2 per cent of thoria in some of these rocks.

Kangankunde carbonatite complex (Garson, 1965a)

The Kangankunde Complex (Fig. 7) differs considerably from all the other large carbonatitic centres in Malawi both in the lack of sövite and the preponderance instead of strontianite-rich ankeritic carbonatites, and also in the virtual absence of associated silicate intrusives bar a few minor dikes and plugs of alnöite and carbonatized nephelinite (?). Other features at Kangankunde, not present or little apparent in the other vents, include the large scale replace-

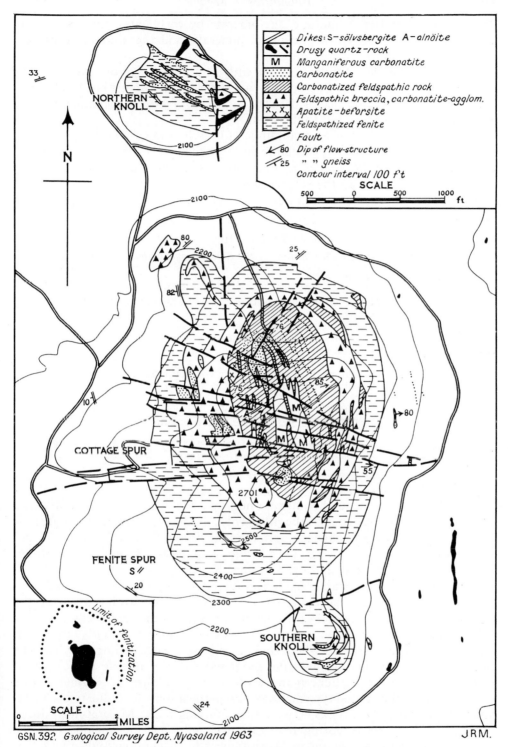

Fig. 7. Geology of the Kangankunde carbonatite complex.

ment of feldspathized fenite and agglomerate by carbonates, the remarkable concentrations of rare earth phosphate minerals, and the abundance of late quartz-rich hydrothermal solutions.

The Kangankunde Complex is apparently at a higher erosion level than the Tundulu and Chilwa Island complexes, and its elongated shape has been partly influenced by the occurrence of the vent in a zone of weakness parallel to, and related to, the main rift fault to the west.

The complex consists of Kangankunde Hill itself, a low ridge rising to about 600 ft above the plain, and the satellite vents on the low Northern and Southern Knolls. On each of the three hills the fenitized gneisses tend to form the lower slopes which give way to the steeper slopes of feldspathized rocks and craggy agglomerate. The carbonatites in general form smooth surfaces on the higher ridges.

TABLE VIII

Summary of the geological history of the Kangankunde carbonatite complex

Tertiary (?)	Faulting.
	Intrusion of alkaline dikes and biotite alnöite.
	Hydrothermal quartz-druse rocks and radioactive rocks.
	Quartz-barite-monazite-carbonate mineralization.
Chilwa Alkaline Province	Formation of manganiferous rocks.
	Intrusion of carbonatite dikes.
U. Jurassic—Cretaceous	Carbonatization, phlogopitization and mobilization.
	Feldspathization.
	Formation of agglomerate and contact breccia.
	Intrusion of plug and dikes of apatite-beforsite (carbonatized nephelinite?).
	Fenitization.
Basement Complex Precambrian or L. Cambrian	Gneisses, granulites, marbles and pegmatites.

Fenitization

The country rocks around Kangankunde have been fenitized up to a distance of half a mile from the foot of the hill. This aureole of alkali metasomatism is roughly oval-shaped and aligned approximately NNW–SSE such that the longer axis of the aureole, which is just over 2 miles long, passes through the Northern Knoll, Kangankunde Hill and the Southern Knoll.

As at Tundulu it is probable that the fenitizing solutions which emanated from the vent initially gained access along a series of cracks produced during the updoming of the country rocks prior to the intrusion of the vent rocks.

Two main types of fenite are present, both of which have counterparts at Tundulu and Chilwa Island where they are not so clearly distinguishable The first type which mainly occupies the outer parts of the aureole is the normal shock zone type of v. Eckermann with veinlets infilled by normal fenitic minerals, while the second type displays also permeation effects due to the metasomatism of parts of the rocks between the ramifying veins. Minerals introduced into the country rocks during fenitization include aegirine, members of the riebeckite–subglaucophane and magnesioriebeckite–magnesioarfvedsonite series,

calcite, magnetite and apatite. The original potash feldspar is altered to orthoclase-microperthite, and the plagioclase is altered to oligoclase or albite, concomitant with replacement by thin shreds of calcite.

Apatite beforsite

Intrusions of an unusual rock, termed 'apatite beforsite' and characterized
by the presence of abundant small phenocrysts of apatite, occur as a small
plug and dikes at several localities on Kangankunde Hill. These rocks, which
were intruded prior to the main brecciation, have been altered by processes
associated with the carbonatites.

Hand specimens are compact, very fine-grained, greyish rocks crowded with
phenocrysts of dark honey-coloured apatite, black magnetite and ilmenite, and
occasional flakes of biotite. In thin section additional constituents are found to
be minute reddish brown cubes of perovskite, olivine altered to antigorite and
carbonates but often with an outer zone of monticellite, turbid carbonatized
laths of melilite, phenocrysts of nepheline and occasional bright yellow crystals
of baddeleyite. The matrix is extensively replaced by carbonates but staining
tests reveal remnants of nepheline altered to cancrinite and thin colourless laths
of melilite.

A chemical analysis and calculated mineral composition of a specimen of
apatite beforsite from the main plug are given in Table IX.

TABLE IX

SiO_2	11.16		
TiO_2	1.18		
Al_2O_3	6.88		
Fe_2O_3	8.46		
FeO	3.48	Apatite	16.9
MnO	0.62	Perovskite	2.0
MgO	10.71	Nepheline	7.3
CaO	34.48	Kaliophilite	0.3
Na_2O	1.59	Gehlenite	11.4
K_2O	0.12	Magnetite	12.3
H_2O-	0.12	Olivine, monticellite	14.2
H_2O+	2.28	Dolomite, brucite, portlandite	35.3
P_2O_5	7.16	W. H. Herdsman, anal.	
CO_2	11.54		
NiO	nil		
Cr_2O_3	0.01		
	99.79		

Brucite and portlandite, calculated because of excess RO and H_2O after
allotting various oxides for the first seven constituents, are not easily distinguishable in thin section if present in a finely-divided state. Portlandite is an important
constituent of the crystallization of carbonatitic liquids in laboratory experiments
(Wyllie and Tuttle, 1960). If present in the apatite beforsites it is probably
associated with later hydrothermal carbonatitic fluids following on the intrusion
of these unusual rocks which originally may have been leucocratic, apatite-rich,
olivine-melilite-nephelinites.

Agglomerate and breccia

The main vent at Kangankunde, prior to the intrusion of carbonatite, was filled with contact breccia and agglomerate which occupied an oval-shaped area with a longer N–S axis of 2500 ft and a shorter axis of about 2000 ft. Most of the marginal areas have been feldspathized and the central parts have been invaded and partly replaced by carbonatite. Similar rocks occur at the two satellite vents, and elsewhere as arcuate belts up to 1 mile from the centre of the main vent.

Feldspathization

Most of the agglomerate and breccia, and extensive stretches of fenite around the satellite vents and extending over 800 ft from the main vent, have been altered by a process of feldspathization similar to that at Tundulu and Chilwa Island. At Kangankunde the association of feldspathization with carbonatite is emphasized by the manner in which zones of feldspathization form 'collars' outlining the vents, and by the increased feldspathization of fenites towards the margins of individual dikes of carbonatite.

Carbonatite agglomerate and carbonatization

In the main vent extensive belts of carbonatite agglomerate comprise an intermediate zone between the outer feldspathized collar and the inner central zone of strongly carbonatized rocks. This agglomerate consists of fragments of feldspathic breccia in a matrix, partly the replacement product of original feldspar by carbonates and partly of intrusive sideritic carbonatite.

The central parts of the main vent consist of variably carbonatized rocks with schlieren and streaks of relict feldspathic rocks, invaded by dikes of intrusive carbonatite. There are indications of local rheomorphism of patches of carbonatized feldspathic material. Many of these carbonatized rocks closely resemble in colour and outward appearance the feldspathic breccia and agglomerate from which they are derived, and can be distinguished only by acid tests and in thin section where it is revealed that the amount of carbonate present is always many times that indicated megascopically. In the most strongly carbonatized varieties most of the original feldspar consists of sideritic carbonate with a turbid pinkish dust of iron oxides outlining crystal faces and cleavages. Thin lustrous black veinlets ramifying parts of these rocks consist of aggregates of brookite crystals.

Phlogopitization

The phlogopitization is associated with the intrusion of numerous ramifying veins of ankeritic carbonatite. In many marginal parts of the vent reddish feldspathic rocks are broken up into a breccia of angular blocks in a white ankeritic matrix with phlogopite-rich reaction rims against the feldspathic blocks.

Feldspathic rocks showing incipient alteration occur on the north western slopes of Kangankunde Hill. In these rocks parts of turbid potash feldspars are replaced by tiny euhedral flakes of pale yellow phlogopite while original biotite is also in part replaced by magnetite and phlogopite, both marginally and along cleavages. More highly phlogopitized rocks on the upper slopes are greyish to dark greenish grey in colour with numerous white veins of ankeritic carbonatite and a few pink spots of relict feldspar. The greyish areas consist of aggregates of fine-grained, pale yellow to green phlogopite, colourless ankerite with accessory sellaite, and small corroded patches of turbid feldspar. Some pseudomorphs after feldspar comprise cores of ankerite and margins of phlogopite outlining crystal shapes. Associated with the carbonate veins are small crystals of anatase, barite, apatite, sphalerite and pyrite.

Refractive index determinations indicate that the phlogopite content of the mica is about 75 per cent to 90 per cent in a range of specimens, while the ankerite has a content of between 50 per cent and 60 per cent of $CaFe(CO_3)_2$ and $CaMn(CO_3)_2$. The sellaite occurs as tiny colourless and white grains with $\omega = 1.380 \pm 0.005$ and $\epsilon = 1.392 \pm 0.005$.

Carbonatites, associated apatite-rich rocks and rare earth mineralization

Much of the area shown on Fig. 7 as carbonatized feldspathic rock could be classified on mineralogical grounds as feldspar carbonatite although this rock type is evidently a product of carbonate replacement. In some areas carbonatized feldspathic rock merges with intrusive carbonatite as if there had been mobilization adjacent to the intrusive rock. In other areas carbonatite dikes are sharply defined with clear intrusive contacts against older rocks.

In the central complex most of the carbonatite dikes conform to an arcuate pattern roughly paralleling the margins of the zone of carbonatized feldspathic rock. A few dikes are arcuate to a plug of carbonatite near the crest of the hill; the Southern Knoll dikes are arcuate to a separate satellitic centre; while the carbonatite dikes on the Northern Knoll are in a tangential trend to the main vent. In general the streaks and bands in the intrusive carbonatites are oriented outwards at angles of 60° or greater from the central part of the complex, in a similar fashion to flow banding of carbonatites at most other carbonatitic vents in Malawi.

Most dikes comprise mixtures of different types of carbonatite, all of which weather to a uniform brown or dark brown colour with the exception of the late leucocratic strontianite-rich dikes which are creamy white to pale greenish grey on weathered surfaces. Apart from the strontianite-rich varieties the carbonatites can be classified into four main groups. These are: firstly, early sideritic carbonatites which are dark brown fine-grained rocks often containing small xenoliths and schlieren of feldspathic rocks; secondly, coarser-grained, mottled, dark and light brown carbonatites with abundant rare earth minerals and in which most of the early siderite is replaced by ankerite; thirdly, leucocratic white, pale grey and light buff, ankeritic carbonatites again with much rare earth mineralization; and lastly, dark purplish brown to black carbonatites rich in iron and manganese oxides apparently associated with pale pinkish apatite-rocks.

The apatite rocks, which are very similar to apatite rocks at Nathace Hill in the Tundulu Complex, occur as segregations up to one or two feet wide and as relict patches in ankeritic and manganiferous carbonatites.

The rare earth mineralization takes several forms. Normally the intrusive carbonatites are impregnated with variable amounts of fine-grained pale green monazite, pink florencite and tiny pearly flakes of bastnaesite, accompanied by small amounts of somewhat drusy quartz and barite. In many cases monazite enrichments occur at the margins of intrusive dikes, especially within sideritic areas. Another type of mineralization is that of ramifying monazite-rich veinlets accompanied by strontianite, ankerite, quartz and barite. The most spectacular form of mineralization occurs within rounded bodies, from 2 in up to 1 ft in diameter, which consist of radiating groups of prismatic pseudomorphs comprising barite, strontianite, quartz, clear carbonate and drusy pale green monazite associated with flaky minerals of the bastnaesite series, and occasionally with sugary pale pink florencite. Semi-radiate structures of similar type also occur, often oriented in bands alternating with, or parallel to, tooth-shaped drusy patches of segregations of rare earth minerals aligned perpendicular to the banding.

The ankeritic carbonates vary in colour from white or pale buff to dark tawny. Refractive index measurements on a range of carbonates indicate that the content of ferro-mangan-dolomite varies from 3.5 per cent to about 36 per cent, such that the megascopically leucocratic ankerites contain most ferro-mangan-dolomite. In the tawny carbonatites, the ankerite has shed as limonitic inclusions most of its iron and manganese carbonate leaving a nearly pure dolomitic carbonate. The strontianite is a very pure variety with over 66 per cent SrO and less than 2.5 per cent CaO.

Pyrochlore is a rare accessory mineral as pale yellow to almost colourless octahedra up to 0.05 mm across.

The monazite is an unusual, almost thorium-free variety which occurs as euhedral pale green crystals from microns up to 3 mm long. The refractive indices are $\alpha = 1.786$, $\beta = 1.787$, $\gamma = 1.840$ and $2V - 5° 6°$.

Bastnaesite with $\omega = 1.702 - 1.709$ and $\epsilon = 1.804 - 1.810$ occurs as thin hexagonal plates and bundles of plates. It is often associated with pink florencite which occurs as pale pink rhombohedra ranging in size from 0.01 mm to 0.05 mm long. ω varies from $1.648 - 1.665$ and ϵ varies from $1.657 - 1.673$ indicating a range of minerals from strontian florencite to nearly pure florencite.

Chemical analyses and approximate mineral compositions of ankeritic carbonatites and strontianite-rich ankeritic carbonatites are given in Tables X and XI.

Late siliceous rocks

Throughout the Kangankunde area there are numerous irregular outcrops of siliceous rocks, many of which occur as areas of irregular disseminations while others form arcuate or dike-like bodies measuring up to 800 ft long by 100 ft wide.

The most abundant of these rocks contain numerous rare earth minerals. They are fine- to medium-grained, greyish buff and speckled rocks with cavities and druses lined by quartz crystals. Up to one third of the rocks consist of opaque rhombohedral carbonate and the rest of quartz-rich bands and druses with associated monazite, bastnaesite, florencite, barite, pyrochlore and sphalerite. Radioactive varieties contain in addition much parisite and thorian goethite similar to that at Chilwa Island.

TABLE X

Chemical Analyses of Carbonatites at Kangankunde

	1	2	3	4	5	6	7	8
SiO_2	1.87	2.13	2.60	3.24	0.40	2.01	1.40	0.65
Al_2O_3	0.20	0.24	0.40	0.20	0.32	2.41	0.25	0.13
Fe_2O_3	2.80	6.97	5.37	11.50	10.69	17.60	3.97	3.30
FeO	10.40	—	—	—	—	—	—	—
TiO_2	nil	nil	nil	nil	nil	nil	nil	nil
MnO_2	—	3.22	2.26	6.35	4.74	2.97	1.80	1.53
MnO	5.00	—	—	—	—	—	—	—
CaO	19.26	24.69	20.80	25.85	25.18	16.99	17.46	15.90
MgO	14.47	15.12	12.05	10.74	16.68	12.01	9.24	10.05
BaO	0.10	0.27	4.26	2.48	0.03	1.50	2.72	2.89
SrO	2.48	3.95	0.71	0.73	0.89	4.76	18.24	15.92
$TR_2O_3 + ThO_2$	1.18	2.92	12.18	2.82	tr.	5.12	8.00	10.98
$(Nb,Ta)_2O_5$	tr.	tr.	0.01	tr.	tr.	0.02	tr.	tr.
SO_3, soluble	0.12	0.10	0.14	0.05	0.06	} 1.22	0.15	0.25
SO_3, insoluble	nil	nil	2.28	0.44	—		1.03	1.58
P_2O_5	0.80	1.49	5.56	1.27	0.05	3.50	5.15	4.76
CO_2	38.36	38.19	30.04	32.62	39.35	25.50	29.80	30.47[b]
H_2O+	nil	0.33	0.28	1.66	1.07	2.52	nil	nil
H_2O-	—	—	—	—	—	0.61	—	—
Zn	0.29	0.26	0.10	0.12	0.35	—	0.62	0.84
	97.33	99.88	99.04	100.07	99.81	98.74[a]	99.83	99.25

[a] Constituents present but not determined include alkalis and fluorine.
[b] Loss on ignition (N. Cogger).

1. Pale buff-coloured carbonatite (G462), upper eastern slopes of North Knoll.
2. Banded ankeritic and sideritic carbonatite (G427), with monazite-rich veins, northern part of central complex.
3. Tawny bastnaesite monazite carbonatite (G1160), 800 ft south west of crest of Kangankunde Hill.
4. Very dark brown bastnaesite-monazite-carbonatite (G1135), 750 ft south south west of crest of Kangankunde Hill.
5. Carbonate-portion of tawny bastnaesite carbonatite (G1135), north western upper slopes of North Knoll.
6. Monazite carbonatite (Sample No. 45), collected by T. Deans in 1951 from area of summit beacon, C. V. Green, anal.
7. Strontianite-rich ankeritic carbonatite (G1148) with much florencite and monazite, Trench No. RCM No. 2.
8. Strontianite-rich ankeritic carbonatite with much monazite (BCA 654/C) collected by Rhodesia Chrane Mines in 1955.
Samples 1–5, 7 and 8 were analysed by D. C. Griffith and Co., and Mineral Resources Division (R. Pickup and N. Cogger).

An apatite-rich quartz-druse rock, about 0.5 mile south west of the top of the Southern Knoll comprises 50 per cent of fine-grained turbid apatite, much carbonate and a little florencite. Dahllite is an accessory mineral in an unusual quartz-fluorite rock which occurs 1 mile north east of the foot of Kangankunde Hill.

TABLE XI

Approximate Mineral Compositions of Carbonatites Calculated from Chemical Analyses

	G462	G427	G1160	G1161	G1135	Sample 45	G1148	BCA 654/G
Quartz	1.87	2.13	2.60	3.24	0.40	} 6.2	1.40	0.68
Orthoclase	—	—	—	—	1.67		—	—
Barite	0.16	0.41	6.49	3.77	0.47	2.3	3.01	4.38
Pyrochlore	tr	tr	0.22	tr	tr	0.03	tr	tr
Sphalerite	0.43	0.39	0.15	0.18	0.52	—	0.92	1.25
Apatite	0.31	0.34	0.67	tr	0.11	3.00	2.18	0.31
Monazite	1.69a	3.79	16.30	3.63a	tr	7.30	7.15	14.96
Florencite	—	0.59	0.93	0.46	—	—	5.00	0.31
Strontianite	3.52	5.66	0.84	0.95	1.27	6.80	25.36	22.64
CaCO₃	33.89	43.77	36.44	46.07	44.79	} 49.2	28.95	28.01
MgCO₃	30.25	31.54	25.11	22.37	34.75		19.32	20.94
FeCO₃	11.70	1.46	1.15	0.61	1.61	—	4.71	0.78
MnCO₃	5.75	0.01	0.44	0.30	0.65	—	2.27	0.37
Fe₂O₃ (as limonite?)	2.80	5.95	4.57	11.06	9.58	20.13	—	2.76
MnO₂	1.45 (MnO)	2.75	1.93	6.12	4.14	2.97	—	1.25
H₂O	0.22	0.22	0.11	1.57	1.07	2.52	—	—

a Includes bastnaesite.
Mineral composition of Sample 45 was determined by T. Deans.

Alkaline dikes and biotite alnöite

The alkaline dikes comprise a few thin sölvsbergites and some trachytic types which are probably mobilized feldspathic rocks.

Two extremely weathered lamprophyric dikes are possibly biotite alnöites which are partly carbonatized. These are pale greenish rocks with pink spots consisting of turbid carbonate replacing insets of nepheline. The remainder of the rocks comprise insets of apatite, titano-magnetite, chloritized biotite and serpentine-carbonate pseudomorphs after olivine in a fine-grained groundmass consisting of biotite, and laths of melilite in an intimate mixture of carbonate, serpentine, analcite and turbid nepheline (?).

II. PETROGENESIS OF CARBONATITES AND ASSOCIATED ROCKS

The carbonatites in Malawi in general have intrusive relations with country rocks and have behaved as igneous rocks. It is evident that they are not mere hydrothermal replacements of pre-existing rocks by carbonate minerals, although a certain amount of carbonatization has occurred at several vents and especially at the Kangankunde Complex. This process, which has evidently operated in the upper levels of these intrusions, in any case does not preclude the presence of igneous carbonatites, for Wyllie and Tuttle (1960) in important laboratory experiments with carbonate melts have found that hydrothermal solutions would result from condensation at lower temperatures of the vapour given off during crystallization. Nor may these carbonatites be explained as mobilized limestones of sedimentary origin, since there is a relative paucity of the latter adjacent to most of the carbonatite centres, and it has been shown that the carbonatites have characteristic trace element distributions which differ significantly from those of sedimentary and metamorphic limestones (Garson and Campbell Smith, 1958). Also there are essential differences in mineral composition between sedimentary or metamorphic limestones and carbonatites, and the characteristic presence of fenites and feldspathic rocks is explicable only through metasomatic processes associated with igneous carbonatites.

Wyllie and Tuttle's (1960) low-temperature liquid can reasonably be accepted as a simplified carbonatite magma with CaO representing the basic oxides, CaO, MgO and FeO of the natural magma. The unresolved question is therefore not the nature of carbonatite but the origin of the carbonatite magma and the genesis of the associated rocks. The petrogenesis of these rocks in Malawi cannot be considered in isolation from similar rocks elsewhere. A study of carbonatite complexes in Africa shows that in general there has been an increase in erosion from Uganda southwards so that a complex range is revealed from upper volcanic levels down to deep-seated stems (Dixey, 1946). The Malawi complexes fit into this pattern as having been eroded down to intermediate volcanic levels just below the cone of volcanic flows and ejectamenta. The main types of typical igneous rocks at various levels may be classified as follows:

1. Volcanic cone

Examples of this level include Kerimasi (James, 1953) with flows of carbonatite and nephelinite, and ejectamenta of nepheline-tuff; Oldoinyo Lengai (Dawson, this volume, pp. 155–167), also with carbonatite lavas (both in Tanganyika), and Napak (King, 1949, this volume, pp. 97–110) in Uganda with a volcanic pile of tuff, agglomerate, trachyte and nephelinite.

2. Intermediate volcanic level

Fine examples of these occur in Malawi and also in the Feira District of Zambia (Bailey, this volume, pp. 127–153). Characteristic rocks are feldspathic breccias and agglomerate intimately saturated by carbonatite. The feldspathic rocks (feldspathic fenites) are the source of the trachytic lavas and ejectamenta of the volcanic cone. There is generally a range of carbonatite types comprising sövitic, ankeritic and sideritic varieties, generally emplaced in that order as if some form of gravitational differentiation has operated. The nephelinitic lavas of the volcanic cone stage are represented by feeders comprising cone sheets, dikes and pipes of similar rocks, and also plutonic stems of ijolitic rocks. Other associated rocks are alnöite, nepheline syenite and related dike rocks. The zone of fenitization around the carbonatites shows an introduction into the country rocks of dominant potash and lesser amounts of soda.

3. Upper plutonic stem

Examples of this level occur in Southern Rhodesia at Dorowa and Shawa (Johnson, this volume, pp. 205–224) and Spitskop in South Africa (Strauss and Truter, 1951). Rock types represented include sövite and dolomitic carbonatite with a zone of fenitization in which the introduction of soda is greater than that of potash (Garson, 1962). Silicate rocks comprise ijolitic and foyaitic varieties, and basic and ultrabasic types such as pyroxenite, dunite and serpentinite or peridotite. No trachytic rocks occur.

4. Deep-seated plutonic stem

Palabora in South Africa (Russell *et al.*, 1955) and Jacupiranga in Brazil (Melcher, this volume, pp. 169–179) are typical examples. Dike rocks are rare and the igneous rocks associated with the carbonatite comprise syenite or ijolite, peridotite, pyroxenite and olivine vermiculite pegmatoid (biotite peridotite?). The pyroxenite is probably a reaction product at the contact of carbonatite with syenitic fenites similar to that recorded on a smaller scale at Tundulu (Garson, 1962).

Dikes associated with deep centres at Tundulu and Alnö comprise beforsitic alnöite at the former locality and beforsitic varieties of alnöite and kimberlite at the latter locality.

James (1958) has stated that the very diversity of rock types associated with carbonatite suggests that marked differentiation from a primary magma has occurred, and that carbonatite, kimberlite and biotite pyroxenite are the deep-seated direct differentiates of this unknown primary magma, all other rock types being due to later differentiation, contamination or processes of alkali metaso-matism. Studies of the association of rock types at carbonatite complexes in Malawi indicate that kimberlite or a kimberlite–peridotite assemblage is the most probable source of carbonatite (Garson, 1962). The concept has been adopted for the following reasons:

1. Mica peridotite or related ultrabasic rocks occur at the deepest plutonic levels of carbonatite complexes.

2. A close association of carbonatite and kimberlite is indicated at the Premier Diamond Mine in South Africa (Daly, 1925), at Alnö and Kalix in Sweden (v. Eckermann 1958; Larsson, 1943) where there are intermediate rock-types, and at the Kiwurungi and Igwisi pipes in Tangan-yika (McKinlay, 1958; Sampson, 1956) where there are pipe rocks suggested to be transitional in composition and mineralogy between carbonatite and kimberlite (Garson, 1962).

3. Trace element studies of rocks including melanephelinites, alnöites and beforsites associated with the deep igneous centre at the Tundulu Complex and of apatite beforsites at the Kangankunde Complex, show that there is a marked similarity between their trace element distribution and that of kimberlite (Garson, 1962; Garson, 1965a).

4. The prevalence of alnöitic rocks is a marked feature of numerous carbonatite localities. At Alnö there are transitional rocks between alnöite and kimberlite, and gradations to olivine-melilitite are also present. Alnöitic rocks are essentially different phases of melilite-basalts which in turn are related to kimberlitic rocks (Taljaard, 1937, pp. 312–315).

It is postulated that carbonatite originates as a concentration of CaO, MgO, FeO and volatiles in the upper portions of highly differentiated kimberlitic fractions above a parental mica peridotite. The rocks of the Igwisi and Kiwur-ungi pipes in Tanganyika are taken to be early stages of this concentration. Modification of the carbonatitic fraction probably occurs as a result of assimila-tion, reaction with wall rocks and gravitational differentiation. Fenitization possibly occurs as the result of varying processes of alkali exchanges due to thermal gradients forming concentration gradients with respect of Na/K ratio in alkali carbonate phases, as indicated by Orville (1963). Alnöitic rocks are formed by desilication of deep-seated peridotitic material due to processes of fenitization, and a further desilication, differentiation and addition of alkalis produces nepheline alnöites as at Winnett, Montana (Ross, 1926) and Alnö (v. Eckermann, 1958) and ultimately olivine melilite melanephelinites and other nephelinitic varieties. The carbonatized melilite-bearing nephelinites at Kangankunde are possibly an intermediate stage between alnöite and nepheli-nite in this igneous sequence.

The association of carbonatites with rift faulting is taken as evidence in favour of the tapping of deep-seated ultrabasic magmas which were already highly differentiated in stable crustal areas over a long period of time.

REFERENCES

Bloomfield, K., 1965, The geology of the Zomba area: *Malawi Geol. Surv., Bull.* **16**.

Daly, R. A., 1925, Carbonate dikes of the Premier Diamond Mine, Transvaal: *Jour. Geol.*, v. **33**, pp. 695–784.

Davies, K. A., 1956, The geology of part of south-east Uganda: *Uganda Geol. Surv., Mem.* **8**.

Dias, M. de B., 1961, Geologia do Monte Muambe: *Serv. de Geol. e. Minas, Bull.* **27**, pp. 37–88.

Dixey, F., 1946, Carbonate pipes and ring structures: *Geol. Mag.*, v. **83**, pp. 289–291.

Dixey, F., Campbell Smith, W., and Bisset, C. B., 1937 (revised 1955), The Chilwa Series of southern Nyasaland: *Nyasaland Geol. Surv., Bull.* **5**.

v. Eckermann, H., 1948, The alkaline district of Alnö Island: *Sveriges Geol. Undersokning, Ser. Ca.*, No. **36**.

v. Eckermann, H., 1958, The alkaline and carbonatitic dikes of the Alnö formation on the mainland north-west of Alnö Island: *Kungl. Vetenskap. Akademiens Handl.*, v. **7**, No. 2.

Garson, M. S., 1955, Flow phenomena in carbonatites in southern Nyasaland: *Colon. Geol. Mineral Resources*, v. **5**, No. 3, pp. 311–318.

Garson, M. S., 1960, The geology of the Lake Chilwa area: *Nyasaland Geol. Surv., Bull.* **12**.

Garson, M. S., 1961, The geology of the Namangali vent, Mlanje District: *Nyasaland Geol. Surv., Rec.* 1959, v. **1**, pp. 51–62.

Garson, M. S., 1962, The Tundulu carbonatite ring-complex in southern Nyasaland: *Nyasaland Geol. Surv., Mem.* **2**.

Garson, M. S., 1963, The geology of the Nkalonje ring-structure: *Nyasaland Geol. Surv., Rec.* 1960, v. **2**, pp. 91–110.

Garson, M. S., 1965a, Carbonatite and agglomerate vents in the western Shire Valley: *Malawi Geol. Surv., Mem.* **3**.

Garson, M. S., 1965b, The geology of the area west of Lake Malombe, Fort Johnston District: *Malawi Geol. Surv., Rec.* 1961, v. **3**.

Garson, M. S., and Campbell Smith, W., 1958, Chilwa Island: *Nyasaland Geol. Surv., Mem.* **1**.

Holt, D. N., 1965, The Kangankunde Hill rare earth prospect: *Malawi Geol. Surv., Bull.* **20**.

James, T. C., 1953, An interim report on recent investigations in the Northern and Central Provinces: *Tanganyika Geol. Surv.* (unpublished report TCJ/18).

James, T. C., 1958, Summary of silicate rocks associated with carbonatite bodies in Tanganyika: *C.C.T.A. Comm. Geol. Leopoldville*, 1958, pp. 307–308.

King, B. C., 1949, The Napak area of southern Karamoja, Uganda: *Uganda Geol. Surv., Mem.* **5** (1948).

Larsson, W., 1943, Sur Kenntnis der alkalinen ultrabasischen Ganggesteine des Kalix Gebiets Nord-Schweden: *Sveriges Geol. Undersokning, Ser. C.*, No. **456**.

McKinlay, A. C. M., 1958, Mineralogy and petrology. Kimberlite intrusions cutting Karoo sediments in the Ruhuhu depression of south-west Tanganyika: *Tanganyika Geol. Surv., Rec.* 1955, v. **5**, pp. 63–80.

Orville, P. M., 1963, Alkali ion exchange between vapor and feldspar phase: *Am. Jour. Sci.*, v. **261**, pp. 201–237.

Pulfrey, W., 1950, Ijolitic rocks near Homa Bay, western Kenya: *Geol. Soc. London, Quart. Jour.*, v. **105**, pp. 425–459.

Reynolds, D. L., 1954, Fluidization as a geological process: *Am. Jour. Sci.*, v. **252**, pp. 577–613.

Richey, J. E., 1948, Scotland. The Tertiary volcanic districts. British Regional geology. *H.M. Geol. Surv. and Museum.* pp. 49–53.

Ross, C. S., 1926, Nephelite-hauynite alnöite from Winnett, Montana: *Am. Jour. Sci.*, v. **11**, pp. 218–227.

Russell, H. D., Hiemstra, S. A. and Groeneveld, D., 1955, The mineralogy and petrology of the carbonatite at Loolekop, eastern Transvaal: *Geol. Soc. S. Africa Trans.*, v. **57**, pp. 197–208.

Sampson, D. N., 1956, The volcanic hills at Igwisi (with petrological notes by K. C. Dunham): *Tanganyika Geol. Surv., Rec.* 1953, v. **3**, pp. 48–53.

Smith, W. C., 1953, Carbonatites of the Chilwa Series of southern Nyasaland: *Bull. Brit. Mus. (Nat. Hist.) Mineralogy*, v. **1**, No. 4.

Strauss, C. A. and Truter, F. C., 1951, The alkali complex at Spitskop, Sekukuniland, eastern Transvaal: *Geol. Soc. S. Africa. Trans.*, v. **53**, pp. 81–125.

Stringer, K. V., Holt, D. N. and Groves, A. W., 1956, The Chambe Plateau ring complex of Nyasaland: *Colon. Geol. Mineral Resources*, v. **6**, No. 1, pp. 3–18.

Taljaard, M. S., 1937, South African melilite basalts and their relations: *Geol. Soc. S. Africa Trans.*, v. **39**, pp. 312–315.

Vail, J. R. and Monkman, L. J., 1960, A geological reconnaissance survey of the Chaone ring complex, southern Nyasaland: *Geol. Soc. S. Africa. Trans.*, v. **63**, pp. 119–132.

Vail, J. R. and Mallick, D. I. J., 1965, The nephelinite-syenite ring-complex of the Mongolowe Hills, southern Nyasaland: *Malawi Geol. Surv., Rec.* 1961, v. **3**.

Wyllie, P. J. and Tuttle, O. F., 1960, The system CaO–CO_2–H_2O and the origin of carbonatites: *Jour. Petrology*, v. **1**, No. 1, pp. 1–46.

B. C. KING and DIANE S. SUTHERLAND

The Carbonatite Complexes
of Eastern Uganda

INTRODUCTION

From the plains of eastern Uganda rise four impressive mountains, Elgon (14,178 ft), Kadam (10,050 ft), Napak (8300 ft) and Moroto (9700 ft), which are the dissected cones of central volcanoes of Tertiary age. To the north lies the eroded stump of a similar volcano forming the Toror Hills (6300 ft) and, to the south, close to Mount Elgon, are the still more eroded complexes of Budeda, Bukusu, Sekululu, Tororo and Sukulu, which are believed to date from the Cretaceous (post-Karroo and pre-Miocene) (Fig. 1). The entire group lies in a N–S belt which continues to the south in the complexes of the Kavirondo area of Kenya.

From his early reconnaissance work Wayland (1920) described the 'Elgon Series' as the remnants of vast flows resulting from fissure eruption, the low angles of dip of the volcanics being compatible with this view. Subsequently, however, it was appreciated that the separate mountains are in fact individual volcanoes having low conical forms (Davies and Bisset, 1935). The nature and origin of the carbonatites in south eastern Uganda, set among Basement granites and gneisses, were for many years problematical; that forming Tororo Rock was at first considered by Davies (1956) to be metamorphic, the surrounding alkaline rocks having been produced by reaction with granitic magma. It was Bisset who, from his experience of the Chilwa Series in collaboration with Dixey, first recognized that the limestones of Lokupoi (Napak), Toror, Tororo and Sukulu are intrusive.

The relation between a volcanic cone and its plutonic substructure is magnificently displayed at Napak where a large amount of the volcanics has been removed by erosion, and carbonatite surrounded by ijolite is exposed at the site of the central vent. Carbonatite is not exposed at Elgon, Kadam or Moroto. At Toror, no volcanics remain and carbonatite is revealed, accompanied by phonolites and trachytes. Volcanics are absent at the older complexes to the south, where carbonatites are associated with alkaline silicate rocks. The best exposures of carbonatite itself are found at Tororo, where it is quarried for cement. The alkaline silicate rocks, however, are very well seen at Budeda, where carbonatite is poorly developed.

The country rocks over the entire region have been assigned to the 'Basement

73

Complex'. The predominant rocks are granitic and include both acid gneisses and homogeneous granites. Of more limited distribution in south eastern Uganda, diorites, tonalites, syenites and granodiorites are recorded by Davies (1956). In southern Karamoja acid gneisses with subordinate quartzo-feldspathic and biotite granulites, amphibolites and pyroxene gneisses and granulites are described by Macdonald (1961) and Trendall (1961).

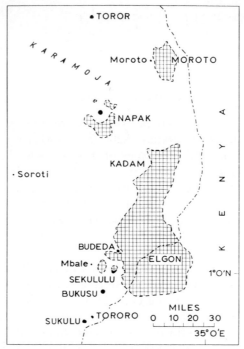

Fig. 1. Map showing locations of alkaline centres of eastern Uganda: volcanics shaded, intrusive centres in black.

THE OLDER COMPLEXES

These complexes are truncated by the surface upon which the Tertiary volcanoes are built. They occur along a line trending NNE-SSW about 40 miles in length in the extreme south east of Uganda and have been ascribed to the Cretaceous merely by analogy with the Chilwa Series which are known to cut Karroo (King and Sutherland, 1960).

They comprise Sukulu, Bukusu, Sekululu, Budeda and Tororo (Fig. 2). Only Budeda and Tororo on which new work has been done (by D.S.S.) are discussed. Summaries of the remainder are given on pages 486–491.

Budeda

The Budeda Complex is about 13 miles ENE of Mbale Township in the Elgon foothills bordering the Siroko valley. Although it is the smallest of the complexes, being less than half a mile across, the outcrops are fresh, and small-scale structures can be examined readily in the water-worn surfaces along the Siroko River and its tributaries (Fig. 3).

The central part of the complex is an arcuate mass, 800 ft in length, ranging from pyroxenite or melteigite to ijolite and urtite with two small areas of carbonatite less than 40 ft across. Several small masses of ijolite are separate from the

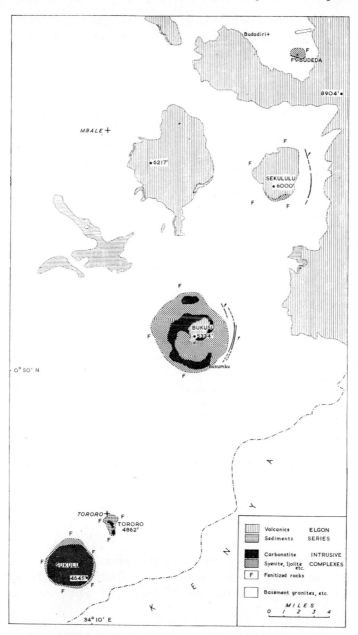

Fig. 2. The older alkaline complexes of south eastern Uganda (after Davies, 1956).

main central mass and all lie within a wide area of syenitic fenites in the granitic Basement rocks. In many places cancrinite syenite is found around the margins of the 'ijolite'. A dike of nepheline syenite and several small dikes of cancrinite phonolite occur. The complex is cut by a fault with an ENE trend.

The country rocks

Most of the area around Mbale is underlain by granitic Basement which is poorly exposed because of the intense weathering. The rocks vary over short

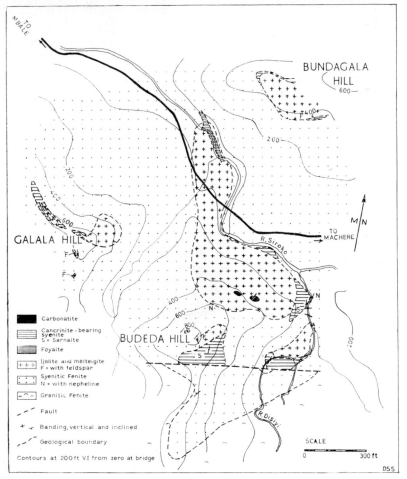

Fig. 3. Geological map of the Budeda Complex (D.S.S.).

distances and are principally granites and granitic gneisses. An unusually potash-rich granite occurs in the stream section south east of Budeda Hill. A partial analysis gives K_2O 7.66 and Na_2O 3.05 wt per cent.

The envelope of fenites

At Budeda, the term fenite embraces three rock-types: fenitized granite (containing quartz); syenitic fenites (with no free quartz); and nepheline-bearing syenitic fenites. Within each group are variations from leucocratic to melanocratic rocks. These rocks form an envelope around the central alkaline masses; only two zones are distinguishable in the field: an outer fringe of fenitized granite grading into country rock, and an inner zone of syenitic fenites, the nepheline-bearing fenites being only sporadically developed in small patches close to the central alkaline bodies.

The sequence of events which can be recognized in the fenites is: (i) crushing, (ii) early metasomatism, (iii) recrystallization, with further metasomatism and (iv) the development of feldspar porphyroblasts, veins and lenses, often of coarse texture.

(a) *Fenitized granite.* The first signs of fenitization appear as minute channels along which feldspar and, to a lesser extent, quartz have undergone granulation. The channels form a random network which is seen in the field as a pattern of hair-like cracks coloured brown by the alteration of dark minerals in the veins. Parts of large crystals become optically discontinuous and separated by granulation channels, and as the proportion of granulated material increases they appear as angular fragments in a recrystallized groundmass. The recrystallizing feldspar becomes oriented along the veins where plagioclase, rather more sodic than the original oligoclase, forms an intergrowth of elongate, subhedral crystals. A potash-rich granite, more intensely granulated, shows the development of a fine-grained groundmass of anhedral potash feldspar and small albite crystals. Ultimately the whole rock becomes recrystallized to a granular mass of albite, potash feldspar and quartz, with the exception of relict crystals of oligoclase, rounded and embayed by albite (An_9).

Along the granulation channels amphibole and pyroxene developed rather later than the recrystallization of feldspar; except in the wider channels (2 mm) none of these minerals shows any marked parallelism. The dark minerals form sheaves of radiating prisms which, where they become abundant, aggregate as a felted mass. The pyroxene is near aegirine, $X: c = 5°$, strongly pleochroic in pale colours, X (blue-green) $>$ Y (green) $>$ Z (yellow), but the colour is patchily distributed even in small crystals and extinction is irregular. It occurs with a pale blue amphibole of similar habit but less idiomorphic, the pyroxene grains tending to lie along the edge of the fenite veins with amphibole among the feldspar crystals inside. The amphibole has a low birefringence and anomalous blue interference tints, with an extinction angle of about 28°. It is weakly pleochroic X (blue-green) $>$ Y (yellow-green) $>$ Z (pink-grey). Where shattering is not restricted to narrow channels the fenite minerals are dispersed through the fine-grained groundmass, and pick out a vague banding, but individual crystals in the layers are not aligned. Pyroxene and amphibole are equally developed, and are especially abundant around pods of quartz. The amphibole here has an extinction angle of over 40° and $X > Y > Z$ (Garson and Campbell Smith, 1958, p. 22). The dark minerals form a sweeping pattern around the relict oligoclase, and the rock in the field has the appearance of an augen gneiss.

(b) *Syenitic fenites.* Whereas the granites show only limited effects of crushing and metasomatic recrystallization, the syenites have been far more intensely affected by both processes and quartz has finally disappeared. The rocks show a

D

TABLE I

Rocks from the Budeda Complex

A. CHEMICAL COMPOSITIONS

	1 Melteigite B27	2 Ijolite B7	3 Nepheline syenite B266	4 Nepheline syenite B302	5 Cancrinite nepheline syenite B247	6 Cancrinite syenite (dike) B262	7 Cancrinite phonolite (dike) B269	8 Syenitic fenite B223	9 Potash syenitic fenite B242	10 Syenitic fenite with nepheline B279
SiO_2	45.68	45.49	49.47	47.71	48.18	47.70	49.55	64.79	59.36	56.71
Al_2O_3	3.33	11.99	15.26	17.35	17.24	13.65	16.80	17.78	15.50	16.30
Fe_2O_3	6.71	7.08	5.05	4.91	2.84	3.27	4.30	2.05	2.43	2.36
FeO	9.50	6.46	4.71	4.73	3.16	3.10	2.92	0.88	2.24	3.03
MgO	6.89	3.82	2.47	1.85	1.34	0.43	0.17	0.40	1.00	1.64
CaO	20.28	12.32	8.61	7.54	8.26	11.23	6.39	2.21	4.43	5.38
Na_2O	2.86	5.45	8.59	8.18	6.91	4.93	8.91	8.42	3.59	7.71
K_2O	0.10	1.35	3.29	4.44	5.64	6.04	4.96	3.19	9.17	4.05
H_2O	0.46	2.94	0.78	0.92	2.14	1.58	1.83	0.33	0.33	1.00
CO_2	0.11	1.01	0.68	0.42	2.71	5.20	3.43	nd	nd	0.30
TiO_2	0.64	0.41	0.57	0.72	0.60	0.49	0.42	0.43	0.41	0.68
P_2O_5	2.10	0.16	1.00	0.43	0.49	0.55	0.35	0.19	0.25	0.54
MnO	0.41	0.35	0.33	0.19	0.16	0.25	0.46	0.09	0.09	0.19
Total	99.07	98.83	100.80	99.39	99.65	98.42	100.49	100.76	100.51	99.89

B. NORMATIVE COMPOSITIONS (C.I.P.W.)

	1	2	3	4	5	6	7	8	9	10
Quartz	—	—	—	—	—	—	—	0.7	—	—
Orthoclase	0.6	8.1	19.4	26.4	33.6	35.8	28.8	18.8	54.3	24.2
Albite	6.0	18.9	7.4	6.3	8.5	15.0	9.6	70.9	21.3	35.8
Anorthite	—	4.3	—	—	—	—	—	1.5	4.0	—
Nepheline	5.6	14.7	28.5	31.5	26.4	11.4	26.7	—	4.6	13.7
Na_2SiO_3	—	—	—	—	—	—	0.6	—	—	—
Acmite	6.6	—	10.7	4.0	1.0	4.8	12.5	—	—	—
Diopside	62.4	31.9	25.3	19.1	17.0	10.3	7.0	2.2	8.3	3.6
Wollastonite	4.8	4.4	1.9	3.8	—	3.2	—	2.4	2.7	16.1
Olivine	—	—	—	—	0.2	—	2.2	—	—	0.8
Magnetite	6.4	10.2	1.9	5.2	3.7	2.4	—	1.9	3.5	1.6
Hematite	—	—	—	—	—	—	—	0.8	—	—
Ilmenite	1.3	0.8	2.0	1.4	1.2	0.9	0.8	0.8	0.8	1.4
Apatite	5.0	0.3	1.3	1.1	1.3	1.2	0.8	0.3	0.5	1.3
Calcite	0.2	2.3	1.6	0.9	6.1	11.8	7.8	—	—	0.7
Total	98.9	95.9	100.0	99.7	99.0	96.8	96.8	100.3	100.0	99.2

strong parallel banded structure, reflecting an early phase of deformation; this banding has often been preserved despite subsequent recrystallization. Many of the syenites contain conspicuous spots of feldspar which are the sole relics of the original granite. The spots, which may be as much as 1 cm in diameter, are often oval with a marked parallelism, and the dark minerals sweep round them. The spotted syenites grade, often rapidly, into unspotted, fine-grained syenites with a banding picked out by layers of dark minerals, and these pass into vaguely streaked syenites with swirling layers of feldspar and pyroxene. These structures are locally modified or obliterated by the development of later feldspar in porphyroblasts, lenses and veins.

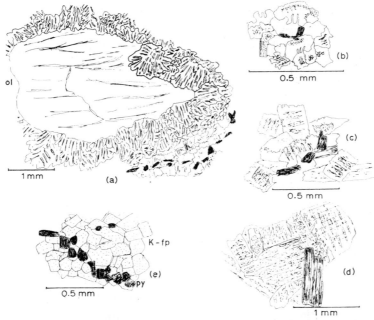

Fig. 4. Syenitic fenites at Budeda. (a) Oligoclase relic surrounded by fringe of feldspar with dactylotypic inclusions, in groundmass of fine-grained antiperthite with pyroxene. (b) Fine-grained antiperthite ground-mass. (c) Medium-grained antiperthite groundmass. (d) Coarse-grained perthosite. (e) Granular mosaic of potash feldspar (potash syenite). (ol-oligoclase, K-fp -potash feldspar, py-pyroxene.)

In thin section the syenites show variation from predominantly sodic rocks to those characterized by potash feldspar.

(i) Soda-syenites (Table I, 8). Recognizable relics of the original rock occur as rounded spots which in thin section are found usually to consist of single crystals of oligoclase (An_{12}) traversed by channels of antiperthite. Around the edges the relics are embayed by a fringe of feldspar crystals up to 0.5 mm in size and of irregular shape, having a characteristic dactylotypic texture owing to the presence of numerous inclusions (Fig. 4a), which in some cases are possibly scolecite. The fringing feldspar though rarely twinned is apparently albite, and all stages in the replacement of oligoclase can be observed. Some spots consist entirely of aggregates of dactylotypic feldspar.

Around the relics is a fine-grained groundmass of recrystallized feldspar, commonly antiperthite; the margins of the crystals are intricately intergrown in a close feathery texture (Fig. 4b). The feldspar (An_8) is twinned only rarely, when it shows a tendency towards a lath-habit. The grain size of the groundmass is around 0.1 mm and often varies in narrow bands a few millimetres wide.

The pyroxene occurs in layers of small granules in the fine-grained bands, and as dispersed larger crystals in the coarser textured bands. Sometimes the granules tend to collect as sieve-like plates and become optically continuous. It is an aegirine-augite with $X: c$ about $36°$. In some of the syenites, particularly those with the spongy-textured pyroxene, amphibole and/or biotite occur. The amphibole differs somewhat from that in the granitic fenites ($Z: c = 21$–$23°$, strongly pleochroic, X (pale grey-brown) $< Y$ (dark grey-brown) $> Z$ (green-grey)). The biotite is pleochroic from red-brown to pale straw. Sphene is a constant accessory mineral.

The fine-grained syenites grade into rather coarser textured varieties (0.2–0.3 mm) (Fig. 4c), having the same mineralogy, but with a less distinct banding. They are sometimes spotted, but these spots consist of recrystallized antiperthite, probably in the place of former relics.

Sporadically distributed among the fenites are much coarser grained rocks, having a grain size from 2–5 mm (Fig. 4d). These rocks are essentially perthosites, the plagioclase rims of neighbouring crystals being intricately intergrown. Pyroxene ($X: c = 28$–$35°$) forms scattered prisms in some rocks, but in others it is confined to veins so that the appearance of the rock is similar to the fenitized granite.

(ii) Potash syenites (Table I, 9) are considered to represent fenitized potash-granite of the Basement. Relic spots up to 1.5 cm in diameter consist of aggregates of interlobing crystals of potash feldspar which enclose elongate blebs of a zeolite having the same properties as the scolecite (?) in the more sodic feldspars. Outside the spots the groundmass consists of a granular mosaic of clear potash feldspar (orthoclase) (Fig. 4e); in contrast with the soda-syenites the grain boundaries are simple and polygonal, and the feldspar is rarely perthitic. Some of the feldspar tends towards rectangular habit and a general parallel orientation. Pyroxene ($X: c = 35$–$45°$) may be concentrated in layers or dispersed between feldspar crystals and around groups of them, and prismatic crystals may show parallel orientation; some zoning occurs. Apatite and pale sphene are constant accessories.

In the more recrystallized syenites, variable amounts of plagioclase occur as albite rims to potash feldspar and sometimes as separate crystals; large porphyro-blastic crystals growing in pods and in the sites of former relics are generally perthite.

(c) *Nepheline-bearing syenitic fenites* (Table I, 10). The nepheline-bearing syenites are sporadically developed in both the soda- and potash-syenitic fenites close to the ijolite masses. Many instances were found, however, of nepheline-free fenites against the ijolite margin and against cancrinite syenite. The nepheline is occasionally sufficiently abundant to be recognizable in the field, but is seen in many specimens of syenitic fenite in thin section. Most commonly it forms round porphyroblasts up to 1 mm in diameter, with irregular margins, enclosing antiperthite. While the porphyroblasts are often dispersed through the syenite, nepheline also congregates in pods of fairly coarse texture. There is evidence that in some cases nepheline accompanied the development of coarse feldspar in the syenites, for it is here confined to the coarse feldspar pods, being enclosed as numerous small blebs. Nepheline also occurs in cross-cutting veins replacing syenite, where it is accompanied by abundant pyroxene; these veins are cut by late coarse-textured veins of antiperthite having characteristic twinned 'chequer albite'. The nepheline was therefore introduced before the latest feldspathization.

Most of the nepheline-bearing fenites show conspicuous development of biotite; it forms aggregates of small flakes and some plates with spongy texture, and replaces pyroxene. Occasionally it is accompanied by a pale brownish-grey amphibole. Some of the nepheline-bearing syenites have cancrinite replacing nepheline, and sometimes a little calcite. In other respects the rocks can be exactly matched by the nepheline-free syenites.

Enclosed within the melteigites on the Siroko River are xenoliths of biotite ijolite, showing a close banding in which the three constituent minerals, nepheline, pyroxene and biotite, occur in varying proportions. The texture of the nepheline and pyroxene is granoblastic, but some of the larger crystals of biotite and pyroxene are poikiloblastic. The rock as a whole bears a strong resemblance to the biotite nepheline syenites in the fenite zone, apart from the absence of feldspar, and is interpreted as the product of extreme fenitization.

The central melteigite–ijolite masses

The bodies of melteigite–ijolite emplaced in the broader fenite zone are probably funnel shaped, spreading to become lenticular at the top, for inward dipping contacts were observed in several places and, at one locality, evidence from fragments in a breccia dike indicate that the melteigite–ijolite mass has a flat-lying lower surface underlain by fenite.

(a) *Pyroxenites and melteigites* (Table I, 1). On the northern slopes of Budeda Hill, in exposures in the Siroko River below, and on the summit of Galala Hill, are medium-grained, dark, compact rocks, which are about 90 per cent pyroxene. On Galala Hill and in the Siroko River exposures, this rock is apatite pyroxenite. The pyroxene[1] forms stout prisms, pleochroic from green to yellow, and is commonly zoned; apatite forms single grains and aggregates probing into the pyroxene. A little cloudy zeolite of low birefringence, and cancrinite, in place of original nepheline, occur interstitially. On the slopes of Budeda apatite is less abundant, and the dark rocks are melteigite, with unaltered anhedral, poikilitic nepheline between the pyroxene prisms; sphene is an abundant accessory, and a little calcite and biotite may be present. Small vugs of spherulitic natrolite, rimmed by limonite, are found in some thin sections, and locally pyrite is common. Within the pyroxenite–melteigites in the bend of the Siroko River are xenoliths

---

[1] A chemical analysis gave a composition corresponding to $Di_{38}He_{38}Ac_{24}$.

up to 9 in across of schistose biotite ijolite. The fact that the direction of the schistosity varies from one xenolith to another shows that the melteigite was originally mobile.

(b) *Ijolites* (Table I, 2). Of the intrusive rocks, dark, fine-grained pyroxenite–melteigite is the earliest phase and becomes replaced by ijolite which traverses the rock in a series of diffuse veins; nepheline porphyroblasts and pods appear in the pyroxenite, and recrystallization and replacement produce very coarse-grained ijolite in several stages. The pyroxenite–melteigite remains as angular xenoliths in heterogeneous ijolite.

The ijolites are extremely varied in composition and texture but, unlike the ijolites of Napak, few minerals occur other than the essential pyroxene and nepheline. Calcite, cancrinite and potash feldspar are the only additions by which the ijolites grade into other rock types.

The ijolites are rarely banded except near the margins of the masses, and are more often patchy, with rapid changes in texture and composition over a few inches. Very coarse-grained areas, with crystals up to a centimetre or so are common, both in diffuse patches and in well defined veins.

Three textural varieties of ijolite can be distinguished. One variety consists of euhedral or subhedral nepheline generally rectangular in outline and often 3 mm or more across, with ragged prisms of pyroxene arranged peripherally; the thin section viewed with the naked eye resembles crazy paving. The nepheline is slightly streaked by zeolite and frequently is partly replaced by cancrinite around the edges. The pyroxene[1] is irregular against nepheline but has mutual boundaries which are straight.

A second type of texture is formed where the pyroxene is enclosed by nepheline. Again, the pyroxene has straight boundaries with other crystals of pyroxene, but is generally lobed against nepheline; the nepheline is anhedral and interstitial.

The two textures can occur in the space of one thin section and are gradational from one to the other; in both cases pyroxene is embayed by nepheline and appears to be replaced by it; where nepheline is less abundant than pyroxene, it takes an interstitial position, but where it becomes more abundant it gradually assumes a euhedral form, leaving the pyroxene around the periphery. In general lighter coloured areas of ijolite have the first texture and darker rock the second type. It is inferred, therefore, that in all these ijolites pyroxene crystallized first and nepheline was a later replacement, despite its frequent euhedral habit. The evidence seen in thin section agrees with the observation in the field that the earliest rock to be emplaced was melteigite, which became nephelinized in patches and veins, to form ijolite.

A distinctive type of ijolite occurs sporadically; this is medium-grained and even-textured, having small, polygonal nepheline crystals and subordinate pyroxene along the interstices. The nepheline may have irregular margins in detail but within the nepheline crystals, inclusions of acicular aegirine-augite ($X: c = 26°$) are regularly arranged in zones. Calcite is a late replacement after nepheline, and pyrite is abundant.

---

[1] Chemical analysis of pyroxene in a typical ijolite gave a composition corresponding to $Di_{27}He_{36}Ac_{37}$.

Among accessories, apatite is ubiquitous but variably distributed; it forms rounded granules, very rarely prisms, and commonly embays pyroxene. Sphene is also common, but again is locally concentrated, especially alongside late ijolite veins and nepheline syenite dikes.

Cancrinite commonly replaces nepheline in small amount, as ramifying, anhedral plates. It is most abundant in the small masses of ijolite, and is least in the main Budeda ijolite. Calcite also occurs as an accessory mineral in the small ijolite masses but does not always accompany cancrinite.

Marginal phenomena between the central masses and the fenites

The ijolite at the margin is often crudely banded parallel with the contact, bands of differing composition and texture a few inches across being observed in two instances to dip steeply inwards; the ijolite bodies in both cases are small ones.

Xenoliths of fenite occur in ijolite south of Galala Hill, where they are unaltered and nepheline-free, but in exposures in the Siroko and Disiyi Rivers the feldspar of the fenite xenoliths is replaced by nepheline, and biotite is conspicuous as porphyroblastic aggregates. A sharp junction between ijolite and fenite can be seen on the summit of Budeda Hill; the fenite is not nepheline-bearing, and the ijolite is unchilled.

The most common phenomenon associated with the marginal zone of the ijolites is feldspathization which converts the ijolite to 'nepheline syenite' (Table I, 4, 5).

In some ijolites there are large poikilitic plates of clear feldspar with a small $2V$, enclosing euhedral nepheline; the nepheline is often streaked with zeolite and the feldspar may be replaced by cancrinite. More commonly, however, the potash feldspar is lath shaped and generally slightly perthitic, transecting and corroding the nepheline, and isolating parts of once continuous crystals. In most of these rocks cancrinite replaces nepheline to a varying extent and is interstitial to the feldspar.

Pyroxene is less abundant in the feldspathized ijolite than in the unaltered rock, and the stout prisms are corroded by adjacent feldspar; some of the pyroxene is now deeper in colour and extinction angles vary around $X: c = 30°$. The pyroxene frequently is partly replaced by calcite. Apatite and sphene are accessory.

Cancrinite-bearing rocks

Cancrinite becomes an important constituent in various feldspathic alkaline rocks around the outside of the ijolite occurrences. The cancrinite-bearing rocks can be classified more appropriately by texture than by mineralogy which has less genetic significance. The first type of cancrinite-bearing rock is derived from ijolite as potash feldspar and cancrinite replace nepheline and some of the pyroxene (Table I, 5). Most have prominent tabular feldspars which are sometimes aligned in trachytoid habit, but may form a felt of small laths. In these rocks, nepheline may or may not be present. Where it does occur, nepheline forms equant or rectangular grains, partly enclosed in feldspar, and sporadically replaced by cancrinite; this mineral may take the form of ramifying plates (which locally corrode feldspar also), aggregates of polygonal granules and small prisms, or large crystals interstitial to laths of feldspar (Fig. 5a). The accompanying pyroxene occurs as ragged acicular prisms, some of them zoned (X: c about 18°). Sphene and apatite are accessory, with occasional biotite after pyroxene. The potash feldspar may be homogeneous or perthitic.

Parts of the cancrinite-bearing masses on the eastern slopes of Budeda Hill contain felted laths of potash feldspar which, in thin section, are seen to enclose elongate prisms of cancrinite (Fig. 5b). Nepheline occurs only sporadically and has a rectangular habit. Pyroxene forms both stout grains (some zoned) and a later crop of small, ragged acicular prisms. Some alteration to red-brown

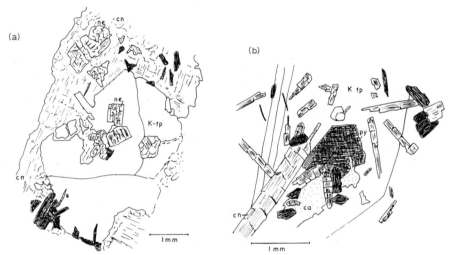

Fig. 5. (*a*) Cancrinite-bearing syenite with relict nepheline and large interstitial plates of cancrinite. (*b*) Cancrinite-syenite *ss.* (särnaite) with prismatic cancrinite enclosed in potash feldspar. (ca-calcite, cn-cancrinite, K-fp -potash feldspar, ne-nepheline, py-pyroxene, s-sphene.)   (Budeda)

biotite is recorded, and other minerals present in small amount arc apatitc, sphene, and interstitial calcite; one specimen has granules of brown melanite. Pegmatitic structures are common in this type of cancrinite syenite; a vague banding is produced on a macroscopic scale by the concentration of prismatic pyroxene and pink cancrinite in layers between feldspathic bands; a comb structure is often shown by the prismatic minerals. Marginally the rock is much replaced by analcite, and veins of calcite and analcite occur. An interesting feature of this type of cancrinite syenite is the euhedral habit of the cancrinite (Fig. 5b); bladed prisms occur singly and in sheaves, and are characterized by a close $10\bar{1}0$ cleavage and an additional basal parting along which some alteration to isotropic analcite (?) has occurred. Whereas in almost all the other cancrinite-bearing rocks of Budeda the cancrinite has obviously replaced nepheline, here its habit is so different from that of nepheline that it cannot be pseudomorphic. It is regarded as primary cancrinite, and indeed the rock closely resembles the original cancrinite aegirite syenite of Törnebohm (Johannsen, 1938, p. 108) which Brögger later called särnaite after the type locality. Primary cancrinite is rarely recorded, but it has been described in syenite surrounding the Lueshe carbonatite (Bethune and Meyer 1956; Bethune, 1957). The syenite is termed 'busorite' and it differs from typical särnaite by the abundance of albite and microcline.

In the field the Budeda cancrinite-bearing rocks are gradational into one another and towards the ijolites. There are, however, dikes, cutting both ijolites and fenites, which consist of cancrinite-bearing rocks analogous to the two main types.

Carbonatite

On the northern slopes of Budeda Hill, and at the margins of some of the smaller ijolite masses, carbonatite invades ijolite along distinct, but swirling channels, surrounding patches of the silicate rock and producing a mixed rock of xeno-lithic aspect (see also Tororo p. 93 and Chilwa, Garson and Campbell Smith, 1958, Fig. 4). Although the carbonatite here has an intrusive appearance, it is of very limited extent, and may well represent replacement by calcite of a somewhat brecciated rock.

The largest mass of carbonatite is on Budeda Hill, and here the contact with the surrounding melteigite is everywhere gradational; calcite initially replaces the interstitial nepheline of the rock and then much of the pyroxene; the remaining pyroxene is at first concentrated in vague schlieren but becomes recrystallized as oriented prisms, picking out a vertical banding. In specimens of transitional rocks nepheline forms almost clear, rectangular crystals with embayed margins, few being in contact with one another, dispersed in a mosaic of calcite. Subhedral prisms of pyroxene are rounded and somewhat embayed against calcite; where the crystals are isolated they tend to be larger and more euhedral. Accessory minerals are relatively abundant: sphene and apatite in the calcite areas, locally partly replaced by calcite, and anhedral pyrite.

The texture of the carbonatite is variable; some parts are granular and medium-grained, and others contain larger calcite crystals (2–3 mm), with finer grained channels around them. All the calcite is anhedral, and crystals are mutually intergrown. Pyroxene is reduced in amount and is noticeably corroded, and nepheline is absent. Sphene occurs as pleochroic wedges and altered granules, and round crystals of apatite are dispersed. The carbonatite develops a conspicuous alignment of many of the prisms of pyroxene, and a coarse, vague banding is produced by the concentration of calcite and pyroxene into separate layers.

Dike rocks

At Budeda there are dikes of nepheline syenite and several types of cancrinite syenite and phonolite (Table I, 6, 7). Nepheline syenite of foyaite type forms quite a large dike at the northern tip of the main ijolite mass and a number of smaller dikes in the ijolite to the south. It is medium grey, with small euhedral nephelines and large, tabular feldspars up to 2 cm in length. In thin section the nepheline is seen to be extensively altered to cloudy zeolite with low birefringence, associated with a little cancrinite and calcite. The potash feldspar is twinned and encloses pseudomorphs of euhedral nepheline; the feldspar has a very small $2V$ and appears to be sanidine. The pyroxene is aegirine-rich with $X: c = 23°$, and forms acicular prisms with pleochroism from deep green to yellow. Biotite and apatite are additional minerals.

Most of the dikes of the area are cancrinite-bearing; two main textural types are represented.

The largest dikes, up to 10 ft in width, are coarse-textured and lack chilled margins; feldspar (twinned orthoclase) is conspicuous by its tabular habit and is generally aligned. Cancrinite occupies an interstitial position in aggregates or large prismatic plates. Pyroxene is not abundant, and forms ragged acicular prisms, sporadically replaced by biotite. Nepheline is present in variable amounts and is replaced by cancrinite. A cataclastic texture is shown by a few of these dikes, which wedge out after short distances. The feldspar is somewhat rounded, and the crystals are separated by channels of fine granular feldspar in which the proportion of albite is high. In the granulated areas cancrinite occurs as flakes and aggregates.

The other main type forms dikes which have chilled margins and contain angular xenoliths of the adjacent rock. They were evidently emplaced at a late stage for they post-date the phase of extensive feldspathization in the fenites. Laths of potash feldspar are aligned in a trachytoid texture; they are twinned and are sometimes marginally replaced by late albite. Cancrinite forms independent prisms of 'primary' aspect, but in some rocks it is extensively altered to cloudy isotropic zeolite so that only ghosts of the original crystals remain. The pyroxene, dispersed between the light minerals, is ragged and acicular, with nearly straight extinction. These rocks, being fine-grained, may appropriately be termed cancrinite phonolites.

Inferred sequence of events

The earliest phase of fenitization is the recrystallization of the country rock to a fine granular texture; this takes place along confined channels in the granite and is widespread through the syenite area. In the outer granite zone, the granulation channels form a random network, but in the syenites, directional stress is involved, for a pronounced layering is inherent in the fabric.

Metasomatism subsequently took place along the fine-grained channels in the granite, and throughout the whole of the granulated syenite area. Intermediate stages in the syenitization of the granite are rarely seen; the transition appears to be abrupt. It is probable that quartz, which is seen to be recrystallized along with feldspar in the granite, disappears with the introduction of dark minerals (aegirine and blue-green amphibole). In the syenites, however, aegirine is absent, and the pyroxene is a more lime-rich aegirine-augite. Locally, nephelinization of the syenites may have taken place at this stage.

The potash-rich syenites are considered to have been derived from the zones of potash granite during the syenitization of the Basement rocks.

The source of the metasomatic emanations is not apparent at Budeda. The alkaline masses themselves were not the direct source, for they were emplaced in already fenitized rocks; the zone of fenitization is widespread, and surrounds all the alkaline masses, and in many instances the intensity of fenitization shows no increase towards these bodies. The source is therefore considered to lie at depth below the complex, and may well underlie the whole of the area of the syenitic fenites.

Fig. 6. Feldspathized syenitic fenites at Budeda (Disiyi exposures). (*a*) Fine banding picked out by feldspathization, with anastomosing feldspar veins, and thin veins of aegirine-augite (width of view 2 ft.) (*b*) Coarse feldspathic veins, superimposed on banded syenite.

Melteigite forms comparatively small bodies emplaced in the broader envelope of fenites; they were mobile and intrusive, since they contain xenoliths of banded fenite. The ijolites, however, were not in general intrusive but developed by the nephelinization of melteigite. The pyroxene became zoned, and was also replaced by nepheline. Several stages of very coarse-grained ijolite were developed in patches in the melteigite and in veins.

Marginal feldspathization of the ijolite–melteigite masses took place with the development of pegmatitic potash feldspar, but this phase was soon followed by the alteration of nepheline to cancrinite and the pyroxene became more aegirine-rich. Locally pegmatitic recrystallization occurred and the cancrinite assumed an idiomorphic habit. The feldspathization not only affected the ijolites but also spread into the surrounding fenites, which became streaked with diffuse pods and veins of perthite, and transected by a series of feldspar pegmatites (Fig. 6).

Some phases of the cancrinite syenites later became mobile; large, coarse-textured dikes had only limited mobility, having brecciated margins and wedging out after short distances, but the late cancrinite phonolites were fluid, and engulfed xenoliths of the marginal rock.

The central carbonatite on Budeda Hill developed by replacement of melteigite. At the same time, vague schlieren of silicate material in the carbonatite became streaked out, and a banded structure was produced which resembles the flow layering in carbonatites from other areas. Here it is believed to have developed by recrystallization under directional stress. On Galala Hill, marginal replacement of the ijolite by calcite has occurred in the brecciated rock.

Summary of metasomatism at Budeda

1. Introduction of CaO (MgO), Fe_2O_3 (FeO), TiO_2, MnO, P_2O_5 } Fenitization of
   Removal of SiO_2.   country rock

2. Introduction of Al_2O_3, Na_2O, K_2O
   Removal of CaO, (MgO), Fe_2O_3, FeO } Nephelinization of melteigite
   TiO_2, MnO, SiO_2 remain constant.

3. Introduction of K_2O, SiO_2, (CO_2 and (OH)) } Feldspathization of
   Removal of FeO, Fe_2O_3, CaO, MgO ijolite and fenite
   TiO_2, MnO remain constant.

4. Introduction of CaO, CO_2, $?P_2O_5$ } Carbonatization of ijolite
   Removal of other basic oxides and SiO_2.

Tororo

Tororo Rock forms a conspicuous landmark in the southern part of eastern Uganda a few miles from the Kenya border, rising to a height of 4862 ft, nearly a thousand feet above the surrounding plain. The Rock itself, with precipitous sides, consists entirely of carbonatite which also occupies the lower hills to the south of the Rock. Limekiln Hill, the southernmost hill, is a separate mass of carbonatite which has invaded a mixed assemblage of alkaline silicate rocks exposed on the flanks (Fig. 7). It is quarried for cement making, and fresh material can be readily examined.

The main carbonatite is approximately pear-shaped in outline and three-quarters of a mile in length, but its contact with the surrounding rock is nowhere exposed. Williams (1952) described the structure of this mass as a series of separately intruded 'collars'. The carbonatite of Limekiln Hill is an elongate mass about a quarter of a mile in length and contains silicate xenoliths which tend to be concentrated in vertical zones only a few feet wide separated by purer carbonatite.

The silicate rocks associated with the carbonatite on Limekiln Hill include syenitic fenites, nepheline syenites and ijolites, which, on the NE side of the hill, have been brecciated and the fragments mixed. The emplacement of the carbonatite was preceded by intensive feldspathization of the breccia fragments, (see also Chilwa: Garson and Campbell Smith, 1958). A number of ijolite–agglomerate dikes cut the carbonatite on this hill, the largest being about 40 ft thick; the assorted fragments are of silicate rocks in a carbonated matrix.

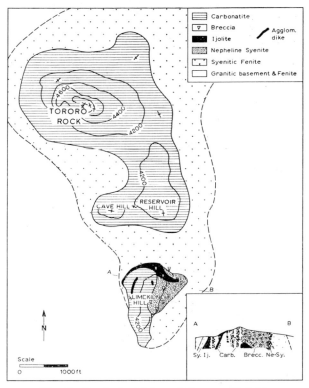

Fig. 7. Geological Map of Tororo (D.S.S.)

Fenitized country rock

The carbonatite complex is emplaced in fenitized granitic rocks of the Basement Complex. The granite is not foliated and consists of oligoclase surrounded by albite, with microcline, quartz and a very small amount of yellowish-brown biotite. The fenites are closely shattered and along a network of irregular channels up to a millimetre or so in width the feldspar is finely granulated and even fragmented in the wider crush zones. Quartz becomes rimmed and veined by the ferro-magnesian minerals associated with fenitization; this replacement affects both the large crystals of the granite and the small, irregular grains in the crush channels, but the small ones are soon entirely replaced, and most of the channels consist only of recrystallized potash feldspar in association with the fenite minerals. The feldspar itself is replaced to a lesser extent. The original biotite of the granite is replaced along the cleavages by potash feldspar and rimmed with iron oxides.

The mafic minerals introduced during fenitization occur mainly in veins and patches along the crush channels, and are rarely aligned with the veins, except occasionally in areas where the feldspar is extensively recrystallized to irregular laths which are themselves aligned. Pyroxene is the most abundant of the dark minerals, generally as acicular tufts of pleochroic green to yellowish aegirine, with high birefringence and straight extinction, but occasional clusters of pale-yellow acmite ($X: c = 8°$) occur near the centres of some veins. Accompanying the pyroxene is the conspicuous blue amphibole typical of fenites; it is pleochroic from pale blue-green to light greyish-buff, and is characterized by low interference colours. Apatite occurs sporadically in some of the fenite veins.

Syenitic fenite

Among the fenitized granites are to be found specimens which contain no quartz, but consist largely of recrystallized feldspar with angular fragments of original granite with veins and aggregates of aegirine and amphibole. Around Limekiln Hill are more continuous exposures of syenitic fenite, good examples of which occur in the mixed rocks of the agglomerate on the east side. Many of these fenites retain the pattern of net-veining found in the granites; foliated rocks of the type seen at Budeda are not found at Tororo. Some contain cloudy, oval feldspars up to 2–3 mm in diameter, which are mainly oligoclase, occasionally twinned, and speckled with sericitic alteration. Around the large feldspars is a groundmass of recrystallized feldspar, variably perthitic, and veins of acicular aegirine in close sheaves. In a few cases the oval feldspars consist of a central crystal fringed by smaller similar crystals, the whole aggregate containing a host of tiny globular inclusions. These ovals strongly resemble the relic spots in the syenitic fenites at Budeda. The groundmass often consists of intricately intergrown streaky perthite, and both aegirine and aegirine-augite in veins and aggregates. The proportion of dark minerals in the fenites varies widely.

Nepheline syenites

Rocks of nepheline syenite composition are frequently encountered in exposures close to the carbonatite on Limekiln Hill. A high proportion of these rocks, however, are feldspathized ijolites (this volume p. 92). The nepheline syenites proper are distinct in character; they are dark and fine-grained, with small, euhedral pink altered nephelines visible in hand specimen. In thin section the nepheline syenites are distinguished from feldspathized ijolites by the acicular habit of the pyroxene and its composition near aegirine rather than aegirine-augite. The euhedral nepheline is extensively replaced by aggregates of cloudy, finely divided zeolite and cancrinite. Some of them contain inclusions of acicular pyroxene in concentric zones. Potash feldspar either forms clear, poikilitic plates or it approximates to intergrown laths, but it is generally interstitial. An almost pure albite accompanies the potash feldspar in some rocks. The pyroxene is generally peripheral to nepheline and often shows alteration to red-brown biotite.

The nepheline syenites, like the ijolites, have been feldspathized near to the carbonatite, and their original character is often obliterated by the development of coarse-textured orthoclase.

Ijolites

On the northern and western flanks of Limekiln Hill ijolitic rocks occur, but are extensively invaded by carbonatite and altered by feldspathization. Ijolites also occur sporadically in the breccia on the north east side of the hill, and specimens of relatively unaltered rock can be obtained from the larger agglomerate dikes.

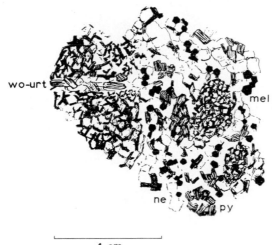

1 cm

Fig. 8. Ijolite, east side of Limekiln Hill, Tororo. Medium-grained ijolite and coarser textured melteigite are transected by a vein of wollastonite-urtite (wo-urt), and replaced by coarse-grained ijolite with euhedral melanite (mel) and much interstitial calcite. (ne-nepheline, py-pyroxene).

The contact between ijolite and syenitic fenite was revealed in 1960 by quarrying on the lower slopes of the pediment west of Limekiln Hill, although it is largely obscured by alteration associated with the invasion by carbonatite. The transition from syenite to ijolite is abrupt, and there is no intervening zone of nepheline syenite as is found on the east side of the hill. The contact, traced across the quarry, dips outwards at around 45° towards the west.

From the few specimens of unaltered ijolitic rocks obtained, it is apparent that, in common with those of other alkaline complexes, they are variable in both texture and mineralogy. Fragments of melteigite–pyroxenite occur in the agglomerate and also as small patches within the ijolites. The subhedral stout prisms of pyroxene are zoned from pale diopsidic cores to rims of aegirine-augite, and nepheline or its alteration products are interstitial. A fine- to medium-grained ijolite with subhedral nephelines and peripheral prisms of pyroxene also occurs as patches in coarser grained ijolite (Fig. 8); an exaggerated form of this texture is found in a dike rock on the east knoll, where euhedral nephelines are embedded in green pyroxene, and the appearance resembles a regular crazy-paving. In this rock, and in a similar but very much coarser-grained ijolite with nephelines 4 mm in size from Limekiln Hill, the nepheline is entirely pseudo-morphed by granules and oriented flakes of cancrinite, and the pyroxene is a felted mass of acicular aegirine.

The melteigite and even-textured ijolite are replaced by later veins and patches of bladed wollastonite and interstitial nepheline, followed by the development of melanite. The garnet varies from chocolate brown to nearly opaque, and from

Fig. 9.   Feldspathized ijolite, Limekiln Hill, Tororo.   Ijolite (dark) transected by veins of potash feldspar and calcite (light).

euhedral granules to ramifying plates around pyroxene. It is often accompanied by interstitial calcite (Fig. 8) but along later calcite veins in some rocks the melanite is altered to iron-titanium oxides. Sphene and apatite are accessory minerals.

Feldspathized rocks

After the emplacement of the alkaline silicate rocks and prior to the intrusion of the carbonatite, extensive brecciation took place which, on the NE side of Limekiln Hill, resulted in the mixing of fragments of syenitic fenite, nepheline syenite and subordinate ijolite in the form of a coarse breccia, but evidently with comparatively little movement from their original positions. The fragments in the breccia- and shatter-zones were then feldspathized along the network of channels, and rims of potash feldspar rock of variable width surround the darker cores of earlier silicate rock (Fig. 9). The feldspar, in the quarries where it is fresh, is light grey or white and consists of a mesh of intergrown needles or coarser laths, but on weathered surfaces it is reddened. In thin section it is identified as twinned orthoclase (Davies, 1956), often slightly cloudy, but in both ijolitic and syenitic rocks, large poikilitic plates of clear potash feldspar with a $2V$ smaller than that of orthoclase are recorded.

Carbonatites

The main mass of Tororo Rock was apparently emplaced as a series of 'collars' around a central plug 10 ft in diameter; the first ring is steeply inclined towards the centre, and the dip of concentric banded structures decreases outward. Williams (1952) records a dip of 57° for ring structures in the region of Cave Hill and Reservoir Hill. Tangential dikes are suggested by Williams to account for linear structures on these hills, and he infers an intersection in the carbonatite of Limekiln Hill. Subsequent examination of the structures revealed by quarrying confirms this view, and there is evidence that the carbonatite of Limekiln Hill was emplaced as a succession of vertical masses, of varying width, separated by bands of xenolithic material from the wall rocks.

The west contact of the carbonatite at the southern tip of the hill dips steeply to the west; here it cuts granitic fenites, but farther north it invades ijolitic rocks. On the eastern side the carbonatite extends irregularly into the feldspathized breccia.

Small-scale structures in the carbonatites are complex and include: (i) xenoliths in varying stages of assimilation; (ii) banding and (iii) a succession of crosscutting veins.

(i) Most of the xenoliths of wall rocks are feldspathized around the edges and alongside intersecting veinlets, and the cores appear to have been afforded a certain measure of protection by the feldspathic rims when the xenoliths were subsequently surrounded by carbonatite. Xenoliths of ijolite less than three inches or so in diameter, however, are generally altered; the nepheline is replaced by cloudy aggregates of natrolite and cancrinite, and the pyroxene shows alteration to orange-red biotite near the edges of the xenoliths. Where calcite has extensively replaced the zeolite aggregates, the pyroxene is decomposed and the crystals remain as streaky aggregates of calcite and aegirine. These may eventually fade to grey ghost crystals, replaced by calcite and speckled with iron oxides. Where the pyroxene was originally zoned, the diopsidic core has been more easily replaced by calcite than the rim, and prisms of aegirine-rich pyroxene commonly occur in the carbonatite without much alteration. The rims and masses formed of potash feldspar in the carbonatite are less readily replaced than the nepheline-bearing rocks, but the feldspar laths are gradually corroded by calcite and the crystals are dispersed in the calcite groundmass. Sphene becomes rimmed with iron oxide and apatite is sometimes concentrated in the xenoliths. Syenitic xenoliths are less altered than the nepheline-bearing rocks, but are gradually replaced by calcite, and the crystals of feldspar and green pyroxene become isolated. Fragments of melteigite–pyroxenite in the agglomerate are altered along calcite veins to blue-green amphibole like that found in the fenites associated with pale aegirine. On weathered surfaces the xenoliths stand out against the less resistant calcite, and the carbonatite frequently has the appearance of sweeping round them in turbulent 'flow', small inclusions of silicate material being strung out in a banded structure.

(ii) Banded structures in the carbonatites are in general produced by irregular layers and streaks of different minerals; on Tororo Rock these are commonly octahedra of magnetite, with subordinate schlieren of reddish silicate material, but on Limekiln Hill the most common inclusions are prisms of pyroxene, an aegirine-rich aegirine-augite. On the west side of the hill bands of biotite crystals occur in the carbonatite. These minerals are probably derived from assimilated xenolithic material.

In detail the banded structures show a number of different styles. Commonly the pyroxene prisms are unevenly distributed in vaguely defined bands, but the prisms show a parallel orientation which may be oblique to the banding; in coarser-textured carbonatites the pyroxene bands may have feathery or dendritic outlines in detail; sometimes the pyroxene is concentrated along the edges of

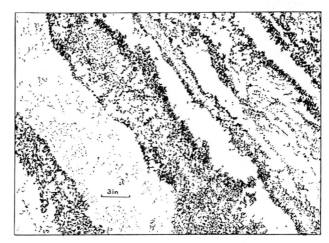

Fig. 10. Banding in carbonatite; limestone quarry, Tororo. The dark mineral is mostly aegirine-augite, which shows concentration along the margins of calcite 'veins'.

bands of almost pure calcite, the prisms of pyroxene being perpendicular to the margins or in parallel or slightly radiating groups (Fig. 10). This structure may be explained by assuming considerable recrystallization and redistribution of the minerals subsequent to the original consolidation of the carbonatite.

A further type of structure develops by shear movements, both the calcite and pyroxene becoming fine-grained and assuming a platy parallelism.

Various structures are seen in thin section, in addition to the macroscopic phenomena. Locally, brecciated feldspathic syenite is minutely veined by late fenite minerals, including small, equant crystals of biotite, and feathery growths of amphibole and aegirine, accompanied by extensive calcite replacement; eventually a granular mosaic of calcite remains, the crystals rimmed and the rock net-veined by fenite minerals, and in some of these rocks the veins, following the main direction in the breccia, are predominantly aligned. In some carbon-atites oval crystals of calcite up to 0.5 mm in diameter are set in a finer grained groundmass of the same mineral. Other minerals which occur sporadically in the various carbonatites include apatite, colourless to purple fluorite in patches and along veins, and a small amount of pyrochlore. Pyrite is a common replacement as ramifying patches, granules and prismatic crystals. Davies (1956) records chlorite, zircon, tremolite and rare quartz in addition.

(iii) All exposures of carbonatite at Tororo are characterized by the presence of narrow veins of carbonatite, from a fraction of an inch to a few inches wide, some grey, some buff coloured, and many of them parallel banded (Fig. 11).

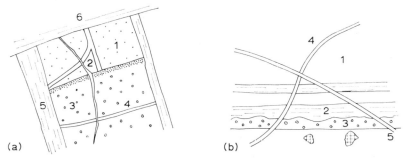

Fig. 11. Veins in carbonatite at Tororo (exposures 3 feet across). (*a*) 1. Medium-grained carbonatite; 2. Blue-grey carbonatite vein; 3. Breccia dike with fine-grained edge; 4. Light calcite vein; 5. Grey streaky carbonatite vein; 6. Yellow-grey carbonatite vein. (*b*) 1. Coarse-grained grey-white carbonatite with apatite, and feldspar relics; 2. Buff coloured streaky carbonatite; 3. Breccia dike; 4. Light grey fine-grained carbonatite; 5. Fine-grained carbonatite vein.

In the late veins of carbonatite the calcite commonly has a lath-like habit and is strongly aligned parallel with the vein; in some cases small rods appear to be pseudomorphs by calcite of an earlier mineral, feldspar or melilite. Some of the larger dikes (3 ft in width) are banded, the dark layers containing coarse calcite with patches of granular magnetite associated with golden biotite partly altered to a vivid greenish-blue, and the light layers consisting of coarse laths of calcite and a small amount of the biotite.

Agglomerate dikes

Agglomerate dikes are fairly common, cutting the carbonatite of Limekiln Hill; they were emplaced before some of the late carbonatite veins (Fig. 11). The dikes trend NW–N and vary in width from 6 in to 40 ft. They are generally of very dark colour, but small ones weather to light grey, and consist of fragments of plutonic rocks and their constituent crystals in a friable calcareous matrix. The size of the fragments varies according to the width of the dike—about 1 cm across in the small dikes and 5–10 cm in the large dikes. They are ellipsoidal and very well rounded. In the quarry exposures the fragments are graded according to size in almost horizontal bands, and the ellipsoids are coaxially aligned. The dikes are bordered by selvedges a centimetre or so wide where the fragments are very small.

The evidence strongly suggests that the plutonic fragments were brought up from below in streams of gas, sorted and suspended in a fluidized system, and simultaneously rounded by attrition.

The most abundant fragments consist of coarse-textured hornblendite; the anhedral crystals of hornblende are 3–5 mm across and are pleochroic in shades of greenish brown. This hornblende predominates also in the crystal fragments of the groundmass. The hornblendite contains subordinate pale green diopside and red-brown biotite and much euhedral apatite. Ijolites of various textures are common among the fragments, consisting mainly of aegirine-augite and nepheline, sometimes accompanied by red-brown biotite and iron-titanium oxide, and occasionally by melanite. Some of the fragments are of feldspathized ijolite. Other rocks represented include carbonatite, trachyte with fluidal texture and phenocrysts of potash feldspar, and biotite-rock; melteigite–pyroxenite, consisting of diopsidic pyroxene with cores of titanaugite, ramifying plates of ilmenite, and nests of apatite, is found occasionally. The crystal fragments in the groundmass consist of the brown hornblende, diopside and aegirine-augite and biotite which varies from yellowish-green/straw to shades of deeper green in patches and streaks. The small dikes on the south side of the hill consist mainly of this biotite and magnetite with abundant apatite in a calcite matrix. Cloudy potash feldspar occurs as small fragments and patches in the ground-mass of many of the larger dikes. Most of the fragments are carbonated; the nepheline is replaced by cancrinite flakes, together with zeolites such as natrolite and analcite, and diopside and hornblende are partly replaced by calcite along cracks and cleavages. Sphene is altered to leucoxene and iron oxide. Between the crystal fragments the groundmass consists of irregular grains of calcite, and occasionally small, euhedral plates of the pale greenish biotite which sweep round the fragments, together with granules of magnetite and apatite.

Trachyte dikes

Trachyte dikes a foot or so wide occur in the fenitized basement to the east of the complex. They are holocrystalline, with a fluidal texture, and consist of phenocrysts of cloudy potash feldspar in a groundmass of feldspar laths with tufts and aggregates of limonite replacing the original ferromagnesian mineral. Like the trachytes of Toror, these rocks are potash-rich (Na_2O, 0.49; K_2O, 13.7 per cent, Fig. 18).

THE YOUNGER COMPLEXES

These are represented by the great dissected volcanoes of Elgon, Kadam, Moroto, Napak and Toror, built up on an erosion surface probably of mid-Tertiary age. A more precise dating is possible for Napak with the discovery by Bishop (1958) of a rich mammalian fauna of Lower Miocene age in sediments associated with the lowest part of the volcanics. Toror is included in this group purely by inference since no extrusive rocks remain.

Napak and Toror are discussed in some detail.

Napak

Napak is unique among the alkaline complexes of eastern Uganda in that both extrusive and intrusive igneous rocks are represented. The extrusive rocks are remnants of a volcanic cone which originally had a basal diameter of over 20 miles, and rest on a domed surface of Basement gneisses and foliated granites

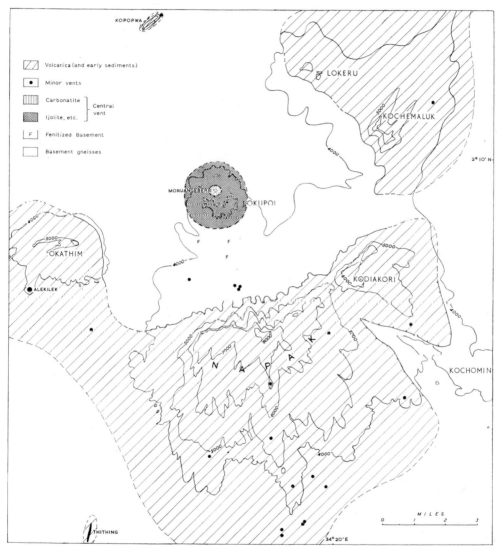

Fig. 12. Outline geological map of the Napak area (after King, 1949).

(Figs. 12 and 13). Over a central area some eight miles in diameter the volcanics have been entirely removed and the site of the main vent is marked by a circular group of hills, Lokupoi, about 1.25 miles across. This is largely formed of ijolites with a small central boss of carbonatite, and is surrounded by a zone in which the Basement gneisses are fenitized.

Volcanics

Only a brief summary is given here, since a detailed description has already been presented (King, 1949).

It is estimated that of the total bulk of the volcanic mountains, not more than 3 per cent consists of lava flows; the remainder is pyroclastics, chiefly agglomerates.

The lava flows are mostly between 10 and 30 ft thick and consist almost entirely of nephelinites and melanephelinites, composed essentially of nepheline and pyroxene, together with varieties bearing olivine and/or melilite (Table II, 6–12). A lava of exceptional composition forms the basal flow on the inner scarp face of Napak. It consists chiefly of plagioclase ($Ab_{65} An_{35}$) and magnetite, together with chlorite, which may represent original pyroxene and was described originally as an andesite (King, 1949), but more recently it has been noted that chemically it compares more closely with mugearite (King and Sutherland, 1960) (Table II, 5).

In the nephelinite series, nepheline commonly forms almost perfectly euhedral crystals and as judged by refractive indices contains 20 per cent or more of the kaliophilite molecule. The pyroxene is usually a pale coloured diopsidic variety, but sometimes contains greener coloured cores. In some of the more leucocratic rocks the normal pyroxene is distinctly green and contains an appreciable proportion of aegirine. The pyroxene of the groundmass is often greenish and is occasionally fringed by minute needles of aegirine. Biotite is present in small amount in some lavas, while small blades of a blue-green amphibole have been recorded. Apart from ubiquitous iron-titanium oxides, the accessory minerals include perovskite and apatite.

In the more leucocratic varieties the matrix to the groundmass is light coloured, of low refractive index and very weakly birefringent. Normative compositions suggest the presence of a mineral (or minerals) with a higher ratio of silica to alkalies and alumina than in nepheline. Analcite or natrolite appear the most likely.

Amygdales are of frequent occurrence in the lavas and similar structures are also widespread in the agglomerates. The principal infilling mineral is natrolite, but other zeolites, chabazite, stilbite and mesolite, have been identified, and calcite is also abundant.

Fragments of lavas of the same types as those of the flows predominate in the agglomerates, but Basement gneisses, early sediments, together with fenites and, at certain horizons, members of the ijolite series also contribute. Locally some of the basal tuffs contain abundant fragments of feldspar.

The central intrusive complex

The melteigite–ijolite–urtite series. Based primarily on field data it has been found possible to recognize a sequence of events, which is summarized in Fig. 14. In any one group of outcrops only a part of the sequence is represented, but the

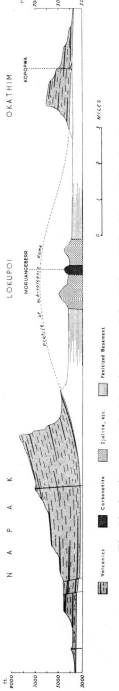

Fig. 13. Section across the Napak volcano (after King, 1949 with modifications).

TABLE II
Volcanic Rocks

A. Chemical Compositions

	1 Ankaratrite (4)	2 Meilite-Ankaratrite (6)	3 Nephelinite (10)	4 Phonolitic Nephelinite (12)	5 Phonolite (14)	6 Meilite-Nephelinite N200	7 Meilite-Nephelinite K222	8 Meilite-Nephelinite N192	9 Nephelinite N89	10 Olivine-Nephelinite K81	11 Nephelinite K74	12 Phonolitic Nephelinite N6	13 'Andesite' K330
	I		ELGON			II				NAPAK			
SiO_2	41.44	41.65	43.59	46.71	53.64	36.79	37.21	38.27	39.36	41.47	43.23	43.50	53.54
Al_2O_3	7.01	9.92	15.07	15.03	19.16	12.79	11.51	12.31	10.88	13.29	14.37	10.30	15.78
Fe_2O_3	3.16	7.03	6.96	5.35	3.61	8.23	8.23	8.89	11.65	8.74	6.99	9.25	12.90
FeO	7.89	6.79	4.54	5.41	0.88	4.87	8.16	6.48	6.08	5.91	4.96	5.26	0.96
MgO	26.48	11.47	3.51	4.13	0.37	7.10	6.72	6.90	6.38	6.97	3.41	9.18	0.44
CaO	8.23	12.23	10.53	7.83	1.18	15.88	16.54	12.36	12.86	12.89	10.09	16.94	4.80
Na_2O	1.83	1.42	6.03	4.86	10.54	5.43	4.58	5.78	5.81	4.87	5.77	1.26	4.40
K_2O	0.94	2.68	3.87	4.24	4.28	3.12	2.14	3.45	2.76	1.81	3.47	1.68	1.80
H_2O+	1.57	1.04	2.57	2.94	5.25	0.43	2.79	—	—	1.99	2.90	—	2.32
H_2O-	0.35		—	1.39	0.35		1.21	—	—	0.23	0.72	—	0.36
CO_2	None	tr	—	—	0.16	1.5	0.18	1.75	None	0.23	None	0.25	0.33
TiO_2	0.72	1.84	2.71	2.41	0.13	2.19	1.85	2.25	2.50	1.11	2.96	2.03	1.03
P_2O_5	0.26	0.47	0.62	0.81	0.49	1.08	0.65	0.92	0.90	0.74	0.97	0.58	1.65
MnO	0.18	0.33	0.25	0.44	0.15	0.22	0.20	0.24	0.27	0.15	0.21	0.18	0.27
Total	100.06	99.83	100.25	101.55	100.22	99.63	100.25[a]	99.60	99.45	100.41[b]	100.30[c]	100.41	100.47[d]

[a] Includes BaO 0.02.   [b] Includes BaO 0.01.   [c] Includes Cl 0.04, S 0.02, BaO 0.11, SrO 0.11.   Includes BaO 0.02.   [d] Includes BaO 0.02.

B. Normative Compositions

	1	2	3	4	5	6	7	8	9	10	11	12	13
Quartz	—	—	—	—	—	—	—	—	—	—	—	—	15.8
Orthoclase	—	8.3	22.8	25.0	25.6	—	—	—	—	9.4	20.6	10.0	10.6
Albite	—	2.6	1.6	12.6	28.0	—	—	—	—	—	6.8	0.5	37.2
Anorthite	8.1	9.5	2.5	6.7	—	1.1	—	—	—	8.9	2.8	17.5	10.8
Leucite	4.4	—	—	—	—	—	4.4	—	—	0.9	—	—	—
Kaliophilite	—	—	—	—	—	10.4[a]	10.0	11.7[a]	9.5[a]	—	—	—	—
Nepheline	8.5	12.2	26.7	15.3	25.1	25.0	21.0	23.8	23.0	22.4	23.0[b]	5.4	—
Acmite	—	—	—	—	10.6	—	—	5.5	6.0	—	—	—	—
Diopside	22.8	38.1	18.8	21.2	2.6	35.6	23.7	35.1	37.5	38.3	18.4	47.5	(2.6)[c]
Wollastonite	—	—	9.2	—	(0.4)[d]	—	—	—	—	—	7.7	—	—
$2CaO SiO_2$	—	1.2	—	—	—	4.5	13.4	2.4	4.4	1.2	—	0.7	—
Hypersthene	1.2	—	—	1.8	1.2	—	—	—	—	—	—	—	1.1
Olivine	46.5	10.5	7.4	7.9	—	1.0	9.0	—	—	12.5	7.9	12.1	—
Magnetite	4.4	10.2	1.9	4.6	—	10.0	9.5	10.2	10.7	2.1	1.6	1.0	0.5
Haematite	—	—	—	—	0.3	1.3	—	—	2.2	—	—	3.8	12.1
Ilmenite	1.4	3.5	5.2	2.0	—	4.1	3.5	4.4	4.7	1.7	5.8	1.3	2.1
Apatite	0.7	1.0	1.3	—	1.0	2.7	1.3	2.0	2.0	0.6	2.4	—	4.0
Calcite	—	—	—	—	—	3.4	0.5	—	—	—	—	—	0.7
Water	1.9	3.7	2.6	2.9	5.6	0.4	4.0	4.0	—	2.2	3.6	0.6	2.7
Total	99.9	99.6	100.0	100.0	100.5	99.5	100.3	99.1	100.0	100.2	100.6	100.4	100.2

[a] Kaliophilite made in preference to calcium orthosilicate.   [b] Nepheline made in preference to olivine.   [c] Corundum.   [d] Cancrinite.

1–5, Quoted from Davies, 1952, 44. 1 and 2, W. H. Herdsman, anal.; 3 and 4, N. Sahlbom, anal.; 5, B. C. King. 7, 10, 11, 13, quoted from King, 1949, 41. B. C. King, anal. 6, 8, 9, 12, new analyses. R. C. Tyler, anal.

order in which the various phases appear is everywhere the same. For this reason it is inferred that essentially only a single cycle of events is represented in the ijolites, and that the existing ijolite-carbonatite complex was formed very largely or even wholly after extrusion of lavas had ceased; it represents the products of consolidation of the immediately parental magma under effectively plutonic conditions. Nevertheless, the occurrence of ijolites as fragments in the agglomerates at various levels in the volcanic cone shows that such rocks had crystallized in the central vent at earlier stages in the history of the volcano. It is

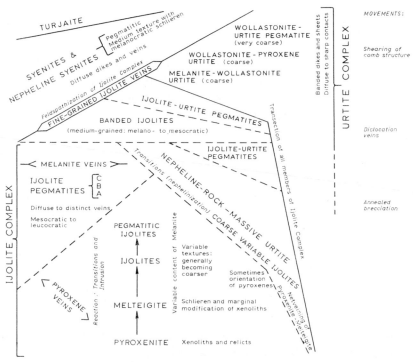

Fig. 14. Schematic representation of relations among the intrusive
formations of Lokupoi, Napak.

presumed that former ijolitic plugs were disrupted during subsequent explosive episodes.

In the field a broad two-fold division was made for descriptive purposes into an earlier 'ijolite complex' of melanocratic and mesocratic rocks, but also including an important urtite phase, and a later coarse-grained 'urtite complex', largely developed in well-defined dike-like masses. Variations in composition chiefly depend on the relative proportions of the two principal minerals, pyroxene and nepheline. Others that are frequently found are melanite, iron-titanium oxides, wollastonite, sphene and apatite. Perovskite and biotite occur in some rock types, while cancrinite, pectolite, calcite and zeolites are mostly found as replacements.

(a) *The ijolite complex*

(i) *Pyroxenite-melteigite-ijolite*[1] *phase.* Invariably the earliest member of the entire sequence is pyroxenite (Table III, 1, 2); it is never found as extensive outcrops, but forms more or less distinct xenolithic masses within the later types (Fig. 15d). It is dark grey and has an even, rather fine-grained texture although coarser-textured varieties occasionally occur. In thin section the rock is seen to contain up to 90 per cent or so of an almost colourless pyroxene, in closely packed anhedral crystals mostly from 0.5 to 1 mm.

An iron-titanium oxide may amount to 5–10 per cent, sometimes occurring in extensive aggregates; it shows a brownish colour in reflected light, probably indicating an ilmenite with considerable Fe_2O_3. Perovskite is a ubiquitous accessory forming somewhat irregular grains, occasionally as much as 1 mm in diameter. It has a distinctive purplish-brown colour and often occurs within, or partly fringing the oxide grains. Apatite is common and locally forms close granular aggregates. Sphene, a nearly colourless variety, is also usually present; sometimes it fringes iron oxide and perovskite.

A bright orange-brown biotite may occur, in places in sufficient abundance for the rock to be termed a biotite pyroxenite. The mineral forms somewhat ragged plates, often in interlocking aggregates; it also occurs around grains of iron oxide, interstitially or fingering along the grain boundaries of the pyroxene aggregates. Certain types in which biotite is abundant contain no iron oxide; this is reflected in the poverty of Fe_2O_3 on analysis. Occasionally nepheline occurs as unevenly distributed grains and aggregates.

The simplest modification of the pyroxenite is to melteigite (Table III, 3, 4). In the field it is generally apparent that the melanocratic xenolithic masses contain cores of pyroxenite margined or enclosed by melteigite, which is recognizable by its dark green colour and often coarser and more variable texture. Nepheline is present in variable amount, and its introduction appears to be an essential feature of the transformation, associated with which is the development of green margins to the pyroxene, marking an increase in the aegirine content (Fig. 16a). At the same time melanite initially invades and ultimately replaces entirely the iron-titanium oxide and perovskite. The biotite similarly is surrounded and replaced. By way of a patchy and marginal metasomatism the pyroxene becomes a medium green aegirine-augite with associated nepheline and variable brown to almost opaque melanite. Sphene is usually an abundant accessory and often appears to be replacing perovskite.

The material surrounding and invading the xenolithic pyroxenite–melteigite is exceedingly variable, both in texture and mineralogy, but can broadly be described as consisting of meso- to leucocratic ijolite (Table III, 5–9). Quite independently of the relative proportions of aegirine-augite and nepheline, melanite shows an exceedingly sporadic distribution and locally varies from being entirely absent to being the principal dark mineral in the rock.

[1] The terminology employed for the members of the ijolite series is essentially that in current use, namely, pyroxenite-95-melteigite-70-ijolite-30-urtite-5-nepheline rock (figures referring to colour indices). Pyroxenite and melteigite are also distinguished according to the nature of the constituent minerals.

TABLE III
Naɔ̨ak (Lokupoi): plutonic rocks

A. Chemical Compositions

	Pyroxenites		Mela-Ijolites		Meso-Ijolites			Leuco-Ijolites		Urtites				
	1 Pyroxenite N35C	2 Biotite Pyroxenite N25	3 'Schistose' Melteigite N163	4 Melteigite N62	5 Variable pyroxenitic ijolite N155	6 Medium-grained ijolite N117	7 Coarse-grained ijolite N152	8 Medium-grained melanite-ijolite N52	9 Leucocratic ijolite N123	10 Wollastonite urtite N29	11 Urtite N123	12 Ijolite pegmatite N517A	13 Turjaite N170	14 Nepheline syenite N121
SiO_2	41.39	43.25	48.31	39.39	40.83	40.20	38.12	41.54	42.80	41.81	40.94	43.25	35.66	51.32
Al_2O_3	4.91	11.49	8.06	15.84	15.77	15.09	14.35	15.05	19.08	18.92	25.42	14.61	23.54	21.92
Fe_2O_3	10.37	0.39	3.39	5.04	5.90	7.07	5.86	6.29	4.46	3.00	4.70	3.13	1.17	5.92
FeO	9.77	12.63	5.27	7.25	4.48	4.49	3.23	4.08	5.84	0.92	1.02	3.12	5.17	2.71
MgO	10.06	8.41	9.62	7.08	4.73	3.90	3.37	2.70	2.08	0.26	0.24	3.08	5.01	0.94
CaO	18.02	12.00	18.28	15.80	16.92	15.18	22.56	15.18	11.99	17.59	8.41	23.68	17.84	3.95
Na_2O	1.52	1.90	4.99	3.77	4.25	7.50	4.65	8.25	7.73	11.68	12.92	4.40	5.65	7.60
K_2O	1.40	4.22	1.17	1.97	2.12	3.84	1.74	2.79	3.17	3.66	5.31	1.41	1.70	5.10
H_2O+	—	1.22	0.20	0.19	0.51	0.11	0.57	0.32	0.68	1.23	—	0.36	0.38	0.11
H_2O-	—	—	—	—	—	—	—	—	—	—	—	—	—	—
CO_2	2.55	3.07	—	—	—	None	—	—	—	—	0.25	1.43	—	0.07
TiO_2	0.02	0.51	0.70	3.28	3.71	2.22	3.90	3.49	1.82	0.63	0.68	0.72	3.36	0.76
P_2O_5	0.21	0.32	0.29	0.80	0.99	0.78	1.21	0.94	0.25	0.01	0.64	0.71	0.23	0.19
MnO	—	—	0.17	0.25	0.02	0.15	0.15	0.05	0.20	0.16	0.07	0.21	0.15	0.16
Total	100.22	99.41	100.45	100.56	100.23	100.53	99.71	100.68	100.10	99.87	100.60	100.11	99.86	100.75

R. C. Tyler, anal.

B. Normative Compositions[e]

	1	2	3	4	5	6	7	8	9	10	11	12	13	14
Orthoclase	—	—	—	—	2.2	—	—	—	1.6	—	—	—	—	30.6
Albite	2.5	—	—	—	—	—	—	—	—	—	—	—	—	19.9
Anorthite	—	10.3	—	20.3	17.5	—	13.1	—	7.8	—	—	—	—	10.3
Leucite	4.7	16.1	4.1	—	8.3	13.0	—	3.9	13.5	12.3	17.7	15.8	—	—
Kaliophilite	6.8	2.5	—	6.6	—	—	6.0	6.6	—	—	—	5.2	7.8	—
Nepheline	—	8.8	18.7	17.3	19.6	30.4	21.3	33.2	35.5	41.5	54.8	20.2	25.8	24.1
Acmite	—	—	6.5	—	—	—	—	7.4	—	9.2	—	0.9	—	—
Diopside	64.2	37.5	62.5	32.0	32.4	22.9	18.2	14.7	25.0	3.2	6.9	20.8	14.8	5.2
Wollastonite	0.9	—	—	3.8	2.7	7.9	15.1	20.9	5.6	13.2	11.5	25.8	—	0.6
2CaO SiO₂	—	—	—	—	—	6.9	9.5	—	—	16.0	2.2	—	9.0	—
Hypersthene	—	—	—	—	—	—	—	—	—	—	—	—	—	—
Olivine	15.1	15.2	3.3	4.8	—	7.0	—	—	—	—	—	—	—	—
Magnetite	—	0.7	1.3	7.4	8.6	—	5.9	3.2	6.5	1.2	1.4	4.6	1.6	7.0
Haematite	4.9	—	1.6	—	—	—	—	1.4	—	—	1.3	1.4	—	1.1
Ilmenite	—	5.9	1.4	6.2	7.1	4.1	7.1	6.7	3.5	—	1.3	1.7	6.4	1.5
Apatite	—	1.3	0.7	2.0	2.4	1.7	3.0	2.4	0.7	2.7[b]	0.6[c]	3.3[c]	0.7	0.3[e]
							0.3[a]						33.4[d]	0.2[e]
Total	99.1	98.3	100.1	100.4	100.8	100.4	99.5	100.4	99.7	99.3	100.4	99.7	99.5	100.8

[a] Perovskite. [b] Na₂O.SiO₂. [c] Calcite. [d] 2CaO.Al₂O₃.SiO₂ (Gehlenite).
[e] Note: Kaliophilite made in preference to calcium orthosilicate.

Excluding the pegmatitic and other veins and dikes, which often constitute a large part of the ijolite complex, variability in the 'host' rocks occurs in a number of ways:

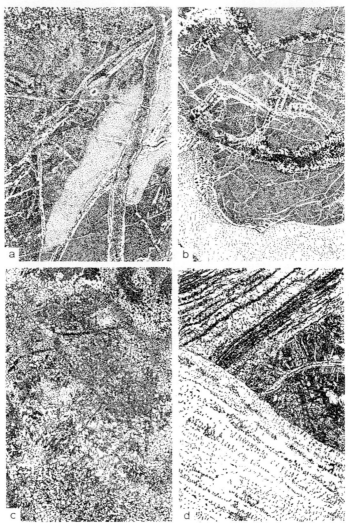

Fig. 15.　Structures in the Ijolites. (*a*) Variable-textured ijolite passing locally into medium-grained urtite and cut by sequence of veins (1/30). (*b*) Medium mesocratic ijolite traversed by succession of pegmatitic veins and sharply cut by early urtite (1/20). (*c*) Variable ijolite developed by nephelinization of pyroxenite-melteigite (1/15). (*d*) Mesocratic ijolite, with xenolithic pyroxenite-melteigite, traversed by pegmatitic veins, and cut by banded ijolite; both are sharply truncated by late banded wollastonite urtite (1/25).

(*a*) Transitions without change in grain size from pyroxenite to melteigite and thence to an even, medium- or fine-textured ijolite; occasionally large masses of homogeneous ijolite appear to have developed in this way.

(*b*) Uneven variations from melteigites to ijolites, sometimes with distinct junctions; the texture is often also variable, the tendency being for the more leucocratic phases to be coarser grained (Fig. 16c).

(*c*) The occurrence of a parallel banded structure, which varies from vague and undulating to straight and regular and arises from several causes. Occasionally it is related to a parallel orientation of the pyroxene prisms, always in rather fine-grained melteigites or mesocratic ijolites; usually, however, it results from variations in grain size and/or mineral composition in the different bands (Fig. 16c and 16d). The most obvious banding depends on varying proportions of nepheline, but wide variations in the relative amounts of pyroxene and melanite are also common.

Among the more homogeneous ijolites two rather different textures are represented; in the one the aegirine-augite, which is either pale and patchily zoned or a medium green variety, occurs in prisms and grains tending when aggregated to form an interlocking meshwork between the nepheline crystals (Fig. 16c); in the other the pyroxene is similarly interstitial but forms larger anhedral grains and often also occurs as tiny blebs and prisms within the nepheline, which itself shows more rounded outlines in contradistinction to the squarish outlines of the other textural variety (Fig. 16a). It is also commonly found that the pyroxene tends to assume euhedral outlines when it is abundant, but in leucocratic varieties it is nearly always anhedral.

Melanite, varying from opaque to a deep brown colour, often unevenly zoned to lighter margins, occurs either as small subhedral to euhedral crystals or as elaborate winding aggregates, insinuating between pyroxene crystals and often enveloping them (Fig. 16b). The larger poikilitic crystals and aggregates show occasional crystal faces. Melanite freely encloses sphene as well as pyroxene.

Melanite has often clearly formed at the expense of both pyroxene and nepheline, for crystals of these minerals become reduced in size and dissected (Fig. 16d). It is sometimes noticeable, too, that the nepheline is corroded to form elongated prismatic shapes that the mineral never otherwise shows.

Other minerals are rare and sporadically developed; a pale orange biotite, sometimes pleochroic to a greenish tint, is occasionally moulded on to pyroxene crystals. Iron-titanium oxides are rare in the ijolites in contrast to their abundance in the pyroxenites. The mineral associations suggest that in the former the ferric iron is accommodated in the aegirine molecule and in melanite.

Where rapid variations in grain size occur, as in the banded varieties, the constituent minerals show no evidence of changes in composition. This is especially apparent in the case of the pyroxene and melanite, wherein compositional variation is readily detectable by differences in colour. The similarity of composition of the aegirine-augite in bands of differing texture is considered a criterion of their simultaneous formation.

(ii) *Ijolite pegmatites.*[1] Transecting the xenolithic and variable ijolite complex is a series of pegmatites, examples of which are to be seen in almost every outcrop. They vary from diffuse and irregular to sharply defined and parallel sided, and

---

[1] The term pegmatite is used to designate a relatively coarse texture, often with a zonal structure, but the actual size of the crystals may be as little as a centimetre.

are mostly a few inches across; in many outcrops at least three successive phases are recognizable (Fig. 15a). It is evident that replacement is an important mechanism in their development 'vein' and this applies to many of those with well-defined margins, for they often show no sign of offsetting earlier structures. In other cases dilation of the vein walls is apparent and it is not uncommon to find

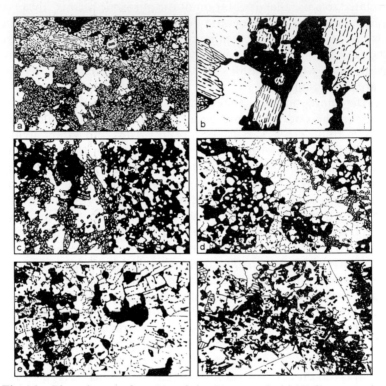

Fig. 16.   Plutonic rocks from Napak (× 50 approx.). (*a*) Medium granular pyroxenite invaded by coarser textured ijolite. Along the contact the pale diopsidic pyroxene of the pyroxenite is transformed to the green aegirine-augite of the ijolite. (*b*) Coarse-grained ijolite showing mantling and replacement of aegirine-augite by melanite. (*c*) Medium-grained banded ijolite; the differences between the bands are partly textural and partly result from variations in the proportions of the three minerals, nepheline, aegirine-augite and melanite. The encirclement of nepheline crystals or aggregates by strings of subhedral or prismatic pyroxene (left of field) is common in some of the finer-textured ijolites. (*d*) Banded melanite-ijolite. The central band is a 'vein' of almost pure nepheline. An even-grained polygonal habit is shown by all the nepheline; replacement by melanite from intergranular boundaries is illustrated. (*e*) Variable melanite bearing urtite; the squat rectangular habit of the nepheline is typical of the early urtite phase. (*f*) Nepheline-bearing syenite. The pyroxene is aegirine-rich and forms aggregates of slender prisms and needles. Large twinned crystals of clear potash feldspar enclose the pyroxene and numerous small grains of similar feldspar. Corroded remnants of nepheline (shown by conventional ruling) occur sporadically. The boundaries of the feldspar crystals have been drawn by viewing the field between crossed nicols.

that dislocation of pre-existing structures parallel to the vein walls has occurred. The pegmatites vary from mesocratic to leucocratic and may show a predominance of dark minerals either along the margins or, very frequently, along the centres of the veins. In most cases the mafic mineral is aegirine-augite, but sometimes melanite is predominant. Usually the orientation of the pyroxene is haphazard, but, especially in later veins, a comb structure is developed with long prisms of aegirine-augite arranged perpendicularly to the vein walls. Thin veinlets composed wholly of pyroxene are common.

In all cases the pyroxene of the veins is richer in aegirine than the host; at the margins of veins this is very obvious since large plates of deep green aegirine-augite are built on crystals of a paler pyroxene in the host rock, a metasomatic alteration of the latter commonly extending outwards from the vein for some millimetres from the contact (Fig. 16a). Melanite sometimes forms a fringe along the contact itself, enclosing the pyroxene and penetrating between grains of nepheline.

A common phenomenon is the development of narrow melanite 'veins' (up to 3 cm) traversing ijolite pegmatites and host rock alike. These may consist of straight continuous aggregates of melanite or discontinuous strings. They are evidently metasomatic in origin.

(iii) *Urtite-nepheline rock (early urtite phase).* This is a phase which is almost ubiquitously developed, but is especially widespread on the northern sector of Lokupoi. The characteristic rock is cream-weathering and medium-textured and often consists almost wholly of nepheline; other distinctive varieties are regularly speckled with melanite or contain small blades of wollastonite.

In many places the nepheline rock elaborately net-veins the ijolite complex, and where the latter consists largely of pyroxenite-melteigite a strikingly colour contrasted pattern of veins and xenolithic blocks is produced. Even where the veins are fairly well defined it is doubtful whether they are intrusive, for it is common to see isolated euhedral crystals of nepheline, sometimes up to a centimetre or more across, in the adjacent melteigite; often too the development of nepheline produces a complementary concentration of pyroxene in the immediately adjacent rock.

In other cases transition zones of ijolite are developed against the urtite and sometimes entire outcrops consisting of variable-textured, but usually rather coarse-grained, ijolite have been produced in this way. The pyroxenes, always deep green in thin section, are in prominent prisms, commonly randomly oriented, but occasionally showing a parallel orientation. The nephelines are typically euhedral, occurring as squat rectangles in the medium-grained varieties (Fig. 16e); in the coarser grained types two stages of growth are often seen: inner euhedral cores with tiny inclusions of pyroxene and outer clear zones with mutually interfering boundaries. In some specimens melanite is moulded against the euhedral cores, but is enclosed by the outer growths.

(iv) *Later phases in the ijolite complex.* Some pegmatite veins and irregular replacements, similar in character to those already described, are demonstrably later than the urtites (Fig. 16a). The urtites are also cut by groups of medium, even-grained melanocratic to mesocratic ijolites which are often banded, reflecting variations in the proportions of the principal minerals. This banding is entirely discordant with any earlier banding in the ijolite complex (Fig. 16d).

(b) *Late urtite phase* (*the urtite complex*)

Dike-like bands of coarse-grained urtite up to several feet in width are prominently developed on the isolated hill in the north western sector of Lokupoi, but they occur sporadically elsewhere. Everywhere they transect all other members of the ijolitic sequence. The commonest rock type is a pegmatitic wollastonite urtite; the wollastonite being more abundant in some parts of a dike than in others produces a crude banding (Fig. 16d). A comb structure is usual, blades of wollastonite several centimetres in length forming perpendicularly to the walls. Other types less commonly developed are melanite-wollastonite urtite and wollastonite-pyroxene urtite, which are evidently earlier than the pegmatites, but nevertheless form a parallel banded pattern with them.

In thin section the nepheline is seen to occur as anhedral crystals of varying size, while the very subordinate pyroxene, a moderately aegirine-rich variety, also has irregular outlines. Wollastonite forms long blades, usually enclosing or moulded against pyroxene, but occasionally being enclosed by the pyroxenes; partial replacement by pectolite is common and the nepheline also may be sporadically altered to cancrinite. Melanite is a translucent brown variety, often zoned to paler margins. Sphene, frequently enclosed by melanite, and apatite are common accessories.

(c) *Deformation of the ijolites and late-stage alterations*

Shearing or brecciation of the ijolites is commonly seen in the field and has formed finer textured granular aggregates of nepheline and pyroxene. Frequently, too, the pegmatite veins have developed along dislocations, while in the late urtites, the blades of wollastonite have often been systematically sheared from their normal positions perpendicular to the dike walls.

Secondary alteration is sometimes associated with shearing, but often occurs in irregular patches or as distinct veins. Most readily affected are the urtites and on the northern and north eastern sectors of Lokupoi extensive belts of the prevalent nepheline rock have become structureless and yellowish-weathering owing to alteration. The chief alteration products of the nepheline are cancrinite, natrolite and other zeolites together with calcite, while wollastonite is converted to pectolite or calcite; the place of melanite is taken by a colourless andradite garnet and aegirine-augite breaks down to obscure turbid alteration products which include hematite and calcite. In secondary veins the same minerals occur, but without pseudomorphic habits after the primary constituents.

Feldspar-bearing rocks

Feldspathic rock which forms dikes and veins, varying from several feet to a few inches in width, cuts the ijolites in a few places, but judging from the distribution of boulders of the rock, it is more widespread than the outcrops suggest.

The rock is typically banded, parallel to dike margins, owing to variations both in texture and composition; the coarser pegmatitic bands are dominated by large laths or plates of potash feldspar up to 3 or 4 cm in length, sometimes arranged perpendicularly to the banding.

In thin section the most characteristic rock is seen to be an aegirine syenite with an interlocking 'background' mosaic of clear to turbid potash feldspar,[1] mostly in twinned laths, and aegirine (or near aegirine) as long slender prisms or a mossy felt of needles, sometimes with a radiating habit (Fig. 16f).

Another closely related dike rock is a cancrinite syenite, ranging from fine- to medium-grained and sometimes showing bands with differing proportions of the essential minerals, potash feldspar and cancrinite. In places large crystals of feldspar enclose a finer grained mosaic of the same mineral. Small amounts of albitic plagioclase occur occasionally, generally as margins on the potash feld- spar, but sometimes producing a perthitic 'flecking'. Cancrinite forms long slender prisms of 'primary' aspect, often numerous and sub-parallel, which transect the potash feldspar; sometimes too it cuts across prisms and needles of aegirine. Calcite 'pods' tend to replace marginally and isolate the feldspar crystals, but hold the aegirine as enclosed prisms; calcite also mantles and replaces cancrinite.

Of particular interest are zones of nepheline syenite which clearly represent replacement of ijolite. Within the potash feldspars relic nepheline sometimes occurs in small rounded and embayed crystals, but the nepheline also shows a tendency to develop euhedral outlines. Locally this rock grades into normal ijolite, composed of nepheline and aegirine-augite. There are, however, some fine-grained nepheline syenites in which the nepheline does not appear to be relict, since it forms euhedral crystals, with tiny needle-like oriented inclusions of pyroxene in the marginal zones, set in a mosaic of larger crystals of potash feld- spar.

Turjaites

Among the ijolites on the eastern flanks of Lokupoi occurs a mass of a uni- form grey, fine-grained but porphyritic rock, containing conspicuous crystals of biotite. The margins of the mass are diffuse and unchilled.

The rock shows affinities with certain of the melilite-nephelinites, both mineralogically and texturally, although it has a coarser grain than any of the lavas. The principal minerals are a very pale diopsidic pyroxene, nepheline and melilite,[2] but each of these may locally be dominant. All three minerals occur both as phenocrysts, occasionally as much as a centimetre across, and as small grains in the groundmass. Larger crystals of melilite often enclose pyroxene and nepheline and sometimes marginally form symplectic intergrowths with the pyroxene. Smaller nephelines may be enclosed both by diopside and melilite, but phenocrysts of nepheline occasionally enclose small grains of both nepheline and melilite. Grains of black iron-titanium oxide are abundant, and perovskite is a common accessory. Biotite is sporadic, but locally abundant, sometimes as

---

[1] $N\alpha$, 1.519; $N\gamma$, 1.525; $2V\,(-) \sim 40°$.

[2] Chemical analysis of the melilite gave a composition corresponding approximately to $Ak_{47}Geh_{22}Fe–Geh_{10}Na\text{-}Mel_{21}$; N^o, 1.634; N_e, 1.625.

E

large sieved crystals; it is pale orange-brown to pale green. Melanite is only rarely found—as films around iron oxide, perovskite and biotite.

Occasional *dikes* with chilled margins cut the ijolites and Basement; they closely resemble the nephelinite lavas (King, 1949).

Carbonatite

Carbonatite constitutes the small central hill, Moruangeberr (0.25 mile in diameter), in the middle of Lokupoi, and forms a number of dikes intersecting the ijolites. The main mass shows a concentric vertical banding. The chief type is a sövite composed largely of calcite with a fine- to medium-granular texture, but siderite forms isolated crystals among the calcite and magnesian carbonates[1] are also variably present (King, 1949). Magnetite is abundant and sometimes forms large euhedral crystals. Patches of coarser-textured calcite appear to be later. Pyrochlore and baddeleyite are accessories.

The carbonatite of the dikes is essentially similar to that of the main mass; wollastonite has been recorded in thin section (King, 1949).

The carbonatites are locally brecciated and in a number of places are sharply cut by small masses of agglomerate, consisting of carbonatite fragments in a ferruginous groundmass.

The peripheral fenites

Between the central intrusive complex of Lokupoi and the elevated pediment of Basement rocks which outcrop along the inner scarps of the volcanic remnants, exposures are almost wholly confined to a low ridge about one mile to the south of Lokupoi. Here the Basement rocks are shattered or sheared and fenitized. The trend of the ridge and the direction of shearing are parallel to the circumference of Lokupoi in this sector, suggesting that concentric faulting or shearing occurred around the central complex similar to that postulated by Davies at Bukusu.

Two drill holes between the fenite ridge and Lokupoi penetrated fenites and ijolites respectively and have served more closely to define the limit of the central complex without, however, providing any information as to the nature of the boundary. The fenites are always unmistakably metasomatic and the transformation is never so great that the original nature of the rock cannot be established.

Among the original Basement rocks coarsely foliated quartz-feldspar gneisses and finer grained granulites are most abundant in the area; they contain variable amounts of biotite and muscovite and sometimes also garnet. Plagioclase usually predominates over potash feldspar (orthoclase or microcline, often perthitic) and ranges from oligoclase to calcic oligoclase.

The fenitized gneisses are traversed by numerous sub-parallel shears or fractures, occupied by fine-grained dark green material, ranging from the merest films to a few millimetres in width. A more irregular small-scale fracturing, similarly emphasized by dark mineralization, is also seen.

[1] Two chemical analyses show MgO, 2.32 and 15.82% and FeO, (total iron) 4.17 and 8.44% respectively.

In detail the course of fenitization shows considerable textural and minera-logical variation. Most of the alteration occurs along shears or fractures, inter-granular boundaries or sinuous ramifying channels, but little or no infilling of actual openings in the rock is envisaged.

The most characteristic newly formed minerals are a deep green aegirine, colourless or brownish acmite, a blue-green amphibole and a grey-green chlorite, occurring in widely varying proportions. The aegirine in particular, but some-times the amphibole, tends to form feathery rosettes of fine needles which fringe the veins and penetrate into adjacent crystals of quartz or feldspar. In other cases the minerals form aggregates of tiny prisms, either in parallel growth or random arrangement. In the pyroxene-garnet gneisses, the garnet is dissected along innumerable cracks by flaky amphibole, which also forms feathery rims to biotite and pyroxene, the hypersthene especially often being completely replaced. Chlorite preferentially replaces biotite. The amphibole varies from a type pleochroic from pale yellowish-green to blue-green, to one ranging from pale to intense blue-green and violet. This distinctively coloured variety, judging from its optical properties, is certainly the same as the eckermannite which has been identified in fenites elsewhere (King and Sutherland, 1960, p. 507). In some of the pyroxene gneisses amphibole forms comparatively large aggregates of parallel fibres, showing marginal zoning to the blue-green-violet variety.

The biotite of the fenites is distinctively pleochroic in shades of orange- or reddish-brown. It is not always clear how much of it represents new crystalliza-tion, for in many cases it can be shown that the original brown biotite of the gneisses has been changed without modification of form. Thus the laths of biotite in an otherwise unmodified pyroxene granulite show pale cores and bright orange marginal zones. Other dark minerals that develop more sporadically are sphene, occasionally forming large crystals, and magnetite.

The transformations affecting the quartz and feldspars are varied and often difficult to trace. It is apparent that quartz disappears owing to replacement both by aegirine and amphibole and by feldspars, but since the amount present in the original gneisses shows wide and rapid variations the extent of quartz replacement in any particular specimen is not easily established.

The original feldspars (and quartz) sometimes show strain and distortion, but this is largely obscured by recrystallization. In thin section areas of granular recrystallization are common along intergranular boundaries and forming irregular patches. Along the shears fine granular and flaky or streaky aggregates of feldspar are often associated with the dark minerals. More extensive recon-stitution is marked by the development of new alkali feldspars, as crystals of the same order of size as the original mosaic. The plagioclase is generally more albitic than that of the gneiss; the potash feldspar is a homogeneous orthoclase. Both varieties, but especially the potash feldspar, often show a diffusely patchy extinction and vaguely defined boundaries, suggesting that they may have replaced granular recrystallized areas of older feldspar. All stages are to be seen in the replacement of the original feldspar, the penultimate one with residual cores being easily recognizable. Where replacement is complete, this fact is less easily appreciated.

Other minerals that occur in the fenites include calcite and zeolites, but it is not clear to what extent these are directly related to fenitization, rather than a later secondary alteration.

Owing to the variability of the gneisses the chemical changes consequent upon fenitization are not easily determined and although a number of analyses of the fenites have been made quanitative assessment of additions and subtractions cannot be attempted. In most cases there has been loss of silica. Judging from the new minerals developed, additions of alkalies and alumina, ferric and ferrous iron have probably always occurred, together sometimes with lime and titania.

Toror

The Toror Hills are situated in Karomoja, to the north of Napak, some 35 miles north west of Moroto and 10 miles south of Kotido. The complex is the most northerly of the group of dissected volcanoes of eastern Uganda, and the volcanics have been entirely removed by erosion. It consists of intrusive rocks of hypabyssal character, including dikes, sheets and vent-intrusions of phonolite, trachyte and agglomerate, and a ring-shaped intrusion of carbonatite (Fig. 17).

The intrusions are emplaced in granitic gneiss of the Basement Complex, and are elevated above the level of the surrounding plain as a group of hills, approximately ring-shaped, the pinnacle of Toror Peak reaching some 2000 ft above the surrounding plains.

A general investigation of the complex was made by DuBois (1957, 1959) and his descriptions have been extensively used in the following account. A detailed re-examination, based on the mapping of two critical areas, was made by one of the writers (D.S.S.) in 1958 and 1960.

Field relations

It appears that the earliest phase of intrusive activity was the emplacement of dikes and sheets of potash trachyte, which are particularly numerous in the northern part of the complex. On the lower slopes of northward-projecting spurs, the trachyte dikes form a highly intricate meshwork in which individual dikes vary from 6–40 ft or so in width. The most prominent trend is 160°, parallel with the foliation of the Basement gneiss, but these dikes cut an earlier set which trend 80°. On the north western slopes, the trend is more commonly 170–180°, suggesting a probable radial arrangement. Several dike-like bodies have the appearance of breccias, with numerous fragments of feldspathic Basement gneiss in a fine-grained trachytic matrix; trachytes containing xenoliths of Basement form an intermediate rock type between such breccias and normal potash trachyte.

The trachyte is fine-grained, and 'chalky' rather than crystalline in aspect; it is light buff and conspicuously stained with shades of purple, red and brown. The small phenocrysts of potash feldspar sometimes show a parallel orientation. Most of the trachytes are considered to be earlier than the carbonatite but a later group of trachytes, sometimes rich in fluorite, occurs as small sheets and dikes cutting the carbonatite. An area, some 400 yd across, in the lower part of the northern valley, consists of trachyte, and appears to represent an early vent. Other areas around the southern periphery of the complex, originally mapped by DuBois as altered Basement, are probably of similar nature (see map, Fig. 17).

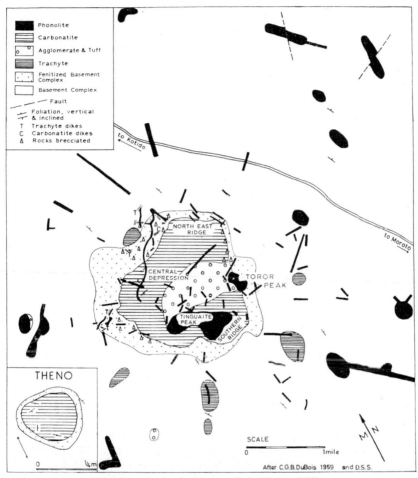

Fig. 17. Geological map of the Toror Hills.

The carbonatite, intruded by the central mass of agglomerate, is now in the form of a partial ring, with a diameter of about two miles. In the north east and south the outer margin of the carbonatite forms steep cliffs above the adjacent Basement; on the west side, cliff features are within the carbonatite, and to the north and north west, cliffs are often formed by the brecciated Basement outside the carbonatite; there is thus no persistent topographic feature marking the outer contact, and the carbonatite outcrops only sporadically on the inner slopes of the hills. The carbonatite is almost invariably brown, with local development of magnetite in vertical bands and sweeping 'flow' lines; on Ironstone Hill the concentration of magnetite is particularly high. Observed contacts between carbonatite and Basement are complicated; on the north side, for example, narrow belts of carbonatite are intercalated with belts of brecciated Basement and the early trachyte dikes, while the contact of the main mass of carbonatite lies, ill-exposed, on the inner slopes of the hills. Several phases of carbonatite emplacement and brecciation are involved for, although carbonatite is seen in more than one place to have a sharp, intrusive, vertical contact against already brecciated Basement, the breccia itself in places contains fragments of carbonatite. Ferruginous veins traverse both carbonatite and surrounding Basement, breccia and trachyte. In some localities, however, the carbonatite contains inclusions which have the appearance of drawn out veins of ferruginous material.

A central mass of phonolitic agglomerate (more appropriately breccia) elliptical and about three quarters of a mile long, occupies the inner slopes to the north west of Toror Peak. It is cut by a number of phonolite intrusions but several types of earlier phonolite and tinguaite have been recognized among the fragments. The fragments are up to two inches across, and largely angular, in a matrix of fine-grained volcanic material with calcite and zeolites. Other vents filled with agglomerates occur on Nyanga Hill (fragments of gneiss and phonolite) and Lozipiri (Basement gneiss).

The latest intrusions of the complex are numerous phonolites and tinguaites in the form of dikes, sheets and plugs. Toror Peak is formed by a phonolite plug which pierces the central agglomerate. Tinguaite Peak to the west of it is a larger mass with a sharp intrusive junction against carbonatite; the tinguaite is altered for a width of 6 in along the contact with carbonatite, but is not chilled. Another recognizable plug forms Nyanga Hill to the south; the top of the hill is crowned with a curved crest of columnar jointed phonolite, and DuBois records the upward streaming of amygdales with flow.

Many of the outlying elliptical masses of phonolite thought by DuBois to be plugs have contacts with the Basement at low angles, in particular at Nakazilet and Moruangnamorj. From a distance on the north east side the phonolites appear to cap the hills like lava flows; the surface of the Basement beneath the sheets, however, is not weathered, but massive, fresh rock and the sheets are evidently intrusive. They appear on average to dip gently to the north, at angles of up to 20°. On the North East Ridge, a prominent dike of phonolite extends south from a knoll probably representing the feeder plug, and a sheeted mass about 30 ft thick passes around the hillside to the west; it dips to the south at a low angle and can be traced to where it cuts the carbonatite. It might appropriately be termed a cone sheet. Near the West Ridge, two other phonolites have a sheet-like habit, one dipping north and one dipping east. Numerous phonolite dikes cut the carbonatite and the central agglomerate; although many are approximately radial to the complex, other trends are recorded (see map, Fig. 17), and cross-cutting relationships testify to several phases of intrusion. The intrusion of the macro-porphyritic varieties generally preceded that of the phonolite crowded with smaller phenocrysts. A few of the phonolites are affected by later faulting.

Three minor intrusions of nephelinite are described by DuBois on the south side of the complex. On the North East Ridge, another small intrusion of nephelinite has the shape of a mushroom, entirely surrounded and roofed by

Basement. It has a diameter of only 10–12 ft, a 'stalk' 2–3 ft in diameter, and a thickness of about 3 ft from the base to the roof.

A small intrusion of carbonatite without associated alkali-silicate rocks occurs at Theno Hill, 5 miles to the west of Toror (Fig. 17). It has a diameter of $\frac{1}{4}$ mile, and flow banding is observed parallel with the margin. The contact is obscured by marginal breccia.

Petrography

The country rocks are predominantly granitic gneisses, having a foliation trending NNW–SSE, ranging from vertical to dipping 80° E. Within these gneisses are bands of garnetiferous hornblende granulite, and locally quartz-feldspar pegmatites follow the strike.

DuBois records that the granitic gneisses consist of orthoclase, often cloudy, subordinate microcline and oligoclase, and quartz forming an interstitial mosaic. Biotite, forming small subhedral flakes, is oriented with the foliation. Magnetite, garnet, amphibole, zircon and apatite occur in small amounts.

The hornblende granulite is closely banded. Hornblende forms anhedral crystals up to 2 mm in diameter, and may be intergrown with garnet. It is pleochroic with X (pale brown) $< Y$ (green-brown) $< Z$ (olive green), and $Z: c = 18°$ (DuBois). The pink garnet is sometimes riddled with inclusions of quartz, and occasional magnetite. Plagioclase ($Ab_{66} An_{34}$), occurring with quartz in the leucocratic layers, is often twinned (DuBois). Magnetite is accessory.

The potash trachytes (Table IV, 3) are usually holocrystalline with a fine-grained felsitic groundmass, locally with fluidal texture, in which are dispersed flakes of brown limonite. Phenocrysts of cloudy orthoclase and sometimes of sanidine, 1–2 mm in length, are sparsely distributed. Baveno and carlsbad twinning are recorded. Amygdales are present in a few specimens, infilled by zeolite and sometimes rimmed by flakes of chloritic material. Intrusions of trachyte containing numerous xenoliths of feldspathized Basement rocks (microcline and orthoclase) have a fine-grained groundmass with felsitic texture, and phenocrysts are rare. Most of the trachytes are veined by limonite, and many have been partly replaced by diffuse carbonate in the groundmass.

Late trachytes cutting the carbonatite are less common. A sheet near the northern margin of the carbonatite is unusual in containing abundant fluorite. It is medium to dark grey in hand specimen, rather darker than most trachytes, and contains tabular phenocrysts of cloudy potash feldspar up to 4 mm in size. The groundmass in thin section consists of laths of feldspar, locally oriented with a trachytoid texture, and streaks of granules of pale yellow-green acmite, largely altered to ferruginous matter and chlorite. These layers sweep round aggregates of purple fluorite. Analyses of the early and late trachytes show that both types are extraordinarily rich in potash,[1] and the late fluorite-bearing trachyte compares closely with the dike rock, borengite, on Alnö (v. Eckermann, 1960). The aegirine trachytes described by DuBois are not fluorite-bearing, but appear to be less altered than the rocks in the north, and may be late intrusions. These

[1] Early trachyte Na_2O, 0.38; K_2O, 13.90%; late trachyte Na_2O, 1.10; K_2O, 12.26% (see also Fig. 19).

rocks are holocrystalline with microlites of feldspar and aegirine forming the groundmass, and phenocrysts of sanidine, or cloudy orthoclase which may be zoned towards more sodic margins.

DuBois classified the phonolitic intrusions on the basis of texture into *phonolites and tinguaites* (although they are mutually gradational), the pyroxene in the latter having a feathery texture and random distribution through the groundmass (Table IV, 1, 2). The porphyritic phonolites contain phenocrysts of nepheline, feldspar and pyroxene in very variable proportions. Commonly, nepheline is more abundant than feldspar. It is euhedral and water clear, with some inclusions of pyroxene, but alteration to kaolin or sericite occurs along cracks, and replacement by natrolite is frequent. In many rocks natrolite also replaces much of the groundmass, often in the form of fibrous rosettes. The refractive indices N_o, 1.538; N_e, 1.534, indicate that the nepheline contains 15 per cent of the kaliophilite molecule (DuBois). Phenocrysts of feldspar are variable in composition, size and abundance. Soda-orthoclase is common as euhedral phenocrysts up to 1 cm in length, but some phonolites contain clear sanidine as thin tablets as much as 1.5 cm long (soda-orthoclase: N_α 1.520; N_β 1.525; N_γ 1.527; $N_\gamma - N_\alpha = 0.007$; $2V(-)$ 63°; sanidine: N_α 1.518; N_β 1.523; N_γ 1.525; $N_\gamma - N_\alpha = 0.007$ $2V(-)$ 6°; DuBois). Pyroxene forms euhedral phenocrysts, commonly zoned from pale green or buff diopsidic cores to bright green pleochroic rims of aegirine-augite. In some phonolites the outermost zones consist of tufted aegirine ($X: c$ around 0°) sometimes accompanied by blue-green sodic amphibole; in others, some of the phenocrysts are approximately pseudomorphed by recrystallized yellow acmite ($X: c = 10°$) in the form of acicular prisms, flecked and tipped with green aegirine. Sphene is also included among the phenocrysts.

The groundmass of most phonolites consists of small laths of feldspar with interstitial nepheline, and is often altered to zeolite and kaolin. Fluidal texture is frequently exhibited by the laths of feldspar and by prismatic aegirine in the groundmass. Accessory minerals in the phonolites are sphene, zircon, granular magnetite, natrolite[1] (often abundant), cancrinite,[2] calcite, sodalite or analcite as isotropic patches and occasional grains, pectolite as colourless laths, and rare phlogopite. Spherulitic texture is found especially in the non-porphyritic phonolites, and amygdales are common.

One example of biotite phonolite is recorded by DuBois; the biotite shows X (very pale brown) $< Y$ (pale orange) $< Z$ (brick red). Accessory minerals are colourless garnet, apatite, sphene, magnetite and chocolate brown, pleochroic enigmatite. Some of the tinguaites contain brown barkevikite mantled with aegirine, a blue-green amphibole and fluorite. Syenitic xenoliths are common in the phonolites, often with conspicuous tabular feldspar, frequently zeolitized, and sometimes with aegirine. Apatite may be abundant in the xenoliths.

Hytönen (1959) from a detailed study of the mineralogy of some of the phonolites represents the history of crystallization as follows:

---

[1] N_α 1.480; N_β 1.485; N_γ 1.492; $N_\gamma - N_\alpha = 0.012$; $2V(+)$ $c \sim 60°$ (DuBois).

[2] N_e 1.498; N_o 1.515.

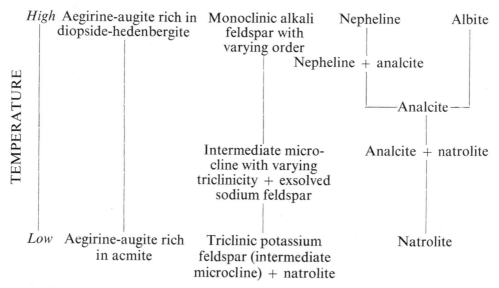

TEMPERATURE

High Aegirine-augite rich in diopside-hedenbergite — Monoclinic alkali feldspar with varying order — Nepheline — Albite

Nepheline + analcite

————Analcite——

Intermediate micro-cline with varying triclinicity + exsolved sodium feldspar — Analcite + natrolite

Low Aegirine-augite rich in acmite — Triclinic potassium feldspar (intermediate microcline) + natrolite — Natrolite

Three occurrences of *nephelinite* are recorded by DuBois, in which nepheline forms up to 20 per cent of the rock, accompanied by microphenocrysts of un-zoned aegirine-augite, in a groundmass of natrolite and cancrinite densely speckled with iron oxides and rods of aegirine. The small mushroom-shaped intrusion on the northern side of the complex is a nephelinite containing numerous xenoliths of variable ijolitic rocks. The nephelinite itself contains euhedral nepheline grains grading in size from 1 mm into the groundmass; partial replacement by cloudy zeolite and cancrinite has occurred. Some enclose small prisms of aegirine-augite. Pyroxene is variable from diopsidic (considered to be indigenous) to green aegirine-augite (often as rounded crystals which may be xenocrysts). Abundant lath-like crystals of colourless melilite occur; it is optically negative but has a higher birefringence than that of melilites from other localities in eastern Uganda, indicating a high content of the $Ca_2FeSi_2O_7$ molecule (Sahama, 1961). Wollastonite is also fairly common. Magnetite crystals are abundant in the groundmass with xenocrysts of melanite. Xenoliths of ijolite in the nephelinite are coarse grained and unaltered, with variable amounts of anhedral nepheline, stout prisms of green aegirine-augite, and granular aggregates of melanite, slightly zoned from orange-brown to dark brown, almost opaque. Apatite is common in the xenoliths.

Part of the groundmass, especially around the xenoliths, is replaced by natrolite in the form of fibres lying perpendicular to swirling structures.

Four main varieties of *carbonatite* occur at Toror: (a) sövite, (b) dolomitic sövite, (c) ferruginous carbonatite, (d) feldspathic carbonatite. The carbonatite, however, is poorly exposed on the inner slopes of the ring of hills, and separate intrusions cannot be recognized.

The sövite consists of a mosaic of calcite, varying from equigranular, fairly fine-grained, to inequigranular with coarser texture. Very finely divided limonite is scattered as dust throughout the entire mosaic. Other minerals are rarely found; apatite is the most common, and is often associated with the late veins of limonite. Unlike the older carbonatites of Uganda, pyroxene is not common, but in one specimen DuBois records large pale green, pleochroic plates of pyrox-

TABLE IV

Phonolites and trachyte from Toror

A. CHEMICAL COMPOSITIONS

	1 Phonolite T174	2 Phonolite T110	3 Trachyte T213
SiO_2	51.17	53.46	58.43
Al_2O_3	19.48	19.31	17.84
Fe_2O_3	1.86	3.25	5.09
FeO	3.62	1.31	nil
MgO	0.46	0.61	0.43
CaO	3.18	2.39	0.80
Na_2O	10.77	10.09	0.38
K_2O	3.01	4.25	13.90
H_2O+	4.71	4.95	1.05
H_2O-	—	—	0.11
CO_2	0.16	nd	nd
TiO_2	0.61	0.41	0.34
P_2O_5	0.05	0.05	0.35
MnO	0.22	0.21	0.42
BaO	0.15	nd	0.18
Total	99.45	100.29	99.32

D. S. Sutherland, anal.

B. C.I.P.W. NORMATIVE COMPOSITIONS

Quartz	—	—	0.5
Orthoclase	17.9	25.1	82.3
Albite	25.8	24.7	3.1
Anorthite	—	—	4.2
Nepheline	31.1	27.5	—
Na_2SiO_3	0.4	—	—
Corundum	—	—	0.6
Acmite	5.4	8.6	—
Diopside	11.0	6.1	—
Wollastonite	—	1.7	—
Hypersthene	—	—	1.1
Olivine	0.8	—	—
Magnetite	—	0.4	0.5
Hematite	—	—	4.8
Ilmenite	1.2	0.8	0.6
Apatite	0.1	0.1	0.7
Calcite	0.4	—	—
Total	94.1	95.0	98.4

ene, many of which enclose calcite, together with granular and fibrous aggregates partly altered to green-blue amphibole. Pyrochlore has a sporadic distribution, forming small honey-yellow isotropic grains, sometimes associated with amphibole and ferruginous material.

In the dolomitic sövite dolomite and calcite occur together as interlocking anhedral plates 0.5–2.0 mm in diameter. Fibrous green amphibole, small flakes of mica (red-brown to dark green), granules of magnetite and occasional grains of pyrochlore are accessory.

Ferruginous carbonatite is apparently the most abundant type at Toror, and is related to the sövites by the development of iron minerals in several ways. In some rocks, magnetite appears as euhedra in strings and layers with a vertical, banded structure, and on Ironstone Hill becomes exceedingly abundant. Some of the carbonatites contain rhombs of siderite with rims of limonite. Veining by hematite which alters to limonite is common, and similar ferruginous veins extend outside the carbonatite margin affecting the surrounding Basement and trachytes for several hundred yards.

The ferruginous carbonatite varies in colour from creamy-white with visible magnetite to black or deep purple when the magnetite is finely divided; an ochraceous appearance is produced by limonite. DuBois states that there is every gradation between sövite in which the constituent crystals of the calcite mosaic are bounded by hair-thin limonitic margins, to rocks where the calcite plates are corroded and set in a dense matrix of magnetite, turgite and limonite.

Ferruginous veins in carbonatite up to 2 cm thick are locally concentrated in swarms. DuBois records 5 per cent of MnO in a specimen of vein material.

Feldspar is rare in calcitic and dolomitic sövites but is found in the more ferruginous carbonatites as anhedral plates and aggregates of clouded orthoclase. Veins of soda-orthoclase cut the sövite-breccia at the north end of the North East Ridge.

Around the outer boundary of the carbonatite concentrations of apatite occur, in thin bands within the carbonatite, and in patches in the adjacent country rock as very fine-grained, buff-coloured apatite rock. Replacement of carbonatite is demonstrable, for locally rhomb-shaped carbonate crystals, probably representing original siderite outlined by rims of limonite, are pseudomorphed by fine-grained apatite. The apatite rock is fragmented by the later ferruginous brecciation. Locally the apatite rock contains notable concentrations of octahedral pyrochlore.

Feldspathic syenite (orthoclasite) consisting of interlocking plates of orthoclase, slightly clouded and often twinned, sometimes with interstitial limonite, occurs in several localities near the margin of the carbonatite; the rock has nearly everywhere been affected by shattering, brecciation and veining by limonite. It appears to be closely associated with trachyte, and may represent a coarsely crystalline equivalent.

Fenitization of the country-rocks at Toror is only slight, by comparison with other alkaline complexes, and quartz-free rocks are rarely developed. Mechanical stresses, however, which generally preceded metasomatism, were widespread and locally intensive, and brecciation is a common feature (see below).

Along narrow channels potash feldspar develops a fine, granular texture, and occasionally shows alignment of small laths. The plagioclase and microcline of the gneiss become partly replaced by anhedral untwinned potash feldspar; biotite, also, is altered to parallel laths of potash feldspar and granules of iron ore. The development of potash feldspar appears to be more conspicuous close to the carbonatite.

Along a network of narrow veinlets and around quartz crystals, aegirine, sodic amphibole, biotite and chlorite are developed. These minerals do not often occur together, but biotite forms the fenite veins at a distance from the carbonatite, while aegirine occurs close to the contact; amphibole, the most common, is found in an intervening area of variable width but up to approximately 100 yd from the contact.

The biotite forms veins and aggregates of small, equant crystals, pleochroic from dark blue-green or olive green to colourless or pale yellow (cf. biotite in the Tororo carbonatite, p. 94), and is partly altered to limonite and magnetite along the cleavages. The amphibole veins consist of aggregates and spherulitic masses of acicular crystals, pleochroic from blue-green to yellow-green or buff, with extinction angles up to 30°. Occasionally the amphibole is fringed by acicular aegirine, which is pleochroic from green to yellow, and has approximately straight extinction. It is often partly altered to limonite.

The later development of limonite and hematite along numerous shatter-veins extends further from the carbonatite than the main fenitization, and is a conspicuous feature of both Basement and trachytic rocks, but is also to be found in the carbonatite itself. It is not clear whether or not the limonite is a replacement of earlier fenite minerals.

Several phases of brecciation occurred at Toror. On the northern hillsides for about 200 yd from the carbonatite boundary the Basement is affected sporadically, the intensity of mechanical break-up varying from mere shattering, and cracking of crystals, to actual brecciation producing angular fragments in a fine-grained groundmass of feldspathic material. The trachytes intruded into the area before this main brecciation are variably affected, sometimes forming resistant blocks, but frequently being themselves fragmented. This phase of brecciation preceded the emplacement of the carbonatite as the latter shows good intrusive contacts against the brecciated country rock. The carbonatite, however, does not penetrate among the breccia channels.

Later brecciation took place locally near the carbonatite margin, and fragments of carbonatite occur, along with basement and trachyte, in a carbonate-rich and often ferruginous groundmass. The carbonatite is locally disrupted and discontinuous. Dike-like masses of breccia occur outside the carbonatite boundary within the country rock. They may be only a few inches wide but are normally of the order of a few feet. The fragments of all these late breccias are mixed and considerable movement of material is apparent. Small veins and dikes of breccia with well defined margins cutting the carbonatite and the country rock are considered to be even later. Their matrix is ferruginous and siliceous.

Derivation of the Toror rocks

By analogy with the Napak volcano, a magma of nephelinite composition is considered to be the immediate parent. Intrusions of such a composition are encountered at Toror only occasionally, but they contain abundant xenoliths of coarse ijolitic material exactly comparable with that found at Napak.

The numerous plugs of phonolite and the probable vents occupied by trachyte suggest the former existence of lavas of corresponding compositions. The trachytes, however, are unusually potash-rich and a direct relationship with the strongly sodic phonolites is unlikely (Fig. 18). The trachytes show greater affinity with potash feldspar rock of the type sporadically developed in the fenites at Toror and abundant at Tororo and other complexes in Africa such as Chilwa (Garson, this vol., p. 52; Garson and Campbell Smith, 1958) and Mbeya (Brown, 1963). They are comparable also with the potash-rich cancrinite syenites at Budeda.

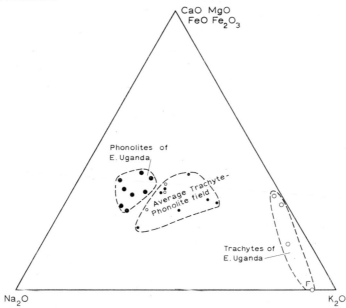

Fig. 18. Distribution of alkalies in the phonolites and trachytes of eastern Uganda compared with that in average rocks of this type (Johann-sen and Daly).
Solid circles: phonolites; open circles: trachytes; f: Feldspar rock, Tororo, included in trachyte field for comparison.

The phonolites may also be the mobilized products of metasomatic rocks (see Budeda, p. 88), but the derivation of some from nephelinite magma cannot be discounted.

CHEMISTRY AND PETROGENESIS

The alkaline igneous rock associations may be summarized as:

Volcanic and Hypabyssal:
    Melanephelinite—nephelinite (nephelinite series)
    Phonolite—trachyte (including trachyandesite)
Plutonic:
    Pyroxenite–melteigite–ijolite–urtite (ijolite series)–carbonatite
    Nepheline syenite—syenite (including fenites and feldspathized ijolites).

Chemical compositions of representative members of these assemblages are given in Tables I–IV. By comparison with members of calc alkaline suites, all assemblages in the complexes of eastern Uganda are characterized by high values

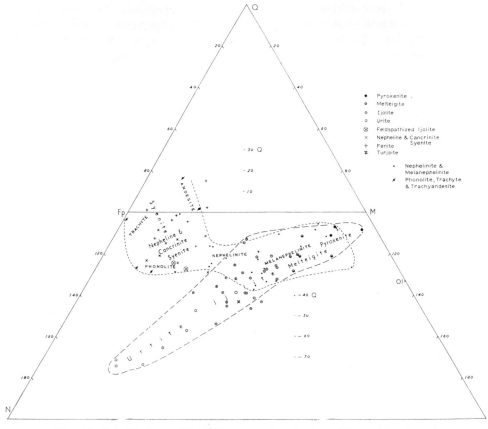

Fig. 19. Modified von Wolff diagram of rocks from Elgon, Napak and Budeda. The volcanic field and main plutonic field are separately outlined. Normative anorthite has been subtracted from L to give Fp (alkali feldspar) and values for Fp and M recalculated accordingly. If An is plotted as a vertical component on a three dimensional graph much of the field of nephelinite–melanephelinite (containing appreciable An) is separated from the ijolite field (containing little or no An). This reflects the tendency for alkalies to be lower in the volcanics than in the plutonics so that in calculation the excess alumina is allocated to lime in An, which in the rocks themselves is expressed as melilite.

for alkalies, especially soda, relative to silica and high alkalies relative to alumina. The nephelinite series and the ijolite series, which represent the predominant volcanic and plutonic assemblages, respectively, also show relatively low values for silica, despite wide variations in the proportions of other constituents, and relatively high values for lime.

In calc alkaline rocks, such as basalt and andesite, lime is partitioned between the two predominant minerals, pyroxene and plagioclase. In the typical alkaline rocks, of the two predominant minerals, pyroxene and nepheline, only the former contains significant amounts of lime. Correspondingly the pyroxene of the alkaline rocks is normally diopsidic and only becomes modified towards heden-bergite and acmite.

The non-appearance of plagioclase in the alkaline series, in spite of the abund-ance of lime, is explicable by reference to the field of plagioclase in the system $CaO-Al_2O_3-SiO_2-Na_2O$, which shows that the presence of a comparatively limited amount of soda suffices to cause initial crystallization of nepheline in place of calcic plagioclase.

Typically the nephelinites consist of diopsidic pyroxene, nepheline, and black ore (ilmenite-magnetite), together often with olivine (Mg-rich) and/or melilite. Perovskite is a common accessory. Analyses suggest that, in many cases, the groundmass contains a mineral such as analcite or natrolite (p. 98). The phono-lites are characterized by alkali feldspar in addition to nepheline and an aegirine-rich pyroxene. They are thus intermediate in composition between the nephelin-ites and trachytes.

Members of the ijolite series consist typically of aegirine-augite and nepheline, together with more or less abundant melanite, while wollastonite is prominent in the leucocratic rocks. By comparison with the lavas there is a notable absence of, or paucity in olivine, melilite and black ore.

Chemically the volcanic and plutonic suites show markedly divergent trends, which reflect the fact that there are no volcanic equivalents of much of the ijolite series (see Fig. 19). A near coincidence of composition is shown, however, between melanephelinite and pyroxenite melteigite. It is in this compositional range, therefore, that the immediately parental magma to both suites is to be sought.

A probable explanation for these divergent trends is provided by the different courses of crystallization suggested by the mineralogy of the volcanic and plutonic assemblages. In the nephelinite series early crystallization of olivine and melilite, in addition to pyroxene, would tend to produce relative enrichment in silica in the later residues, leading to the formation of analcite or alkali feldspar in place of nepheline. In the ijolite series, on the other hand, the crystallization of pyroxene alone would maintain a lower proportion of silica in residual melts, so that nepheline would continue to crystallize.

The contrasting courses of evolution of the volcanic and plutonic series is also shown by plotting the total iron oxides to magnesia ratio against the lime to magnesia ratio (Fig. 20). Whereas relative enrichment in iron oxides is characteristic of both series, the ijolite series alone shows a striking enrichment of lime relative to magnesia. Indeed, many wollastonite urtites and ijolite pegma-tites show higher absolute values for lime than melteigites or ijolites and calcite is often present as a primary, although late-forming mineral. It is this trend towards absolute enrichment in lime and the separation of calcite as a final phase of crystallization that is regarded as providing the key to the derivation of the carbonatites.

Although a common parent magma is postulated for both the volcanic and the plutonic series, slight differences in composition achieved at an early stage might initiate the divergence in trends. Thus in the system $CaO-Al_2O_3-SiO_2-Na_2O$ a slightly higher content of soda (or of total alkalies) would favour migration towards an alkali silicate end-point, rather than a course in which crystallization of nepheline would ultimately be joined by alkali feldspar. Comparison of chemical analyses shows that for particular values of, for example, alumina or silica, the plutonic series has higher values for alkalies than the volcanic.

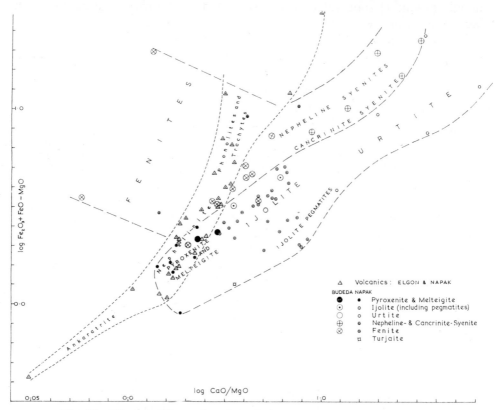

Fig. 20. Diagram illustrating the relations between the ratios $Fe_2O_3 + FeO/MgO$ and CaO/MgO in the alkaline rocks of Mt. Elgon, Napak and Budeda. The fields of volcanics and of the ijolite series are outlined.

It is suggested that the fundamental difference between the two series was that the volcanic rocks evolved as an open system, whereas the plutonic rocks resulted from crystallization in a closed system. In an open system loss of volatiles may be expected which would also have the effect of raising the temperature of the beginning of crystallization, with the consequent separation of olivine. Retention or loss of the anion $(CO_3)^{2-}$ may be expected to exercise an important influence on the association of anions and cations in mineral formation. Retention of volatiles, under plutonic conditions, would, in systems in which there was also a tendency for enrichment in alkalies and lime, lead to the late crystalliza-tion not only of hydrous silicates but also of carbonates of these constituents. The tendency for alkalies to escape during the course of crystallization may also provide an explanation for fenitization, while the more specific process of feldspathization may reflect the mobility of the late stage alkali carbonates and their readiness to react with silica and aluminous minerals in the surrounding rocks. The feldspathization associated with the carbonatites is commonly highly potassic, which probably results from the tendency for potash to accumul-ate in residual melts, since nepheline is the only mineral among the main crystal-lizing phases which accommodates potash; even so, the extent of substitution by potash is limited.

There is good evidence in the field that rocks of syenitic and nepheline syenitic compositions may arise by more than one process. The possibilities may be summarized:

(*a*) The formation of phonolites and trachytes by crystallization-differ-entiation from nephelinitic magma.

(*b*) The development of syenites and nepheline syenites by fenitization of pre-existing rocks; the mobilization of the products would give rise to intrusive equivalents or fine-grained intrusive or extrusive trachytes and phonolites.

(*c*) The development of nepheline syenites by the feldspathization of ijolites.

REFERENCES

Bethune, P. de, and Meyer, A., 1956, Les carbonatites de la Lueshe (Kivu, Congo belge): *Acad. Sci. Paris Comptes rendus*, v. **243**, pp. 1132–1134.

Bethune, P. de, 1957, La busorite, une roche felspathoïdale nouvelle, du Kivu: *Soc. Belge Géol. Bull.*, v. **65**, pp. 394–399.

Bishop, W. W., 1958, Miocene mammalia from the Napak volcanics, Karamoja, Uganda: *Nature*, v. **182**, pp. 1480–1482.

Brown, P. E., 1964, The Songwe Scarp carbonatite and associated feldspathization in the Mbeya Range, Tanganyika: *Geol. Soc. London, Quart. Jour.*, v. **120**, pp. 233–240.

Davies, K. A., 1947, The phosphate deposits of Eastern Province, Uganda: *Econ. Geol.*, v. **42**, pp. 137–146.

Davies, K. A., 1952, The building of Mount Elgon, East Africa: *Uganda Geol. Surv., Mem.* 7.

Davies, K. A., 1956, The geology of part of south-east Uganda: *Uganda Geol. Surv., Mem.* **8**.

Davies, K. A., and Bisset, C. B., 1935, *Uganda Geol. Surv., Bull.* 2, p. 37.

DuBois, C. G. B., 1957, *The geology of the Toror Hills, central Karamoja, Uganda:* Ph.D. thesis, Univ. London.

DuBois, C. G. B., 1959, The Toror Hills alkaline complex, central Karamoja, Uganda: *Internat. Geol. Congr., 20th Sess.*

v. Eckermann, H., 1960, Borengite: a new ultra-potassic rock from Alnö Island: *Arkiv. f. Mineral. Geol.*, v. **2**, pp. 519–528.

Garson, M. S., 1962, The Tundulu carbonatite ring-complex in southern Nyasaland: *Nyasa-land Geol. Surv., Mem.* **2**.

Garson, M. S. and Campbell Smith, W., 1958, The geology of Chilwa Island: *Nyasaland Geol. Surv., Mem.* **1**.

Hytönen, K., 1959, On the petrology and minerology of some alkaline volcanic rocks, north eastern Uganda: *Bull. Comm. Géol. Finlande*, v. **184**, p. 75–132.

King, B. C., 1949, The Napak area of southern Karamoja, Uganda: *Uganda Geol. Surv.*, *Mem.* **5** (1948).

King, B. C., 1965, Petrogenesis of the alkaline igneous rock suites of the volcanic and intrusive centres of Eastern Uganda: *Jour. Petrology*, v. **6**, pp. 67–100.

King, B. C. and Sutherland, D. S., 1960, Alkaline rocks of eastern and southern Africa: *Sci. Progress*, v. **48**, pp. 298–321, 504–524, 709–720.

Macdonald, R., 1961, Explanation of the geology of sheet 36 (Nabilatuk): *Uganda Geol. Surv.*, *Rept.* 5.

Sahama, Th. G., 1961, Thermal metamorphism of the volcanic rocks of Mt. Nyiragongo (Eastern Congo): *Bull. Comm. Géol. Finlande*, v. **196**, pp. 151–174.

Trendall, A. F., 1961, Explanation of the geology of sheet 45 (Kadan): *Uganda Geol. Surv.*, *Rept.* 6.

Wayland, E. J., 1920, *Uganda Geol. Surv. Ann. Rept.*, p. 37.

Williams, C. E., 1952, Carbonatite structure: Tororo Hills, Eastern Uganda: *Geol. Mag.*, v. **69**, pp. 286–292.

D. K. BAILEY

Carbonatite Volcanoes and Shallow Intrusions in Zambia

'Well, you're a long hole, and a deep hole, and a mighty singular hole
altogether . . . . . .'

Baker's Bluejay Yarn
Mark Twain. *A Tramp Abroad*

At the root of many of the arguments about carbonatites lies the question of
whether these rocks are truly igneous, and it might be expected from this that the
possibility of carbonatite volcanicity would be a central issue, particularly as
many carbonatite complexes are subvolcanic in character (Dixey *et al.* 1937;
v. Eckermann, 1948; King, 1949). Until recently, however, there has been little
discussion of the nature of the subaerial activity that might be expected to
accompany the emplacement of carbonatite in dikes, cone sheets and volcanic
vents. This is all the more surprising because the only active volcano in East
Africa, Oldoinyo Lengai, in northern Tanganyika, has erupted carbonate ashes
several times this century, one record of such an eruption being available to every
student of geology in S. J. Shand's well-known textbook (1927), and having the
added piquancy that the author was the outstanding exponent of Daly's theory
of limestone syntexis. In more recent years other evidence of effusive carbonatite
activity has come to light: James (1956) has described carbonatite of uncertain
origin in the crater and on the flanks of the Kerimasi volcano immediately to the
south of Lengai; von Knorring and DuBois (1961) have drawn attention to the
carbonatitic lava flows of the Fort Portal field of Uganda; and in 1960 Oldoinyo
Lengai began erupting lavas consisting essentially of sodium, calcium, and potassium carbonates, within its crater (Dawson, 1962a,b; this volume, pp. 155–167;
Hobley, 1918; Richard, 1942; Guest, 1956, DuBois, *et al.* 1963). Most of these
carbonatite volcanics show marked compositional differences from intrusive
carbonatite and represent only a fraction of the total effusive products, which are
mainly silicate rocks, so that a new aspect of the activity came to light with the
discovery, in 1956, of the Rufunsa province in Zambia. The Rufunsa volcanoes
seem to have erupted only calcium and magnesium carbonate ashes, and they
are eroded sufficiently for the intrusive and extrusive activity to be studied
together. Also within this province is the remarkable Kaluwe sill which affords a
clear instance of one process by which highly mobile carbonatite can be intruded
under a shallow cover. The description which follows will present, firstly the

127

regional setting and history of this carbonatite province; secondly, a description of the various facets of the activity as seen in the four main complexes; and thirdly, an assessment of how this knowledge can further our understanding of the nature of carbonatite.

REGIONAL SETTING AND GEOLOGIC HISTORY

All seven known carbonatites in Zambia are found in the mid-Zambezi–Luangwa rift zone, which runs NE–SW along the south eastern margin of the country and constitutes the most marked structural and topographic break in the Zambia plateau. The main elements of the rift are the colinear troughs of the mid-Zambezi and Luangwa valleys, which are separated by higher ground where the rift crosses the E–W rift of the lower Zambesi (inset to Fig. 1). This upland region at the major rift intersection is broken up by several small divergent rifts and it is around the intersection of one of these, the Rufunsa rift, with the south eastern margin of the Luangwa rift that the Rufunsa carbonatites erupted (Fig. 1. See also Bailey, 1961a). Essentially, the area consists of Karroo terrestrial sandstones and mudstones (Upper Carboniferous–Lower Jurassic) down-faulted between blocks of pre-Karroo crystalline basement, consisting dominantly of granitic gneisses and quartzite. Dixey (1955), has shown that the major Karroo-filled troughs in southern Africa were formed during a phase of earth movements which closed the Karroo period, and that in many cases—the Luangwa valley is an example—these troughs were then eroded to something like their present form, being later filled with Cretaceous sediments, and then re-excavated by Tertiary and later erosion cycles. Within this framework it has been possible to work out the general sequence of the Rufunsa carbonatite activity (Bailey 1960).

During the initial post-Karroo rifting a wedge of Karroo sediments in the angle between the Rufunsa trough and the south eastern margin of the Luangwa rift was compressed, forming an anticline and syncline, the folds growing intermittently with each movement on the bounding faults (Bailey 1960, Plate III). Each compression of the syncline opened up a zone of low stress parallel to the bedding along which carbonatite was injected, and in this way the composite Kaluwe intrusion was built up in the core of the fold. During the ensuing excavation of the rift troughs the roof of the Kaluwe intrusion was eroded off and carbonatite activity apparently ceased until early Cretaceous time when renewed earth movements probably triggered the volcanic outbursts in the region. The earliest and largest volcanic centre, the Uma, formed exactly on the intersection of the Rufunsa and Luangwa rift lines, and thence the activity migrated south east through Mwambuto, along the line of the Rufunsa rift, terminating in the Chasweta volcanoes. The volcanoes of these three main centres, and other smaller vents, mantled the surrounding early Cretaceous valley floor with carbonatite ash and agglomerate, and after activity had ceased were buried with the later Cretaceous sediments that filled the rift troughs. Subsequent re-excavation of the troughs has restored the landscape to something resembling its early Cretaceous form, with relics of the volcanoes surviving.

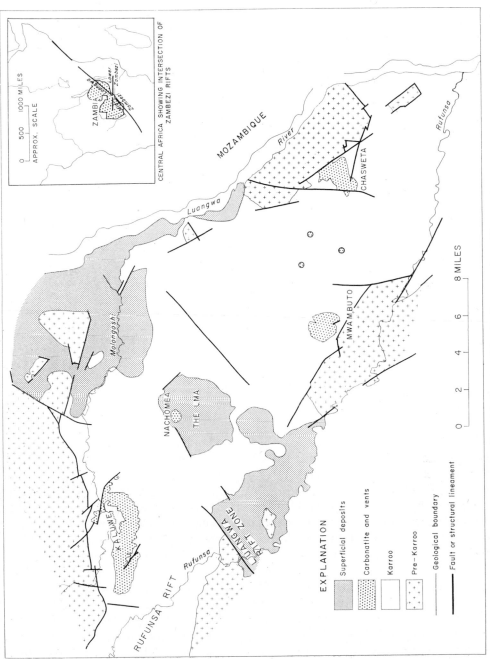

Fig. 1. **Simplified map of the Rufunsa carbonatite province.**

KALUWE

The Kaluwe carbonatite is quite unlike any other. It is a tilted synclinal mass, up to 800 ft thick, outcropping as a low curving scarp, 8 miles long, with a gentle backslope giving an outcrop width of 0.75 to 1.5 miles. This structure is essentially conformable with that of the Upper Karroo sandstones forming the envelope of the carbonatite (Fig. 2) although exposure of the featureless, coarse-bedded Karroo rock is poor, so that minor structural discordances, if they exist, are not detectable. The synclinal axis of the carbonatite pitches north west at 15°, below a resistant core of Karroo sandstone hills; its long south west limb is homologous

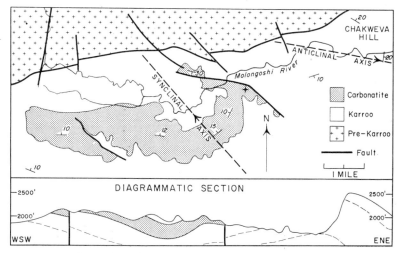

Fig. 2. Simplified map of the Kaluwe carbonatite.

with the gentle northerly regional dip of the Karroo of the Rufunsa valley, but its short north east limb is twisted and broken along a zone parallel to the axis of the adjacent Chakweva anticline. Folding of this type is unusual in the Karroo and is undoubtedly connected with movements on the big E–W Karroo boundary fault immediately to the north. This fault zone is equally unusual for it is filled with large amounts of vertically-banded siliceous breccias, which stand out as a chain of razor-back ridges. In addition to the breccias, which record a complex history of crushing and dilation along the fault, there are smaller injections of carbonatitic veins, and the zone as a whole shows anomalously high thorium and niobium contents. Mineralization of this character, including silicification, can be matched in the various carbonatite complexes to the south, and there are, therefore, cogent reasons for suggesting a link between the folding and faulting of the Karroo and the emplacement of the Kaluwe carbonatite.

Probably the most striking features of the Kaluwe carbonatite are its sill-like form and exceptional size, but in structure and fabric it is no less remarkable, being made up of numerous layers of fragmental sövite. These layers range from a few inches to a few tens of feet thick, while the fragment size ranges from microscopic to boulders a foot in diameter. The layering is chiefly marked by changes in fragment-size, the bulk of the fragments in each band falling into a different size-range from that of adjacent bands, the junctions being macroscopically sharp. Because most layers have finely fragmental matrices, however, the layer-boundaries are not easy to detect in thin section and there are signs, in some cases, of a zone of mixing at this scale. Sorting of fragment sizes into different layers may therefore be described as good, but within each unit the sorting can at best be described as fair, and there are only rare instances of a coarse to fine gradation from bottom to top of a bed. Rounded to subrounded carbonatite fragments predominate in the middle layers of the Kaluwe mass but the lower layers contain, in addition, angular quartz fragments, while the upper layers contain numerous angular fragments of Karroo sandstone and conglomerate. This variation, coupled with colour changes, has been used to divide the carbonatite into an upper, middle and lower facies, which have other less obvious differences suggesting that the division is a fundamental characteristic of the carbonatite.

The middle facies consists dominantly of coarse agglomerate layers, composed of fragments of a wide variety of medium- to coarse-grained sövites, distinguished by variations in colour, grain size, texture and banding and especially by their content of the minor and accessory minerals, martite, apatite, vermiculite and pyrochlore. Fragments of massive or granular martite, up to several inches in diameter, are fairly common in the agglomerates and locally form an important minor component. Fragments of quartz and Karroo argillite and conglomerate are rare. The matrix of the agglomerates appears in hand specimen to be a grey or buff marble, and thin sheets of similar rock are found interbanded with the agglomeratic layers; rare veins of similar material are found also cutting across the layering. Martite and apatite are common accessories in this rock and there are some layers, a few inches thick, which contain as much as 50 per cent martite. Most of this apparently homogeneous carbonatite is found in thin-section to be fragmental, being composed essentially of rounded grains of calcite or carbonatite in a fine- to medium-grained calcite base, or set in a clear, coarse carbonate mosaic which is in optical continuity with the grains. Apatite and martite are usually present in minor amounts; pyrochlore is an accessory; these minerals, especially apatite, frequently show signs of alteration. Not all the bands of buff marble are fragmental carbonatite, however; some consist of a felted mesh of apatite prisms almost completely pseudomorphed by calcite, but with some 10 per cent apatite still persisting.

The rocks of the lower facies are essentially similar to those just described but finer-grained agglomerates are more common; they are chiefly distinguished by their predominantly red colour and by conspicuous amounts of angular quartz fragments. Fragments of Karroo sandstone, conglomerate and argillite are less common, but some of the fine-grained layers near the base are full of sand grains derived from the Karroo, so much so that they resemble flaggy, calcareous sandstone. Another unusual rock, a white, chalky limestone, forms an intermittent layer a few feet thick at the base of the lower facies and may be carbonatized Karroo mudstone. The other fine-grained layers and the matrices of the agglomerate layers are, as in the middle facies, finely fragmental but with grains of quartz, microcline, orthoclase, orthoclase aggregates, phlogopite and martite in addition to the carbonate and carbonatite grains. Many quartzite grains are partly feldspathized, and many of the small books of dark brown biotite, present in some samples, are partly carbonated or pseudomorphed by limonitic material.

The upper facies is similar to the lower but more coarsely agglomeratic. To the west of the synclinal axis of the carbonatite the upper facies can be divided into two zones, a lower zone in which the bulk of the fragments are carbonatite (Fig. 3) and an upper zone in which there are increasing amounts of angular Karroo sandstone and conglomerate fragments towards the top (Fig. 4). The lower zone is distinguished from the underlying middle facies by the reddish or brown colour of its carbonatite fragments and its coarse, white calcite matrix, which frequently has the appearance of anastomosing veins. In thin section this matrix is seen to have partly replaced fragments, and presumably formed, at least in part, by upward streaming of volatiles from the middle facies; there is, too, a wild fluctuation in phosphorus content through the upper facies, consistent with the late-stage replacement of apatite in the rocks below. Calcite veins, stringers and vugs are also common in the top of the underlying facies. Furthermore, the middle facies has a greater content of martite fragments, and large sövite fragments with conspicuous martite, apatite, pyrochlore and vermiculite, than the lower or upper facies. It is distinctly richer in niobium and phosphorus than the lower facies, and is probably slightly richer in these elements than the upper facies. This evidence, plus the fact that the middle facies thins in the limbs of the intrusion and appears to be absent in the extremities, strongly suggests that this facies represents a distinct and later period in the formation of the Kaluwe carbonatite.

In form, structure and fabric the Kaluwe carbonatite has no known analogue, and for this reason three diverse possibilities must initially be considered for its mode of formation: sedimentary conglomerate, extrusive volcanic, and intrusive. If either of the first two alternatives apply the carbonatite must have formed while Karroo sediments were still accumulating. A sedimentary origin is thus virtually ruled out for this would require source areas of carbonatite sufficient to exclude other types of detritus, and moreover there are no normal conglomerates of comparable thickness at the same level elsewhere. If, on the other hand, Kaluwe represents a pile of extrusive agglomerates and ashes, then in fabric, texture and chemistry these are quite unlike the extrusive volcanics to the south; also against such an origin are the rounding of the carbonatite fragments, their large size in thin beds of wide areal extent, the thin layers of apatite rock in the sequence, and the existence of the middle facies sheathed in the lower and upper facies. The most serious objection springs from the necessity that the volcanicity be contemporaneous with Karroo sedimentation, for the carbonatite should then grade laterally and vertically into Karroo sediments containing carbonatite detritus. In fact the converse is true, no carbonatite debris has been found in the overlying Karroo; instead the upper layers of the carbonatite contain angular Karroo fragments that must have been already indurated on incorporation. Such a relationship is consistent with intrusion of the carbonatite and incorpora-

Fig. 3. Layered agglomerate in the lower part of the upper facies at Kaluwe. The fabric is typical of the Kaluwe agglomerate layers and in this example coarse-grained white calcite forms the matrix.

Fig. 4. Layered agglomerate near the top of the upper facies of the Kaluwe carbonatite. The angular fragments are Karroo xenoliths; the softer, rounded fragments carbonatite.

tion of the roof rocks. It is, however, a highly unusual intrusion, composed of numerous thin layers of fragmental carbonatite of great lateral extent, indicating great mobility during emplacement. Fragmental material such as this must have been emplaced in a fluidized condition (Reynolds, 1954), either as a liquid–solid or as a dense-gas–solid system, with the latter alternative being favoured by the probable temperature range, the richness in CO_2, the rounding of fragments and general lack of elutriation. Each layer of agglomerate would thus represent the emplacement of a mobile, continuous expanded bed, the discontinuous gas phase being discharged presumably as fumaroles and surface springs, with some of the CO_2 being precipitated as carbonate during cooling and gradual solidification of the bed. The angularity of the accidental fragments in the upper and lower facies would be consistent with their late incorporation when the bed was approaching the quiescent expanded stage.

Gradual build-up of the intrusion by a series of injections can be related to intermittent flexing of the Karroo syncline, produced by movements along the fault zone to the north. The syncline pitches towards the fault and this would therefore be the logical place to look for a feeder for the intrusion. Hence it is suggested that deep-seated carbonatite intrusions along the fault were shattered by spasmodic fault movements, allowing the passage from below of carbonatite fluids which carried up the fragments of shattered carbonatite as a fluidized system. Each movement on the fault opened a dilation zone parallel to the bedding by flexing the Karroo syncline, giving access to the carbonatite rising along the fault plane, and in this way a series of injections built up the intrusion in the growing fold.

NACHOMBA HILL

By early Cretaceous time erosion had reduced the rift troughs to a form approaching that seen today and it was about this time that carbonatite activity was renewed along the Rufunsa trough. The earliest phase of activity is marked by the Nachomba carbonatite, forming an isolated hill in the northern part of the Uma flat (see Fig. 1). The Uma is a circular depression 3.5 miles in diameter, with no external drainage; it is floored by laterite and ringed with Karroo sandstone hills, at the base of which is a fairly persistent horizon of argillite. A similar depression with a diameter of 2 miles occurs immediately to the south. These two depressions appear to mark the site of former domes in the Karroo sediments, and the presence of carbonatite in the Uma, and small amounts of feldspathic breccia and other carbonatitic mineralization around the peripheries, strongly suggests that they are volcanic collapse- or explosion-structures. Descriptions of the peripheral rocks will be omitted, because these are similar to those of the Mwambuto Complex, to the south east, where they are much better exposed. Nachomba is, however, a good example of advanced late-stage alteration of carbonatite and is a valuable piece in constructing the pattern of activity in the volcanic vents.

Nachomba Hill is largely composed of silica–iron oxide rock produced by alteration of carbonatite. The limited remnants of unaltered carbonatite consist of a breccia of medium- to coarse-grained brown and grey carbonatite in a net vein matrix of paler, buff carbonatite. Both types are ankeritic, the matrix more so than the fragments, and both contain accessory martite, barite and pyrochlore. In some of the fragments the carbonate grains have a mosaic texture but more often the texture is granular, with limonite outlining the grain boundaries and cleavages, and in some cases there is a mortar of smaller grains separating the larger ones. The texture of the buff matrix around the fragments is different, consisting of interfering zoned rhombs, which in some parts of narrow veins seem to have grown inwards from the walls. The zonal structure of the crystals indicates that at some stage during emplacement this buff carbonatite was in the form of a mush of crystals, the interstitial fluid fluctuating slightly in composition.

Most exposures of the carbonatite are cut by thin quartz veins, and close to these the carbonatite shows the various stages of silicification. In this process the carbonate grains undergo progressive replacement, both internally and along the margins, residual iron oxides being swept to the edges of the replaced areas. The end product is a mesh of limonitic oxides in a quartz mosaic and it is this composition and general texture that characterize the flinty, buff-brown rocks that form the bulk of Nachomba Hill.

Quartz veinlets are also common in the silicified rocks and close to such veins the limonite content of the rock diminishes, the end product being a nearly pure quartz-rock, with accessory barite and fluorite. White or cream streaks, up to 2 ft wide, are also common and are composed of fine-grained apatite and fluorite. The paragenetic sequence appears to be barite and apatite followed by fluorite and quartz. There is in addition a small amount of very fine-grained monazite and possibly bastnaesite in the silicified rocks, but the thorium content of most of the rock is too high to be assigned to the visible thorium minerals and is assumed to be in the limonite.

There are no indications that the main mass of the silica–limonite rock was ever mobile, it appears to have formed *in situ* by metasomatism of earlier carbonatite around a stockwork of silica veins. This represents an important hydrothermal event in the history of the complex, and the production of late-stage, silica-rich residuals must find a place in any proposals about the nature and evolution of carbonatite fluids.

MWAMBUTO

Nine miles south east of Nachomba a second volcanic complex forms the isolated ring of the Mwambuto Hills (Fig. 5). The outer ring of hills, 3 miles in diameter, is made up of metasomatized Karroo mudstone surrounding a collar of feldspathic breccia, and it encircles a mile-wide depression which has formed in the carbonatite volcanics and intrusive carbonatite that constitute the core of the complex. Except for the SW side, the annular outcrop of mudstone is surrounded by the overlying Karroo conglomerate and sandstone, indicating doming of the sediments around the complex. On the SW side the mudstone is brought up against granitic rocks of the pre-Karroo by a fault which is part of the

Rufunsa rift system. Small satellite vents filled with carbonatite pyroclastic rock are concentrated along the outer foot of the hills, the pipes presumably having exploited the tension zone in the fold hinge, around the base of the dome in the Karroo sediments. Subsidence along this zone would produce a caldera about the size of the Uma depression. Patches of pyroclastic rubble in the surrounding flat country may mark the site of satellite vents, but the large irregular area of pyroclastics along the NE foot of the hills is probably a relic of the outpourings from the Mwambuto volcano.

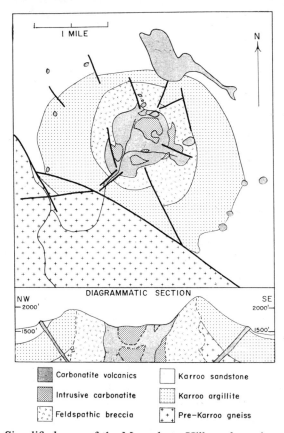

Fig. 5. Simplified map of the Mwambuto Hills carbonatite complex.

An irregular collar of feldspathic breccia forms the outer zone of the main Mwambuto vent and underlies the inner slopes of the depression. Where least brecciated, this is a coarse, hypidiomorphic rock composed almost entirely of creamy orthoclase (MacKenzie and Smith, 1955, p. 711), but the brecciation is so intense that even the individual crystals are usually cracked and broken. The matrix consists of a network of veinlets of comminuted feldspar streaked with limonite, and the whole rock is cut by later veinlets of silica and iron oxides, sometimes accompanied by a little barite. No signs of a shear fabric are seen in the rock and the feldspar grains show remarkably few strain effects. In some places in the western part of the outcrop the breccia contains quartz. Some of this material is a mechanical mixture of quartz, orthoclase and argillite fragments and is probably confined to fault zones; other specimens have highly strained quartz in a mosaic of orthoclase that has clearly replaced quartz. This material is taken to represent feldspathized crystalline rocks from the pre-Karroo below the complex, and suggests that the feldspathic breccia represents highly meta-somatized country rock that was fluidized and entrained by fluids from the volcanic stem, and thence carried up to its present level.

The feldspathic breccia, except where later volcanic activity has cut into it, passes inwards into intrusive carbonatite, through a zone in which the two rocks are mixed. There is a passage from breccia that is erratically laced with carbonatite, through a zone composed of irregular lenses in which breccia and carbonatite alternatively predominate, into carbonatite with streaked-out masses of breccia. This mixed zone resulted either from simultaneous emplacement of the two rocks or, more likely, from intrusion of carbonatite into the feldspathic breccia.

Intrusive carbonatite forms relatively small, highly irregular patches around the edges and within the vent area, these patches being separated by carbonatite pyroclastics, which form lower ground. Vertical or steeply dipping banding is well developed and the concentric strikes of the bands in the various patches of carbonatite indicate that they are all parts of a single plug which has been dismembered by later pyroclastic eruptions. The carbonatite is exceedingly variable, the predominant type being a buff fine-grained ankeritic carbonatite in various stages of silicification, with lesser amounts of medium- to coarse-grained grey sövite, the two types being complexly interbanded. Adding to the complexity are thin bands rich in martite, apatite and barite, associated with the silicification; variable contents of xenolithic material, mainly feldspathic breccia, in streaks and trains; and irregular veins of silica, calcite, and calcite-barite cutting all the other rocks. Adjacent bands may be a few inches to several feet thick, varying in colour, grain-size and accessory mineral content. The banding is wavy, even contorted in places, and dips steeply into or away from the axis of the vent.

A few thin cone sheets of buff carbonatite, one to two feet thick, outcrop sporadically through the volcanics in the north east sector of the vent; some of these have a texture suggestive of replacement of an earlier platy mineral and may be altered alnöitic or sölvesbergitic dikes. Numerous intersecting veins and dikes, a few inches thick, of fine carbonatite and tuffisite ramify the volcanics in the SW half of the vent. These rocks represent episodes of intrusive activity after the main phases of effusion that broke through the carbonatite plug. Yet another late phase of activity, perhaps the latest, is represented by the hydrothermal veins of coarse calcite, barite, and barite-calcite which cut all the rocks of the vent complex.

The common, buff ankeritic carbonatite at Mwambuto is fine-grained (up to 1 mm), the texture varying from an interlocking mosaic to a highly irregular interfering texture, which may well be of replacive or recrystallization origin. Common accessories are martite and barite, with, more rarely, pyrochlore. In some instances the fine ankeritic carbonate forms a matrix containing grains of coarse calcitic carbonatite, this being one of many indications that the ankeritic carbonatite is later than, and at least partly replaces the sövite. Much of the ankeritic rock is itself cut by stringers of clear carbonate and barite, and even more commonly it shows signs of incipient silicification similar to that at Nachomba, accompanied in the advanced stages by barite, apatite, fluorite, bastnaesite, and monazite. Associated with the silicification are bands rich in barite, apatite, fluorite and martite, or mixtures of these minerals. Some fine-grained barite bands have coarse patches of quartz-calcite-barite indicating a link with the late hydrothermal activity. Evidence from a zone of heavy martite and apatite mineralization in the largest mass of carbonatite indicates that this material is not simply a metasomatic product. Specimens of the apatite-martite rock have a trachytic or fluidal texture with trains of apatite prisms sweeping around the grains of martite. It is possible that there was extrusion of such material, which would be similar to that reported as surface flows in Chile (Park, 1961).

The grey sövite at Mwambuto is similar in all essentials to that at Chasweta, and is described in the subsequent section (p. 141).

A large part of the Mwambuto vent is filled with red carbonatite pyroclastic rock, ranging from tuff to very coarse agglomerate. This consists of fragments of earlier pyroclastic material, carbonatite and associated rocks, with lesser amounts of Karroo and pre-Karroo fragments, in a fine, red, carbonate-tuff base. Similar material fills the satellite vents at Mwambuto and the other minor vents in the Rufunsa valley, and is best developed in the Chasweta complex; detailed description and discussion of the volcanics, therefore, will follow the description of Chasweta (p. 141). Most of the lower ground in the SW half of the Mwambuto vent is underlain by tuff and fine to medium agglomerate. The agglomerate is predominantly made up of rounded grains or tuff pellets up to a centimetre in diameter. This rock and the associated tuff mark the site of the more sustained effusive activity in the complex, after the intrusion of the carbonatite plug. Discrete areas of distinctly different, medium and coarse agglomerates in the eastern part of the vent emphasize this point. These contain angular feldspar rock, carbonatite and country rock fragments and mark the site of short-lived parasitic vents. One of these produces the marked embayment in the south east sector of the main vent and was most likely a large, branching satellite pipe from the parent stem, its early establishment being shown by the parallel irregularity in the intrusive carbonatite outcrop. In the border zones of many of the smaller vents, both in and around Mwambuto, the agglomerate is densely packed with fragments of the adjacent country rock in a sparse volcanic base, grading, within tens of feet, into normal agglomerate. Examples are found in pipes penetrating Karroo rocks, carbonatite and feldspathic breccia. The presence of such zones of 'stagnant tuff formation' (Reynolds, 1954), is significant, for they appear to be characteristic of the border zones of gas-tuff streams (Cloos, 1941).

The broad outline of the sequence of events in the Mwambuto volcano may be summarized as follows:

(1) Probably the earliest signs of activity were movements on the Karroo boundary fault, followed by slow doming of the rocks above the rising carbonatite stem.

(2) The dome was pierced by volcanic outbursts which gradually widened the conduit and built up a cone. Rocks lining the vent had been extensively metasomatized, and some of the orthoclase rock so formed was moved to higher levels as fragments entrained in rising fluid streams around the periphery of the conduit.

(3) A small carbonatite plug was intruded below the volcanic pile, partly incorporating the feldspathic breccia lining the vent.

(4) As activity waned the carbonatite was successively invaded by ankeritic and siliceous fluids with accompanying barite, apatite, martite, fluorite, thorium and rare earth mineralization.

(5) An important period of low activity and denudation followed.

(6) Renewed volcanism in multiple episodes decimated the carbonatite plug and broke out along satellite pipes.

(7) Finally thin cone sheets and irregular veins and dikes of fine-grained carbonatite and tuff were emplaced, followed by injection of hydrothermal quartz-calcite-barite veins.

CHASWETA

Seven miles east of Mwambuto lies the Chasweta Complex, an eroded twin volcano, with numerous satellite vents (Fig. 6). The twin vents are marked by shallow crater-like depressions, a third and a quarter of a mile in diameter, in the tops of two adjacent hills of carbonatite pyroclastics. These two hills form part of a larger irregular area of pyroclastics which, together with outlying patches of the same rock, are the remains of a much larger volcanic superstructure. The pyroclastics are mainly agglomerates with little signs of any bedded structure, the few exposures of bedded tuff showing a rather puzzling lack of systematic disposition which is attributed to later explosive disturbance and collapse around the vents. The greater extent of the pre-existing superstructure is indicated by the wide distribution of small satellite vents: these are filled with agglomerate similar to the extrusive material, with the exception of one small vent filled with an agglomerate of perfectly rounded fragments of altered country rock (Bailey, 1960, p. 13 and Plate IV). Thin carbonatite dikes, some with concentrically disposed strikes and similar to those at Mwambuto, are also found as far as 3 miles from the main centre.

The smaller of the two main vents is filled with massive tuff, with minor amounts of fine agglomerate, cut by thin veins and stringers of coarse quartz-barite-calcite. It is merely a large tuff-pipe cutting the older pyroclastics. The larger vent, however, represents only the last big episode of pipe formation on the site of a much larger conduit that had previously been filled by a carbonatite plug, the remains of which now form a broken ring around the vent. Prior to the drilling of the vent this plug had been exposed by erosion because the vent is fringed on the north and west by inward-dipping beds of tuff and agglomerate, containing abundant carbonatite fragments and representing early post-carbonatite eruptions. These rocks were presumably erupted within an old crater and are probably the youngest sub-aerial pyroclasts preserved in the Rufunsa valley. Between the east side of the vent and the sövite ring there are small hills of massive, coarse agglomerate containing carbonatite fragments and having zones of mixing at the sövite contact; these are probably parasitic vents, similar to those at Mwambuto, which post-date the reopening of the main vent and represent the final stages of effusive activity. One other distinguishing feature between the volcanics within the sövite outcrop and those without, is that the latter are

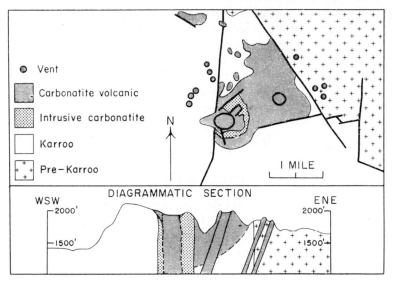

Fig. 6. Simplified map of the Chasweta carbonatite complex.

conspicuously veined with pink carbonatite and carbonatite tuff, whereas there is little sign of such veining in the post-carbonatite pyroclastics.

In structure the intrusive carbonatite at Chasweta is similar to that of Mwambuto, showing the same concentric banding with vertical or steep dips into or away from the intrusion axis, but it differs in composition, being dominantly calcitic (Table I). Several large lenses, up to 300 yd long, of brecciated and comminuted feldspar rock and argillite are enclosed in the carbonatite close to the walls and were clearly carried up from zones, similar to those of Mwambuto, lower in the vent. Debris of the same type, as well as fragments of pre-Karroo rocks, are widely distributed through the carbonatite. Late-stage activity affecting the carbonatite was varied. Net-veins of red jaspilite cut the carbonatite in many places, and sometimes coalesce to form dike-like masses; together with small patches of partly silicified carbonatite they indicate the existence of late siliceous fluids in the complex. Calcite, calcite-barite, and quartz-calcite-barite veins are also present, and thin calcite-pyrolusite veins occur sporadically. Probably related to the latter are scattered patches of dark grey carbonatite, containing much disseminated manganese oxides, and also clots of botryoidal pyrolusite-limonite which seem to be filling small cavities in the carbonatite.

The carbonatite itself is dominantly a medium- to coarse-grained calcitic marble, coloured with disseminated iron and manganese oxides, and containing martite, barite, pyrochlore, monazite, phlogopite, orthoclase, and clots of limonite and pyrolusite as the main accessories. Other varieties are numerous and include some ankeritic carbonatite, and opaque black carbonatite, full of manganese oxides. The texture ranges from an interlocking mosaic to granular, in which the grain boundaries and cleavages are marked by films of limonite. In many cases the rock is ramified by veinlets and patches of clear carbonate and barite, this texture grading into one in which fragments of carbonatite are set in a clear, coarse calcite mosaic: in a few instances fine quartz and chalcedony form the matrix for such a fragmental carbonatite. Late fluid residua were evidently an important component of the rock immediately prior to complete solidification, and the carbonatite may have been finally emplaced as a mush of crystals and fragments lubricated by such residua.

At the outer edges of the carbonatite belt, at the boundary with the older pyroclastics, there is a zone, a few feet wide, of fine-grained pink carbonatite, which is generally free of inclusions and similar to the irregular veinlets which cut the older volcanics. This material closely resembles vent tuffisite and may have been produced by the rapid effusion of volatiles around the margins of the intrusion; the existence of such a peripheral zone of high fluid pressure means that the carbonatite could have been extruded upwards through the vent as a solid plug!

The commonest rock in the Chasweta Complex is the red carbonatite agglomerate around the main vents, ranging from very coarse agglomerate to the finest grades. Fragments in the coarser varieties may reach 6 in. in diameter, but the average size is 2–3 in. Most of the fragments are subrounded pieces of earlier tuff or agglomerate with rarer, recognizable fragments of country rocks, which are usually more angular. The matrix consists of fine agglomerate and tuff particles set in a very fine-grained carbonate base, which is heavily stained with red-brown iron oxides: it is typically dolomitic or ankeritic in composition (Table I). Quartz grains are discernible in most samples, and grains of calcite, barite, vermiculite and greenish clusters of phlogopite and chlorite may also be present. A few patches of agglomerate at Chasweta and Mwambuto contain sufficient phlogopite as single flakes and fragments of phlogopite rock to impart a greenish tinge to the rock; the phlogopite shows signs of mechanical damage indicating that it did not form *in situ* and suggesting the presence of a zone of phlogopite-rock at depth.

The younger, bedded agglomerate, around the main vent piercing the intrusive carbonatite, differs from the older agglomerates in that it contains abundant angular fragments of carbonatite and feldspathic breccia, which establish the time of its eruption. Different grade-sizes of fragments in the different beds of agglomerate and their interbedding with tuffs indicate multiple effusive episodes of varying intensity.

Extrusive tuff, especially that post-dating the carbonatite, usually shows some

F

signs of bedding and ranges from a very fine-grained, soft rock resembling mud-stone to one resembling sandstone; it frequently grades down into fine agglom-erate, more rarely into coarser agglomerate, in the same bed. The very fine-grained tuff is composed of the same fine, ferruginous carbonate that forms the matrix of all the other volcanics and must represent the finest carbonate ash erupted from the volcanoes. The graded bedding and other sedimentary features such as cross bedding in some of the older tuffs and ripple marking in the younger deposits, are invaluable indications of the sub-aerial deposition of these rocks. In contrast to this the tuffisite in the main vents is massive and structureless, the associated fine agglomerate being the rounded-pellet variety, similar to that in the Mwambuto vent.

At the microscopic scale the great variability of the sub-aerial volcanics is even more marked than in outcrop, with essential, accessory and accidental fragments present in widely varying proportions. Carbonatite fragments, carbonate grains, orthoclase and orthoclase aggregates are common, and grains of barite, phlogopite, phlogopite aggregate, and iron ores are present in many specimens. Some of the feldspathic grains have porphyritic and andesitic textures and presumably came from underlying sölvesbergite intrusions, which were probably formed by rheomorphism of feldspar rock. The most common fragments are quartz grains derived from the Karroo sandstones lining the vents. Fragments of Karroo argillite and quartz-microcline-muscovite from the pre-Karroo are of sporadic distribution. In contrast with this the tuffisite of the main vents is predominantly composed of well-rounded essential or accessory fragments. The small rounded pellets in the intrusive fine agglomerate are composed of fine-grained clear carbonate, often with rims of iron oxide and cores of other material such as barite, quartz, microcline, argillite and phlogopite.

At the edges of the tuff pipes there are stagnant tuff zones, which, with features such as rounding of the fragments in the central zone, show that the vents are not the result of catastrophic blasting, but of progressive penetration by rising gas-tuff streams.

In all these pyroclastic rocks the carbonate is an essential, primary constituent. That it is no mere secondary cement is shown by its bulk, the fragments of earlier pyroclasts in the rocks, and the preservation of sedimentary structures in rocks largely composed of carbonates. Replacement of an earlier matrix is ruled out by the preservation of all types of fragments at all distances from the vents. The most striking evidence is the coating of fine-grained clear carbonate on accessory and accidental fragments in the vent-agglomerates, indicating that the fragments were already in an environment of carbonate deposition before consolidation of the rock. Preservation of the primary structures in the pyro-clastic rocks also excludes the possibility of any large amounts of alkali carbon-ates having originally been present, and since removed in solution, so that this effusive carbonatite was quite different from the ash at present being emitted from Oldoinyo Lengai, which is rich in sodium carbonate. The fine grain of the carbonate and the inclusion of so much extraneous material in the pyroclastics make it difficult to assess fully its affinities with the various types of intrusive carbonatite. It is, however, characteristically ankeritic and its lack of well-crystallized magnetite, apatite and pyrochlore make a close relationship with sövite unlikely. The same considerations, together with the common appearance of barite in the rock, suggest a closer link with the ankeritic carbonatite, and it is suggested that both these ankeritic rocks represent equilibrium assemblages for lower temperatures and pressures than are required for the crystallization of sövite. This does not rule out the possibility of similar calcitic pyroclasts, for indeed some of the Chasweta rocks are not richly ankeritic, and some of the very fine sövite agglomerate at Kaluwe is similar in texture to the effusive volcanics; eruption of sövite ash would require merely slightly different conditions or source material.

ALTERATION OF COUNTRY ROCKS

New minerals introduced into the country rocks of the Rufunsa complexes are quartz and chalcedony, limonitic iron oxides, potash feldspar, carbonates and a little barite. All these are found filling cracks and cavities in the country rocks; that is they have been mechanically emplaced, but some, especially the feldspar and carbonates, have also been metasomatically introduced.

The only pre-Karroo rocks in proximity to a large vent are the granitic gneisses south west of Mwambuto. Near to the complex they have been ruptured and brecciated, with the injection of veinlets of feldspar and iron oxides, followed by silica and iron oxides. In some samples the original microcline is sericitized, in others partly replaced by untwinned potash feldspar, which also replaces the quartz and muscovite. Two hundred yards further from the volcanic complex the only alteration in the granitic gneisses is sericitization of the feldspars, with shattering of the quartz lenticles and penetration by iron oxides. Xenoliths of pre-Karroo in the carbonatite complexes show a similar, but more intense, alteration; carbonates sometimes accompany the other introduced materials and have replaced original quartz. At Kaluwe some potash feldspar is replaced by phlogopite; no direct formation of phlogopite in undoubted country rock has been observed. The more extensive alteration of the xenoliths underlines the restricted nature of the alteration of the granitic gneisses at the level now exposed south west of Mwambuto; the strong indications that the feldspathic breccia represents altered pre-Karroo rocks imply, however, that at deeper levels the alteration may be very far reaching.

Probably the most interesting, and certainly the most extensive alteration is potash metasomatism of the Karroo mudstone around Mwambuto and the Uma, the same rock occurring as xenoliths at Chasweta and Kaluwe. Apart from shattering and mild brecciation, accompanied by silica and iron oxide veining, the only apparent difference from normal mudstone is the degree of induration in the altered rock, which is flinty and porcellaneous. There is little sign of change even in thin section, the rock consisting of silt and sand grade particles of quartz, with a little microcline and muscovite, in a 'paste' of very fine-grained low-polarizing material; this matrix, however, always has a low aggregate refractive index. Partial analyses of the rock for alkalis give potash contents corresponding to a range of 60–90 per cent orthoclase (Bailey, 1960, Table I), and x-ray diffraction patterns show very high contents of completely disordered potash feldspar, confirming that this mineral has replaced the largely kaolinitic matrix of the mudstone. Some specimens, especially those from the Uma, show even more advanced feldspathization in which first the silt-grade particles and finally the sand-grades are replaced. It is not difficult to understand why the mudstone should have been so susceptible to feldspathization, for, chemically, its original aluminous composition would favour addition of potash to form feldspar and, physically, it offered an enormous surface area for reaction. Replacement of quartz and other minerals in the mudstone and in other rocks, however, shows that the feldspathization was not limited to aluminous host materials.

A similar pattern of alteration is found in the arenaceous Karroo rocks. Bordering the argillite belt at Mwambuto is a zone of conglomerate and feldspathic grit which shows the characteristic shattering and penetration of feldspar, silica and iron oxide veins. In some specimens the matrix of the conglomerate is completely replaced by potash feldspar and, although the quartz pebbles have largely resisted attack, there is extensive replacement of the chert pebbles in the conglomerate. Feldspathization of the same type affects the xenoliths of Karroo sandstone and conglomerate in the Kaluwe intrusion, specimens from the middle facies showing replacement even of quartz pebbles. The Karroo sandstones of the envelope of Kaluwe do not show feldspathization, the only observed effect being infiltration of carbonate and iron oxides between sand grains, and replacement of some of these, especially chert grains, by carbonate. It may be remembered, too, that the thin 'chalky' layer that outcrops intermittently along the base of the Kaluwe intrusion may be a carbonatized mudstone bed in the Karroo sandstones.

A COMPOSITE PICTURE OF THE RUFUNSA ACTIVITY

Each of the complexes in the Rufunsa province exhibits different, but overlapping aspects of the activity, which can be combined to give an integrated picture of the chemistry and the mechanism of carbonatite intrusion and volcanicity.

Eighteen rock analyses covering the range of variation shown by the complexes are given in Table I. Calcium and magnesium are expressed in terms of carbonates; iron, because of the wide variety of forms in which it occurs in the rock, has been expressed simply as Fe_2O_3, which is its most characteristic form, although part of the iron is undoubtedly in the form of ankerite in some, but not all, the dolomitic rocks. Specimens from Kaluwe are all sövites low in magnesium and barium, and consistently lower in manganese and higher in phosphorous than the carbonatites in the volcanic vents. The typical grey carbonatite at Chasweta is also sövite, with only small amounts of dolomite or ankerite, and differs markedly from the ankeritic and dolomitic carbonatites of Mwambuto and Nachomba. In terms of its higher manganese and barium, and lower phosphate, however (and also lower niobium, not expressed in Table I), it shows affinities with the Mwambuto and Nachomba rocks, rather than with the Kaluwe sövites. The carbonatite volcanics, with the exception of the ripple marked pyroclastic are typically dolomitic, their affinities being with the Mwambuto and Nachomba

TABLE I

	Sample number	Apatite %	CaCO₃ %	MgCO₃ %	Fe₂O₃ %	MnO₂ %	BaSO₄ %	Molecular ratio Magnesite/Calcite	Brief description
Volcanic	860	0.9	26.4	1.5	4.3	0.3	0.1	0.05	Ripple marked pyroclast, Chasweta.
	780	0.8	34.6	24.0	7.0	1.2	0.3	0.82	Fine-grained volcanic, central depression, Chasweta.
	861	0.4	36.4	28.2	9.3	1.8	0.3	0.92	Phlogopite-rich volcanic, Chasweta.
	999	5.2	33.8	28.4	9.0	1.1	—	1.0	Phlogopite-rich volcanic, Mwambuto.
Fault Carbonate	971	0.6	20.4	14.6	5.9	—	—	0.86	Buff, fine-grained fault carbonate, Nyalusu Hill.
Carbonatite:									
Mwambuto	1005	0.2	36.3	14.0	13.7	6.8	6.8	0.46	Manganese-rich carbonatite.
	984	0.4	53.0	29.6	1.3	2.8	—	0.66	Fine-grained buff carbonatite.
	791	0.2	47.8	36.5	7.0	2.0	1.74	0.91	Buff carbonatite dike.
Nachomba	1050	0.2	50.8	33.1	9.9	1.7	3.1	0.77	Fine-grained buff carbonatite; breccia-matrix.
Chasweta	1051	0.2	66.6	30.0	5.3	1.4	—	0.54	Coarse brown fragments in breccia.
	873	0.4	72.4	6.5	3.9	2.6	0.1	0.11	Grey carbonatite-marble.
	841	0.2	75.8	0.6	14.0	1.7	0.3	0.01	Dark-grey marble.
Kaluwe	906	4.9	79.4	0.8	9.3	1.3	—	0.01	Homogeneous carbonate layer.
	908	11.0	79.2	0.9	4.3	0.1	—	0.01	Homogeneous carbonate layer; carbonate replacing abundant apatite.
	922	6.8	73.6	1.5	4.3	0.1	—	0.02	Agglomerate; middle facies.
	958	2.8	64.2	1.4	4.3	0.6	0.1	0.03	Lower facies.
	961	6.8	85.5	1.4	2.6	0.6	—	0.02	Fragment rich in martite, apatite, pyrochlore.
	966	5.2	86.8	1.2	2.9	0.5	0.1	0.02	Upper facies.

E. W. Fowler, anal. (Published by courtesy of Director of Geological Surveys, Zambia) intrusive dolomitic carbonatites. The ripple marked rock is one of the early post-sövite eruptions at Chasweta and its low dolomite content may be due to inclusion of fine sövite debris from the vent walls. A specimen of one of the carbonate veins in the big fault-zone north of Kaluwe also has a similar composition to the ankeritic carbonatites in the volcanoes.

A knowledge of the petrography and mutual relations of these various carbonatites makes it possible to put them in sequence. The fragmental Kaluwe rocks are coarse-grained sövites, with large crystals of martite, apatite, and pyrochlore, and a low content of manganese and barite, representing early crystallization at

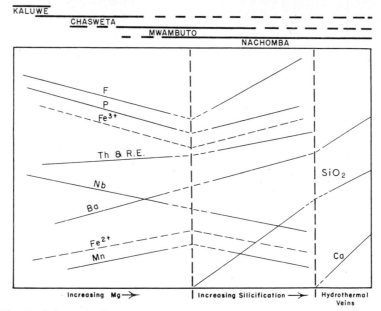

Fig. 7. Schematic diagram of the chemical variation through the various phases of activity. The relative position and amount of slope of each line has been chosen arbitrarily.

depth of iron-, phosphorus-, and niobium-rich sövite, under conditions suitable for the formation of magnetite. Subsequently the magnetite was oxidized and the phosphate extensively replaced by calcite—presumably by residual liquids which were themselves enriched in phosphorous and possibly iron by this process. At higher levels, or at a more advanced stage of crystallization, the carbonatite, as represented by the sövites at Chasweta, is still calcitic but with increasing amounts of dolomite, manganese and barite, while the pyrochlore is fine-grained and less abundant and the apatite content very low. This is followed by the crystallization of finer grained, buff dolomitic and ankeritic carbonatite, which is found as a replacement of the earlier sövite and as a later intrusive phase: this is characterized by even less pyrochlore and erratically distributed high concentrations of barite. Closely following the crystallization of the ankeritic carbonatite is a phase of silicification of the earlier carbonatites, with the introduction also of barite, fluorite, iron oxides, thorium and rare earths, and a second generation of apatite. Veins of coarse quartz-barite-calcite cut all the rocks of the complexes and probably represent the crystallization of the last residual solutions in fissures. Each of the above phases overlaps slightly, both chemically and spatially, and the conclusion that they represent the crystallization series of an original carbonatite fluid is inescapable. The trend of chemical variation through this series, as shown by chemical analyses and mineralogy, is depicted schematically in Fig. 7. An interesting arrangement exists at Kaluwe, where it seems that the flat form and wide extent of the sövite intrusion was unfavourable to any extensive invasion by the later, more tenuous fluids ascending the fault-zone feeder to the north; these were constrained to continue along the fault-zone where the mineralization is essentially the same as that of the late stages in the volcanoes.

The serial nature of this activity is clear at Rufunsa, but the same general sequence has been observed elsewhere, emplacement of ankeritic carbonatite after sövite being described from several localities (see Campbell Smith, 1956); a closely comparable example is the roughly contemporaneous Chilwa Island complex of Malawi (Garson, this volume, p. 52) where in addition there has been later silicification and hydrothermal activity identical with that of the Rufunsa valley.

By relating the crystallization sequence with the physical arrangement of the rocks in the vents the following sequence of activity has been deduced:

(1) Doming of the country rocks by the first ascending fluids in the stem, which were probably the source of the intensive potash metasomatism of the country rocks.

(2) Surface eruption of ankeritic pyroclastics, with intrusion of fluidized feldspathic breccia along the walls of the newly formed vent, this major effusive episode being the surface expression of rising, crystallizing sövite deeper in the complex.

(3) Intrusion of sövite below the new cover formed by the volcanic cone.

(4) Intrusion of ankeritic carbonatite, and ankeritization of the sövite plug, representing the expulsion of the residual fluids from sövite crystallizing deeper in the stem. This was probably expressed at the surface as the dying phases of tuff and agglomerate effusion.

(5) Silicification of the earlier rocks by H_2O-rich residuals, the CO_2 being nearly exhausted by crystallization of the carbonates. This process follows closely the crystallization of ankerite and was probably manifested at the surface by hot springs and mineral springs.[1]

(6) Injection of coarse quartz-calcite-barite veins into fissures in all the older rocks.

At Mwambuto and Chasweta the disruption of the carbonatite plugs indicates that this major cycle was repeated at least once, probably several times, but on a smaller scale, such that only the upper parts of the later cycles are seen at the present erosion level. It is by this fortunate accident that remnants of the well-bedded pyroclastics are still preserved at Chasweta.

---

[1] At the present time there are brackish springs issuing along the continuation of the Luangwa rift line, to the south west.

Temperature and vapour composition

Several lines of evidence lead to the conclusion that during this activity the temperatures were low. Country rocks and xenoliths show a conspicuous lack of thermal affects: strained quartz is not annealed; biotite and epidote are replaced by limonite; and the mudstone, which should have been a sensitive temperature indicator, shows only potash metasomatism. This evidence suggests PT conditions below those of the albite-epidote hornfels facies, with an implication of temperatures below 300°C (Fyfe, Turner and Verhoogen, 1958). In the metasomatized zone, orthoclase coexists with limonite, fine quartz and chalcedony, and, remarkably, with original microcline and muscovite, suggesting rapid metastable formation of the disordered feldspar at low temperature. Spencer (1938) proposed temperatures below 400°C for the formation of orthoclase and recent evidence indicates that the mineral may form even below 40°C (Hay, 1962).

Within the complexes the coexistence of carbonates and quartz and the lack of magnesium and calcium silicates also point to low temperatures. The limited experimental data on carbonate-silicate assemblages make it impossible to fix the temperature but an upper limit around 700°C is clearly imposed by the absence of wollastonite (Greenwood, 1962), and the absence of talc and tremolite demands still lower limits. One possible index of the physical conditions in the carbonatites is the presence of potash feldspar or phlogopite, or the coexistence of these minerals, as, for instance, in the feldspar xenoliths rimmed with phlogopite in Kaluwe. With this in mind a study has been made (Bailey, 1964c) of the conditions controlling the reaction: orthoclase + dolomite + water $\rightleftharpoons$ phlogopite + calcite + carbon dioxide. At 1 kb total pressure the temperature of this reaction ranges from 300°–640°C and is strongly dependent on the proportions of CO_2 and H_2O in the vapour phase. At high concentrations of CO_2, orthoclase + dolomite remains stable to relatively much higher temperatures (640°C) than it does in a hydrous atmosphere (300°C); over a broad range of intermediate vapour compositions the reaction takes place around 500°C, and temperatures of this order probably represent an upper limit for dolomitic carbonatite containing orthoclase. As well as fixing an upper limit of temperature for the Rufunsa carbonatites, therefore, this reaction reveals interesting aspects of the variation of vapour composition during activity. Where fragments of feldspar have reacted to give phlogopite it may be an indication of their being subjected to higher temperature on incorporation in the intrusion, but it is more probable that the reaction took place during cooling and resulted from the decrease in CO_2 concentration brought about by the crystallization of carbonates. With increasing depth a temperature will be reached at which orthoclase cannot coexist with dolomite and, instead of the orthoclase rock typical of the Rufunsa carbonatites, phlogopite would be expected in the metasomatized zone. These conditions are exemplified at Nkumbwa Hill (Reeve and Deans, 1954) and Palabora (Russell, Heimstra and Groeneveld, 1954) and possibly in the phlogopite-rich volcanics poured out at Rufunsa. It may be noted, too, that the stability of potash feldspar and phlogopite fixes similar limits for the conditions in high-level kimberlites, which commonly contain carbonates. Further details and a discussion of the applications of the results will be found in the preliminary account of this study (Bailey, 1964c).

Mechanism of emplacement

Perhaps the most unusual feature of the Rufunsa province is the lack of igneous silicate rocks associated with the carbonatites. But this is an advantage to the understanding of the activity for it leaves no doubt that carbonatite is the agent responsible for all the observed effects. The notion that carbonatites must always be replacement or hydrothermal deposits, or end-stage intrusions in a previously established alkaline complex, is untenable; at Rufunsa, carbonatite is independently involved in volcanic activity, and thereby gives some clues to the nature of deep-seated carbonatite.

The Rufunsa volcanic vents are filled with ankeritic tuffisite, which was emplaced by rising gas streams with solids in suspension. During periods of eruption these streams were moving rapidly and transporting solids through the vents; during quiescent periods the gas streams were merely maintaining solids in suspension, causing gradual rounding by mutual attrition. Such conditions represent different aspects of fluidization, both requiring certain minimum rates of gas flow. Constant flow of gas requires constant supply but with increasing depth in a pipe the pressure will increase, with a correspondingly slower flow required to supply the volume of gas moving through the higher levels. At some depth, therefore, the system should eventually be a slowly rising liquid or near-liquid phase generating the gases which accelerate up through the vent. At Rufunsa this was probably a hydrous carbonatitic liquid akin to those produced experimentally in the system $CaO-CO_2-H_2O$ (Wyllie and Tuttle, 1960), which by loss of pressure during uprise, and by crystallization, generated increasing amounts of vapour. Adiabatic expansion and cooling of the vapour phase would cause further crystallization of solids from the associated liquid, thereby promoting the process. As the volcanics are typically ankeritic it must be supposed that their source-liquid was of this type, which itself was probably derived from the crystallization of sövite. This suggests that the ankeritic liquid was streaming away from a mass of crystallizing sövite, or moving in advance of a slowly rising stem of crystallizing sövite, which eventually would become a dense suspension of sövite grains carried along by its own residual fluids.

Several lines of reasoning indicate that the intrusive carbonatite plugs were emplaced as a mush of fragments in a residual fluid, the Rufunsa rocks providing abundant evidence of an eventual fragmental texture in the carbonatite. Experimental studies have shown that liquids in the simplified carbonatite systems are so thin as to permit crystal settling in fifteen-minute runs (Wyllie and Tuttle, 1960). If such conditions obtain in nature then any static mass of carbonatite liquid should show extreme crystal fractionation. But the actual case is quite the contrary—carbonatites are characterized by their heterogeneity, both in fabric and composition, with dense minerals such as magnetite and barite unsystematically mingled with carbonates and fluorides. This, together with the concentric vertical banding in carbonatite plugs, and the streaking out and pulling apart of xenolithic schlieren, leave little doubt of the viscosity during final emplacement. Either the experimental results are inapplicable or the carbonatite plugs were already largely crystalline on emplacement; the Rufunsa evidence favours the second alternative.

The carbonatite is therefore considered to originate as a hot, carbonatic liquid (possibly a dense supercritical gas), and its close relationship to the great rift structures (Bailey, 1961a), strongly suggests that its source is below the crust. Given a zone of weakness such as a rift or rift intersection it starts to rise and expand. Cooling causes precipitation of sövite minerals, which are carried along by the residual liquids enriched in ankeritic components. The leading edge of this liquid fraction grades into a higher, accelerating vapour phase sweeping along its own precipitated ankeritic solids (thereby transforming from a rising liquid to a gas-solid fluidized system) finally erupting at the surface as carbonatite pyroclasts.

That the two processes, intrusion and surface eruption, are parts of a single process can be seen in another way by comparison with the deeper-seated Chilwa series complexes of Malawi. These have similar intrusive rocks but no tuffisite pipes such as those cutting the Rufunsa carbonatite plugs, indicating that the exposure level in the Chilwa vents is below the transition point from intrusive carbonatite to tuffisite.

OTHER CONSIDERATIONS

One element has been neglected in the previous discussions; this is potassium. Although potash is abundant in the feldspathic breccias and metasomatized rocks, there is no sign of the previous presence of alkali carbonates in the carbonate rocks. Fragments in the volcanics show little or no sign of feldspathization, and the intrusion of carbonatites into feldspathic breccia indicates that intensive metasomatism preceded their emplacement. Accordingly it is suggested that streams of more tenuous fluids containing potassium, probably as dissolved carbonate, preceded the main phase of carbonatite intrusion, the potassium continuously reacting with the wall-rocks. Loss of potash would release carbon-dioxide resulting in increased pressure and expansion of the system; such a process may have provided the mechanism for initial drilling of the conduit, and would certainly go a long way to explaining the doming and fracturing of the roof rocks of the embryonic volcano. The early separation of a more volatile phase containing most of the alkali carbonates would account for the lack of such materials in most carbonatite complexes. The lack of soda in the Rufunsa complexes is puzzling. This may have been an intrinsic property of the primary carbonatite liquid, but if there were an early separation of a phase rich in alkali carbonates another explanation is possible. Under low temperature conditions, in the presence of abundant potash, soda would be unreactive with respect to the wall rocks (Orville, 1963) and was probably expelled at the surface during the earliest activity as hot brines, and showers of soda-rich ashes similar to those erupted from Oldoinyo Lengai (James, 1956; Dawson, 1962).

The lack of igneous silicate rocks in the Rufunsa complexes calls attention to the basic problem of distinguishing easily recognizable carbonatite mineralization from carbonate-rich hydrothermal deposits (Bailey, 1961b; Heinrich, 1962). Possibly no real distinction exists, for carbonate liquids simply reflect particular physico-chemical conditions and may form by convergent processes from different sources, and then may develop along divergent paths. In the case of the Keshya and Mkwisi intrusive limestones (Bailey, 1961b) the evidence is strongly in favour of their being large carbonatite hydrothermal bodies. Their $^{86}Sr/^{87}Sr$ ratios led to this view being challenged (Hamilton and Deans, 1963) but in fact the lower values obtained were consistent with those of the upper range of accepted carbonatites, and the xenolithic contamination of these intrusions makes the use of $^{86}Sr/^{87}Sr$ ratios unsafe as a criterion of origin (Bailey, 1964a). This conclusion has recently been supported by the similar high values of $^{86}Sr/^{87}Sr$ obtained from the Songwe carbonatite dike (Brown, 1964) which is probably also contaminated with sialic strontium.

The question of classification or petrological affinities does not arise with the Rufunsa carbonatites, which are typical in their chemistry, but the very lack of associated silicate magmatism demands serious consideration for a primary origin for the carbonatite. Even when account is taken of the common association of similar carbonatite with alkaline rocks this view is not necessarily modified, for some workers contend that the alkaline rocks are rheomorphic fenites, and the intense potash metasomatism around the Rufunsa complexes favours this possibility.

Alternatively, the localization of the carbonatites at a rift intersection indicates a probable source in the mantle, with its implication of a link with ultrabasic rocks. There are indications of an association between carbonatites and kimberlites (Daly, 1925; Dawson, 1962c), and v. Eckermann (1960, 1961) and Saether (1957) have suggested that carbonatite is a perimagmatic phase of kimberlite magmatism, citing evidence of carbonates replacing earlier silicates. While it is by no means clear that the carbonatite is derivative, the association is undeniable and raises the question of the nature of kimberlite volcanism, which in the past has been discussed almost as little as carbonatite volcanism. As was shown in a recent consideration of the tectonic environment of alkaline and carbonatite magmatism (Bailey, 1964b), the major kimberlite provinces of Africa are distinctive in that they are not related to the rift valley pattern. Typical kimberlite breccia is probably mantle material that has not been molten under crustal conditions. In the rift valleys the melilite basalt association appears to be the chemical equivalent of kimberlite and is related through nephelinite (ijolite) to carbonatite. Recent work on the system $Na_2O-Al_2O_3-Fe_2O_3-SiO_2$ (Bailey and Schairer, 1963; 1966) indicates that ijolitic liquids are probably of residual type, and would be expected to form by partial melting of bulk compositions such as melilite basalt. This information, combined with a knowledge of the localization of alkaline and carbonatite activity along crustal upwarps, has led to the concept of the whole family of rocks resulting from relief of lithostatic load on the lower crust and upper mantle (Bailey, 1964b). The different expressions of the activity that may result from this are shown in Fig. 8. In this scheme carbonatite figures as the volatile-rich fugitive fraction from the upper mantle, not necessarily related through any fractionation process to kimberlite, though naturally cogenetic in the sense of being derived from a common source region in the mantle. The fact that carbonatite is capable of independent generation

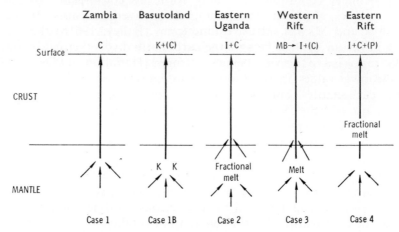

Fig. 8. Diagrammatic section through the crust illustrating the common surface relationships between carbonatite (C), ijolite (I) and nepheline syenite (phonolite, P), and interpreting these as residua or early fusion products resulting from relief of pressure. C is the volatile-rich, low-temperature residuum from the mantle; I is the low-melting fraction from highly undersaturated rocks such as melilite basalt (MB); and P is the low-melting fraction from alkali basalt. The cluster of arrows at the base of each column represents collection of fugitive constituents from the underlying and surrounding mantle. Case IB represents transport of kimberlite (K) from the mantle with no melting under crustal conditions. In cases 2 and 3 the higher arrows indicate the ascent of melt into the crust with subsequent modification or differentiation. Case 4 combines partial melting of basaltic materials in the crust with the release of hyperfusibles from the mantle. The localities chosen are all African to give a consistent picture. (Reproduced by permission of the Journal of Petrology.)

and can be the sole agent in normal igneous processes is the most unusual, and probably the most significant lesson to be gained from the Rufunsa province.

REFERENCES

Bailey, D. K., 1960, Carbonatites of the Rufunsa valley, Feira district: *N. Rhodesia Geol. Surv., Bull.* **5**.

Bailey, D. K., 1961a, The mid-Zambezi–Luangwa rift and related carbonatite activity: *Geol. Mag.* v. **96**, pp. 275–284.

Bailey, D. K., 1961b, Intrusive limestones in the Keshya and Mkwisi valleys, Northern Rhodesia: *Geol. Soc. London Quart. Jour.*, v. **117**, pp. 419–446.

Bailey, D. K., 1964a, Isotopic composition of strontium in carbonatites: *Nature*, v. **201**, p. 599.

Bailey, D. K., 1964b, Crustal warping—a possible tectonic control of alkaline magmatism: *J. Geophys. Res.*, v. **69**, pp. 1103–1111.

Bailey, D. K., 1964c, Temperature and vapour composition in carbonatite and kimberlite: *Carnegie Inst. Wash. Yearbook*, **63**, pp. 79–81.

Bailey, D. K. and Schairer, J. F., 1963, Crystallization of rock-forming silicates in the system $Na_2O–Al_2O_3–Fe_2O_3–SiO_2$ at 1 atm: *Carnegie Inst. Wash. Yearbook*, **62**, pp. 124–131.

Bailey, D. K. and Schairer, J. F., 1966, The system $Na_2O–Al_2O_3–Fe_2O_3–SiO_2$ at 1 atm. and the petrogenesis of alkaline rocks: *Jour. Petrology*, v. **7**, pp. 114–170.

Brown, P. E., 1964, The Songwe scarp carbonatite and associated feldspathization in the Mbeya Range, Tanganyika: *Geol. Soc. Lond. Quart. Jour.*, v. **120**, pp. 223–240.

Cloos, H., 1941, Bau und Tätigkeit von Tuffschloten; Untersuchungen an dem schwäbischen Vulkan: *Geol. Rundschau.*, v. **32**, p. 709.

Daly, R. A., 1925, Carbonatite dikes of the Premier Diamond Mine, Transvaal: *Jour. Geol.*, v. **33**, pp. 659–684.

Dawson, J. B., 1962a, Sodium carbonate lavas from Oldoinyo Lengai, Tanganyika: *Nature*, v. **195**, pp. 1075–1076.

Dawson, J. B., 1962b, The geology of Oldoinyo Lengai: *Bull. Volcanol.*, v. **24**, pp. 349–387.

Dawson, J. B., 1962c, Basutoland kimberlites: *Geol. Soc. America Bull.*, v. **73**, pp. 545–559.

Dixey, F., 1955, Some aspects of the geomorphology of central and southern Africa: *Geol. Soc. S. Africa Trans.*, v. **58**, annexure.

Dixey, F., Campbell Smith, W. and Bisset, C. B., 1937, (revised 1955), The Chilwa series of southern Nyasaland: *Nyasaland, Geol. Surv. Bull.* **5**.

DuBois, C. G. B. *et al.*, 1963, Fresh natro-carbonatite from Oldoinyo Lengai: *Nature*, v. **197**, pp. 445–446.

v. Eckermann, H., 1948, The alkaline district of Alnö Island: *Sverig. Geol. Undersok.*, *Ser. Ca.*, **36**.

v. Eckermann, H., 1960, The Alnö alkaline region: *Internat. Geol. Congr., 21st sess.* Guide to excursion C27.

v. Eckermann, H., 1961, The petrogenesis of the Alnö alkaline rocks: *Geol. Inst. Univ. Uppsala, Bull.*, v. **40**, pp. 25–36.

Fyfe, W. S., Turner, F. J. and Verhoogen, J., 1958, Metamorphic reactions and metamorphic facies: *Geol. Soc. America Mem.* **73**.

Garson, M. S. and Campbell Smith, W., 1958, Chilwa Island: *Nyasaland Geol. Surv. Mem.* **1**.

Greenwood, H. J., 1962, Metamorphic reactions involving two volatile components: *Carnegie Inst. Wash. Yearbook*, **61**, pp. 82–85.

Guest, N. J., 1956, The volcanic activity of Oldoinyo L'engai, 1954: *Tanganyika Geol. Surv. Rec.* 1954, v. **4**, pp. 56–59.

Hamilton, E. I. and Deans, T., 1963, Isotopic composition of strontium in some African carbonatites and limestones and in strontium minerals: *Nature*, v. **198**, pp. 776–777.

Hay, R. L., 1962, Origin and diagenetic alteration of the lower part of the John Day Formation near Mitchell, Oregon: in Petrologic Studies: *Geol. Soc. America, Buddington Volume*, pp. 191–216.

Heinrich, E. Wm. and Levinson, A. A., 1961, Carbonatic niobium-rare-earth deposits, Ravalli Country, Montana: *Am. Mineralogist*, v. **46**, pp. 1424–1447.

Hobley, C. W., 1918, A volcanic eruption in East Africa: *Jour. E. Africa Uganda Nat. Hist. Soc.*, v. **4**, pp. 339–343.

James, T. C., 1956, Carbonatites and rift valleys in East Africa: *Tanganyika, Geol. Surv.* Unpublished report, TCJ/34.

King, B. C., 1949, The Napak area of southern Karomoja, Uganda: *Uganda Geol. Surv. Mem.* **5**.

Knorring, O. von and DuBois, C. G. B., 1961, Carbonatite lava from Fort Portal area in western Uganda: *Nature*, v. **192**, p. 1064.

MacKenzie, W. S. and Smith, J. V., 1955, The alkali feldspars: 1. Orthoclase microperthites: *Am. Mineralogist*, v. **40**, pp. 707–732.

Orville, P. M., 1963, Alkali ion exchange between vapor and feldspar phase: *Am. Jour. Sci.*, v. **261**, pp. 201–237.

Park, C. F., 1961, A magnetite 'flow' in northern Chile: *Econ. Geol.*, v. **56**, p. 431.

Reeve, W. H. and Deans, T., 1954, An occurrence of carbonatite in the Isoka district of Northern Rhodesia: *Colon. Geol. Mineral Resources* v. **4**, pp. 271–281.

Reynolds, D. L., 1954, Fluidization as a geological process, and its bearing on the problem of intrusive granites: *Am. Jour. Sci.*, v. **252**, pp. 577–614.

Richard, J. J., 1942, Volcanological observations in East Africa. I. Oldoinyo L'engai. The 1940–1941 eruption: *Jour. E. Africa Uganda Nat. Hist. Soc.*, v. **16**, pp. 89–108.

Russell, H. D., Heimstra, S. A. and Groeneveld, D., 1954, The mineralogy and petrology of the carbonatite at Loolekop, Eastern Transvaal: *Geol. Soc. S. Africa. Trans.*, v. **57**, pp. 197–208.

Saether, E., 1957, The alkaline rock province of the Fen area in southern Norway: *Det. Kgl. Norske Vid. Selsk. Skr*, v. **1**.

Shand, S. J., 1927, *Eruptive Rocks:* London, Murby, 1st Ed., p. 36.

Smith, W. Campbell, 1956, A review of some problems of African carbonatites: *Geol. Soc. Lond. Quart. Jour.*, v. **112**, pp. 189–220.

Spencer, E., 1938, The potash-soda feldspars II. Some applications to petrogenesis: *Min. Mag.*, v. **25**, p. 87.

Wyllie, P. J. and Tuttle, O. F., 1960, The system $CaO–CO_2–H_2O$ and the origin of carbonatites: *Jour. Petrology*, v. **1**, pp. 1–46.

J. B. DAWSON

Oldoinyo Lengai—an Active Volcano with Sodium Carbonatite Lava Flows

INTRODUCTION

The volcanics of the Neogene volcanic province of northern Tanganyika are divided into two main groups—(*a*) the Older Extrusives comprising the olivine basalt trachybasalt–trachytc–phonolite volcanoes of the Crater Highlands, Gelai, Kitumbeine, Tarosero and Monduli (Fig. 1); and—(*b*) the Younger Extrusives which include the composite cones of Mosonik, Oldoinyo Lengai, Kerimasi, Essimingor, Burko and Meru. Most of the Younger Extrusive centres are carbonatite volcanoes. These two main groups are separated by a major phase of faulting, the most spectacular example of which is the western boundary fault of the Gregory Rift Valley, which runs from the Kenya border in the north to Lake Manyara in the south (Dawson, in press).

The carbonatite cone of Oldoinyo Lengai, situated some 10 miles south of Lake Natron is still active. There have been 10 recorded eruptions since 1880 and these have recently been summarized by Richard and van Padang (1957) and Dawson (1962a). The steep, cone-shaped volcano (see frontispiece) is approximately 5 miles in diameter and stands 6500 ft above the surrounding plains. The cone is dissected by deep, radial gullies, and on the lower northern, eastern, southern and south western slopes are small parasitic cones, explosion craters and tuff rings.

The summit of the mountain is occupied by two craters separated by an E–W ridge. The inactive southern crater, which was the eruptive vent during the earliest major phase of activity, is now a shallow oval depression filled with grey ash and scattered volcanic bombs. The active northern crater is a collapse feature formed as the result of a major eruption in 1917; it is roughly elliptical in shape, measuring 500 by 700 yd and the precipitous walls vary from 400 to 800 ft in height. The main vent is situated excentrically on the eastern half of the crater floor and is surrounded by an area 70 to 100 yds in diameter consisting of scoria cones, recent ejectementa and minor lava flows.

STRATIGRAPHY

The following stratigraphic sequence has now been established:

    6. Modern sodium carbonate lavas of the northern crater.

5. Variegated carbonate ashes of the active crater; soda ash deposit of the summit area; black and grey, poorly consolidated ashes.

4. Melanephelinite extrusives.

3. Black nephelinitic tuffs and agglomerates.

2. Grey pyroclastics of the parasitic cones and tuff rings.

1. Yellow ijolitic tuffs and agglomerates with interbedded lavas.

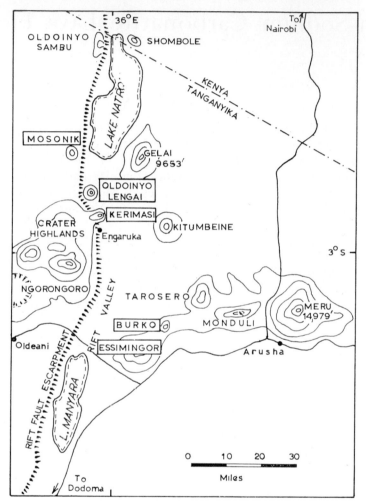

Fig. 1. Map showing the location of Oldoinyo Lengai. Other carbonatites in the area are boxed.

PYROCLASTICS

The yellow ijolitic pyroclastics constitute the main mass of the volcano with the younger pyroclastics forming merely a thin veneer above them. In the best exposures some 1200 ft of yellow pyroclastics are exposed. The individual units vary considerably both in thickness and lateral extent. The finer grained members are crystal tuffs, consisting of nepheline and pyroxene in a matrix of carbonate, limonite and zeolites, and grade into agglomerates containing blocks of nephelinite, phonolite, urtite, ijolite, melteigite, jacupirangite, biotite pyroxenite and fenite. The rocks of the urtite–melteigite series consist of varying proportions of nepheline and sodic pyroxene, with apatite, sphene, melanite and titaniferous magnetite as accessories; biotite is found in some of the melteigites which, with the disappearance of nepheline, grade into jacupirangite. The biotite pyroxenites consist of biotite and diopsidic augite. The strongly veined and fractured fenite blocks are sacharoidal in texture, and consist of varying proportions of quartz, orthoclase, perthite, albite, aegirine and aegirine-augite, sphene, nepheline, apatite and biotite.

The grey pyroclastics of the parasitic cones and tuff rings are agglomerates, and crystal and lithic tuffs. The lithic tuffs, which consist of lapilli of black nephelinite and crystals of biotite grade into crystal tuffs in which crystals of mica, pyroxene, olivine and nepheline predominate over the lapilli; the main cementing mineral is white carbonate. In the agglomerates, blocks of olivine basalt, ijolite and yellow agglomerate have been found.

The black pyroclastics which form a thin veneer over the yellow pyroclastics, grade from lithic tuffs to agglomerates. The tuffs are formed mainly of lapilli of black nephelinite, and, less commonly, of small fragments of ijolite and fenite, and crystals of nepheline, pyroxene and mica, all cemented by zeolites and carbonate. The agglomerates, with their dark matrix of nephelinite lapilli, contain blocks similar to those in the ijolitic pyroclastics with the addition of wollastonitites, wollastonite ijolite, sövite and carbonatized urtite. The wollastonitites consist of radiating masses of wollastonite, with small amounts of nepheline, glass, magnetite and apatite. Gradation from wollastonitite to ijolite within single hand specimens, combined with evidence of wollastonite over-growths on pyroxene, suggest that these rocks are the result of calcium metasomatism of earlier ijolitic rocks. X-ray studies of some of the wollastonite prove it to be intergrowths of triclinic wollastonite and monoclinic parawollastonite (Dawson and Sahama, 1963).

The variegated ashes and soda deposits of the summit area, with the black and grey semi-indurated ashes, are the products of historic explosive eruptions. The black–grey ashes consist of lapilli of nephelinite and small crystals of biotite. These ashes are intermingled with, encrusted and overlain by white and buff deposits of soda-rich carbonate ash.

The variegated soda ashes are found on the steep inner slopes of the active crater and on the crater rim; in colour they are light green, pale buff, pink and white, and consist mainly of carbonate with occasional lapilli of nephelinite, and scattered crystals of pyroxene and nepheline.

Partial analyses of soda-rich ejectementa, collected by Richard (1942) following the 1940–1941 eruption are shown in Table I.

According to earlier workers (Uhlig, 1907; Reck, 1914) blocks of gneiss were found in the southern crater prior to the 1917 eruption.

TABLE I

Partial analyses of soda-rich ashes and rocks

	1	2	3
SiO_2	0.16	—	—
Fe_2O_3	11.99	—	—
CaO	6.82	—	—
MgO	0.38	—	—
Na_2CO_3	40.0	—	—
Na_2SO_4	5.4	—	—
Na_2O	—	24.32	24.69
K_2O	0.16	4.97	5.33

1. Powdery boulder altering to brown powder containing carbonate and magnetite.
2. Nepheline-bearing rock altering to white powder.
3. Block of whitish-grey mud.
All analyses from Richard (1942).

TABLE II

Analyses of silicate lavas from Oldoinyo Lengai

	1	2	3	4	5	6	7	8	9
SiO_2	53.42	53.35	49.15	48.87	46.59	43.93	42.44	39.66	37.13
TiO_2	0.85	0.97	1.15	0.64	0.98	2.76	2.15	2.01	3.92
Al_2O_3	20.53	19.96	18.53	18.33	19.60	13.84	12.20	11.49	12.11
Fe_2O_3	3.04	3.29	6.07	4.28	4.08	2.40	6.33	6.70	7.25
FeO	1.24	2.37	0.84	2.07	2.86	5.42	3.14	3.56	3.45
MnO	0.15	0.42	0.22	0.18	0.20	0.44	0.34	0.33	0.20
CaO	2.91	3.12	3.64	5.44	4.49	14.43	10.73	17.54	19.34
MgO	0.03	0.79	0.27	0.98	0.10	7.47	1.03	1.90	4.27
Na_2O	10.15	9.48	9.10	9.36	12.60	5.59	14.24	7.84	6.13
K_2O	5.30	4.46	6.00	3.88	4.93	2.13	5.19	3.52	2.54
H_2O^+	—	1.06	—	1.85	—	0.58	0.19	0.30	0.26
H_2O^-	0.20	0.52	1.62	1.68	1.22	0.14	0.46	1.31	0.12
P_2O_5	0.24	0.08	0.31	0.23	0.13	0.51	0.60	1.03	2.82
CO_2	0.13	tr	0.63	2.02	—	—	0.50	2.54	—
F	—	—	—	—	—	—	0.28	0.43	—
S	—	—	—	—	—	—	—	0.28	—
Loss on ignition	1.90	—	2.78	—	2.11	—	—	—	—
Total	100.13	99.87	100.21	100.01	99.89	99.86	99.82	100.44	99.54
Total iron as FeO	3.97	5.83	6.30	5.92	6.53	7.58	8.83	9.59	9.97

1. Phonolite (Guest, 1953).
2. Phonolite (Dawson, 1962a).
3. Phonolite (Dawson, 1962a).
4. Nephelinite phonolite (Guest, 1953).
5. Phonolitic nephelinite (Dawson, 1962a).

6. Melanephelinite (Guest, 1953).
7. Nephelinite (Richard, 1942).
8. Nephelinite (Richard, 1942).
9. Melanephelinite (Guest, 1953).

SILICATE LAVAS

Oldoinyo Lengai is formed mainly of pyroclastics, but lava flows of two ages have been found:

(*a*) Nephelinites and phonolites interbedded with the yellow pyroclastics.

(*b*) Melanephelinites which post-date the black pyroclastics.

In the phonolites phenocrysts of sanidine, aegirine-augite and nepheline are set in a glassy matrix with numerous microlites of sanidine and aegirine. Nepheline in the matrix is usually interstitial and may be partly replaced by analcite or cancrinite. Sphene is a common accessory and calcite and zeolites are common in the vesicles. The texture is often trachytic. In the nephelinites, the place of the feldspar has been taken by nepheline, and wollastonite, melilite and sodalite may occur; the wollastonite is possibly xenocrystic. In other respects the nephelinites resemble the phonolites and there is every gradation between them.

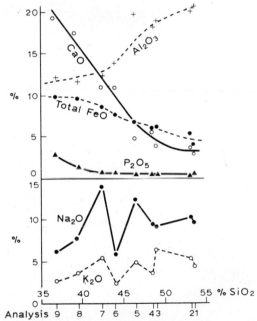

Fig. 2. Plots showing the variation with silica content of some oxides in the Oldoinyo Lengai silicate lavas.

The melanephelinites occur in two small flows on the upper west slopes of the volcano, and in four small, aligned cones on the lower north slopes. Mineralogically, these rocks are nephelinites with a high proportion of pyroxene; sphene is absent, its place being taken by its undersaturated equivalent, perovskite.

Analyses of nine silicate lavas from Oldoinyo Lengai are shown in Table II. From the phonolites to the melanephelinites there is a steady decrease in the silica and alumina content, while calcium, total iron, phosphorus and titanium increase (Fig. 2). Alumina and silica vary sympathetically, as do sodium and

Fig. 3. A flow of blocky sodium carbonate lava on the floor of the active
crater, Oldoinyo Lengai, October 8th, 1960.

Fig. 4. Mobile *pahoehoe* flows (in the foreground) and a blocky *aa* flow
of sodium carbonate lava in the active crater of Oldoinyo Lengai. Note
the textural differences between the two flow types.

potassium, and calcium and magnesia. The soda and potash content, however, has no relationship to the silica content. Some of the lavas contain high amounts of lithium, gallium, rubidium, strontium, yttrium, zirconium, niobium, barium and lanthanum (Table III).

TABLE III

Trace elements of some lavas in Table II

	2	3	5
	ppm	ppm	ppm
Li	300	300	750
Ti	> 3000	> 3000	> 3000
V	150	150	300
Cr	5	—	5
Co	20	20	50
Ni	40	50	40
Ga	50	50	30
Rb	450	450	450
Sr	10,000	10,000	10,000
Y	30	60	20
Zr	> 450	> 450	> 450
Nb	800	800	250
Ba	10,000	10,000	10,000
La	200	500	200

P. Bowden, anal.

SODIUM CARBONATE LAVAS

Lavas consisting mainly of soda and carbon dioxide were extruded on to the floor of the crater in January, June, September and October 1960, and August 1961, (Dawson, 1962a, 1962b). They were extruded both as highly mobile

Fig. 5. Close-up view of the surface of a *pahoehoe* flow showing a miniature driblet cone, nahcolite encrusting cracks (na) and *aa* bomb (ab).

pahoehoe flows and as viscous, blocky *aa* flows, (Figs. 3 and 4). In every way they behaved like silicate lavas, the *pahoehoe* lavas showing ropy structures, small squeeze-ups and minor driblet cones (Fig. 5). Cracks on the *pahoehoe* flows were coated with sublimated nahcolite ($NaHCO_3$). A noticeable feature of the flows is that although they were black in colour when first extruded, they began to turn white after a very short time (24–36 hours). After a matter of 6–7 days the lava becomes light grey-white in colour; in this state it is deliquescent.

Aa flows, similar to those observed in 1960, were again extruded in early August 1961.

Another feature of interest is that the carbonate lavas are not incandescent. Moving flows of lava, observed from the crater floor during daytime, did not appear to be incandescent, and this was confirmed when the crater was kept under observation at night; lava could be heard surging about in the vent and splashing back on to the crater floor after small gas explosions, but it did not glow. This is in contrast to observations made during the 1940 eruption (Richard, 1942) and during minor activity in 1954 (Guest, 1956). The temperature of the magma was not ascertained but in view of the unusual chemistry of the lavas it is unlikely that the temperature would be greater than 500°C.

Analyses of the 1960 lavas (Table IV) show their highly unusual nature. The outstanding feature of their chemistry is the extremely high alkali and volatile content (37 and 49 per cent respectively) combined with a virtual absence of silica and alumina; fluorine, chlorine and sulphur trioxide are also very high. They are unlike any other magmatic carbonate so far recorded, containing relatively little lime and magnesia, and the alkalies are not present in silicate minerals. The strontium content is in the same order as in calcite and dolomitic carbonatites but the barium (probably substituting for potassium) is present in greater concentrations in these lavas. The high lithium and rubidium content is unusual, but the lanthanum is believed to be characteristic of the Tanganyika carbonatites as a group (Bowden, 1962). The high water content 8–9 per cent reported in the 1960 lavas may be due to absorption of atmospheric moisture after collection, as later samples, taken while hot in 1961 and put promptly into sealed containers, show only 1.8–1.9 per cent water (see DuBois, C. G. B., Furst, J., Guest, N. J. and Jennings, D. J., (1963) and Guest (1963)). The four available analyses of these lavas are shown in Table IV. With regard to the individual elements, sodium predominates over potassium, which is in keeping with the overall sodic character of the magmatism in this part of the Gregory Rift Valley, while calcium out-weighs magnesium, a general feature of most of the residual carbonatites in Tanganyika (the exception being the dolomitic dikes at Wigu Hill). It has been pointed out (Rankama and Sahama, 1950, p. 430; Taylor *et al.*, 1956) that both the Na/K and K/Rb ratios decrease during the normal differentiation of a magma. Compared with the silicate lavas (Table V), however, the soda ashes and lavas have higher Na/K and K/Rb ratios, the inference being that these later eruptives are not differentiates of the earlier silicate rocks. Poole (1963) found that the 1960 lava contained 4.3 ppm thorium and 34.5 ppm uranium. The uranium and radium are in radioactive equilibrium, and the high content of uranium is noteworthy.

Mineralogically, the lavas consist of stumpy, prismatic crystals up to 1.5 mm

TABLE IV—*Sodium Carbonate lavas*

	1	2	3	4
SiO_2	Trace	Trace	1.18	1.12
TiO_2	0.10	0.08		
Al_2O_3	0.08	0.09	} 1.64	1.70
Fe_2O_2 (total)	0.26	0.32		
MnO	0.04	0.24	—	—
CaO	12.74	12.82	19.09	17.52
BaO	0.95	1.05	1.05	1.02
SrO	1.24	1.20	0.89	0.85
MgO	0.49	0.41	1.43	2.35
Na_2O	29.53	29.70	29.00	30.00
K_2O	7.58	6.58	6.90	7.50
P_2O_5	0.83	1.06	—	—
H_2O (total)	8.59	8.27	1.81	1.91
CO_2	31.75	32.40	31.98	30.73
F	2.69	1.84	—	—
CI	3.86	2.64	2.07	3.03
SO_3	2.00	2.18	2.79	2.88
S			0.08	0.13
	102.73	100.88	99.91	100.74
Less O for F, CI and S	2.00	1.36	0.57	0.75
	100.73	99.52	99.34	99.99

Trace elements in ppm		
Li	100	100
Ti	25	25
V	75	100
Rb	200	400
Nb	15	—
La	400	400

Cr, Ni, Co, Ga, Y, Zr were sought but not detected.
1. *Pahoehoe* lava extruded between October 1st and 8th, 1960.
2. *Aa* lava extruded 12.05 p.m. October 9th, 1960. (Major elements from Dawson (1962b). Trace elements from Bowden (1962)).
3. Lava L1 from uppermost flow, August 1961 (DuBois *et al.*, 1963).
4. Lava L4 collected very hot from flow beneath L1 (*ibid.*).

TABLE V

	Na/K	K/Rb
1	1.69	82
2	1.92	110
3	1.35	
4	2.16	
5	1.92	91
6	2.34	
7	2.45	
8	1.99	
9	2.16	
R2	4.37	
R3	4.14	
BD 114	3.48	315
BD 118	4.03	173

1–9 Oldoinyo Lengai silicate lavas (see Table II). R2 and R3 Soda-rich ejectementa (Table I).
Bd 114 and 118 Sodium carbonatite lavas 1 and 2 (Table IV).

long set in a brown-grey, turbid iosotropic matrix. The crystals are of a new mineral which has not yet been named, as investigations of the detailed crystallography and chemistry are not complete. On the prism faces the crystals exhibit high birefringence (third order greens and reds) but basal sections have low birefringence (first order greys) and show polysynthetic twinning; exsolution lamellae can be seen on some of the basal sections. The mineral is hexagonal, uniaxial negative; relief is low to moderate, all refractive indices being less than 1.54. Preliminary chemical tests indicate that the phenocryst mineral is a complex sodium calcium potassium carbonate sulphate chloride containing considerable amounts of barium and strontium. The groundmass is mainly hydrated sodium carbonate. Minute crystals occurring in the groundmass have been identified as fluorite.

GENESIS OF THE VOLCANO

The important features to be remembered in the genesis of Oldoinyo Lengai are:

(1) The extrusion of a Na, Ca, K carbonate magma from a carbonatite volcano; and

(2) evidence from the extruded rocks of a decreasing silica content during the successive eruptions, the trend being from ijolitic pyroclastics with nephelinites and phonolite →nephelinitic pyroclastics →melanephelinites → soda-rich carbonate ashes and lavas.

At the present time the hypotheses postulated for the genesis of carbonatites and their associated alkaline complexes may be divided into two groups:

(*a*) Hypotheses which assume a basic or ultrabasic parental magma which differentiates to carbonatite. This parent magma has been interpreted as pyroxenite (Davies, 1952), peridotite (Strauss and Truter, 1951); kimberlite (Saether, 1957; Garson 1961) and alkali peridotite or nephelinite (King and Sutherland, 1960, this volume, p. 121). It should be pointed out that some of these hypotheses have been based upon the well-documented fact that, hitherto, the residual carbonatite has been found to be calcitic or dolomitic with subordinate sideritic or ankeritic carbonate.

(*b*) Hypotheses in which carbonatites and their complexes are derived from primary carbonate magmas or carbon dioxide of unknown origin. v. Eckermann (1948), in the case of the Alnö Island Complex has proposed a potash-rich carbonate magma reacting with gneisses to give the fenites and ultra-alkaline basic plutonic rocks, with residual calcitic and dolomitic carbonatites. For the genesis of the ultrabasic potassic rocks of south western Uganda, however, Holmes (1950) has postulated a parental cafemic carbonatite magma. The concept of carbonatite magma has received support from Higazy (1954), Russell *et al.* (1955), von Knorring and DuBois (1961), and, on experimental evidence, from Wyllie and Tuttle (1960).

v. Eckermann's hypothesis (1948) of the existence of an alkaline carbonate magma was based partly on the necessity of some source for the alkalies introduced into the country rock during the fenitization process. His proposal has not gained general support since alkaline carbonate had never been found, and the workers who derived their carbonatites from ultrabasic parents have mainly cited rocks of the ijolitic suite as the source of the fenitization alkalies. The now proved existence of alkaline carbonate in magmatic form at Oldoinyo Lengai, strongly supports v. Eckermann's hypothesis, and gives a possible explanation of the phenomena seen around centres such as Chilwa Island, Toror and Panda Hill, and along certain carbonatite dikes (Fockema 1952; v. Eckermann, 1961) where the country rocks in direct contact with carbonatites have been fenitized without the intervention of ijolitic rocks. The soda carbonate ashes and lava on Oldoinyo Lengai have proved to be very soluble in water, and this could explain the absence of alkaline carbonate at older centres; they are preserved on Oldoinyo Lengai only because of their very recent age.

Starting with a parental magma of the approximate composition of the sodium carbonate lavas, Oldoinyo Lengai is believed to be the result of at least four main phases of carbonatite intrusion as follows:

Phase 1. Intrusion of a Na, K, Ca carbonatite magma into crystalline basement rocks with formation of a metasomatic envelope varying from 'granite' through fenites to melteigite, due mainly to the action of the alkaline carbonates. High pressure due to carbon dioxide released during this reaction causes the upper part of the envelope to be fragmented and ejected as the yellow pyroclastics. The interbedded phonolites and nephelinites are due to mobilization of chemically similar zones of the metasomatic envelope.

Phase 2. Intrusion of a carbonatite markedly richer in calcium (possibly a residuum from the Phase 1 carbonatite magma). Reaction with the already partly desilicated envelope results in the formation of rocks lower in silica which are erupted as the black nephelinitic pyroclastics. The higher calcium content of the carbonatite is reflected in the metasomatism of earlier rocks to give the wollastonitites, wollastonite ijolites and carbonatized urtite.

Phase 3. Similar to Phase 2 but silica contamination is even less and mela-nephelinites result.

Phase 4. Intrusion of Na, Ca, K carbonate magma. The envelope surrounding the magma chamber is now so desilicated, due to the earlier carbonatite stages, that the magma is virtually uncontaminated. It is erupted as the soda-rich carbonate ashes and lavas.

In summary, the volcano is believed to be the result of successive intrusions of carbonate magma, each intrusion being less contaminated with siliceous material than its predecessor. The sodium carbonate ashes and lavas are regarded as approximating to the uncontaminated parental magma of the sub-volcanic complex.

GENERAL CONSIDERATIONS

With the proved existence of magmatic alkali carbonate there is an indication of the source of the alkalies needed for the fenitization process. It is possible that variations in the soda and potash content of carbonatite magmas may account for the differences in fenitization, feldspathization and nephelinization seen around different carbonatite intrusions.

From the evidence of certain dikes mentioned above, in which it is apparent that the carbonatite is the source of the fenitization alkalis, it would appear that, relative to the cafemic fraction of a carbonate magma, the alkaline carbonates have a preferred or selective ability to react with 'granitic' wall-rock material.

Although no definite hypothesis has yet been advanced to explain the source of carbonatite magmas, v. Eckermann (1958) has suggested, '. . . the upper basalt level with the earth's crust as a possible locus where we have to look for the origin of the carbonatites and their associated rocks'. The close link between basaltic rocks and carbonatites is demonstrated by the fact that many carbonatites are erupted at the close of major periods of basaltic magmatism, examples being the Brazilian carbonatites, the Dorowa and Shawa Complexes of Rhodesia, and the Rangwa group of Kenya; Parsons (1961) has suggested that the Canadian carbonatites in the region east of Lake Superior may be related to the Keweenawan volcanism. The association is certainly very intimate in the case of the Neogene carbonatites of northern Tanganyika. Moreover, the concentration of carbonatite complexes within areas of crustal flexuring and rift faulting, previously pointed out by numerous authors, is clearly demonstrated in northern Tanganyika where the carbonatite centre lies very close to the western boundary fault of the Gregory Rift Valley (Fig. 1) or on major faults resulting from the same major phase of crustal warping.

These two features—the appearance of carbonatites at the close of major cycles of basaltic volcanic activity and the role played by major upwarping and the associated faulting—cannot be fortuitous. It is suggested that carbonatite magma accumulated during the extrusion of the earlier basaltic rocks, either by differentiation or by preferential gas streaming during migration of material into the zone from which the basalts were tapped. The irregular surface of the basaltic layer/crustal layer interface in the period immediately following major warping and/or faulting could lead to localization of the accumulated gases (possibly due to tilting of crustal blocks acting as gas traps), while the faults would provide access to higher parts of the crust and the earth's surface.

Acknowledgements. Dr. R. Pickering of the Tanganyika Geological Survey accompanied the writer on the descent into the active crater of Oldoinyo Lengai and assisted in the collection of the soda carbonatite lava. Messrs. W. K. L. Thomas, G. Luena, A. P. Muley and Dr. P. Bowden carried out some of the analyses. The Commissioner for Geological Survey, Tanganyika is gratefully acknowledged for permission to publish these analyses.

REFERENCES

Bowden, P., 1962, Trace elements in Tanganyika carbonatites: *Nature*, v. **196**, p. 570.
Davies, K. A., 1952, The building of Mount Elgon (East Africa): *Uganda Geol. Surv. Mem.* 7.
Dawson, J. B., 1962a, The geology of Oldoinyo Lengai; *Bull. Volcan.*, v. **24**, pp. 349–387.

Dawson, J. B., 1962b, Sodium carbonate lavas from Oldoinyo Lengai, Tanganyika: *Nature*, v. **195**, pp. 1075–1076.
Dawson, J. B., The Northern Province Volcanics, in Summary of the Geology of Tanganyika: *Tanganyika Geol. Surv. Mem.*, **1**, Pt. 4, *Petrology*, in press.
Dawson, J. B. and Sahama, Th. G., 1963, A note on parawollastonite from Oldoinyo Lengai, Tanganyika: *Schweiz. Min. Pet. Mitt.*, Parker Volume, v. **43**, pp. 131–133.
DuBois, C. G. B., Furst, J., Guest, N. J., and Jennings, D. J., 1963, Fresh natro carbonatite lava from Oldoinyo L'Engai, *Nature*, v. **197**, pp. 445–446.
v. Eckermann, H., 1948, The alkaline district of Alnö Island: *Sverig. Geol. Undersok.*, *Ser. Ca.* **36**.
v. Eckermann, H., 1958, The alkaline and carbonatite dikes of the Alnö formation on the mainland North-East of Alnö Island: *Kungl. Vetenskap. Akademiens Handl. Fjärdel*, *Ser.*, *Bd.* **7**, No. 2.
v. Eckermann, H., 1961, The petrogenesis of the Alnö alkaline rocks: *Geol. Inst. Univ. Uppsala Bull.*, v. **40**, pp. 25–36.
Fockema, R. A. P., 1952, The geology of the area around the confluence of the Elands and Crocodile Rivers: *Geol. Soc. S. Africa Trans.* v. **55**, pp. 155–171.
Garson, M. S., 1961, *The Tundulu Carbonatite Complex in Southern Nyasaland:* Ph.D. Thesis, University of Leeds, England.
Guest, N. J., 1953, *The Geology and Petrology of The Engaruka—Oldoinyo L'Engai—Lake Natron Area of Northern Tanganyika:* Ph.D. Thesis, University of Sheffield, England.
Guest, N. J., 1956, The volcanic activity of Oldoinyo Lengai 1954: *Tanganyika Geol. Surv. Rec.* 1954, v. **4**, pp. 56–59.
Guest, N. J., 1963, Description of exhibit of fresh 'natro-carbonatite' from Oldoinyo Lengai, Tanganyika: *Geol. Soc. London. Proc.*, No. 1606, pp. 54–57.
Higazy, R. A., 1954, Trace elements of volcanic ultrabasic potassic rocks of south western Uganda and adjoining parts of the Belgian Congo: *Geol. Soc. America Bull.*, v. **65**, pp. 39–70.
Holmes, A., 1950, Petrogenesis of katungite and its associates: *Am. Mineralogist*, v. **35**, pp. 772–792.
King, B. C. and Sutherland, D. L., 1960, Alkaline rocks of Eastern and Southern Africa: *Sci. Progress*, v. **47**, pp. 298–321, 504–524, 709–720.
v. Knorring, O. and DuBois, G. G. B., 1961, Carbonatitic lava from Fort Portal area in Western Uganda: *Nature*, v. **192**, pp. 1064–1065.
Parsons, G. E., 1961, Niobium-bearing complexes East of Lake Superior: *Ontario Dept. Mines, Geol. Rpt.* **3**.
Poole, J. H. J., 1953, Radioactivity of sodium carbonate lava from Oldoinyo Lengai, Tanganyika: *Nature.* v **198**, p. 1291.
Rankama, K. and Sahama, Th. G., 1950, *Geochemistry:* Chicago University of Chicago Press.
Reck, H., 1914, Oldoinyo Lengai, ein Tätiger Vulkan in Gebeite der Deutsch Ostafrikanischen Bruchstufe: *Branca Festschrift*, v. **12**, pp. 373–409.
Richard, J. J., 1942, Oldoinyo L'Engai. The 1940–1941 eruption. Volcanological observations in East Africa: *Jour. East Africa and Uganda Nat. Hist. Soc.*, v. **16**, pp. 89–108.
Richard, J. J. and van Padang, N., 1957, Catalogue of the active volcanoes of the world. Pt. 4, Africa and the Red Sea: *Naples.*
Russell, H. D., Hiemstra, S. A. and Groenveld, D., 1955, The mineralogy and petrology of the carbonatite at Loolekop, Eastern Transvaal: *Geol. Soc. S. Africa Trans.* v. **57**, pp. 197–208.
Saether, E., 1957, The alkaline rock province of the Fen area in Southern Norway: *Det. kgl. Norsk. Vid. Sel'sk. Skr.*, No. **1**.
Strauss, C. A. and Truter, F. C., 1951, The alkali complex at Spitzkop, Sekukuniland, Eastern Transvaal: *Geol. Soc. S. Africa Trans.* v. **53**, pp. 81–125.
Taylor, S. R., Emeleus, C. H. and Exley, C. S., 1953, Some anomolous K/Rb ratios in igneous rocks and their petrological significance: *Geochim. Cosmochim. Acta*, v. **10**, pp. 224–229.

Uhlig, C., 1907, Der sogennante gross Ostafrikanische Graben zwischen Magad (Natron See) und Lawa ya Mueri (Manyara See): *Geogr. Zeit.*, v. 13, pp. 478–505.

Wyllie, P. J. and Tuttle, O. F., 1960, The System CaO–CO$_2$–H$_2$O and the origin of carbonatites: *Jour. Petrology*, v. 1, pp. 1–46.

GERALDO C. MELCHER

The Carbonatites of Jacupiranga, São Paulo, Brazil

INTRODUCTION

During the last few years the existence of carbonatites has been recognized in several alkalic rock provinces in Brazil. Carbonate rocks, previously assumed to be sedimentary limestone that had been metamorphosed by subsilicic igneous rocks, are now being interpreted as intrusive carbonatites at some localities. The location of known alkalic rock occurrences in southern Brazil is shown on Fig. 1. Carbonatites are known to exist at Jacupiranga, Serrote, Itapirapuã, Araxá and Anitápolis. They probably occur also at Lajes, Tapira, Itatiaia and Catalão but at these localities the carbonate rocks are difficult to observe, due to deep weathering, and have not yet been studied in detail.

Jacupiranga is the classical Brazilian locality of undersaturated and ultrabasic rocks. Bauer (1877) discovered the district and the first descriptions were made by Derby (1891) and Hussak (1892, 1895, 1904). Later many references were made to Jacupiranga, especially by R. A. Daly and J. S. Shand, who cited it as an example of the limestone syntexis theory. Melcher (1954) mapped the area and many striking similarities to African carbonatites were noted. The discovery of a phosphate deposit by Knecht (1940, 1948) and the mining of the residual weathered mantle that capped the limestone has now exposed almost the whole carbonatite area and permitted its detailed observation and sampling (Melcher, 1962). Furthermore, from 1961 to 1964 the economic potential of the unweathered carbonates was investigated by underground workings and drill holes.

REGIONAL GEOLOGY

The alkalic complex of Jacupiranga occurs at the contact of tightly folded mica schists and a syntectonic granodiorite belt, belonging to the Precambrian Açungui series which extends over a large area along the coast in southern São Paulo and eastern Paraná. The general strike of the metamorphic rocks is SW–NE. With the exception of the three alkalic plugs of Jacupiranga, Serrote and Itapirapuã, several small acid intrusions and diabase dikes related to the triassic Paraná basalt flows, no younger igneous rocks are known in the area. Major tectonic features, such as rift valleys, which could be of significance for the location of the intrusions, are suspected to exist, but the regional geology is not yet known with enough detail to permit their positive identification.

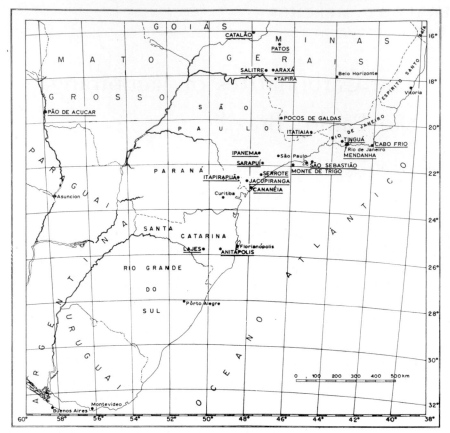

Fig 1. Map of southern Brazil showing the location of alkalic igneous rock occurrences. Some localities are known by several names or include more than one occurrence. Patos is also known as Coromandel; Araxá as Barreiro; Salitre includes the neighbouring intrusion of Serra Negra; Mendanha the alkalic rocks of Marapicú and Gericinó; São Sebastião the island of Buzios; Ipanema is also designated as Araçoiaba, and Serrote has been described as Juquiá.

ALKALIC ROCKS

The oval shaped igneous complex (Fig. 2), underlies an area of about 65 sq km. Leucocratic alkalic rocks surround the basic types and form two major bodies east and west of the main body. At some contacts nephelinization of the Precambrian country rocks can be observed. The quartz content decreases, biotite is replaced by a sodic pyroxene and feldspars recrystallize around their margins. Where fenitization is more advanced, quartz is absent, feldspars recrystallize completely into soda-orthoclase or anorthoclase, and nepheline and small amounts of calcite appear. In the less altered varieties the attitude of the metamorphic rocks is sometimes preserved.

Peridotites occur in the northern part of the intrusion and consist of fine-grained olivine (Fo_{90}), partly altered into serpentine. Near the margin of the dunitic body and to the south the proportion of pyroxene increases and the rocks grade into members of the ijolite–jacupirangite series. The relative amounts of nepheline and pyroxene also vary gradually. The pyroxene of the ijolites is more or less sodic, but is common augite in the pyroxenites. Typical jacupirangites surround

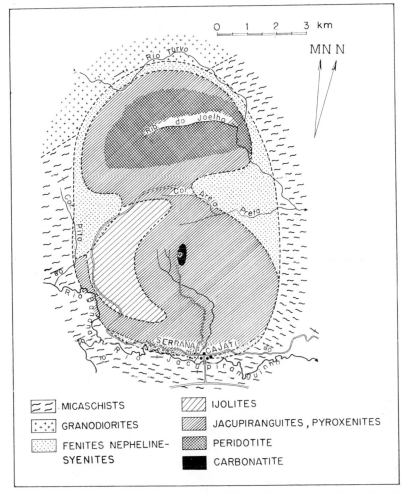

MICASCHISTS

GRANODIORITES

FENITES NEPHELINE-
SYENITES

IJOLITES

JACUPIRANGUITES, PYROXENITES

PERIDOTITE

CARBONATITE

Fig. 2. Geological map of the Jacupiranga alkalic complex. Reproduced
from Melcher (1954).

the carbonatite plug and consist almost exclusively of titanaugite and magnetite, with a small amount of nepheline and biotite. In many places this rock exhibits parallel structure.

Many essexite, ijolite, monchiquite and tinguaite dikes cut irregularly through the whole area but cannot be mapped in detail because of the deep weathering mantle.

It seems probable that two separate intrusive stages occurred within the basic complex. In its northern half the peridotitic body was first emplaced and then surrounded by pyroxenites. South of this and partly cutting it, the almost circular jacupirangite plug was intruded, and partly differentiated into the concentric, crescent-shaped ijolite body. The carbonatites occupy a central position in this later intrusion. The areas east and west of the contact between the two main intrusions seem to have been more favourable for the location of leucocratic alkalic rocks, which probably are mostly rheomorphically mobilized fenites.

GENERAL STRUCTURE OF THE CARBONATITES

The carbonatites crop out on an oval shaped hill 1000 by 400 m, called Morro da Mina, which has a maximum elevation of 225 m above sea level (Fig. 3). The lowest contact between carbonatite and jacupirangite is 70 m above sea level, and diamond drilling shows that the carbonatite body extends to at least 60 m below sea level. The carbonatite body has a highly irregular karst topography, which results from differential leaching of the carbonates, particularly along radial and concentric joints. In many places these joints form an evenly spaced grid and provide channel ways for surface waters, leaving a series of pinnacles or pyramids of fresh carbonatite, 3–20 m high, the space between them being filled with residual weathered material.

The contact between carbonatites and jacupirangites can be well observed at the southern part of the area, although the jacupirangites are always partly decomposed by weathering. The contact has a steep dip, slightly outwards from the carbonatite. This and the fact that the E–W diameter of the plug on the surface is smaller near the top of the hill than at the lower parts, indicates that the intrusion has a conical form in depth. The mineralogy and texture of both the carbonatites and the jacupirangites show no change away from the contact, and there is no evidence of metamorphism or metasomatism, except for the possible carbonatization of jacupirangites indicated by small amounts of calcite in a few unweathered outcrops.

The carbonatite is cut by numerous dikes, 0.1–1.0 m thick, made up of carbonate minerals, apatite, phlogopite and magnetite in varying proportions. In some places the dike minerals are oriented parallel to the walls of the dikes (Fig. 5). The dip is always near vertical, but owing to the subtle differences in grain size and proportions of the accessory minerals, it is usually difficult to distinguish the dikes from the wall rocks and to map them accurately.

Three larger and many smaller, almost vertical faults cut the carbonatite (Fig. 3). Their displacement was also vertical but the slip cannot be determined. These faults do not extend beyond the carbonatite. Their planes were especially favourable for the circulation of later solutions, which widened them, the openings being filled by apatite and magnetite, partly cemented by secondary iron-stained reddish carbonates. The southernmost of the larger faults cuts almost the whole carbonatite body and is filled by a 1m thick breccia, with angular fragments of different carbonatite varieties cemented by calcite. Another large breccia occurs on the east end of the contact between the two main carbonatite intrusions.

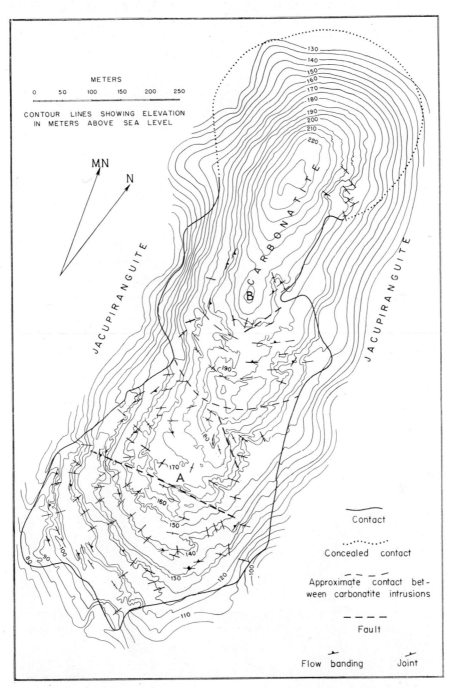

Fig. 3. Geological map of the Morro da Mina carbonatites. The letters A and B are at the approximate centres of the two carbonatite plugs.

G

The most conspicuous structural feature of the whole carbonatite body are the many joints. In the southern part there is a clear radial and concentric system, which has its centre approximately at point A (Fig. 3). The radial joints are all subvertical but the concentric joints have dips that vary from 40–80°, all

Fig. 4. Olivine-rich carbonatite showing flow structure. Fig. 5. Carbon-atite with parallel stringers of magnetite. At the right of the pick a 10 cm thick carbonatite dike fills a fault. The dike contains magnetite and olivine, and also shows parallel structure.

towards the centre of the intrusion. A similar arrangement can be observed at the northern part, with centre at point B.

At many outcrops the carbonatite has a clear planar or linear structure. Either some minerals, as mica and apatite show parallel arrangement or the dark accessories, mica, olivine and magnetite are concentrated in layers which alternate with bands of almost pure carbonates (Figs. 4, 5). Sometimes these bands curve around jacupirangite xenoliths. Most probably they can be interpreted as flow structures. Their orientation is usually parallel to the concentric, inward dipping joints and also indicates a conical structure of the whole carbonatite bodies, although local irregularities are common.

PETROGRAPHY OF THE CARBONATITES

The carbonatites of Morro da Mina are typical sövites, made up predominantly of medium- to coarse-grained calcite. On fresh outcrops the dark minerals are

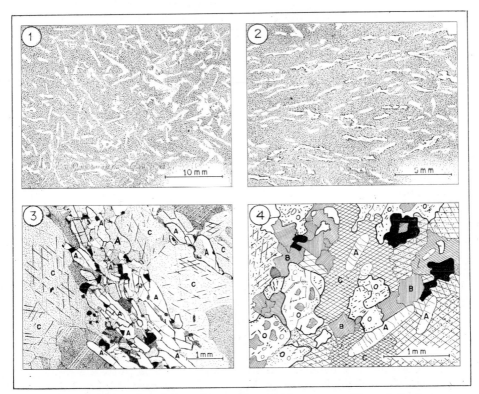

Fig. 6. 1. Apatite sövite with pseudo-ophitic texture. The calcite has been stained with silver nitrate and potassium chromate.
2. Stained apatite sövite. The apatite prisms (white) show oriented texture due to flowage.
3. Typical carbonatite crossed by a small apatite-rich vein.
4. Carbonatite rich in olivine and biotite. Note the corrosion of the olivines by the carbonates.

readily distinguished, concentrated either in bands or in irregular clusters. Apatite stands out on slightly leached surfaces and sometimes forms aggregates in veinlets a few centimetres thick. The peculiar granular texture of the rock can be observed by staining the carbonates with silver nitrate and potassium chromate (Fig. 6). It is very similar to an ophitic texture, with calcite in the place of pyroxene and dolomite or apatite in the place of plagioclase. The texture may also be oriented, probably due to flowing.

The minerals occurring in the rock are calcite, dolomite, apatite, magnetite, forsterite, serpentine, clinohumite, phlogopite, pyrite, pyrrhotite, galena, ilmenite, spinel, pyrochlore, baddeleyite, barite and perovskite.

Calcite occurs in xenomorphic crystals with diameters of 0.1–1 cm. Twinning is common and frequently the lamellae are curved. Many crustal boundaries are recemented by homogeneous unstrained calcite. A peculiar feature of some carbonates in the sövite is the occurrence of many, very small (0.01–0.03 mm in diameter) worm-like empty channels, which sometimes lend the aspect of a graphic texture to the rock. Separation of the carbonates with heavy liquids showed that the proportion of dolomite is always somewhat lower than the values that were calculated from the chemical analyses. Probably the calcite contains some dolomite.

Eighty per cent of representative surface samples from the carbonatite contain 5–15 per cent apatite, which is the most important accessory mineral. It occurs with two distinct habits: (a) small isolated ovoid-shaped grains within the carbonate minerals, with a diameter of 0.1–1 mm. These apatite crystals usually are slightly rounded and corroded. Davies (1956) observed a similar habit of apatite from the Sukulu and Tororo carbonatites. (b) Idiomorphic prisms, 1–5 mm in diameter, in parallel aggregates. These aggregates form either rounded clusters or, more frequently, veinlets or schlieren with a thickness of several centimetres within the carbonatite. Frequently some of the apatite crystals are broken, the fragments slightly displaced and the intervals filled with calcite. Small liquid and gas inclusions are common. The apatite contains 42.2 per cent P_2O_5; and 55.3 per cent CaO. The specific gravity is 3.11 and the optical characteristics $n_\varepsilon = 1.635$, $n_\omega = 1.638$. It is therefore probably largely fluorapatite, but with some hydroxyl-apatite.

Magnetite and ilmenite are ubiquitous in the carbonatite, frequently associated with the apatite concentrations. Most of the titano-magnetite crystals have diameters from 0.2–4 mm. Their shape is usually irregular and intergrowths with apatite are common. Maghemite partly substitutes the magnetite. Ilmenite occurs exclusively within the magnetite, either as thin exsolution lamellae or as irregular corroded inclusions. Chemical analysis of a pure titano-magnetite concentrate showed 90.4 per cent Fe_2O_3; 1.8 per cent MgO; 1.3 per cent Al_2O_3; 0.7 per cent, MnO_2; 0.4 per cent CaO; and 2.5 per cent TiO_2. v. Eckermann (1948) noted the high proportion of other spinel molecules (15–20 per cent) in the titano-magnetite from Alnö. Russell, Hiemstra and Groeneveld (1954) also published an analysis of the magnetite from Palabora, which contains 2.5 per cent MgO; 0.75 per cent Al_2O_3; and 0.55 per cent V_2O_5.

A green phlogopite mica occurs in thick tabular to short prismatic crystals.

Its optical characteristics are $n_\alpha = 1.573$, n_β and $n_\gamma = 1.604$, $2V = 5–10°$, weak colour absorption.

The olivine is a very common accessory and is almost pure forsterite (Fo_{98} Fa_2) as determined both by the optical characteristics and x-ray analysis. It is always partly serpentinized and many crystals have a rounded, irregular surface, due to corrosion and substitution by carbonates (Fig. 6). Red clinohumite occurs in frequent association with the olivine.

A peculiar, dark, shiny iron sulphide occurs in flat tabular crystals, which gave an x-ray pattern similar but not identical to pyrrhotite. It is strongly radioactive owing to the presence of uranium. Further studies will be necessary to establish the exact identity of this mineral.

Pyrochlore is a rare accessory in some parts of the carbonatite, seldom exceeding 0.1 per cent in surface samples. It occurs in the same areas as the unidentified iron sulphide which is readily detectable by stronger radioactivity. The pyrochlore forms yellow to brown dodecahedra (0.05–1.0 mm in diameter) combined with octahedra and cubes. Most crystals are imperfect, very friable, and have pitted surfaces, resulting from intergrowth with apatite. The mineral is metamict but gives a typical pyrochlore x-ray diffraction pattern after being heated to 600° C for an hour. Thermoluminescence of a strong orange colour is produced above 250°C. The specific gravity is 4.8, slightly higher than the values of 4.2–4.4 of normal pyrochlore. The mineral is strongly radioactive owing to a high uranium content, with thorium practically absent. It may be classified as an intermediate member between pyrochlore and microlite.

The baddeleyite from Jacupiranga was discovered by Hussak (1892), who described the mineral and proposed the name brazilite, but assumed that it contained niobium and tantalum. Later, however, a chemical analysis showed that it consisted of zirconium and was identical with the baddeleyite from Ceylon, which had been described in the meantime. In the carbonatite baddeleyite is always associated with pyrochlore, and occurs as small plates attached to or partly intergrown with the pyrochlore dodecahedra, parallel to the cubic planes.

CHEMICAL COMPOSITION

A grid was established and more than 400 representative samples were taken to determine the variations in chemical composition of the carbonatites. The contents of the more important oxides, with the exception of calcium oxide, are shown in Fig. 7. The average values for the whole area are: 4.58 per cent P_2O_5; 2.89 per cent Fe_2O_3; and 1.24 per cent MgO. Average samples made up by 20 or more chips collected from 20 by 20 m squares did not bring out any systematic relationship between the major elements, since different carbonatite varieties often were included in one sample. However, analysis of individual fragments showed a consistent parallelism between P_2O_5 and Fe_2O_3. The southern carbonatite body has a core that is comparatively poor in phosphorus, surrounded by somewhat irregular areas of higher grade. The distribution of iron is given in percentage of Fe_2O_3 although it occurs mainly as Fe_3O_4, and shows no apparent systematic pattern. The most striking difference in composition

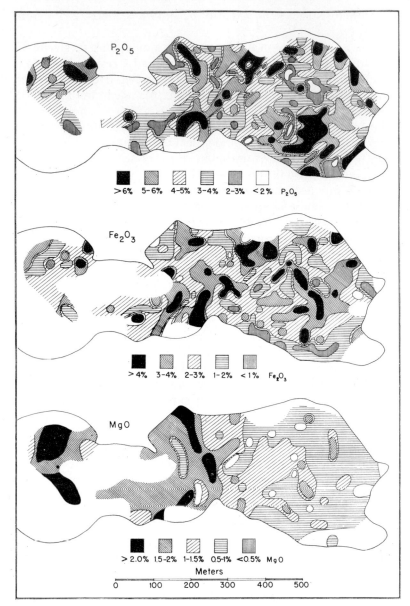

Fig. 7. Maps of the carbonatite showing distribution of P_2O_5, Fe_2O_3 and
MgO on part of the surface.

between the northern and the southern carbonatite plugs is their content of
magnesium. The average value for the southern intrusion is about 0.8 per cent
MgO; compared to approximately 2.0 per cent MgO in the northern plug. It is
also interesting to note that most of the higher values of the first intrusion are
situated in an almost circular zone around the centre.

Calcium oxide and carbon dioxide make up most of the balance of the analyses of the carbonatite, with carbon dioxide sometimes occurring slightly in excess of the calculated values allowed for carbonate minerals.[1] Except for samples which contain olivine and mica concentrations, the carbonatite averages less than 1 per cent SiO_2. The magnetite contains 2.7 per cent TiO_2, which corresponds to 0.08 per cent TiO_2 in the rock.

Among the rarer elements, niobium, tantalum and zirconium total less than 0.05 per cent of most rock samples and always occur together in intergrowth of pyrochlore and baddeleyite. The tantalum: niobium ratio of 1:4 is unusually high for pyrochlores from carbonatites. An interesting chemical feature of the Jacupiranga carbonatites is the presence of about 0.003 per cent uranium and total absence of thorium. The distribution of barium in different samples is very erratic but never exceeds 0.1 per cent Ba. Small quantities of lead (about 0.005 per cent) occur usually in samples which contain pyrochlore and baddeleyite. Rare earth elements are practically absent.

In comparison to the Scandinavian and most African carbonatite occurrences, the Jacupiranga carbonatite has an unusually simple and homogeneous composition. The average content of silica is extremely low owing to the scarcity of silicates, but the P_2O_5 values are somewhat higher than at most known carbonatites.

INTRUSION OF THE JACUPIRANGA CARBONATITES

The carbonatites of Morro da Mina offer an interesting example of the successive emplacement of two carbonatite plugs at one locality.

The present level of erosion most probably was at considerable depth below the surface at the time of magmatic activity. No extrusive rocks are found in the area or its surroundings.

The Precambrian rocks of the Açungui series have been deeply eroded since the Tertiary, with a relief now of over 1200 m in the coastal range of São Paulo and Paraná. The intrusion probably took place at a time when the Precambrian formations were still covered by Paleozoic and Mesozoic sediments which today are only seen farther inland. The alkalic rocks also may have cut part of these sediments. The total amount of erosion to reach the present level at Jacupiranga would then have been over 1500 m. It is interesting to note that the Serrote carbonatite, 50 km NE of Jacupiranga, occupies a very similar topographic position; the Itapirapuã carbonatite, at an elevation of 400–500 m also intrudes Precambrian rocks, but lies only a few kilometres from the contact with Devonian sediments. At Ipanema no carbonatites are found but alkalic and basic igneous rocks cut through Carboniferous sediments. It is quite possible, however, that some of these intrusions belong to different age groups, as is the case with the African carbonatites.

Several phonolite dikes that must be related to the alkalic rocks of Jacupiranga, are found in the basement rocks, a few kilometres from the intrusion, at elevations of 600–700 m. No radial or concentric carbonatite dikes cut either jacupirangites or the surrounding basement.

The structure and the homogeneous constitution of the two adjoining carbon-

---

[1] See also v. Eckermann, this volume p. 19.

atite plugs point to cooling under tranquil conditions, without large scale movement. Fluidal structures are developed mainly in the outer parts of the plugs
and may be the result of some movement at a time when the rock was not yet
wholly consolidated. Broken apatite crystals that have been re-cemented by
carbonates, and twinned and deformed calcite grains also are found in the
peripheral areas and indicate some dynamic strain on already solid rock. On
the other hand, at one time during their emplacement the carbonatites had
sufficient movement and viscosity to incorporate and carry the large jacupirangite xenoliths.

In the light of what is known at present, the cooling history of the carbonatites
may be tentatively summarized as follows: in a magmatic conduit with a cross-
section corresponding to the southern plug, the carbonatites ascended as a
partial or total melt. Either crystallization had already started at greater depth
or proceeded from the walls inwards, while some movement was still going on.
Pyrochlore and baddeleyite are early-formed minerals, together with olivine.
The apatite of the first generation then crystallized simultaneously with calcite,
the carbonates partly corroding the olivine. Phlogopite and part of the magnetite also belong to this stage. It seems likely that some fractionation took place
on a small scale, with the formation of a rest fluid enriched in phosphorus, fluorine, some iron and sulphur. This produced the small veinlets of apatite, magnetite and sulphides that cut the carbonatite generally parallel, but in some cases
discordant to the flow structure. The whole process must have been one of rapid
solidification rather than slow cooling, since no settling of crystals occurred, no
difference in grain size or composition between the inner core and the contact
zone is observed, and no extensive reaction with the wall rocks or the xenoliths
took place.

The second carbonatite plug was intruded at a later stage and then crystallized
in a similar manner. It also must have acquired its present homogeneous
composition at a deeper level of the crust and it seems remarkable that it is
practically identical in composition with the first intrusion, except that the second
always shows a small but consistently higher content of magnesium.

There is little evidence in Jacupiranga that would support the hypothesis of
metasomatic or pneumatolitic origin of the carbonatites. Although the carbonate
melt reacted with the olivine on a small scale, the carbonatization of a large
mass of jacupirangite is hardly conceivable. This would call for the removal of an
enormous amount of silica and also the substitution of magnesium by calcium
through some unknown process.

The potassium-argon age of two phlogopite samples from the carbonatite was
determined by Amaral, Cordani, Kawashita and Reynolds in the new laboratory
at the University of São Paulo. The results were 151 and 134 million years,
placing the intrusion in the Upper Jurassic or Lower Cretaceous.

PHOSPHATE DEPOSITS

Solution of the carbonate minerals on the surface of the carbonatite and chemical
weathering of the silicates produced a 1–10 m thick residual soil blanket which

covers the irregular surface of the fresh rock. Apatite and magnetite are more resistant to weathering and were incorporated into the soil, which averages 22 per cent P_2O_5; and 26 per cent Fe_2O_3. This phosphate ore is being mined and concentrated by washing and magnetic separation. The annual production averages 50,000 tons of phosphate concentrate with 39 per cent P_2O_5.

The apatite appears to be very little altered by the weathering process and the same ovoid-shaped crystals that occur in the fresh carbonatite also are found in the residual ore. Many of the phosphate grains are covered by a thin coating of iron oxides. Conversely, some of the magnetite crystals are enclosed in a shell of secondary iron-rich phosphates.

Baddeleyite and pyrochlore are chemically resistant but very fine-grained and the niobate is so friable that it crumbles into minus 200 mesh fragments upon washing. These minerals are enriched in the soil compared to their content in the underlying carbonatite, but the total amount of ore is small and the grade too low to justify any attempt to recover them economically.

The unweathered carbonatite is a large potential source of phosphates and of limestone for the manufacture of cement, since 100 million tons of rock could easily be mined. Extensive ore dressing experiments were conducted and led to the development of a froth flotation process by which phosphate concentrates with 38 per cent P_2O_5 and carbonate tailings with less than 1.0 per cent P_2O_5; were produced. A pilot plant was constructed in 1962 and successfully operated, confirming the feasibility of this process.

REFERENCES

Davies, K. A., 1956, The geology of part of South-East Uganda: *Uganda Geol. Surv. Mem.*, **8**.

Derby, O. A., 1891, The magnetite ore districts of Jacupiranga and Ipanema, São Paulo, Brazil: *Am. Jour. Sci.*, v. **41**, pp. 311–321.

v. Eckermann, H., 1948, The alkaline district of Alnö Island: *Sveriges Geol. Undersök.*, ser. *Ca*, **36**.

Hussak, E., 1892, Ueber Brazilit, ein neues Tantal (Niob) Mineral von der Eisenmine Jacupiranga: *Neues Jahrb. Min. Geol. Pal.*, v. **2**, pp. 141–159.

Hussak, E., 1895, Ueber den Baddelit (syn. Brazilit) von der Eisenmine in Jacupiranga in São Paulo: *Tschermaks Min. Petr. Mitt.*, pp. 395–411.

Hussak, E., 1904, Ueber die microstructur einiger brasilianischer Titanmagneteisensteine: *Neues Jahrb. Min. Geol. Pal.*, Jg. 1904, v. **1**, pp. 94–113.

Knecht, T., 1934, Os minerais e minérios do Estado de São Paulo: *Boletim de Agricultura*, ser., **32**, pp. 237–323.

Knecht, T., 1939, As ocorrencias de minérios de ferro e pirita no Estado de São Paulo: *Bol. Inst. Geogr. Geol.*, No. **25**, São Paulo.

Knecht, T., 1940, Os minérais nao metálicos do Estado de São Paulo: *Bol. Inst. Geogr. Geol.*, No. **27**, São Paulo.

Knecht, T., 1948, Novas ocorencias nos municipos do Extremo Sudoeste Paulista: *Min. e Met.*, v. **13**, No. 73, Rio de Janeiro.

Melcher, G. C., 1954, Nota sôbre o distrito alcalino de Jacupiranga, São Paulo: *Div. Geol. Min.*, *Notas. Prelim.*, No. **84**, Rio de Janeiro.

Russell, H. T., Hiemstra, S. A. and Groeneveld, D., 1954, The mineralogy and petrology of the carbonatite at Loolekop, Eastern Transvaal: *Geol. Soc. S. Africa, Trans.* v. **57**, pp. 197–208.

W. WIMMENAUER

The Eruptive Rocks and Carbonatites of the Kaiserstuhl, Germany

INTRODUCTION

This work is essentially a summary of the author's previous publications on the petrography of the Kaiserstuhl (Wimmenauer, 1957–1963). Geological and petrographical details, rock and mineral analyses, and detailed bibliographies are to be found there. For general geological and topographical orientation, the 'Geologische Exkursionskarte des Kaiserstuhls' at 1:25,000 published by the Geologisches Landesamt in Baden-Württemberg is recommended (available from the Landesvermessungsamt Baden-Württemberg, Stuttgart).

A publication of the mineralogy-geochemistry division of *EURATOM* (van Wambeke *et al.* 1964) gives many new geochemical, mineralogical and geophysical data concerning the Kaiserstuhl. Some of the most important mineralogical and petrographical contributions of this group were made available for the present work through the kindness of Dr. van Wambeke, which is gratefully acknowledged.

GEOLOGICAL SYNOPSIS

The tertiary eruptive province of Central Europe

The tertiary eruptive province of central Europe extends from eastern France over large parts of Germany and Czechoslovakia as far as Silesia. Among the major volcanic centres of the province are the Eifel, Westerwald, Vogelsberg, Hessian Highlands, Rhön, Duppau Range and Bohemian Mittelgebirge. In these regions predominantly basaltic lavas were emitted, characterized by a more or less distinctly alkaline trend of differentiation. On the fringes of the province and between the larger centres mentioned there are in addition a great number of smaller volcanoes, dikes and volcanic necks. They are composed, for the most part, especially in eastern France and southern Germany, of olivine nephelinite and melilite ankaratrite and related variants.

The Kaiserstuhl lies near the SW boundary of the province in the Tertiary Upper Rhein Graben between the Vosges Mountains and the Black Forest. The volcanic activity can be dated, with great probability, as middle Miocene (Burdigalian to Helvetian). Furthermore, the main period of Tertiary volcanism in central Europe occurs in the Miocene, but significantly older occurrences are

Corrected page 183 for Tuttle & Gittins/CARBONATITES

also known (e.g. Katzenbuckel near Heidelberg, with an age of 66×10^6 years according to the K–Ar method; Lippolt, Gentner and Wimmenauer, 1963). On the other hand the volcanism of the Eifel extends into the Holocene.

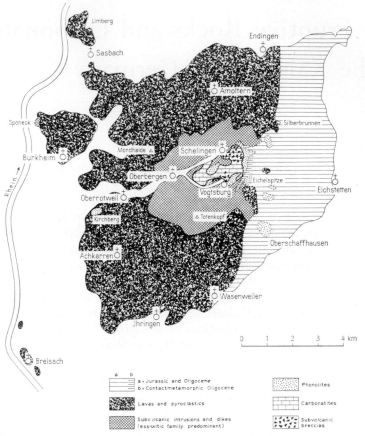

Fig. 1.   Simplified geological sketch map of the Kaiserstuhl, without loess cover.

The geological structure and the development of the Kaiserstuhl

The Kaiserstuhl lies about 15 km NW of Freiburg im Breisgau in the Upper Rhein Graben, which is a plain approximately 40 km wide at this point.

It has been established by drilling that about 1200 m of old Tertiary and 800 m of Mesozoic deposits underlie the volcanics and rest on pre-Hercynian gneiss and Hercynian granites, which at depth connect the two basement blocks, the Vosges Mountains and the Black Forest.

The Kaiserstuhl has a roughly rhombic outline with a major axis of nearly 16 km in a SW–NE direction and maximum width in a SE–NW direction of approximately 12.5 km. The most important topographic feature is the horse-shoe shaped main ridge, which is open to the west and reaches a height of 557 m in the Todtenkopf. The altitude of the surrounding plain is between 170 and

200 m. In the immediate vicinity of the Rhein lie the small volcanic hills of Limberg and Luetzelberg and of Breisach, which are separated from the Kaiserstuhl proper by Quaternary alluvium.

More than three quarters of the Kaiserstuhl hills is covered by loess, which may reach a maximum depth of 30 m. Because of this, only an approximate reconstruction of the geological structure is possible.

Three major geological units can be distinguished (Fig. 1):

   I. The sedimentary platform in the east (predominantly Oligocene and some Jurassic).
  II. The Kaiserstuhl volcano itself (lavas and tuffs).
 III. The Centre, composed of subvolcanic rocks. To the subvolcanic formations belong also the phonolite stocks and numerous intrusive dikes appearing in units I and II outside the Centre.

The sedimentary platform in the eastern Kaiserstuhl is composed of calcareous sandstone, marls and clays of Oligocene age. On the easternmost fringe of the range Dogger rocks also occur. The stratigraphic succession of Oligocene in the Kaiserstuhl, according to Hasemann (1959) extends from the lower Sannoisian, through the Pechelbronner, up to the Meletta beds and the Cyrena marls of the Upper Stampian. From the unconnected exposures, it is possible to reconstruct an arch whose culmination lies in the vicinity of the subvolcanic centre. In the individual cases the stratification is very irregular. The direction and sense of the faults, which must have caused considerable disarrangement of individual fault blocks is not discernible. This tectonism appears to be chiefly prevolcanic. Since the tuffs and lavas of the earliest volcanic phases lie on various units of the Oligocene, it is assumed that there is an erosion phase between the tectonic disturbances and the beginning of volcanism.

Between the platform and the subvolcanic centre, there is a contact metamorphic zone in the Oligocene up to 100 m wide.

The formation of the Kaiserstuhl volcano begins in the eastern part of the mountain range with accumulation of polygenetic tuffs and breccias which lie directly on the prevolcanic erosion surface in the Oligocene sediments. Among the volcanic fragments are carbonatites and carbonate fenites. Lava flows and tuffs of predominantly leucite tephrite composition overlie the polygenetic tuffs. These constitute the largest volume of rocks in the Kaiserstuhl and make up a complex stratovolcano of numerous alternating layers. The remains still surviving today give only an incomplete impression of the former external form, height and extent of the volcano. Petrographic and volcanological differences lead to the conclusion that several eruptive centres existed, each with its own character and history of development. Thus, the volcano of Sponeck-Burkheim, recently examined by Keller (1964), is characterized by the occurrence of tephrite sills and several phases of activity interrupted by dormant periods during which differentiation took place in the volcanic vent. According to drilling and geophysical data the lava flows extend beneath the Rhein alluvium for several kilometres to the west and south.

From the stratification of the lavas and tuffs, it is further evident that there are deeper and older volcanics to the east and higher and younger volcanics to the west. The younger lavas in the peripheral part of the western Kaiserstuhl also differ in composition from the older ones; they include olivine-bearing tephrite, limburgite, alkali feldspar nephelinite and olivine nephelinite. In Breisach, near the Sponeck and on the Limberg, these rocks are interlayered with minor phonolitic tuffs. Especially on the Limberg olivine nephelinite, limburgite and alkali feldspar nephelinite lavas as well as polygenetic and phonolitic tuffs accumulated in abruptly changing succession. The pyroclastics contain fragments of carbonate fenite and carbonatite just as do the polygenetic tuffs of Wasenweiler. Fifteen metres of Miocene marls, calcareous sandstones and conglomerates are interbedded with the volcanic series.

The intrusive magmatic activity in the subvolcanic centre probably began at a time when surface volcanism persisted. The phonolites and related rocks of the Badberg and the eastern part of the main ridge belong to the oldest components. Whether the phonolite stocks in the eastern Kaiserstuhl and on the Kirchberg are of the same age as these oldest phonolites, can not as yet be decided. Certainly they are older than the dike suite of the essexites.

Following the oldest phonolites in the centre are the intrusions of the essexite-theralite subvolcanic rocks. The form and size of the intrusive body or bodies of this phase have been so modified by massive younger dike-formation and the emplacement of carbonatites that a reconstruction is hardly possible any longer. The contact of the essexite intrusions of the centre with the lavas is nowhere directly visible; instead, numerous dike equivalents (essexite and theralite por-phyrites) cut the lavas. A smaller essexite intrusion cuts the lavas and tuffs near Sponeck castle in the extreme west of the Kaiserstuhl.

The dike rocks which belong to the essexite family (essexite and theralite porphyrites, monchiquites, monzonite porphyries, etc.), are for the most part younger than the essexite intrusive rocks. A part of the older essexite por-phyrites of the centre can perhaps be interpreted as the marginal facies of the essexites.

The dikes of this group are especially abundant in the centre, so that often dikes are crowded against one another over distances of tens of metres, in which case the oldest essexite country rock is limited to remnants and wedges of a few metres extent. Even north and south of the centre, in the region of the lavas numerous closely spaced dikes appear. The generally parallel trend of the dikes is obviously caused by frequently repeated tensional movements normal to the predominant regional strikes (N–S and NW–SE).

Subvolcanic breccias occur more extensively in the central Kaiserstuhl, especially in the immediate vicinity of the carbonatites. They are composed chiefly of fragments of the subvolcanic rocks (essexites, phonolites, dike rocks); in some places they also contain fragments of carbonatites. According to Hubaux (1964) there is a direct causal relationship between the formation of the breccias and the intrusion of the carbonatites.

Carbonate rocks occupy an area of about 1 sq km in the central Kaiserstuhl; they make up large parts of the Badberg, the Haselschacher Buck and the

Orberg. The interpretation of the whole carbonate complex as carbonatite intrusions, which the author has held since 1958, is based on numerous observations in the Kaiserstuhl itself and also on comparisons with similar rocks in other regions (Wimmenauer, 1959c, 1962a).

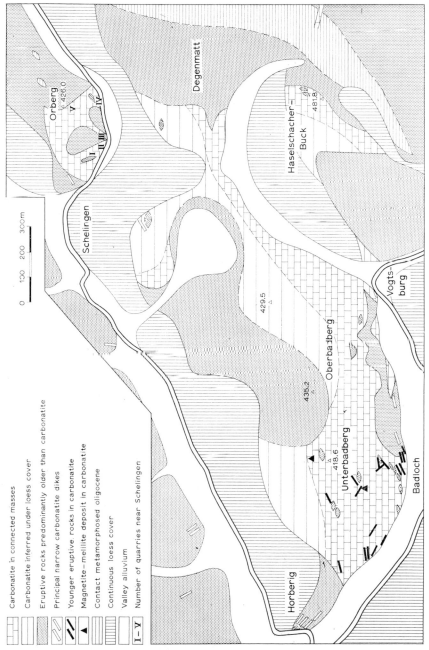

Fig. 2. Simplified geological sketch map of the central Kaiserstuhl.

Arguments supporting the carbonatite interpretation are:

(*a*) Intrusive behaviour in relation to the predominant rocks of the centre.
(*b*) Occurrence of inclusions of the older country rocks.
(*c*) Alteration of the country rock (biotitization and carbonatization).
(*d*) The geochemical properties.
(*e*) Certain macrostructural phenomena.

The situation, form and size of the carbonatite intrusions of the centre can be understood from the map (Fig. 2).

The intrusive behaviour is immediately evident in several cases. The best known example is the dike about 10 metres wide in quarry III near Schelingen (Metschke, 1938).[1] The carbonatite which borders the dike on the west and dips gently ESE also has an intrusive relationship to the surrounding subvolcanic breccias. Thinner carbonatite dikes are also numerous in other places. The large limestone mass of the Badberg can also be interpreted as a sheet dipping steeply to the north. It breaks through the assemblage of older eruptive rocks in its vicinity (essexites, phonolites, essexite porphyrites, subvolcanic breccias); the carbonatites are not cut by apophyses of these rocks, but, on the contrary, contain inclusions of them.

Numerous narrower carbonatite dikes cut the eruptive rocks of the centre; they are younger than all the other rocks of the region. Individual dikes of this group even occur on the east slope of the Kaiserstuhl; the phonolite stock of the Kirchberg contains one narrow dike and two others have been discovered by Deutzmann in the vicinity of the stock.

Inclusions of the older country rocks support the intrusive carbonatite interpretation. Fragments of the subvolcanic breccia in the carbonatite are clearly visible in various quarries near Schelingen; phonolite inclusions also appear there in sizes ranging from a centimetre to several metres. In Badloch quarry a zone several metres wide, rich in inclusions, has been opened up. The size of the inclusions varies between a few centimetres and more than a metre. Originally a phonolite-like rock they have been altered to hauynite diopside carbonate rock in contact with the carbonatite. Similar lime-silica rocks have been found in other places in the Badberg carbonatite, which in part still show relics of the phonolite or essexite mineralogy and texture.

The petrographical and geochemical properties of the carbonatites are dealt with later under Petrography (p. 195).

The latest and most highly differentiated eruptive rocks of the central Kaiserstuhl are younger than the Badberg carbonatite. These are dike rocks, which were intruded in the following order according to cross-cutting relationships and chill-zone formation:

Monchiquites
Phonolites
Tinguaites, Hauynophyres, Mondhaldeites
Bergalites

[1] Concerning the history of views about the carbonate rocks of the Kaiserstuhl, see Wimmenauer 1963a.

Gauteites, Shonkinite porphyries
Youngest dike carbonatites

Postmagmatic tectonism apparently had but little importance in the Kaiserstuhl. Whether or not the attitude of the depositional surface of lavas and tuffs on the Oligocene (dip 3% to west) is prevolcanic can not as yet be ascertained. The erosion of the volcanic mountain took place essentially during the long period of time between middle Miocene and early Pliocene. Several hundred meters of the former volcanic covering is absent from the centre. Summits in the west of the Kaiserstuhl on the other hand appear to be less deeply eroded. Judging from the attitude of the oldest loess and gravels in the valleys of the Kaiserstuhl, it is evident that the general form of the mountain today was formed in the early Pliocene.

Dating of Kaiserstuhl volcanism

In the Kaiserstuhl, the Oligocene succession ends with the Cyrena marls of the lower Chattien. A phase of faulting and erosion is assumed some time in the Aquitan (see p. 185); after this follow the first tuff and lava eruptions. The only paleontological time marker for the Kaiserstuhl volcanism is provided by the mammalian fauna in tuffs on the Limberg (Tobien 1959). They belong to the younger Burdigalian and hence date one of the youngest phases of the volcanic activity.

The succession of the eruptive rocks appears to be satisfactorily determined for the lavas and tuffs on the one hand, and for the intrusions and dikes on the other hand, while the time relationship of the two mentioned groups is only incompletely determinable. The essexites of the centre and their dike series are certainly younger than the tephrites which surround the centre itself. However, significantly younger lavas and tuffs are present on the periphery of the Kaiserstuhl. Having regard to all the geological and petrographical arguments, the following succession is proposed:

	Lavas and Tuffs	Subvolcanic Rocks
		Carbonatite dikes
		Gauteites, shonkinite porphyrites
		Mondhaldeites, bergalites
		tinguaites, hauynophyres
		Dike phonolites
Time relationship to the subvolcanic rocks uncertain.	Limburgites, olivine nephelinites, phonolitic and polygenetic tuffs, olivine-bearing tephrites	Larger carbonatite intrusions Subvolcanic breccias of the centre Monchiquites, essexite porphyrites and theralite porphyrites
	Younger leucite tephrite lavas and tuffs	
	Older leucite tephrite lavas and tuffs; polygenetic tuffs of the eastern Kaiserstuhl (?)	Essexites, theralites Oldest phonolites of the centre, Phonolite stocks (?)

K–Ar age determinations on minerals and rocks of the Kaiserstuhl were made by H. L. Lippolt (Lippolt, Gentner and Wimmenauer, 1963). The peculiar character of the rocks causes high argon loss and so the ages have a wide scatter and to some extent contradict the geological relationships. In view of all these circumstances the following dates can be regarded as most probable:

Main volcanic phase (Tephrites)	18 to 17.5 $\times$ 10^6 years
Younger volcanic formations	
(Limberg, particular phonolitic tuff t_3)	16.5 $\times$ 10^6 years
Subvolcanic activity in the centre	17.5 to 16 $\times$ 10^6 years

The age of the phonolitic tuffs t_3 designates approximately the Burdigalian-Helvetian boundary.

PETROGRAPHY

General

On the basis of characteristic mineral associations, the majority of silicate eruptive rocks of the Kaiserstuhl can be divided into two main families:

A. The essexitic family: Rocks with plagioclase + augite ($\pm$ magnetite, olivine, amphibole, leucite, nepheline, analcite; alkali feldspar and hauynite are also present although not normally characteristic of such rocks).

B. The foyaitic family: Rocks with alkali feldspar + sodalite (or hauynite) + aegirine-augite ($\pm$ melanite, wollastonite, nepheline, analcite, titanite; plagioclase and leucite are also present although not normally characteristic of such rocks).

Rocks whose classification is questionable are few. Both families have relatively acid, intermediate and basic members; both are represented among the lavas or tuffs, the dikes and the subvolcanic intrusive rocks. The rocks of the essexite family surpass those of the foyaite family repeatedly in surface area and volume. The olivine nephelinites and bergalites do not belong directly to either of these families.

The olivine nephelinites

Olivine nephelinite lavas, agglomerates and tuffs appear on the Luetzelberg near Sasbach and in the Kaiserstuhl near Oberschaffhausen. They are distinguished from the basic members of the essexite family by the absence of plagioclase. It is a special type of rock, also extensively distributed in the central European eruptive province, which, according to Wimmenauer (1963b) possibly represents the parent magma for the eruptive rocks of the Kaiserstuhl.

Mineral composition: olivine phenocrysts, augite, nepheline, titano-magnetite, and a little biotite. The titano-magnetite in the red agglomerates is altered to hematite + pseudobrookite $\pm$ spinel (Frenzel 1956; Wimmenauer 1959b, p. 134 and Table 17); the lavas contain numerous olivine rock inclusions with chrome diopside, enstatite and picotite.

The rocks of the essexitic family

Most lavas, agglomerates and tuffs of the Kaiserstuhl are composed of leucite tephrite. Hauynite-bearing tephrites, leucite-poor tephrites and latites appear as variants. Olivine-bearing tephrites are present on the periphery of the volcano, especially to the south west and west.

For the mineral composition, see Fig. 3. Phenocrysts: augite, leucite, plagioclase ($\pm$ olivine); Groundmass: augite, plagioclase (An_{50}–An_{60}), alkali feldspar, leucite, analcite, zeolites, iron-titanium oxides. The leucite is mostly altered to analcite.

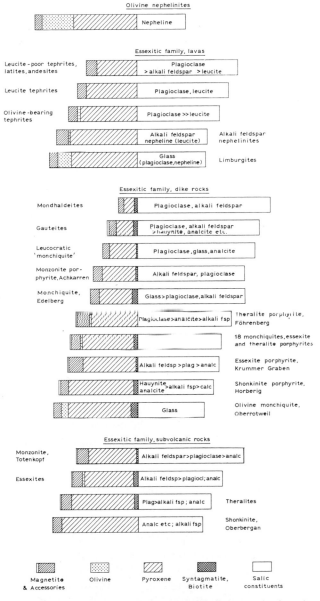

Fig. 3.   Mineral composition of olivine nephelinite and of rocks of the essexitic family (in volume per cent).

In the explosion-tuffs of Sponeck-Burkheim, Keller (1963) observed signs of pipe-differentiation[1] with concentration of alkali pyroxene, biotite, melanite and leucite. The leucitophyre breccia of Burkheim (Soellner, 1912), accordingly could be the final end product of such a differentiation.

The limburgites are distinguished from the tephrites by a higher content of olivine and a lack of alkali feldspar; in accord with the definition, they mostly possess a glassy base; the groundmass is also locally crystallized to plagioclase (An_{40}) and nepheline. Phenocrysts: olivine, titanaugite; Groundmass: augite, titano-magnetite (in part skeletal crystals), glass, rhönite flakes, apatite (Fig. 3). An alkali feldspar nephelinite occurs as the youngest lava on the Limberg. (See Fig. 3 for the mineral composition.) The especially basic lavas of the Limberg-Luetzelberg volcano (olivine nephelinite, limburgite, alkali feldspar nephelinite) within the boundaries of the Kaiserstuhl alternate with phonolite and polygenetic tuffs.

The essexite-theralite intrusive rocks are more or less uniformly fine- to medium-grained. The principal components are titanaugite, plagioclase (An_{45}–An_{55}), alkali feldspar, analcite, titano-magnetite, syntagmatite, biotite, rare olivine, nepheline or leucite (Fig. 3). The most numerous types are essexites and theralites with monzonite seldom observed and shonkinite found only once. The colour index varies between 33 and 66 and the nomenclature of the rocks depends on the leucocratic components:

Monzonite: (Plagioclase + alkali feldspar) > feldspathoids
(incl. analcite)

Essexite: Plagioclase + alkali feldspar + feldspathoids
(incl. analcite)

Theralite: (Plagioclase > alkali feldspar) + feldspathoids
(incl. analcite)

Shonkinites: alkali feldspar + feldspathoids
(incl. analcite)

Under the microscope, metasomatic textures are frequently observed (Rein, 1950): Plagioclase is replaced by alkali feldspar or analcite, titanaugite is transformed to syntagmatite or biotite. Near the contact with the carbonatites there is additional biotitization of the augite as well as impregnation by calcite (Wimmenauer, 1962a, p. 7; this chapter, p. 188).

In the peripheral parts of the Kaiserstuhl as well as in the centre, rocks closely related to the essexite–theralite group occur as very numerous dikes (essexite and theralite porphyrites, monchiquites, monozonite and shonkinite porphyries). In addition to these there are dike rocks which can be considered as differentiation products of essexitic–theralitic magmas: mondhaldeite, gauteites, olivine monchiquites. All of the rocks mentioned are linked by transitional types.

The quantitative mineral composition of the most important rocks of this group is presented in Fig. 3. As phenocrysts, augite to titanaugite and titanomagnetite usually appear; in individual rock types in addition there are olivine

[1] Differentiation within the volcanic neck. Ed.

(olivine monchiquites), plagioclase (essexite porphyrites, gauteites, a few mondhaldeites), hauyne (gauteites, shonkinite porphyrites), and rarely leucite. Practically all rocks contain analcite, zeolites and calcite in the groundmass; the calcite is especially abundant in strongly differentiated gauteites and

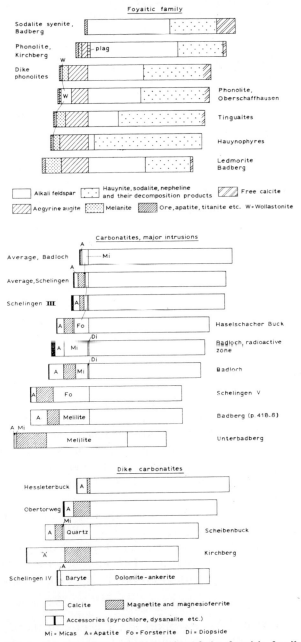

Fig. 4.   Mineral composition of the rocks of the foyaitic family and of carbonatites (in volume per cent).

shonkinite porphyries. The matrix of the monchiquites is largely glassy, but in part finely crystalline owing to devitrification.

The rocks of the foyaitic family

The rocks of the foyaitic family appear as stock-like intrusions, as dikes and as components of tuffs. The chief minerals are alkali feldspar, hauyne or sodalite, aegirine-augite, melanite and wollastonite. The rock types range from feldspar-rich phonolites through tinguaite (hauyne > feldspar) to feldspar-free hauyno-phyre (Fig. 4). The evolution of this series can be considered as a consequence of fractionated crystallization differentiation. The widely distributed wollastonite is probably the result of supplementary assimilation of lime.

The alkali feldspar of these rocks is in general anorthoclase and not sandine. The phonolite from the Kirchberg contains approximately 2 volume percent of plagioclase (An_{30}–An_{40}) as cores of the alkali feldspar phenocrysts. Sphene is a characteristic accessory component of the phonolitic tuffs and of many phonolites and tinguaites.

Outcrops of sodalite syenite and ledmorite, as well as inclusions in the phono-lites of sodalite syenite, tawite and jacupiranite occur as representatives of the subvolcanic facies proper. Hydrothermal alteration and neomineralization are very common; the feldspathoids are often wholly altered to zeolites, analcite or calcite (e.g. phonolite from Oberschaffhausen). The phonolite stock of the Kirchberg in the western Kaiserstuhl contains narrow carbonatite dikes (Wimmenauer 1962b) and two more were found by Deutzmann (1955) in the tephrite country rock of the phonolite. Bitumen appears in fractures and as pigment in the phonolites of Kirchberg and Oberschaffhausen respectively.

The radioactivity of the rocks of the foyaitic family is on the average much higher than the essexitic family. According to Kirchheimer (1959, pp. 30–37) the milk opals and hyalites, which occur in fractures of the two phonolites mentioned, contain uranium (0.2–0.9% U).

The phonolites contain widespread inclusions of granite and gneiss from the underlying rocks. These are frequently fenitized (quartz is resorbed, plagioclase altered to alkali feldspar, biotite to aegirine-augite). Moreover there are often hydrothermal products (calcite, zeolites). In other cases there is a predominance of thermal transformation without large compositional changes such as feldspars with high temperature optics; biotite → spinel (or magnetite) + corundum, etc. (Eigenfeld, 1954; Wimmenauer, 1962b).

The eruptive components of the phonolitic tuffs from Limberg and from Breisach are mostly strongly decomposed. The tuffs of the Limberg contain, besides phonolite fragments, many blocks of the underlying Mesozoic and Tertiary as well as of gneiss and granite. The latter show thermal metamorphic changes, fenitization and carbonatization (see p. 200 and Wimmenauer, 1959b).

The bergalites

These rocks, which occur in a few dikes in the centre of the Kaiserstuhl, were first described and analysed by Soellner (1913). They are characterized by the association melilite + hauyne, with augite, magnetite, perovskite, biotite, nepheline and apatite in addition. Most fresh bergalites are rich in calcite; individual rocks contain glass in the matrix. The silica content is extremely low (33%).

Polygenetic tuffs and breccias

Polygenetic subvolcanic breccias form the immediate country rock of the carbonatites in the centre of the Kaiserstuhl. Predominantly, they contain fragments of essexites, essexite porphyrites, monchiquites and phonolites, as well as individual occurrences of carbonatite fragments. The matrix is made up of small rock and mineral fragments of the same origin, as well as abundant calcite, biotite and an isotropic substance. The biotite along with calcite is characteristic of the immediate contact zone of the carbonatites; it is formed principally at the expense of augite (Wimmenauer, 1962b).

Among the polygenetic tuffs, that of Wasenweiler is especially interesting because of the variety of its components. Among the larger fragments (> 1 cm) are: granite, gneisses, Triassic sandstone, tephrite and related rocks (hauyne tephrite, latite), essexite porphyrite, olivine nephelinite, phonolite, as well as fenite-like and carbonatite-like rocks (Wimmenauer, 1959b).

Additional occurrences of polygenetic tuffs and breccias of various character have been described by Cissarz (1932), Soellner (1939) and Wimmenauer (1959b; 1962b).

The carbonatites

The carbonatites of the Kaiserstuhl are quite variable in respect to their texture and mineral composition (Fig. 4). The larger intrusions are clearly different from the smaller, younger carbonatite dikes. The carbonatites of the larger intrusions and larger dikes are medium- to coarse-grained, less frequently fine- or coarse-grained rocks, which in the large exposures display a layered structure and jointing parallel to it. The layered structure is determined by a varying content of non-carbonate minerals as well as by differences in the grain size. Mica in mica-rich carbonatites is more or less distinctly oriented (Figs. 5 and 6).

A 'migmatite-like' schlieren structure with coarse-, to giant-grained portions of pegmatite-like habit is exposed in quarry V near Schelingen. Calcites with crystal edges up to 30 cm long display, even macroscopically, twin lamellae $(01\bar{1}2)$. The crystals are stretched obliquely to the c-axis so that individual long-extended cleavage surfaces $(10\bar{1}1)$, roughly parallel to the elongation of the individuals, appear on the broken surfaces of the rock.

The quantitative mineral composition of a few typical carbonatites is presented in Fig. 4. The average composition of the rocks from the Badloch quarry and from Schelingen was determined by a chemical and physical separation of minerals from channel samples weighing several kilograms. The rocks of the Badberg are predominantly calcite—mica carbonatites (sövites), those from Schelingen are characterized by a higher content of magnetite, apatite and forsterite. Dolomitic–ankeritic carbonatites with barite appear as younger intrusions near Schelingen. The majority of the narrow carbonatite dikes in the centre consist of calcite rocks with magnetite, apatite and a little mica as

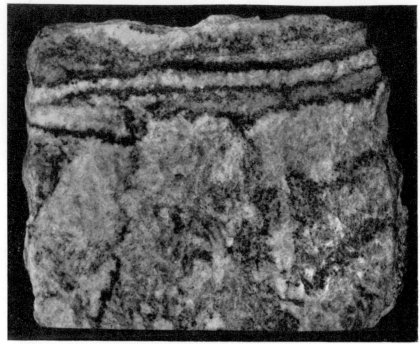

Fig. 5.   Carbonatite; Schelingen, Quarry V. Layered and schlieren texture
with enrichment in magnetite, forsterite and apatite.
Polished slab approximately × 0.6.

Fig. 6.   Carbonatite with inclusions of lime silicate rock; Quarry on the
Badloch. Inclusions have biotite rims; flow texture in the carbonatite is
indicated by sheafs of hydrobiotite.
Approximately × 0.6.

accessory constituents. In addition to the minerals mentioned, others, such as diopside, olivine, melilite and quartz quantitatively play only a local role. In the magnetite-rich and melilite-rich deposit on the Unterbadberg discovered by Deutzmann (1964) the melilite constitutes about 50 per cent by volume.

The calcite of the carbonatite occurs in the most varied grain sizes, from less than 0.01 mm to over 10 cm. Among the smaller grains the predominant habit is generally irregular polyhedral forms with clear cut boundaries while among the larger grains more irregular habits prevail. Twinning parallel to $(01\bar{1}2)$ is extremely widespread, especially in the larger grains. Normally all the other constituents of the carbonatites are idiomorphic against the calcite; nevertheless, it not infrequently happens that apatite, forsterite and others are corroded by calcite. Metschke (1938) distinguished two contrasting textural types among the carbonatites from Schelingen, based on the relationship of calcite to the other constituents: (*a*) the other constituents lie principally on the grain borders of the calcite; (*b*) the other constituents also lie within the calcite grains.

Ankeritic dolomite is the chief constituent of the fine-grained carbonate-barite rocks in quarries IV and V near Schelingen.

Apatite is an almost universal constituent of the carbonatites sometimes amounting to 10 per cent by volume. The crystals display short to long prismatic habits and they are mostly rounded at the ends. In the coarser grained carbonatites of Schelingen there are individual crystals with a length of several millimetres and radiating clusters which are at times visible to the naked eye. The very abundant cavities in the apatite, elongated parallel to the *c*-axis or more or less rounded, are, with their filling, of special interest. Under high magnification, liquids and gas bubbles as well as mineral precipitates are frequently recognizable. The latter are in part cubic and optically isotropic, but also in part clearly anisotropic. In spite of their minuteness the anisotropic crystals display interference colours of first order red or second order blue, so that it can be presumed that they are tiny carbonate crystals. According to microchemical tests, the cubic crystals are halite and sylvite.

Magnetite usually forms well developed octahedra up to 4 mm in size (Schelingen); in the narrow carbonatite dikes it appears also as exceedingly fine-grained pigment dust with a grain size of only a few microns. The mineral contains up to 8.6% MgO and 6.6% Al_2O_3, according to analyses by Knop (1892) and Hugel (1912). Magnetite is abundant in individual localities in the Badberg carbonatite, e.g. on the Unterbadberg in polyhedral crystals up to 1 cm in size (Deutzmann, 1964), and in the quarry of the Badloch in severely corroded grains, up to 4 mm in size (see also Fig. 4).

Various micas are characteristic accessory constituents of the carbonatites. On the Badberg, they are chiefly pale-brown biotite and phlogopite-like minerals which occur in layers up to a centimetre thick. Knop (1892) has already made reference to the vermiculitic-like behaviour of the mica from the Badloch. His analyses show that, compared with biotite and phlogopite, the mineral is impoverished in potash, but richer in water. Powder patterns obtained by Dr. Brauner in the Mineralogical Institute of the University of Freiburg, are very similar to those of hydrobiotites and hydrophlogopites.

In the carbonatites near Schelingen a barium phlogopite appears in flakes up to a centimetre wide which are in part thick and polyhedral. A chemical analysis obtained by Daub (1912) showed 5.11% BaO and 8.17% CaO (Wimmenauer, 1963b).

Omenetto and Weber (1963) describe manganophyllite as a rare component of various carbonatites near Schelingen. The mineral is distinguished in thin section by its red-brown colour and the fact that its plane of maximum absorption is at right angles to that of biotite.

Forsterite is limited to the carbonatites of Schelingen and its surroundings. The mineral forms rounded to idiomorphic grains with a maximum size of 2–3 mm, which frequently show the beginnings of serpentinization. Omenetto and Weber also found olivine in quarry II near Schelingen.

Diopside occurs in small quantities in a few mica-rich layers of the carbonatite from the Badloch.

Melilite is a principal component of the magnetite-rich deposit on the Unterbadberg. According to Omenetto and Weber (1963) the mineral is close to akermanite. Melilite also appears elsewhere in the Badberg carbonatite (Fig. 4).

Pyrochlore (='Koppite') since its first mention by Fischer (1865), is certainly the most discussed component of the carbonatites (Knop, 1875; Knop, 1892; Daub, 1912; Brandenberger, 1931; Metschke, 1938; Kirchheimer, 1957). A summary of chemical analyses is given by Wimmenauer, 1963b, The mineral forms octahedra which are chestnut-brown to cherry-red in colour, with edges up to 3 mm long; in general, however, the crystals are only a fraction of one mm long. Not infrequently the octahedra are blunted by rhombic dodecahedral faces; Kiefer (1932) mentioned a step-like succession of octahedral faces; Metschke (1938) also mentions the appearance of cubic faces. The koppite appears yellow-brown to dark-yellow in thin section; the larger individuals are zoned. Inclusions of apatite are numerous; those of magnetite are less frequent.

The uranium- and thorium-bearing koppite of Schelingen and the Badloch, described by Kirchheimer (1957) is noteworthy as a special variant. This koppite is a distinctly brighter yellowish-brown than the usual form. Zoned crystals with a dark brown core and lighter rim have also been observed on the Badloch. The highest content of uranium and thorium determined is 11.1% and 5.5% respectively.

The dysanalite (Ca, Ce, Na) (Ti, Nb, Fe) O_3 is characteristic of the carbonatite of the Badberg. The mineral forms black cubes with edges up to 3 mm; usually, however, the crystals are only a fraction of a millimetre in length. The dysanalite is transparent dark brownish or dark greenish, and displays a very weak double refraction which reveals the subdivision of the original cubic crystals into a mosaic of rhombic segments (Soellner, 1912). In the few available analyses (compiled by Wimmenauer, 1963b) the TiO_2 content varies between 12.3% and 48.3%, and the Nb_2O_5 content between 16.2% and 49.0%.

Barite appears isolated in fissures in the carbonatite on the Badloch in crystal aggregates up to a centimetre in diameter. It is an essential component of the dolomite–ankerite carbonatites in quarries IV and V near Schelingen (Fig. 4).

In addition to the minerals already mentioned, the following appear in the carbonatites in small amounts:

Monticellite (Daub, 1912; exact locality unknown)—Pyrrhotite (Schelingen)—Pyrite (in narrow carbonatite dikes of the centre)—Quartz (Badberg, isolated; more abundant in a carbonatite dike on the Scheibenbuck; Fig. 4)—Pyrolusite, kryptomelane (as a weathering product in the ankeritic–dolomitic carbonatites; Schelingen, Degenmatt)—limonite (extensive as a product of weathering)—Fluorite (narrow carbonatite dikes in the phonolite of the Kirchberg).

The following main types of texture may be distinguished among the small carbonatite dikes:

Fine-grained to very fine-grained texture with irregular-polyhedral or slightly embayed calcite without visible orientation.

Fine-grained to very fine-grained texture which can be best described as intermediate between porphyritic and mortar structures. Larger calcite grains, oval-shaped and elongated to lath-shaped, lie in a very fine-grained groundmass.

Amygdaloid-like texture. In this type occur round or elongated patches which contain no pigmenting minerals and are frequently somewhat coarser grained than their surroundings. In the dike carbonatite discovered by Deutzmann on the Kirchberg the 'bubbles' are in part empty; their long axes are normal to the dike walls.

Highly porous texture. Typical in a carbonatite dike near Oberschaff-hausen which is not now exposed (Wimmenauer, 1963b).

Textures with columnar calcite which is mostly oriented normal to the dike walls. A layered structure is very often combined with this texture and it arises through an alternation of the grain size of the calcite and interlayers of other minerals.

Strontium enrichment characterizes the Kaiserstuhl carbonatites, as it does the majority of carbonatites throughout the world, and markedly distinguishes them from the sedimentary limestones in the immediate vicinity. A few strontium analyses, determined by Dr. W. Käss are listed in Table I.

TABLE I

Strontium contents of carbonatites and sedimentary rocks of the Kaiserstuhl (in ppm)	
Carbonatite, Badloch quarry, channel sample	9550
Carbonatite from a radioactive zone, Badloch quarry	8000
Dike carbonatite, Hessleterbuck	8000
Carbonatite, Schelingen quarry V, channel sample	7650
Dolomitic–ankeritic carbonatite, Schelingen	7350
Dike carbonatite, Oberbergen (Gehöft König)	6350
Marl of the Meletta beds, Silberbrunnen	270
Calcareous sandstone of the Meletta beds, Silberbrunnen	220
Contact metamorphosed Oligocene, Rütte	330
Main Oolite of the Dogger, Merdingen am Tuniberg	150
Strontium content from carbonatites of various sources (from Van Wambeke, 1960)	2500–7750
Average strontium content of sediments (according to Turekian and Kulp, 1956)	640

The abundance of the isotopes ^{18}O and ^{13}C in carbonates was investigated by Baertschi (1957) on many samples of different origin. The following departures from the standard values were found for two carbonatite samples from the Kaiserstuhl.

	O%	C%
Schelingen	− 21.1	− 8.8
Badloch	− 21.0	− 9.3

These values lie in the field of typical carbonatites and indeed in the immediate vicinity of samples from Alnö (Sweden), Iron Hill (Colorado) and Spitzkop (Transvaal).

The inclusions in the carbonatites

The occurrence of inclusions in the carbonatites has already been discussed briefly on p. 188. In a few cases the original material is readily identifiable because only a slight alteration has taken place, e.g. phonolite with alkali feldspar phenocrysts, and essexite with larger augites. The more altered inclusions, the 'lime silicate rocks' according to Wimmenauer (1959a) are, on the other hand, quite different from their original materials. Most numerous are the fine-grained to very fine-grained, mostly grey to dark grey rocks, in which wollastonite, lime-iron garnet, calcite and isolated pyrite grains are megascopically recognizable. Also very characteristic are rims of dark mica in contact with the surrounding carbonatite (Fig. 6).

Microscopically, the lime silicate rocks show hornfels-like texture, i.e. the principal constituents are more or less xenomorphic intergrown with one another in an irregularly embayed manner. The most important components of these rocks are: a mineral of the sodalite group, chiefly hauyne (often altered to calcite or zeolites); diopside (present practically everywhere); brown lime-iron garnet; wollastonite (in part altered to calcite or pectolite); calcite (by itself or as an alteration product of hauyne and wollastonite); nepheline; alkali feldspar (in part relict phenocrysts, mostly recrystallized to xenomorphic or xenoblastic form); pale brown biotite and phlogopite (at the contact with the carbonatite); melilite (in one occurrence only); apatite and pyrite.

The quantitative mineral composition is subject to very great fluctuations.

TABLE II

Mineral composition of lime silicate rocks

	a	b		
Hauyne and alteration products	41	52	volume per cent	
Diopside and aegirine-diopside	41	25	,,	,,
Lime-iron garnet	0.5	19	,,	,,
Wollastonite and alteration products	10.5	—	,,	,,
Nepheline	4	—	,,	,,
Alkali feldspar	1.5	—	,,	,,
Independent calcite	—	3.5	,,	,,
Apatite	1.5	<0.5	,,	,,
Pyrite	—	<0.5	,,	,,

Table II illustrates the composition of two typical samples from the Badberg (*a*) and from the Badloch (*b*).

Carbonatites and carbonate fenites as fragments in tuffs

Fragments of carbonatites and carbonate fenites were found in several occurrences of the polygenetic and phonolitic tuffs (Wasenweiler, Meisensatz and Limberg). Among the carbonate fenites there is a gradational series from gneisses (rarely granites) to alkali feldspar—aegirine-augite—calcite rocks. In the process quartz, plagioclase and biotite are more or less completely replaced. The strontium content of these carbonate fenites (at 2500–5900 ppm) is significantly high like that of the carbonatites of the centre and is of great importance with regard to the origin of the carbonatites (see p. 199 and Wimmenauer, 1963b).

The contact metamorphosed Oligocene

On the eastern rim of the subvolcanic centre Oligocene marls and calcareous sandstones in contact with intrusive phonolitic rocks are thermally metamorphosed in a zone about 100 m wide. With more pronounced metamorphism, dense banded carbonate hornfelses have developed which are composed of quartz, feldspars, calcite and diopside. Compared with their original material these rocks are poorer in carbonate and richer in silica. In this they are in contrast with the carbonatites, which, on the whole, are richer in carbonate. The carbonatites can in no case be derived from the carbonate hornfelses through progressive metamorphism. In at least one place a coarse-grained carbonatite dike cuts the metamorphosed oligocene with sharp contacts.

THE ORIGIN OF THE SILICATE AND CARBONATITE MAGMAS OF THE KAISERSTUHL

The Tertiary volcanic rocks in the immediate vicinity of the Kaiserstuhl and in the general area are predominantly olivine nephelinite and melilite ankaratrite. Hundreds of occurrences of such rocks lie in the following districts of eastern France and southern Germany: Lorraine, Vosges Mountains, Upper Rhein graben, Black Forest, Hegau, Urach volcanic region, Odenwald, Palatinate, Rhön, Hassberge and Upper Palatinate. The petrographic consanguinity of the widely scattered and often isolated dikes and necks indicates a common genesis; their similarity shows that they could have undergone only minor individual changes through differentiation and assimilation. They are rather to be regarded as representatives of a primary magma of the Tertiary period for the region. It should perhaps be characterized as very undersaturated alkali basaltic magma which is very evidently different from the magma of the usual plagioclase olivine basalts; it may obviously occur independently of the latter. Olivine nephelinite lavas and pyroclastics occur in the Kaiserstuhl on the Limberg and near Oberschaffhausen (see p. 190).

If one assumes such an undersaturated alkali basaltic magma as the original magma for the Kaiserstuhl, then the problem arises, how the other types of magma present there are derived from this one. With this it can be seen that the development of the essexitic and especially of the foyaitic derivative magmas probably is not possible without assimilation of sialic material. A hypothetical calculation, based on the average analysis of the olivine nephelinites, shows that a combination of fractional crystallization differentiation and assimilation of 16% 'granite' could cause the step-wise development of an alkali gabbroic and a foyaitic magma (Wimmenauer, 1963b). Numerous, often fenitized granite and gneiss inclusions in the phonolites of the Kaiserstuhl give evidence that reaction between the magma and these rocks has actually taken place (Eigenfeld, 1954). For the further development of the individual varieties of rocks, the proposed fractional crystallization seems to be responsible. The majority of the phonolitic rocks furthermore, show signs of limestone assimilation.

The abundant appearance of minerals of the sodalite-hauyne group with their chloride and sulphate content, was attributed to the assimilation of saline deposits of the underlying Tertiary by Schneiderhöhn (1948).

Only conjectures can be made about the origin of the carbonatites. Geochemical data do not support an origin by mobilization of the underlying Mesozoic and Tertiary limestones. Thus the strontium content (6350–9550 ppm) is many times higher than that of the Tertiary and Jurassic sediments in the eastern Kaiserstuhl. Similarly the phosphorus, barium, niobium and uranium of the carbonatites could not be derived from sediments. Further, fenitized fragments of basement rocks, in part very rich in calcite, occur in the phonolitic and polygenetic tuffs of Wasenweiler and the Limberg. They show that high concentrations of carbonate were possible even at the level of the Basement rocks. The strontium content of this carbonate fenite, at 2500 to 5900 ppm, is as high as that of the carbonatites. Under these circumstances the genesis of carbonatite magmas at depth seems to be possible without participation of sediments. The association of narrow carbonatite dikes with the phonolites of the Kirchberg permits the assumption that the formation of carbonatite is here related to the foyaitic magma but this conclusion cannot of course be generalized.

According to experience in other carbonatite areas and of experimental studies (this volume, pp. 309–350), it is probable, that the carbonatites are derived from a strongly undersaturated magma. The magmas of the olivine nephelinites and melilite ankaratrites, mentioned above, offer themselves as such possible sources. Although this supposed connection is not visible in the Kaiserstuhl itself, many of the small olivine nephelinites outside of the Kaiserstuhl show a marked tendency to generate carbonatic differentiates. The concentration of Sr and Nb in and near the carbonatic vugs is a very remarkable analogy with the geochemical properties of the true carbonatites.

REFERENCES

Baertschi, P., 1957, Messung und Deutung relativer Häufigkeitsvariationen von ^{18}O und ^{13}C in Karbonatgesteinen und-mineralen: *Schweiz. Miner. Petrogr. Mitt.*, v. **37**, pp. 73–152.

Brandenberger, E., 1931, Die Kristallstruktur von Koppit: *Z. Krist.*, v. **76**, pp. 322–334.

Cissarz, A., 1931, Der Gesteinsinhalt der Schlotbreccie im Gewann Nonnensohl in der Gemarkung Oberschaffhausen, Kaiserstuhl: *Ber. naturforsch. Ges. Freiburg i. Br.*, v. **31**, pp. 273–286.

Daub, R., 1912, Beiträge zur Kenntnis der Kontaktmineralien aus dem körnigen Kalke des Kaiserstuhls: *Inaugural Dissertation, Freiburg i. Br.*, 45 pp.

Deutzmann, W., 1964, in Wambeke, L. van, 1964.

Eigenfeld, R., 1954, Zur Genese von Alkaligesteinen: *Ber. Phys.-Med. Ges. Würzburg*, v. **66**, pp. 95–114.

Fischer, H., 1865, Short contribution in: *Leonhard's Jb. Miner.*, pp. 435–449.

Frenzel, G., 1956, Zur Kenntnis der Eisen-Titanoxyde in thermometamorphen Gesteinen: *Heidelb. Beitr. Miner. Petrogr.*, v. **5**, pp. 165–170.

Hubaux, A., 1964, in Wambeke, L. van, 1964.

Hugel, E., 1912, Über den Dysanalyt von Vogtsburg im Kaiserstuhl: *Inaugural Dissertation*, 54 pp,

Keller, J., 1964, Zur Vulkanologie des Burkheim-Sponeck-Gebietses im westlichen Kaiserstuhl: *Ber. Naturf. Ges. Freiburg i. Br.*, v. **54**, pp. 107–130.

Kiefer, H., 1932, Das Alter der kontaktmetamorphen Kalke im zentralen Kaiserstuhl: *Fortschr. Geol. Paläont.*, v. **11**, pp. 461–501.

Kirchheimer, F., 1957, Bericht über das Vorkommen von Uran in Baden-Württemberg: *Abh. Geol. Landesamt Baden-Württemberg*, v. **2**, pp. 1–127.

Kirchheimer, F., 1959, Über radioaktive und uranhaltige Thermalsedimente, insbesondere von Baden-Baden: *Abh. Geol. Landesamt Baden-Württemberg*, v. **3**, pp. 1–67.

Knop, A., 1892, Der Kaiserstuhl im Breisgau: Eine naturwissenschaftliche Studie, 534 pp.

Lippolt, H. J., Gentner, W. and Wimmenauer, W., 1963, *Altersbestimmungen nach der Kalium-Argon-Methode an tertiären Eruptivgesteinen Südwestdeutschlands:* Jh. Geol. Landesamt Baden-Württemberg, v. **6**, pp. 507–538.

Metschke, H., 1938, Koppitkarbonatit und Koppitmarmor von Schelingen im Kaiserstuhl: *Ber. naturforsch. Ges. Freiburg i. Br.*, v. **36**, pp. 28–56.

Omenetto, M. and Weber, K., van, *et al.*, 1964, Les roches alcalines et les carbonatites du Kaiserstuhl: *EURATOM publication* EUR 1827, d,f,e.

Pfannenstiel, M., 1933, Die Geologie des Kaiserstuhls In: Der Kaiserstuhl: Bad. Landesver. Naturkunde u. Naturschutz, pp. 18–127.

Rein, G., 1950, Über Essexite und Tephrite des zentralen Kaiserstuhls und deren Umwandlungsprodukte: *Fortschr. Miner.* , v. **28**, pp. 70–72.

Schneiderhöhn, H., 1948, Neue Beobachtungen und Hypothesen im Kaiserstuhl: *Mitt. bad. Geol. Landesanst*, p. 30–36.

Soellner, J., 1912, Die optischen Eigenschaften des Dysanalytes von Vogtsburg und von Schelingen im Kaiserstuhl: *Zbl. Miner.* pp. 310–317.

Soellner, J., 1912, Über ein neues Vorkommen von Leucitophyr und Leucitophyrbreccie im Kaiserstuhl: *Zbl. Miner.* pp. 571–574.

Soellner, J., 1913, Über Bergalith, ein neues melilithreiches Ganggestein aus dem Kaiserstuhl: *Mitt. bad. Geol. Landesanst.*, v. **7**, pp. 415–466.

Soellner, J., 1928, Über essexitisch-theralithisch-monzonitische Tiefengesteine aus dem Kaiserstuhl: *Mitt. bad. Geol. Landesanst.*, v. **10**, pp. 1–93.

Soellner, J., 1939, Über den vermeintlichen Schlot vom Gewann Nonnensohl auf der Gemarkung Oberschaffhausen Kaiserstuhl: *Zbl. Miner. Abt. B.*, pp. 433–442.

Tobien, H., 1959, Miozän. *In: Erläuterungen zur geologischen Exkursionskarte des Kaiserstuhls*, 1: 25000. Geol. Landesamt in Baden-Württemberg, pp. 21–23.

Wambeke, L. van, 1960, Geochemical prospecting and appraisal of Niobium-bearing carbonatites: *Econ. Geol.*, v. **55**, pp. 732–758.

Wambeke, L. van, *et al.* 1964, Les roches alcalines et les carbonatites du Kaiserstuhl: *EURATOM publication* EUR 1827, d,f,e.

Wimmenauer, W., 1957, Beiträge zur Petrographie des Kaiserstuhls, Einführung und Teil I: *N. Jb. Miner. Abh.*, v. **91**, pp. 131–150.

Wimmenauer, W., 1959a, *Abschnitte über Petrographie und Petrogenese in: Erläuterungen zur* geologischen Exkursionskarte des Kaiserstuhls, 1: 25000: ed. Geol. Landesamt Baden-Württemberg.

Wimmenauer, W., 1959b, Beiträge zur Petrographie des Kaiserstuhls, Schluss von Teil I, Teile II und III: *Neues Jb. Miner. Abh.*, v. **93**, pp. 133–173.

Wimmenauer, W., 1959c, Karbonatite im Kaiserstuhl: *Fortschr. Miner*, v. **37**, pp. 67–69.

Wimmenauer, W., 1962a, Zur Petrogenese der Eruptivgesteine und Karbonatite des Kaiserstuhls: *N. Jb. Miner. Mh.*, pp. 1–11.

Wimmenauer, W., 1962b, Beiträge zur Petrographie des Kaiserstuhls, Teile IV und V: *N. Jb. Miner. Abh.*, v. **98**, pp. 367–415.

Wimmenauer, W., 1963a, Beiträge zur Petrographie des Kaiserstuhls, Teile VI und VII: *N. Jb. Miner. Abh.*, v. **99**, pp. 231–276.

Wimmenauer, W., 1963b, Die Stellung der Olivinnephelinite und Melilithankaratrite im tertiären Vulkanismus Mitteleuropas: *N. Jb. Miner. Mh.*, pp. 278–282.

R. L. JOHNSON

The Shawa and Dorowa Carbonatite Complexes, Rhodesia[1]

INTRODUCTION

The Shawa and Dorowa carbonatite complexes are situated about 10 miles apart (see Fig. 1), and with the associated small intrusions of ijolite and nephelinite have been in the granitic gneisses of the Archaean craton of eastern Rhodesia (Johnson, 1961). The age of 209 ± 16 my (probably Triassic) which has been established for these complexes (Nicolaysen, Burger and Johnson, 1962) indicates that they represent part of the intense vulcanicity which took place throughout southern Africa in Late-Karroo[2] and early post-Karroo times (Fig. 2). Consequently, although the complexes are geographically isolated from other areas where Karroo volcanic rocks are preserved, their petrogenesis must be considered in relation to the whole volcanic episode. This point will receive particular emphasis in the present account, and a recent attempt to demonstrate a possible genetic link between magmas parental to carbonatite complexes and the more common type of Karroo magmas will be discussed (Johnson, in Cox et al., 1965).

The smaller Dorowa Complex (Fig. 3) is composed largely of syenites, which have formed in situ by fenitization of the Basement gneiss. These rocks show a progressive increase in the degree of metasomatism from the exterior inwards towards central areas occupied by intrusions of ijolite and other nepheline-rich rocks. The syenites are cut by a small plug and several dikes of carbonatite. Both the syenites and the ijolites are intersected by dikes and veins of rocks consisting of various combinations of the minerals magnetite, apatite, serpentine and vermiculite.

The larger Shawa complex (Fig. 4), which has a diameter of about 3.5 miles, consists of a plug of dunite, now largely serpentinized, enclosed by an irregular zone of fenite which grades outwards into the country rocks. Arcuate bodies of ijolite have been intruded between the ultrabasic plug and the surrounding fenite, and a ring dike of dolomitic carbonatite intersects the ultrabasic rocks.

---

[1] Formerly Southern Rhodesia.
[2] The Karroo System covers the period from the Upper Carboniferous to the Lower Jurassic (Du Toit 1954).

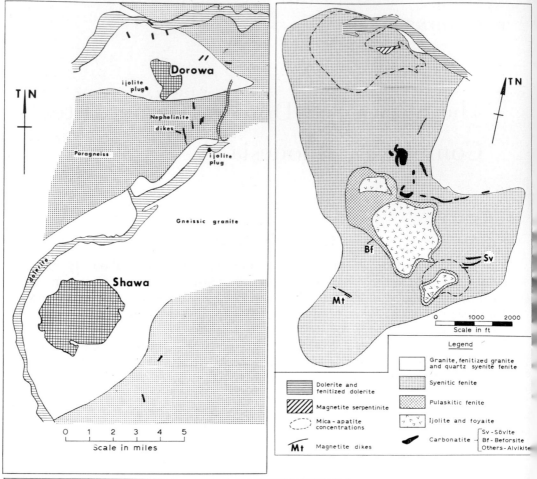

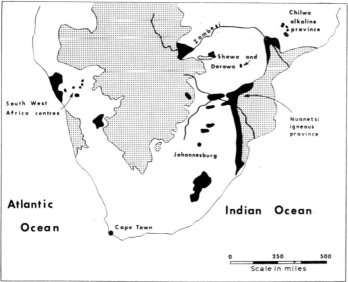

Fig. 1 (*top left*). Regional geological setting of the Shawa and Dorowa carbonatite complexes.

Fig. 2 (*left*). Location of the Shawa and Dorowa carbonatite complexes in relation to the Karroo igneous cycle in southern Africa.

Fig. 3 (*top right*). The Dorowa complex.

Legend

Dolerite and fenitized dolerite

Magnetite serpentinite

Mica - apatite concentrations

Mt   Magnetite dikes

Granite, fenitized granite and quartz syenite fenite

Syenitic fenite

Pulaskitic fenite

Ijolite and foyaite

Carbonatite {
  Sv - Sövite
  Bf - Beforsite
  Others - Alvikite
}

COUNTRY ROCKS

The granitic country rocks (see Fig. 1) form part of one of the gregarious batho-liths (Macgregor, 1951) which, with the intervening narrow arcuate belts of metamorphosed ancient sedimentary and volcanic rocks constitute the

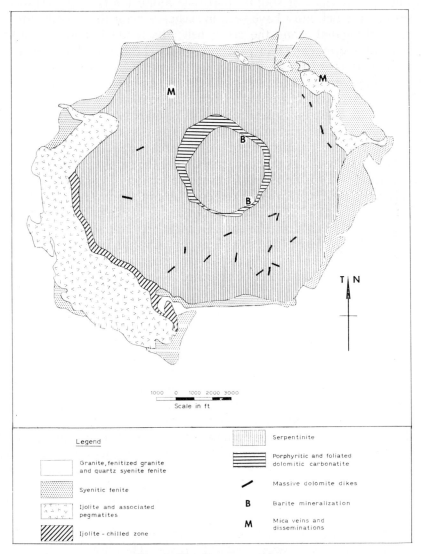

Fig. 4. The Shawa complex.

Archaean of Rhodesia. The country rocks also include members of a widespread suite of thick and extensive dolerite sheets, with subordinate dikes. Isotopic age determinations carried out by Dr. J. A. Miller and quoted by McElhinny and Opdyke (1964) show that these dolerites, which post-date the Archaean meta-morphism, are at least 1600 my. old.

The Rhodesian craton area has been a rigid block free from orogenic disturbance since early Precambrian times. The Dorowa and Shawa Complexes are not situated near any known major faults, although a number of NNW and ENE trending shatter belts, which may represent old fault lines, traverse the country rocks. The Dorowa Complex is located on a crush belt of the former trend and the presence of sodium pyroxene along joints in the crushed zone, indicates that the belt must have been in existence prior to the fenitization. The complex is elongated along the crush belt; the fenite boundaries, dikes and areas of apatite-vermiculite mineralization tend to be arranged parallel to the two fracture directions in the country rocks. It would appear therefore that the position of the complex and the asymmetrical arrangement of the rock groups within it, are due to the controlling influence of the fracture pattern in the country rocks. In contrast the much larger Shawa Complex is not situated on a known line of fracture, and the geological boundaries tend to be concentric in plan.

A most interesting structural feature of the area is the doming of the Basement gneisses and dolerite sheets that occurred during the emplacement of the carbonatite complexes. This is apparent from the deflection of the strike of one of the dolerite sheets (see Fig. 1) which extends in an arc around the Shawa Complex and dips outwards at 10–20°. The size of the arc indicates a dome about eight miles across, similar in diameter to that under the Napak volcano in Uganda (King, 1949; this volume, p. 99) and at the Kwaraa volcano in Tanganyika (James, 1956). A similar, though smaller, structure appears to be present around the Dorowa Complex, but here the evidence is less complete.

FENITES

At Dorowa and Shawa, the gradual transition from granitic country rocks to syenite, and the persistence of textural features of the granitic gneiss into the syenites, shows that fenitization as originally demonstrated by Brögger (1921), has operated at these localities. The granitic rocks around Dorowa and Shawa comprise broad belts of uniform, poorly foliated adamellite gneiss, separated by well-foliated, more basic paragneiss belts, but the fenites were formed almost entirely by metasomatic alteration of adamellite gneiss. The fenites are of special interest and will be described in rather more detail than the other rock groups since, unlike those at many carbonatite complexes, they are not complicated by variations in the composition of the enclosing rocks, and at Dorowa a complete sequence is available from granitic country rocks to nepheline bearing types.

Three fenite zones, surrounding a central area of predominantly ijolitic intrusive rocks have been recognized at Dorowa. They are:

(*a*) fenitized gneiss and quartz syenitic fenite;
(*b*) syenitic fenite;
(*c*) pulaskitic fenite.

Only the first two of these have been recognized at Shawa, and in the following account the description of the first two zones applies to both Dorowa and Shawa, except where it is stated otherwise. Modal and chemical analyses of fenites from Dorowa are presented in Table I.

TABLE I

Analyses of representative fenites from the Dorowa carbonatite complex

Chemical analyses	Granitic gneiss	Granitic fenite	Syenitic fenite	Pulaskitic fenite
SiO_2	71.67	70.66	61.76	60.43
TiO_2	0.25	0.10	0.08	0.19
Al_2O_3	14.42	14.66	13.50	15.74
Fe_2O_3	0.76	0.98	3.26	3.24
FeO	1.25	0.50	0.80	1.19
MnO	0.03	0.03	0.13	0.08
MgO	0.83	0.44	3.13	1.51
CaO	2.20	2.71	5.68	4.23
Na_2O	3.73	5.64	5.91	7.15
K_2O	4.27	3.20	4.39	4.56
H_2O+	0.42	0.27	0.58	0.17
H_2O-	0.06	0.10	0.20	0.46
P_2O_5	0.09	0.13	0.51	0.72
CO_2	nd	0.60	nd	0.30
	99.98	100.02	99.93	99.97
Modal analyses				
Original Minerals				
Quartz	33.8	22.9	—	—
Potash feldspar	27.0	15.0	—	—
Plagioclase	38.2	29.2	—	—
Micro-perthite	—	—	37.5	—
Biotite	0.2	1.5	—	—
Iron Ores	0.8	0.2	—	—
'New' Minerals				
Potash feldspar	—	6.1	—	—
Plagioclase	—	13.6	21.7	—
Micro-perthite	—	—	13.5	62.7
Myrmekite	—	7.5	1.5	—
Nepheline	—	—	—	8.8
Zeolite	—	—	—	4.4
Pyroxene	—	3.4	25.5	21.5
Apatite	—	—	0.3	2.3
Calcite	—	0.6	—	0.3
Magnetite	—	—	—	—
	100.0	100.0	100.0	100.0

Chemical analyses by Mrs. E. Padget. nd = Not determined.

Fenitized granitic gneiss and quartz syenitic fenite

Since the outer limits of this zone are indefinite and poorly exposed a boundary is not drawn on the map. The first visible signs of fenitization are normally found about 3000 ft from the outer boundary of the syenitic fenite zone, where narrow veins of aegirine-augite ($X: c = 15°$) appear along joints in the granitic gneiss. Metasomatic alteration of the main body of the gneiss is, however, confined to a region within a few hundred feet of the syenitic fenite zone, in which aegirine and aegirine-augite progressively replace biotite and quartz.

The pyroxene usually replaces the rims of the grains first, and at this stage corroded biotite grains are commonly separated from the encroaching pyroxene by narrow rims of micro-crystalline feldspar. Veins of green aegirine and aegirine-augite are distributed sporadically throughout the rock at this stage. Along the inner margin of the zone, all the biotite and most of the quartz has been replaced or removed, giving quartz syenite, usually with a cellular texture. The cavities, which are usually lined with fresh acicular pyroxene crystals and correspond in size to the original quartz grains, indicate the removal of a greater volume of silica than was replaced by pyroxene. The final disappearance of quartz marks the boundary with the syenitic fenite zone.

The syenitic fenite zone

Syenitic fenite is more resistant to denudation than either the associated nepheline-bearing rocks and serpentinite or the enclosing granitic gneiss; consequently this zone occupies high ground at both complexes.

The syenites consist essentially of feldspar and pyroxene with minor amounts of apatite. The green aegirine-augite occurs as compact aggregates, and is the chief component of narrow veins of pyroxene, feldspar and apatite, which ramify throughout the rock. In thin section the feldspars are seen to be composite; the centres are remnants of the feldspar of the gneiss, while the rims comprise mosaics of new feldspar developed during fenitization. The mosaics consist of crystals of perthite, rectangular in section and about 0.2 mm in length, in which rims of albite–oligoclase enclose cores of intimately intergrown albite–oligoclase and potassic feldspar. At Dorowa the prismatic aegirine-augite crystals contain about 20 per cent of the acmite end member, but the syenite at the Shawa Complex has a more sodic pyroxene with around 50 per cent. acmite The cellular syenitic fenite, which is confined to the outer parts of this zone, has considerably less aegirine-augite than the normal type and the pyroxene is concentrated around the cavities which characterize the rock. The original feldspar is replaced or recrystallized to a limited extent only, in this variety.

Pulaskitic fenite

Pulaskite is not present at Shawa, but is an important feature of the Dorowa Complex, where it occupies a narrow, poorly exposed strip of ground between the widespread syenitic fenite zone and the central areas of intrusive ijolite. It is a coarse-grained rock which can be distinguished in the field from the syenitic fenite by the dark grey or pink colour of the feldspar and by the very dark green pyroxene. The small amount of nepheline which characterizes this type of fenite is not visible in hand specimen. At this stage it is no longer possible to distinguish between the feldspars developed during fenitization and those of the original gneiss. The feldspar, which is always perthitic, forms crystals with irregular outlines and of the order of 0.25 mm in length. Very small nepheline crystals less than 0.02 mm in diameter are developed among the perthite, both at crystal boundaries and within grains, while larger nephelines occur in groups associated with the smaller perthite crystals. The aegirine-augite crystals, with which accessory apatite is normally associated, have about 55 per cent acmite end member.

The analyses in Table I show that the progressive change from granitic gneiss to pulaskitic fenite is predominantly a decrease in silica content. Associated with this is an increase in sodium, potassium and iron. Calcium and magnesium are present in much greater amounts in the syenitic fenite zone of Dorowa, than in the adjacent ones; the syenite zone must therefore correspond to a front of calcium-magnesium metasomatism. This front is reflected in the mineralogy of the rock since there is more aegirine-augite in the syenite than in the quartz syenite and pulaskite, but the mineral is much more diopsidic than the aegirine augite of the adjacent fenite zones.

There are no independent grains of sodium and potassium feldspars in the syenitic and pulaskitic fenite; the feldspar in these rocks is entirely micro-perthitic. The temperature during fenitization must, therefore, have been high enough to permit crystallization of a homogeneous sodium-potassium feldspar. From a consideration of the solvus in the system $NaAlSi_3O_8$–$KAlSi_3O_8$–H_2O (Tuttle and Bowen, 1958), and the composition of the normative feldspar, this temperature must have been above 650°C.

IJOLITES AND NEPHELINITES

Intrusions of ijolite form an integral part of the Dorowa and Shawa Complexes. Similar rocks are the major constituents of two small independent plugs, which, together with a number of nephelinite dikes, form a suite of minor intrusions which extend over an area of about 100 sq miles around the two complexes.

At Shawa, there are two main ijolite intrusions, which with a number of small poorly exposed bodies, form an incomplete ring of intrusions between the central ultrabasic plug and the encircling zone of fenitized country rock. The largest ijolite intrusion at Shawa (on the west side) is characterized by a very coarse texture except along its eastern margin, where it is chilled against the ultrabasic plug. A further chilled zone may be present along the western edge of the body, but this region is poorly exposed, and the situation is further obscured by the presence of ijolitic and syenitic pegmatite bodies at or near the outer contact of the ijolite. One specimen of micro-ijolite from the inner chilled zone has the following modal composition: nepheline 37.6%; aegirine-augite (with about 35% acmite end member) 55.6%; biotite 0.2%; iron oxides 1.2%; apatite 5.4%. The major part of this intrusion is composed of a very coarse ijolite consisting of prisms of dark green pyroxene, which is largely augitic but has very narrow rims of aegirine-augite (with about 55 per cent acmite end member), and anhedral grey nepheline, with accessory biotite, apatite, magnetite and sphene. A number of textural types are covered by this description, all of which are characterized by a marked tendency for the nepheline and pyroxene to be segregated. In the commonest variety urtitic schlieren are enclosed in a pyroxene-rich base. The schlieren are frequently elongated and arranged parallel with one another forming pyroxene-rich and nepheline-rich bands 1–2 cm in width. The dips of these bands are quite random in magnitude and direction, although in places small scale folding appears to have affected them. Irregular, indefinitely bounded patches of melteigite complementary to the urtitic schlieren occur sporadically, and more rarely, sharply bounded angular fragments of the same rock can be seen. In places the parallel alignment of columnar pyroxenes produces a conspicuous comb structure. Irregular veins of very coarse ijolite, ranging from a few millimetres to several centimetres in width, cut the ijolite but apart from a

TABLE II

Analyses of ijolitic rocks from the Dorowa Carbonatite Complex and from the plug to the west of the Complex

	1	2	3	4
SiO_2	42.40	44.09	42.81	47.26
TiO_2	1.00	1.43	1.28	0.32
Al_2O_3	20.82	11.76	18.91	15.53
Fe_2O_3	4.37	5.31	4.20	4.46
FeO	2.73	4.96	5.58	2.16
MnO	0.14	0.17	0.18	0.11
MgO	3.30	10.17	4.10	4.84
CaO	6.45	12.17	8.31	11.16
Na_2O	11.69	5.99	9.59	7.69
K_2O	3.40	2.02	3.02	3.51
H_2O+	1.57	0.45	0.41	0.81
H_2O-	0.04	0.24	0.15	0.20
P_2O_5	1.00	1.07	1.38	1.87
CO_2	0.74	nd	nd	nd
SrO	tr	nd	nd	nd
Cl	0.03	nd	nd	nd
S	0.18	nd	nd	nd
V_2O_3	0.03	nd	nd	nd
BaO	0.04	nd	nd	nd
	99.93	99.83	99.92	99.92

1. Ijolite. Plug to the west of the Dorowa Complex. P. I. Brewer (Swift, 1952), anal.
2. Olivine Ijolite. Plug to the west of the Dorowa Complex. Mrs. E. Padget, anal.
3. Nephelinite. Plug to the west of the Dorowa Complex. Mrs. E. Padget, anal.
4. Ijolite. Dorowa Complex. Mrs. E. Padget, anal.
nd = Not determined.

rather higher content of accessory sphene and biotite, these veins have a similar composition to the rocks they cut. Pale green apatite is a common accessory mineral, occurring as single crystals and small patches of sugary grains. In places, however, it is concentrated to form irregularly shaped, rather ill-defined pods of apatite-rich ijolite or melteigite, or in many cases, an apatite-pyroxene rock in which apatite takes the place of nepheline in the texture of the rock.

The ijolite body in the north east is smaller than that in the west and consists of a fairly homogeneous medium-grained biotite ijolite. Several other outcrops of medium-grained ijolite occur along the fenite-serpentinite contact, but are too small to appear on the accompanying map.

A number of small bodies of very coarse, often pegmatitic, syenite and ijolite intersect both the ijolite and the fenite near the ijolite-fenite contact. These bodies are not well exposed, but appear to be roughly oval in plan with a major diameter varying from a few tens of feet to several hundred feet. They include mesotype pegmatites which are composed largely of aegirine-augite and perthitic feldspar, but often contain nepheline especially where they cut the ijolite. The melanocratic pegmatites and coarse syenites are commonly melteigitic and malignitic in composition and consist of about 75 per cent green aegirine-augite and various proportions of nepheline and potassium feldspar.

At Dorowa the central part of the complex is occupied by three areas of nepheline-rich rocks. Medium-grained ijolite (see analysis in Table II) is the commonest type, although foyaites, malignites and apatite-pyroxene rocks are developed locally. The rocks have a hypidiomorphic texture in which subhedral prisms of green aegirine-augite, having about 35 per cent acmite end member, are ophitically or poikilitically enclosed by anhedral nepheline grains and, where the rocks are foyaitic, by anhedral potassium feldspar crystals.

Lack of exposure hinders the determination of the inter-relationships of these rocks, or the character of the contact with the pulaskite fenite, though the latter is believed to be sharp since ijolite and fenite have been seen in places within a few yards of each other. In addition, sharply bounded xenoliths of fenite have been found in loose blocks of ijolite.

In view of this relationship and the fact that the predominant rock type is similar in composition and texture to the rocks of the chilled zone of the western ijolite intrusion at Shawa, these areas are regarded as representing three ijolite intrusions, or, more probably, three cupolas above a single intrusion.

MINOR INTRUSIONS

These comprise two small plugs of ijolite and a widespread suite of nephelinite dikes. The plug immediately west of Dorowa consists largely of ijolite with lesser amounts of olivine-ijolite and porphyritic nephelinite (see analyses in Table II), while the intrusion to the SE of the complex consists entirely of olivine ijolite. The constituent minerals of the ijolites of the two plugs are similar to those in the western ijolite at Shawa, except for the presence of olivine (Fa_{13}) in the olivine ijolites, and a brown amphibole with optical properties similar to those of soda tremolite, occurring interstitially in the ijolite and nephelinite at the first-mentioned plug.

The nephelinite dikes are commonly about two feet in width and are usually vertical or dip steeply. Their strikes show no regional pattern except in the vicinity of Dorowa where a NNW trending swarm corresponds in position and direction to a fracture-zone in the gneisses. The dikes have a fine blue-grey groundmass and vary mainly in the number and composition of the pheno-crysts. The groundmass consists predominantly of nepheline and ragged prisms of aegirine-augite; nepheline is usually replaced by zeolites or calcite. In addition small amounts of biotite, magnetite, apatite and fluorite are frequently also present. The commonest phenocrysts are nepheline, occurring usually as well-shaped tabular crystals, and augite, with aegirine-augite rims. Brown horn-blende, biotite and olivine are less common as phenocrysts.

THE ULTRABASIC ROCKS AT SHAWA

The major part of the Shawa Complex is underlain by serpentinite. Dunite is found only in the south, as small outcrops enclosed by serpentinite and as loose blocks scattered over it.

The dunite consists almost entirely of fresh green olivine with minor magnetite, and, locally, magnetite-rich bands. The normal dunite is about 96 per cent olivine and 4 per cent magnetite. Spinel and colourless clinopyroxene are also present, but the amount of clinopyroxene is too small for precise identification. The olivine is colourless in thin section and forms subhedral to anhedral grains ranging in diameter from 1 mm to 1 cm. The refractive indices (± 0.002) of two crystals are as follows:

$$1. \quad \alpha = 1.647 \quad \beta = 1.666 \quad \gamma = 1.691$$
$$2. \quad \alpha = 1.654 \quad \beta = 1.665 \quad \gamma = 1.685$$

These indicate a composition Fa_{17} (Poldervaart, 1950). The serpentinite is usually weathered and brown in hand specimen, and is seen in thin section to be largely replaced by calcite and quartz. Veins of very fine-grained magnesite with accessory phlogopite intersect the serpentinite.

MICACEOUS AND MAGNETITE–APATITE–OLIVINE ROCKS

WNW trending veins and disseminations of hydrated micas are concentrated at two localities at Shawa. Immediately NW of the ring dike, veins of a brown mica, with a slight exfoliation potential are enclosed by serpentinite, while in the extreme NE part of the complex a golden mica with the physical properties of vermiculite is developed in the serpentinite and adjacent ijolite and fenite.

At the northern end of the Dorowa Complex, dikes, veins and stringers of yellow friable vermiculite-apatite rock intersect the fenite and in places form a valuable phosphate ore. In the richer parts of the ore bodies the vermiculite-apatite rock is greatly in excess of the syenitic fenite which is reduced to the form of narrow lenticular screens. A partial analysis of the mica gave 0.04% total alkalis, indicating that it is vermiculite. One apatite analysis gave 3.38% fluorine and 0.10% chlorine, and a crystal gave the following figures for the refractive indices: $N_\varepsilon = 1.635 \pm 0.002$, $N_\omega = 1.639 \pm 0.002$. Accessory constituents of the rock include magnetite and more rarely baddeleyite.

The vermiculite-apatite rock and enclosing fenite are cut by a series of veins composed of magnetite and apatite with subordinate serpentine. The veins have the following approximate modal composition: apatite 70%, magnetite 25%, serpentine 5%. The minor, but extremely interesting, serpentine component is usually silicified, but in many cases has clearly replaced well-developed olivine crystals occurring as isolated individuals in the apatite matrix.

There is also a group of magnetite dikes, which vary from 6–15 ft in thickness and dip NNE at angles of 40°–80°, emplaced in the syenitic fenite zone at the

SW corner of the complex. Magnetite comprises more than 95 per cent of the dikes, and is very coarse throughout, with no finer grained, marginal phase. The crystals average about 20 cm across and are generally anhedral, although in places there are pockets of sugary apatite, against which the magnetite has developed octahedral and subordinate dodecahedral faces.

A large mass of magnetite-serpentine rock, which is enclosed by syenitic fenite in the northern part of the Dorowa Complex will be mentioned here, although it may be genetically related to the serpentinite at Shawa rather than to the vein and dike assemblage of Dorowa. The serpentine, which is silicified, has replaced the olivine of a magnetite-dunite or magnetite-peridotite, which originally contained 80–90 per cent of olivine.

CARBONATITES

Carbonate rocks occupy only a small part of the area of the two complexes, but show a considerable variety of composition and texture. The carbonatites of the two complexes differ somewhat in composition being dolomitic at Shawa and predominantly calcitic at Dorowa.

At Dorowa three types of carbonatite have been recognized: alvikite, sövite and porphyritic beforsite.

Alvikite—Fine-grained calcitic carbonatite

This, the most abundant type of carbonatite at Dorowa, makes up the plug and most of the dikes. The weathered surfaces of the rock usually have a banded structure which in the dikes is very steeply dipping or vertical, and parallel to the walls. In the plug the banding has a concentric strike, dips steeply outwards and is parallel to the outer contact of the plug where it is exposed in the extreme SE. The banding does not reflect any textural or compositional variation visible in thin sections which show a very fine-grained aggregate of rather irregularly shaped groups of calcite grains, which often radiate from points or planes. It seems probable that the banding reflects an original texture which has been obliterated by subsequent recrystallization. Magnetite, an important minor constituent of the rock, occurs as octahedral grains, often with spinel law twinning, and sometimes broken into irregular fragments separated by the calcite matrix; some have embayments suggestive of corrosion.

Sövite—Coarse-grained calcitic carbonatite

Three dikes of sövite have been located at Dorowa. They consist largely of white, coarsely crystalline calcite, with accessory magnetite, phlogopite, apatite and pyrite.

Porphyritic Beforsite—Dolomite phenocrysts in a fine-grained dolomitic matrix

Dolomitic carbonatite is found in only small amounts at Dorowa. In the SE part of the plug there is a steeply dipping sheet about 10 ft thick, with margins concordant with the banding in the enclosing alvikite. In addition, one dike consists solely of porphyritic beforsite, and another dike of alvikite contains concordant lenticular inclusions of porphyritic beforsite. The large phenocrysts of dolomite which characterize this rock are distributed throughout a fine-grained, buff-coloured matrix. They are colourless, up to 4 cm across, and tend to be rhombohedral in shape, but with rounded edges and embayments suggestive of corrosion. They are enclosed by coronae of fibrous dolomite crystals several millimetres in length, arranged with their long axes perpendicular to the margins of the phenocrysts. The matrix is made up of dolomite fibres identical to those of the coronae, but randomly orientated. A few patches and stringers of small, rhombohedral grains and an occasional small magnetite grain are scattered throughout the groundmass. The large dolomite crystals have the refractive index $N_\omega = 1.684 \pm 0.003$. Spectrographic determinations indicate that the matrix and phenocrysts are identical in composition as far as the major elements are concerned, within the limit of the method, which is about ± 15 per cent of content.

At Shawa dolomitic carbonatite occurs as dikes enclosed in serpentinite. These fall naturally into two groups:

    1. The ring dike of foliated and porphyritic dolomite.
    2. Dikes outside the ring dike, of massive even-grained dolomite.

The ring dike has a diameter of about 5000 ft, is oval in plan and ranges in width from 100 to 1000 ft. The margins are not clear-cut. Within about 50 ft of the contact, veins of dolomite anastomose through the serpentinite, and these increase in abundance towards the mapped boundary, within which the serpentinite occurs as lenticular fragments enclosed in the carbonatite of the ring dike, their long axes parallel to the foliation. Porphyritic beforsites occur in the eastern and northern sections of the ring dike, where they arc generally much richer in phenocrysts than the Dorowa beforsites described above, and in many places the dolomite crystals are very large indeed, and may be as much as 10 cm across, in which case they make up a major part of the rock.

In the southern section the dike is finer grained and consists almost entirely of parallel lenticular dolomite crystals $N_\omega = 1.684 \pm 0.003$, which give the rock a strong foliation that is vertical in attitude and has a concentric strike parallel to the margins of the dike. Phlogopite, magnetite and apatite are common accessory minerals. The dimensional orientation of the carbonate grains is accompanied by a marked lattice orientation; the c-axes of the dolomite crystals have a strong tendency to be normal to the foliation giving a fabric with a strong orthorhombic symmetry.

The foliation does not flow round the serpentinite inclusions, but is truncated by them; it is also developed in narrow veins of dolomite cutting the inclusions, and is there independent of the orientation of the vein, but parallel to the foliation in the enclosing dolomite.

The fabric in the dolomite of the southern section of the ring dike (Johnson, 1961, Fig. 5) resembles that which has been produced experimentally (Turner *et al.*, 1956, p. 1275, Fig. 9A) by compressing specimens of Yule Marble. The grains in the artificially deformed rock are elongated normal to the direction of compression, and the c-axes form a narrow ring maximum around the compression axis. The dimensional and lattice orientation patterns are thus the same as those in the Shawa dolomite, except that the latter yields a double point maximum rather than the ring maximum of the deformed Yule Marble. If the resemblance between the artificial and natural fabrics is taken to imply a similarity in the stress patterns which controlled the development of the two fabrics, and if the relation of foliation to inclusions is taken to imply that the foliation was developed after emplacement of the veins, then the ring dike at Shawa must have been deformed and recrystallized under a radial compressive stress. Such a stress pattern could possibly have been due to the volume increase consequent on the serpentinization of the dunite.

Sixteen quantitative spectrographic determinations have been made on specimens of carbonatite from Shawa and Dorowa (Johnson, 1961, Table 7). No correlation has been found between trace element variation and the ratio of magnesium to calcium, nor has any systematic variation between the different types of carbonatite body been detected. The general statement made by Higazy (1954) that, compared with limestones of sedimentary origin, carbonatites are rich in barium, strontium, lanthanum and yttrium and have Sr > Ba is borne out by the present work. Narrow barite veins have been noted at two localities at Shawa cutting serpentinite (Fig. 1). However, Higazy's assertion that La > Y, is not in accordance with the figures from Shawa and Dorowa where yttrium is equal to, or slightly in excess of lanthanum. Rare earths are, however, low at these two carbonatite localities, compared with others, and yttrium and lanthanum together do not exceed 210 ppm. Cerium was sought but not detected, the limit of detection being 300 ppm. Niobium is also low, 30 ppm being the highest content recorded. Thorium and uranium were not detected (limit of detection 100 ppm), and all the rocks of the two complexes give a lower background radioactivity than the enclosing gneisses.

PETROGENESIS

The emplacement of the carbonatites

Wyllie and Tuttle (1960) have demonstrated that liquids in the system $CaO-CO_2-H_2O$ which correspond to simplified carbonatite magmas can exist over a wide pressure range at moderate temperatures. Gittins and Tuttle (in press) have recently drawn attention to the textural similarity between the porphyritic beforsite, developed at Dorowa and Shawa, and some of their quenched charges in carbonate systems. They suggest that the porphyritic beforsite represents a dolomitic liquid which contained dolomite crystals in equilibrium with it. This implies that the Shawa ring dike, which has porphyritic beforsite as an important component, and one of the dikes at Dorowa which is made up entirely of this rock were both emplaced as magmas. There is no conclusive evidence concerning the mode of emplacement of the massive dolomite dikes at Shawa or of the alvi-kite plug and alvikite and sövite dikes at Dorowa. In the absence of any evidence to the contrary, however, it seems reasonable to suggest that all the carbonate bodies at the two complexes were emplaced in the same state, i.e. as magmatic liquids.

Source of the carbonatite magma and fenitizing fluid

At Shawa and Dorowa the carbonatite magmas were intruded into earlier members of the association, and little direct evidence is available concerning their origin. At several of the younger carbonatite-bearing complexes in Uganda and Tanganyika extrusive rocks are preserved, which are almost entirely ijolitic in composition and occupy large volumes in comparison with the size of carbonatite bodies, which were emplaced at a late stage in the history of the centre. These relationships have been stressed by King (1949), King and Sutherland (1960; this vol., p. 98) and James (1956), who regard the carbonatite as a derivative of a carbonated ijolite magma. Although no extrusive rocks are preserved at the much older Shawa and Dorowa centres, small ijolite plugs and a widespread suite of nephelinite dikes testify to the availability of ijolitic magma over an area of 100 sq miles or more. This contrasts with the limited distribution of the carbonatite rocks, which are confined to the two centres, and even within these occupy a lesser area than the associated ijolite intrusions. It seems highly probable that Shawa and Dorowa represent more deeply eroded members of the nephelinite–carbonatite association, as exemplified by centres such as Napak in Uganda (King, 1949; King and Sutherland, this vol., p. 97) and that at these two localities ijolitic magma was parental to the carbonatite magmas.

At Dorowa the fenite zones are arranged around areas of ijolitic rocks but show no regular spatial relationship to the carbonatite bodies, which appear to have been emplaced after the fenitization. There seems little doubt, therefore, that at Dorowa the source of the fenitizing fluids lay in ijolitic rather than carbonatitic magmas. At Shawa the evidence is less clear, but the distribution of the fenite zones is consistent with an ijolitic rather than a carbonatitic source for the fluids.

At several other carbonatite localities, notably those of the Chilwa Alkaline Province in Malawi (Garson and Campbell Smith, 1958; Garson, this vol., pp. 51–53), some at least, of the fenitization is related to sövite intrusions. This contrast in the composition of the source magmas is less remarkable if the carbonatite magma itself is regarded as a residual fluid derived from ijolitic magma.

The emplacement of the dunite at Shawa

The problem of the genesis and emplacement of the ultrabasic rocks at Shawa cannot be solved by invoking special processes or circumstances, since similar ultrabasic rocks have been described from a number of other carbonatite complexes in Africa and elsewhere.

v. Eckermann has suggested (1948) that at the Alnö carbonatite complex in Sweden, olivine was produced by the dedolomitization of a dolomitic carbonatite magma, through the agency of silica withdrawn from the wall rocks during fenitization. At Shawa, however, the dolomitic carbonatite intrudes the ultrabasic rocks and, moreover, there is no sign of the large volumes of calcite which would be liberated by such a process. Although some other metasomatic process cannot be ruled out, a magmatic parentage for the Shawa dunite, possibly involving gravity differentiation, is consistent with evidence from other rocks belonging to the alkali suite at this locality, and from elsewhere. Olivine is a common accessory mineral in the intrusive ijolites associated with the Shawa and Dorowa Complexes, and olivine-rich intrusive and effusive rocks are associated with nephelinites of a similar age in the Nuanetsi Igneous Province (Cox *et al.* 1965).

Generation of the alkaline magma

The development of present ideas on the generation of Karroo alkaline magmas in general, and those parental to the Dorowa and Shawa carbonatite complexes in particular, is dependent on a consideration of the disposition of the Karroo volcanic rocks in space and time. It is therefore necessary in this discussion to give a brief outline of the Karroo igneous activity of southern Africa.

The Karroo lavas are about 4500 ft thick in the Karroo Basin, but are much thicker (about 27,000 ft) in the east. Walker and Poldervaart (1949) have divided the volcanic areas into three provinces: a central province in which the lavas are essentially basaltic, and eastern and western provinces where, in addition to basalts, there are rhyolites, basic alkaline lavas and their intrusive equivalents. The western province includes the plutons of Erongo, Messum, Cape Cross and Okonjeje in South West Africa and can now be extended to include a number of carbonatite complexes recently described (Martin *et al.*, 1960) from the same territory.

The Shawa and Dorowa carbonatite complexes are associated with the eastern province, which will be discussed with special reference to recent work (Cox *et al.*, 1965) in the Nuanetsi Igneous Province of south eastern Rhodesia, about 150 miles south of the two carbonatite localities.

The Nuanetsi Province includes a thick sequence of Karroo lavas, developed in a deep and extensive ESE plunging volcano-tectonic depression, the Nuanetsi Syncline. The southern limb of this syncline curves into, and is continuous with, the eastward-dipping Lebombo Monocline and its NE extension to the Lupata Gorge. These monoclines separate the uplifted central part of southern Africa from the depressed continental margin to the east, and mark a zone of intense vulcanicity which corresponds to the eastern province of Walker and Poldervaart. North of the Lupata Gorge in Malawi lies the post-Karroo, Chilwa Alkaline Province (Garson and Campbell Smith, 1958) comprising a group of post-Karroo intrusive rocks which include carbonatite-bearing complexes.

Cox *et al.*, 1965, have shown that the volcanic sequence in the Nuanetsi Igneous Province consists of a lower group of basalts, followed by rhyolitic extrusives with interbedded basalts. The lower basalts form a continuous series from olivine-rich limburgites in the lower part of the succession to over-saturated normal tholeiites beneath the rhyolites. The lower part of the limburgite succession contains numerous intrusions of picritic rocks, many with strong alkaline affinities. Nephelinites and related nepheline-bearing rocks are found in small quantities among the earliest flows, and comprise the very significant Lower Alkaline Group.

A volcanic sequence similar to the above is also found along the Lebombo Monocline (Du Toit, 1929) where, as in the Nuanetsi Province, a thick sequence of basalts with limburgites and nephelinites at the base in the north, are followed by rhyolites. Then follows a further series of basalts unrepresented at Nuanetsi, where the rhyolites dip under the unconformable base of the Cretaceous. These upper basalts of the Lebombo include basanites, tephrites and phonolitic rocks.

The phonolites of the Lupata Gorge (Dixey and Campbell Smith, 1929) overlie the Karroo rhyolites and basalts unconformably and are similar to the Upper Alkaline Group of the Lebombo in contrast with the Lower Alkaline Group of Nuanetsi and the Lebombo.

Cox, (Cox, *et al.*, 1965), in considering the petrogenesis of the rocks of the Nuanetsi Province argues that for a number of reasons, not all the Karroo volcanic rocks can be considered as differentiates of a single magma available in Karroo times. These reasons include the vast volumes of acidic rocks which have been erupted, and the fact that the observed chemical variations in the basalts of Nuanetsi cannot be interpreted in terms of conventional crystal fractionation of the observed phenocrysts. It is proposed that the major variations in the Lebombo-Nuanetsi zone are due to a thermal disturbance, producing a large range of primary magmas by the remelting of a simple layered substructure at different levels. The symmetry in the volcanic succession leads to the concept of the Karroo Volcanic Cycle, an essentially thermal event, consisting of a waxing phase during which the geo-isotherms rise; a culmination when the geothermal gradient reached its steepest inclination; and a waning phase during which a normal geothermal gradient was re-established. Rocks with alkaline affinities, having a deep-seated origin were erupted at the beginning and end of the cycle, while rhyolites were produced by the melting of the crust at the culmination. The waxing phase represents the ideal environment for rock variation by melting processes, whereas the waning phase provides conditions conducive to crystallization differentiation. The position of the Lower Alkaline Group at the very base of the succession is difficult to reconcile with any hypothesis that these rocks originated by some process of differentiation of a magma of more normal composition, and it seems more probable that they were produced by partial fusion of an earth layer as the geo-isotherms began to rise.

Yoder and Tilley (1962) have produced experimental evidence that fractionation of peridotite melts at very high pressure may produce alkaline derivatives. If these results may be applied in principle to partial fusion then the suggested origin of the Lower Alkaline Group by partial fusion becomes theoretically possible. Yoder and Tilley apply their depth control mechanism to explain the succession in the volcanoes of the Hawaiian Islands. They state that 'the appearance of large volumes of tholeiitic lavas, followed in the closing stages of the activity by alkali-type lavas suggests that the source of the magma increases in depth with time'. There is a likely parallel between this sequence and that developed in the waning phase of the Nuanetsi cycle leading to the eruption of the Upper Alkaline Group. By contrast the Lower Alkaline Group of the waxing phase shows the reverse sequence as the geo-isotherms begin to rise and the reverse process of partial melting ensues.

It has been suggested above that the generation of magmas in the Nuanetsi Igneous Province, including those of an alkaline composition, can be explained in terms of a cyclical rise, culmination, and fall of geo-isotherms through a layered earth structure. At Shawa and Dorowa, ijolitic magmas believed to represent the parent magmas of the association, were available over a wide area, and no rocks intermediate between ijolite and basalt are in evidence. It seems probable, therefore, that the ijolites and nephelinites at Shawa and Dorowa, like those in the Nuanetsi Province originated by some process other than the fractional crystallization of basalt.

Since the age determination has indicated that Shawa and Dorowa can be considered as features of Karroo Vulcanicity, it is suggested that the process of partial fusion of an ultra-basic layer under high pressures, in the mantle, which has been argued for the origin of the nephelinite at Nuanetsi, was also responsible for the generation of the parent magmas at Dorowa and Shawa where, however, the rise of the geo-isotherms apparently culminated at a relatively lower level, before they had risen to a sufficient extent to produce basalt.

It is possible that the dunite at Shawa, which must be regarded as an essential part of the alkaline association, may be related to, or derived from magmas similar to those represented by the olivine-rich rocks which are to be found in the Nuanetsi Province. Significantly, these latter rocks occur as lavas and minor intrusions associated with or immediately following the nepheline-bearing rocks of the Lower Alkaline Group. They include limburgites with up to 20 per cent olivine and picrites with up to 50 per cent olivine. Both rock groups contain olivines with a composition similar to that of the Shawa dunite (Cox *et al.*, 1965).

The concept of the Karroo Volcanic Cycle can be further extended in an attempt to explain the puzzling contrast, even allowing for differences in erosion level, between Dorowa and Shawa on the one hand and the Chilwa Alkaline Province (Garson and Campbell Smith, 1958) on the other. In the latter area large intrusions of quartz syenite, syenite and nepheline syenite are associated with the carbonatite centres, and there is a much greater variety of rocks than at Dorowa and Shawa, where the associated igneous intrusions are restricted to nephelinites and ijolites.

Bloomfield (1961), however, has quoted an age of 138 ± 14 my for the Chilwa Province and Garson (1961) has equated it with the Lupata Alkaline Volcanics. More recently Snelling (1965) has obtained an age of 123 ± 6 my for micas from a carbonatite at Kangankunde in the Chilwa Province. By contrast the Shawa and Dorowa Complexes are considerably older (209 ± 16 my). On this basis the Dorowa and Shawa Complexes can be equated with the waxing stage of the complete cycle, as developed in Nuanetsi, or with the culmination of the thermal cycle at a much lower level, whereas the Chilwa Province is clearly equivalent in both age and general variety and types of rocks to the waning phase of the complete Karroo Volcanic Cycle, fully developed in the neighbouring Lupata Area.

Another important area where Karroo or early post-Karroo alkaline rocks were developed, is in South West Africa (Martin *et al.*, 1960). Here there are a number of carbonatite complexes, which include granites, syenites, nepheline syenites and small amounts of ijolitic rocks within their limits. Their age, relative to the other Karroo extrusive and intrusive rocks is not known. However, at a number of the other Karroo ring-complexes of South West Africa, notably

Okonjeje (Simpson, 1954) and Messum (Korn and Martin, 1954), alkaline rocks similar to those forming part of the carbonatite complexes, were developed at a late stage in the history of the centres. These can clearly be referred to the waning stage of the local Karroo cycle, and it seems highly probable that the South West Africa carbonatites, like those of the Chilwa Province, can also be related to the waning phase of the igneous cycle. Again the contrast between the varied series of magmas developed in the South West Africa carbonatite complexes, and the very limited range of magma type at Dorowa and Shawa can be related to their generation at different stages in the thermal cycle.

The hypotheses concerning alkaline magma generation discussed in this chapter are of a tentative nature, but they clearly indicate that any general study of carbonatites should take into consideration the possible fundamental differences between parental magmas produced at difference stages of a volcanic cycle.

SUMMARY OF CONCLUSIONS

The Shawa and Dorowa carbonatite complexes were emplaced in Karroo times and contain examples of the four contrasting rock types, each of unusual composition, which characterize carbonatite associations. These four groups and their representatives at Shawa and Dorowa are:

1. Alkaline intrusive rocks—ijolites, olivine ijolites and nephelinites.
2. Fenites—quartz syenitic, syenitic and pulaskitic fenite.
3. Ultrabasic rocks—dunite, serpentinite and magnetite–apatite–olivine rocks.
4. Carbonatites—dolomitic and calcitic carbonatites.

The carbonatites were emplaced as magmatic liquids which, with the fenitizing fluids, were derived, probably as residua, from a parental ijolite magma. Ijolitic magmas were among the earliest products of the Karroo Igneous Cycle in the nearby Nuanetsi–Lebombo zone, and have been attributed to the partial melting of deep-seated ultrabasic rocks at high pressures, as the geo-isotherms began to rise. It is suggested that the ijolitic magmas parental to the Dorowa and Shawa carbonatite complexes were generated by the same process, either at the beginning of the waxing phase of the thermal cycle or at its culmination at a relatively low level. Picrites and olivine-rich limburgites are associated with the nephelinites at Nuanetsi, and olivine-rich magmas of a similar deep seated origin may have been parental to the Shawa dunite. The concept of a thermal cycle with a waxing phase, culmination, and waning phase is extended to explain the contrast between the magmas of the Chilwa Alkaline Province of Malawi and of the Karroo alkaline rocks of South West Africa which correspond to the waning phase of the Karroo Cycle on the one hand, and those of Dorowa and Shawa corresponding to the waxing phase or low level culmination of the cycle on the other.

I am indebted to Professor W. Q. Kennedy and Professor R. M. Shackleton for critically reading the manuscript, and to my co-workers in the Nuanetsi area for discussion and information. The work was carried out in the Leeds University Research Institute of African Geology, which was founded through the generosity of the Anglo-American Mining Corporation of South Africa.

REFERENCES

Bloomfield, K., 1961, The age of the Chilwa Alkaline Province: *Nyasaland Geol. Surv. Rec.*, v. **1**, p. 95.

Brögger, W. C., 1921, Die eruptivegesteine des Kristianiagebietes—IV. Des Fengebiet in Telemark, Norwegen: *Vidensk. Selsk. Skr.* 1, *Math. Nat. Kl.*, No. **9**.

Cox, K. G., Johnson, R. L., Monkman, L. J., Stillman, C. J., Vail, J. R., and Wood, D.N., 1965. The geology of the Nuanetsi igneous province: *Roy. Soc. London Phil. Trans.*, *ser. A.*, v. **257**, pp. 71–218.

Dixey, F. and Campbell Smith, W., 1929, The rocks of the Lupata Gorge and the north side of the lower Zambesi: *Geol. Mag.*, v. **66**, pp. 241–259.

Du Toit, A. L., 1929, The volcanic belt of the Lebombo—A region of tension: *Roy. Soc. South Africa Trans.*, v. **18**, p. 189.

Du Toit, A. L., 1954, *The Geology of South Africa:* Edinburgh and London, Oliver & Boyd, 3rd. Ed.

Garson, M. S., 1961, *The Tundulu Carbonatite Ring-Complex in Southern Nyasaland:* Ph.D. Thesis, Leeds University, England.

Garson, M. S., 1962. The Tundulu carbonatite ring complex in Southern Nyasaland: *Nyasaland Geol. Surv. Mem.* **2**.

Garson, M. S., and Smith, W. C., 1958. Chilwa Island: *Nyasaland Geol. Surv.*, Mem. **1**.

Gittins, J. and Tuttle, O. F., Further evidence for the existence of carbonate liquids: (in press).

Higazy, R. A., 1954, Trace elements of volcanic ultrabasic potassic rocks of South-Western Uganda and adjoining parts of the Belgian Congo: *Geol. Soc. America Bull.*, v. **65**, pp. 39–70.

James, T.C., 1956, Carbonatites and rift valleys in East Africa: *Int. Geol. Congr.*, *20th sess.*, *Assoc. des Serv. Geol. Africains*, p. 325 (abstract only).

Johnson, R. L., 1959, *The Geology of The Dorowa and Shawa Carbonatite Complexes, Buhera District, Southern Rhodesia:* Ph.D. Thesis, Leeds University, England.

Johnson, R. L., 1961, The geology of the Dorowa and Shawa carbonatite complexes, Southern Rhodesia: *Geol. Soc. S. Africa Trans.*, v. **64**, pp. 101–146.

King, B. C., 1949, The Napak area of Southern Karamoja, Uganda: A Study of a dissected late Tertiary volcano: *Uganda, Geol. Surv. Mem.* **5**.

King, B. C. and Sutherland, D. S., 1960, Alkaline rocks of Eastern and Southern Africa, Parts I, II and III: *Sci. Progr.*, v. **48**, pp. 298–321, 504–524 and 709–720.

Korn, H. and Martin, H., 1954, The Messum igneous complex in South West Africa: *Geol. Soc. S. Africa Trans.*, v. **57**, p. 83.

MacGregor, A. M., 1951, Some milestones in the Precambrian of Southern Rhodesia: *Geol. Soc. S. Africa Trans.*, v. **54**, p. xxvii-lxxi.

Martin, H., Mathias, M. and Simpson, E. S. W., 1960, The Damaraland subvolcanic ring complexes in South West Africa: *Int. Geol. Congr.*, *21st sess.*, Pt. 13, pp. 156–174.

Mathias, M., 1956, The petrology of the Messum igneous complex South West Africa: *Geol. Soc. S. Africa Trans.*, v. **59**, pp. 23–58.

McElhinny, M. W. and Opdyke, N. D., 1964, The palaeomagnetism of the Precambrian dolerites of eastern Southern Rhodesia, an example of geologic correlation by rock magnetism: *Jour. Geophys. Res.* v. **69**, p. 2469.

Nicolaysen, L. O., Burger, A. J. and Johnson, R. L. 1962, The age of the Shawa carbonatite complex: *Geol. Soc. S. Africa Trans.*, v. **65**, pp. 293–294.

Poldervaart, A., 1950, Correlation of physical properties and chemical composition in the plagioclase, olivine and orthopyroxene series: *Am. Mineralogist*, v. **35**, pp. 1067–1079.

Simpson, E. S. W., 1954, The Okonjeje igneous complex, South West Africa: *Geol. Soc. S. Africa Trans.*, v. **57**, pp. 125–172.

Snelling, N. J., 1965. Age determinations on three African carbonatites: *Nature*, v. **205**, p.491.

Swift, W. H., 1952, The geology of Chishanya, Buhera District, Southern Rhodesia: *Edin. Geol. Soc. Trans.*, v. **15**, pp. 346–359.

Turner, F. J., Griggs, D. T., Clark, R. H. and Dixon, R. H., 1956, Deformation of Yule Marble. Part VII: Development of oriented fabrics at 300°C–500°C: *Geol. Soc. America Bull.*, v. **67**, pp. 1259–1293.

Tuttle, O. F. and Bowen, N. L., 1958, Origin of granite in the light of experimental studies in the system NaAISi$_3$O$_8$–KAISi$_3$O$_8$–SiO$_2$–H$_2$O: *Geol. Soc. America, Mem.* **74**.

v. Eckermann, H., 1948, The alkaline district of Alnö Island: *Sver. Geol. Undersok., Ser. Ca.* **36**.

Walker, F. and Poldervaart, A., 1949, Karroo dolerites of the Union of South Africa: *Geol. Soc. America Bull.*, v. **60**, pp. 591–706.

Wyllie, P. J. and Tuttle, O. F., 1960, The System CaO–CO$_2$–H$_2$O and the origin of carbonatites: *Jour. Petrology*, v. **1**, pp. 1–46.

Yoder, H. S. and Tilley, C. E., 1962, Origin of basalt magmas: an experimental study of natural and synthetic systems: *Jour. Petrology*, v. **3**, p. 342.

T. F. W. BARTH and I. B. RAMBERG

The Fen Circular
Complex

INTRODUCTION

The small ring complex of carbonatites and peralkaline rocks at Fen in Telemark
with its satellitic vents and diatremes is in southern Norway 2 km west of the
Oslo graben (Fig. 1). The peculiar rock association at Fen was discovered by

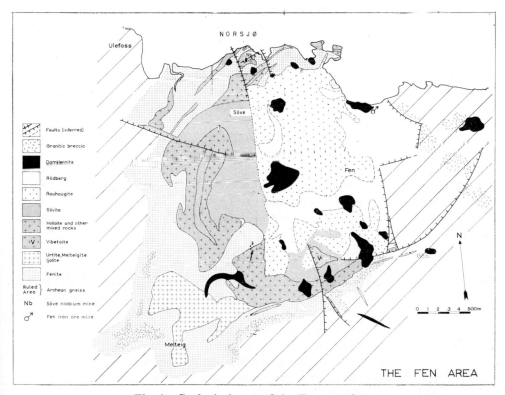

Fig. 1   Geological map of the Fen complex.

Goldschmidt in 1918 but it is known primarily through the classic studies of
Brögger (1921) who proposed the existence of a carbonate-rich magma. The
age was also put as Jotnian or Eocambrian and thus much older than the in-

225

trusives of the Oslo area. This has subsequently been confirmed by radioactive dating.[1]

Brögger's interpretation was criticized by Bowen (1924, 1926), who believed that the carbonatite represented carbonated silicate rocks, but Brauns (1925, 1926), a man carrying great weight among German-speaking geologists, strongly supported Brögger. 'Die Abhandlung von Bowen ist nicht geeignet, diese Anschauung zu erschüttern.'

TECTONIC SETTING

The Fen volcanism is related to faults striking parallel to the margins of the Baltic Precambrian shield. Similarly located are the carbonatites of Alnö, Sweden, and of the Kola Peninsula, U.S.S.R.

The last movements in the Oslo area are of Permian age but the faults at Fen are Eocambrian and consequently much older (560 my against 240 my) and contemporaneous with the formation of the sparagmite basin about 200 km N of Fen. Nevertheless there is much evidence to show that the Fen and Oslo fault systems represent the initial and concluding phases of the epoch. Like the African rift valleys whose pattern originated in Precambrian time, the Oslo–Rhine rift valley seems to have had a long history. At the time of the stepped subsidence of the sparagmite basin the initial break-throughs of the magmatic fluids rich in carbon dioxide and other volatiles took place in the Oslo rift. For three hundred million years the evolution of the rift continued together with the slow generation of the Oslo magmas that were finally erupted in Permian time.

The area around the Fen complex is characterized by breccia zones, and concentric and radial faults which, in part, show appreciable vertical displacements.

Fen is only one of the many explosion sites; a large number of smaller vents or diatremes are distributed over the same system of fissures. Some are spatters of quenched magma (partly tinguaitic, etc., partly kimberlitic) while others are simply explosion vents filled only with brecciated fragments of the surrounding gneisses.

Faults

The faults radiating from the central parts of the area continue up to several hundred metres into the surrounding gneisses. They caused brecciation and mylonitization of the silicate rocks, but the carbonatites of the central parts reacted more plastically and became strongly foliated parallel to the directions of the faults. The concentric faults, with centres at the Fen mines (Saether, 1957) often mark the contacts of the Fen complex, but some of them are within the carbonatites. Always the central parts have sunk relative to the outer rocks, i.e. typical cauldron subsidence.

[1] Saether (1957) Th/Pb on koppite, zircon and columbite: 420 and 570, 570, 590 my.

Kley and Schmidlin (1960) K/Ar on alkali feldspar from hollaite pegmatite: 413 my.

The most reliable figure is given by Faul, Elmore and Brannock (1959). K/Ar on biotite from biotite-sövite: 565 my. It is of interest that v. Eckermann and Wickman (1956) give 563 my for U/Th on pyrochlore from Alnö.

Breccia

The breccias are of two types: granitic and damkjernitic.

Granitic breccias are abundant in the immediate Fen area, but extend, although more thinly distributed, for many kilometres to the north and south.

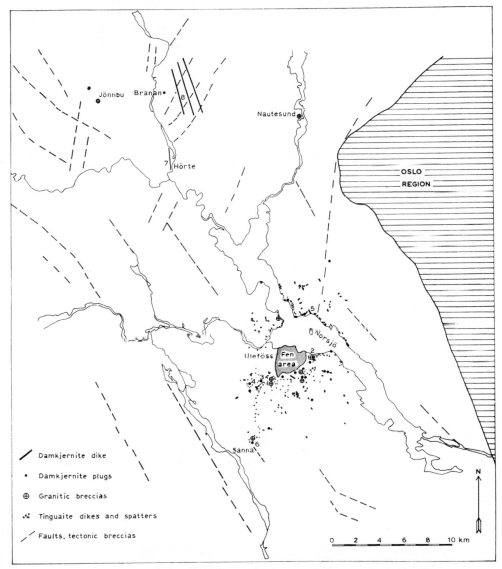

Fig. 2   The geological setting of the Fen explosion vent. The vent is about 5 km across and filled with a suite of peralkalic igneous rocks, carbonatites and mixed silicate-carbonate rocks. It is situated on a system of faults of regional extent striking N to NW, parallel to the western border of the Oslo graben, and congruent with the characteristic fissure system developed within the graben.

They are composed of fragments, up to 0.5 m across, in a fine-grained ground-mass of quartz and alkali feldspar having aplitic structure.

The damkjernite breccias comprise fragments of gneiss, fenite, rocks of the ijolite—melteigite series, sövite and rauhaugite in a damkjernite matrix showing signs of reiterated fragmentation. In extreme cases the amount of damkjernitic matrix is very small compared to that of the fragments. Transitions between granitic breccias and damkjernite breccias are seen in several places (Bergstöl, 1960), a fact which does not support Saether's idea that each of the two kinds of breccia initiates a new volcanic period with eruptions and subsequent subsidence.

Breccias and dikes perforate the surrounding gneisses over a much wider area than the Fen complex proper. (Fig. 2, also Ramberg and Barth, in press).

Tinguaite

The gneisses around Fen are thickly studded with innumerable dikes and spatters of tinguaite (Bergstöl, 1960). They seem to be ubiquitous; wherever the gneiss is exposed, tinguaite spatters abound—from mere spots the size of a coin to relatively large bodies. The petrography of them is treated on page 247.

Damkjernite

Damkjernite occurs both within the Fen complex as a large number of irregularly-shaped bodies with diffuse borders, and in the surrounding gneisses as pipes and dikes generally on visible pressure lines and shatter zones (Figs. 2 and 8). The dike-like bodies are usually rather small, 20 cm to 5 m wide, and up to 200 m long.

The following localities are shown on Fig. 2:

1. The type locality is at Damtjern[1] just south of the Fen complex. It is a dike, 3 m wide, striking WNW, containing numerous inclusions of peridotite, but no gneiss fragments.

2. At Gruveåsen is a breccia of irregular shape, transitional between damkjernite and granite breccia.

3 and 4. At Vindsås and Steinsrud are circular plugs. Minor pipes, only about 2 m across, are also known.

5. At Valebö is a dike about 20–30 cm wide, striking NW for at least 100 m (Brögger, 1932).

6. At Sanna, 7 km SSW of Fen, is an elliptical volcanic plug, 100 m across, consisting of fragments of gneiss, juvite, sövite, etc., in a damkjernite matrix. (Sannaite of Brögger.)

7. At Hörte is a large dike with a northerly strike.

8. At Brånan, in Bö, about 20 km NW of Fen, are three dikes of damkjernite striking NW over a distance of more than 5 km (Werenskiold, 1910).

---

[1] The proper spelling of the geographical name is as given here. For the rock name Brögger (erroneously) used *k* instead of *t* (damkjernite); this is retained in the present paper. But, for example, Saether writes damtjernite.

The surface areas of the three largest damkjernite pipes at Fen are as listed below. They compare in size with the kimberlite pipes in South Africa (Wagner, 1914; Dawson, 1962a).

Sanna pipe	about 0.032 sq km
Vindsås pipe	0.008 sq km
Steinsrud pipe	0.003 sq km

The petrography of the damkjernite is treated on page 244.

PETROGRAPHY

Brögger described a large number of rock types from the Fen complex. They can be arranged into 5 groups: peralkalic silicate rocks, carbonatites, transitional rocks, metasomatic rocks and kimberlites (see Table I). To these rocks Brögger

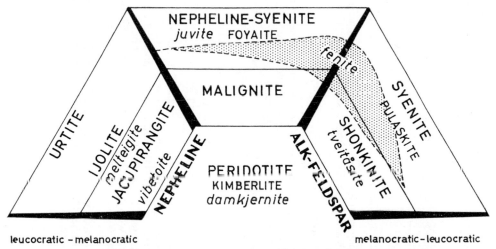

leucocratic – melanocratic   melanocratic – leucocratic

Fig. 3   Mineralogical classification of the silicate rocks of the Fen complex.

gave a large number of names of the type-locality variety. For some of them new names have been proposed by Saether who simplified the terminology, for example by changing kåsenite, ringite and hollaite to pyroxene sövite, feldspar-pyroxene sövite and sövitic melteigite respectively. Fig. 3 shows graphically the classification of the silicate rocks based on the presence of alkali feldspar, nepheline and dark minerals. In addition there are carbonatites and carbonate silicate mixed rocks.

The Archean Bedrock

The rocks around the Fen complex are Precambrian gneisses and gneissic granites forming part of the migmatite area of Telemark. Amphibolites and mica schists occur to the east and south, and on the north the gneisses pass into granitic rocks.

TABLE I

Survey of Petrographic Types

Type	Rock Name	Mineral Contents	Cafemic Index
Metasomatic Rocks	(a) Fenite	85 microperthite, 8 aeg-aug, 5 cc, 3 ap, zirc, sphene	16
	(b) Pulaskite	79 $(Or_{45}Ab_{55})$, 11 (di + hbl), 5 aeg, 4 sodalite + ne, 1 sphene, ap, ore	17
Silicate Rocks	(a) Urtite	82 ne, 9 aeg, 7 ab, 2 ap	11
	(b) Ijolite	52 ne, 39 aeg, 5 ap, 4 sphene, cc	48
	(c) Melteigite	21 ne, 47 aeg-di, 6 bi, 5 cc, 16 sphene, canc, garnet, ore	74
	(d) Malignite	20 ne, 49 aeg-di, 21 or, 6 ap, 4 bi, sphene, ore	59
	(e) Jacupirangite	1 ne, 80 ti-aug, 19 mt, 1 ne, ap, perov	100
	(f) Vibetoite	64 (hbl + ti-aug), 14 cc, 10 bi, 9 ap, 3 sphene, ore ± ab, ne	100
	(g) Tinguaite	46 $(Or_{65}Ab_{35})$, 32 ne, 21 aeg ± bi, 1 ap	22
Carbonate Rocks	(a) Sövite	74 cc, 8 bi, 8 ore, 8 ap, 2 koppite, barite	100
	(b) Rauhaugite	90 ankerite, 8 ap, 2 feldsp, barite, mt	99
	(c) Rödberg	70 cc + ankerite, 28 hm, 2 q, ab, barite, ap	99
Transitional Rocks	(a) Juvite	51 $(Or_{77}Ab_{23})$, 36 ne (canc + musc), 7 aeg-di ± bi, 3 cc, 3 sphene, ap, ore	13
	(b) Kamperite	45 alk.feldsp, 42 bi, 10 plag, 3 ap, ore	45
	(c) Tveitåsite	75 aeg-di ± bi, 15 $(Or_{50}Ab_{50})$, 6 ap, 4 sphene, 3 cc, zirc, ore	85
	(d) Hollaite	55 pyroxene, 16 cc, 10 ne, 6 garnet, 4 ap, 9 bi	90
	(e) Kåsenite	25 pyroxene, 57 cc, 7 ap, 5 ne(musc), 6 chlor, feldsp, sphene, ore	93
	(f) Ringite	20 aeg, 66 cc, 6 alk.feldsp, 5 ap, bi, sphene, ore	94
Kimberlites	(a) Damkjernite	32 ti-aug, 24 bi, 17 ne(musc), 8 ep, 6 perthite, 3 cc, 9 ap, sphene, perov, ore	77
	(b) Sannaite	29 perthite, 14 aug (+ aeg), 12 hbl, 16 chlor + 11 cc, 7 aeg, 5 ne(musc), 6 ap, sphene, ore	66

Fenite

Fenite is a metasomatic rock forming an aureole around the volcanic vent. Indeed, genetically the fenite is the contact metamorphic aureole of the Fen eruptive rocks. It was first described and named by Brögger, and was later found to be present around most other carbonatite complexes.

Fenite is highly variable and passes imperceptibly into the surrounding gneisses that are fenitized to varying degrees.

The first trace of fenitization is that biotite in the gneiss changes into aggregates of aegirine or iron oxides. By increasing temperature a homogeneous alkali feldspar is formed that upon cooling exsolves to form microperthite;

TABLE II
Fenite from Melteig, Fen Area

	Weight % (Brögger, 1921)	Cation %
SiO_2	62.17	56.8
TiO_2	0.44	0.3
ZrO_2	0.05	—
Al_2O_3	15.04	16.3
Fe_2O_3	3.20	2.2
FeO	1.05	0.8
MnO	0.11	0.1
MgO	0.40	0.6
CaO	3.01	3.0
BaO	0.15	0.1
Na_2O	5.25	9.6
K_2O	7.16	8.2
P_2O_5	0.05	—
CO_2	1.61	2.0
H_2O	0.41	—
F, Cl	tr	—
S	0.09	—
	100.19	100.0

quartz and plagioclase are replaced by alkali feldspar and the gneissic structure of the rock is simultaneously changed into a mortar structure. The most common type of fenite has microperthite and some albite as the only light minerals, but some types carry a small amount of nepheline. A volume to volume replacement of gneiss by fenite requires but a small material exchange.

By using the standard cell as unit (volume containing 160 ions of oxygen and approximately 100 cations) the exchange consists of the gneiss losing 7.0 ions of Si and 0.4 ions of Fe^{2+}. In return the gneiss receives the following cations: 2.6 Al, 0.2 Mg, 2.1 Ca, 2.9 Na, 2.4 K, 0.2 P, 2.6 C.

Fenite is typically developed in the south-western part of the area, from where the analyses of Table II are taken. There are several varieties:

Hornblende fenite carries soda amphibole instead of aegirine and is found along the coast of Norsjö. Pulaskite fenite with massive structure is locally

developed with aggregates of muscovite as alteration products after nepheline.
In places it grades into juvite.

The minerals of the fenites are:

Feldspars: Microcline perthite usually in large crystals rimmed by albite
and surrounded by a matrix of small polygonal grains of albite and non-
perthitic microline (mortar structure). It is typically mesoperthitic with
about equal amounts of potassium and sodium feldspar. In places the
sodium component increases and albite antiperthite dominates the rock.
The composition of the feldspars proves that fenite was formed above
650° C. A similar conclusion has been reached in other areas. (e.g. Johnson
1961).

Pyroxenes are aegirine and aegirine-augite in irregular aggregates between the feldspar crystals, and in idiomorphic crystals.

The composition is (see Table III):

$$K_2Na_{45}Ca_{45}Mg_{25}Ma_5Fe_{75}Ti_6Al_{10}Si_{190}O_{600}.$$

Hornblende, if present, is a sodic amphibole exhibiting the usual pleochroism in blue, green and yellow colours. The composition is:

$$K_4Na_{17}Ca_{10}Mg_{34}Fe_{17}Ti_1Al_2Si_{75}O_{220}(OH)_{20}.$$

Apatite, sphene and zircon are present as accessories.

Genesis

Fenite is the result of the specific action of a carbonatite magma or solution
on the wall rocks. It is not probable that the silicate magma (urtite–melteigite–
magma) could bring about this kind of alteration, for around intrusions of non-
carbonated alkalic magma the wall rocks are not fenitized. But in almost all
cases of carbonatite magma intrusions, fenitization is present. The urtite–
melteigite body in the south-western part of the Fen area is surrounded by
fenite. Since it could not itself produce the fenitization, it must have been emplaced in a fenite that already existed as a result of an earlier action of a carbonatite magma, i.e. the sövite–magma. Consequently, at least part of the sövites
came first and the urtite-melteigite series later. This is parallel to the evolution
in the Alnö area, where v. Eckermann (1948, 1960) has shown that a carbonatite
magma was first extruded from a reservoir at a depth of 9 km below the present
surface; subsequently alkalic silicate rocks came from a reservoir at a depth of
5 km. Of particular interest is a composite dike that demonstrates the fenitizing
action of the carbonatite, whereas the silicate dike rock is inactive (v. Eckermann, 1961, Fig. 1).

It can be concluded, therefore, that in the Fen area, as in Alnö, a rather pure
carbonatite magma was succeeded by an alkalic silicate magma. An interesting
question is, therefore, whether these two magmas ever coexisted as immiscible
phases in the same reservoir. This will be discussed further on p. 253.

As a further comment on fenitization it should be emphasized that low-
temperature metasomatism and wall-rock alteration continued for a long time

TABLE III

Data on minerals of Fen (after Saether 1957)

Mineral:	Pyroxene			Amphibole			Biotite			
Colour:	Green	Green	Brown-violet	Brown	Brown	Bluish	Brown	Brown	Reddish	Light greenish
Refractive index α	1.725	1.72	1.715	1.67	1.66	1.655	1.673	1.630	1.623	1.60
Refractive index γ	1.76	1.75	1.74	1.693	1.682	1.666				
Parent rock:	Fenite	Melteigite	Vibetoite	Vibeto te	Damkjernite	Sövite	Melteigite	Vibetoite	Damkjernite	Sövite
Locality:	Holla	Melteig	Vibeto	Vibeto	NE of Damtjern	Hydro's quarry	Melteig	Vibeto	NE of Damtjern	Hydro's quarry
Si	19	18	16.5	58	58.4	75	27	24.5	26.5	28
Al	1	2.5	3	23.5	28.2	2	14	14	15.8	12
Ti	0.5	1	1	3.5	3.3	1	2	1.5	2.3	—
Fe^{3+}	4.5	4	3	6	2.3	6	—	4	0.3	—
Fe^{2+}	3	2	—	8	6.7	11	16	5	4.2	2.4
Mn	0.5	0.3	—	0.2	0.1	0.3	0.5	0.1	—	—
Mg	2.5	4	6	34	35.6	34	8	19	20.3	28
Ca	4.5	5	9.5	16	16.9	10	2	1	0.8	0.7
Ba	—	—	—	—	—	—	—	—	0.1	—
Na	4.5	3	1	7	5.3	17	2.5	3.3	—	0.7
K	0.2	0.3	0.1	4	4.3	4	8	7.5	9.7	8
	40	40	40	180	161.1	160	80	80	80	80
O	60	60	60	222	226.7	220	102	100	103.3	100
OH, F	—	—	—	18	13.3	20	18	20	16.7	20
O	60	60	60	240	240	240	120	120	120	120
Density:	3.50	3.35		3.20			3.00			

after the emplacement of the main rock types. This late metasomatism obscures many of the primary features. To use the words of Brauns (1926), it covers the primary rocks with a veil which, if caution is not exercised, may lead to erroneous interpretation of the mineral succession.

Peralkalic Silicate Rocks

The urtite–ijolite–melteigite series are feldspar-free, hypidiomorphic rocks. The grain size is usually 1–5 mm, but pegmatitic varieties occur. They make up an irregularly shaped body in the south-western part of the complex; and they are not sharply separated from each other, but occur as local variations within the body. They are always surrounded by fenite; a narrow zone (1 m) of transitional rocks is developed at the contact. Just north of this body are a few outcrops of nepheline syenite and malignite. They are feldspar-bearing, but otherwise similar to the urtite–melteigite series. Vibetoite forms a small body near the southern border of the complex. It is surrounded by sövite, carbonatized at the contact, and coarsely crystalline; the minerals, 5–20 mm long, are xenomorphic with curved and jagged outlines; parallel growths of amphibole and pyroxene are common. It is transitional into kimberlite.

Chemical analyses of these rocks are given in Table IV and the modes in Table I. Minor constituents always present are titanomagnetite, apatite, pyrite, sphene and calcite. Frequently present are biotite, a lime garnet (melanite), and microlite (var. koppite). Cancrinite occurs in reaction rims between nepheline and calcite. Zircon is present in minute quantities. Nepheline in all these rocks has a fairly constant composition. It is low in potash (K_2O 5.2 per cent, CaO 1.0 per cent) and is thus different from the nephelines in the Alnö rocks which contain 7–12 per cent K_2O (v. Eckermann, 1948). Its composition can be expressed as:

$$K_{16}Na_{75}Al_{97}Si_{104}O_{400}$$

In the Nc–Ks–Qz diagram it has the parameters 17–81–2 respectively, which in itself does not indicate a magmatic temperature (Barth, 1963).

Pyroxene is diopsidic (except in vibetoite which carries titanaugite) with a small content of aegirine and is some times zoned with the rim richer in aegirine than the core. Analyses of pyroxene from melteigite and from vibetoite are listed in Table III.

Carbonatites

Sövite–rauhaugite–rödberg form a series of carbonatites. Sövite and rauhaugite are essentially monomineralic and dominated by calcite and ankerite respectively. Rödberg is a metasomatic rock consisting of calcite, ankerite and much hematite. Apatite is always present and may attain 10 per cent. The mineral contents of these rocks are shown graphically in Fig. 4.

Saether calculated the composition of the carbonate minerals from the rock analyses. More accurate compositions are given in Table V according to new analyses of calcite and dolomite separated from the sövite-rauhaugite contact at Tuftestollen.

TABLE IV

Peralkalic rocks of Fen
(after Brögger, 1921)

Rock name:	Urtite	Ijolite	Melteigite	Malignite	Melteigite jacupirangite	Vibetoite
Locality:	Melteig	S. of Melteig	Melteig	Tveitåsen	Melteig	Vibeto
SiO_2	39.50	40.50	40.64	43.75	43.58	30.15
TiO_2	0.25	1.94	2.24	1.48	2.51	3.47
ZrO_2	0.01	0.08	0.10	0.04	0.04	0.18
Nb_2O_5	—	0.70	—	—	—	—
Al_2O_3	30.25	18.95	10.58	15.77	7.80	9.10
Fe_2O_3	1.02	3.53	4.18	5.58	4.23	6.07
FeO	1.23	3.70	4.18	3.77	6.09	6.81
MnO	0.06	0.20	0.28	0.25	0.22	0.20
MgO	0.29	3.46	6.47	0.29	6.46	8.67
CaO	4.86	12.21	19.91	11.73	21.93	20.71
BaO	0.06	0.09	0.11	0.04	0.02	0.13
Na_2O	13.38	8.64	4.75	7.36	1.10	1.66
K_2O	5.60	3.41	1.86	4.17	1.33	1.28
P_2O_5	0.44	0.71	1.91	1.38	2.58	3.51
CO_2	2.62	1.66	2.08	3.41	0.10	6.30
H_2O^-	(0.07)	(0.14)	(0.14)	(0.13)	(0.07)	(0.17)
H_2O^+	0.37	0.30	0.27	0.32	1.27	0.48
Cl	0.02	0.02	0.03	0.11	0.02	0.02
F	0.05	0.07	0.12	—	0.24	0.30
S	0.02	0.13	0.05	0.27	0.21	0.48
	100.10	100.44	99.90	99.85	99.80	99.69

Cation %						
Si	33.0	35.9	37.4	39.9	42.5	28.6
Ti	0.2	1.2	1.5	1.0	1.8	2.4
Zr	—	—	0.1	—	—	0.1
Nb	—	0.3	—	—	—	—
Al	29.6	19.8	11.3	17.0	9.0	10.0
Fe'''	0.7	2.3	2.8	3.9	3.1	4.4
Fe''	0.9	2.7	3.2	2.9	5.0	5.3
Mn	0.1	0.2	0.3	0.2	0.2	0.2
Mg	0.3	4.8	8.9	0.4	9.5	12.4
Ca	4.2	11.6	19.6	11.5	23.0	21.0
Ba	—	—	0.1	—	—	0.1
Na	21.7	14.8	8.5	13.0	2.0	3.1
K	5.9	3.8	2.2	4.9	1.7	1.5
P	0.4	0.5	1.5	1.0	2.1	2.8
C	3.0	2.1	2.6	4.3	0.1	8.1
	100.0	100.0	100.0	100.0	100.0	100.0

It is interesting that ankerites from sövite and from rauhaugite, taken only a few centimetres apart, exhibit significant differences in composition. These compositions are plotted on the experimental diagram of Goldsmith *et al.* (1962) (Fig. 5) and indicate rather low temperatures of (re)crystallization, suggesting that exsolution, recrystallization and movements have taken place in the solid state.

Chemical analyses of the rocks are listed in Table VI. Sövite makes up the western part of a circular, but in detail irregular, carbonatite area (2 km across) in the centre of the Fen complex. The streaky sövite dips steeply inwards and

TABLE V

Composition of calcite and ankerite

Weight %	Calcite from sövite	Ankerite from sövite	Ankerite from rauhaugite
CaO	54.57	31.75	30.35
MgO	0.51	18.02	18.80
FeO	0.52	4.24	3.10
MnO	0.47	0.85	1.31
SrO	0.18	0.48	0.91
BaO	0.05	trace	trace
Mol %			
$2(CaCO_3)$	94.7	4.0	0.5
$CaMg(CO_3)_2$	2.4	82.0	86.6
$CaFe(CO_3)_2$	1.4	10.8	8.0
$CaSr(CO_3)_2$	0.4	1.0	1.6

strikes concentrically. The complex is divided into arcs by screens of silicate rocks (fenite, melteigite, vibetoite, etc.) which are more or less altered. In part they exhibit sharp contacts against the white sövite, and are brecciated and invaded by sövite veins; in part they are drawn out to diffuse streaks.

Outside the main sövite complex there are numerous sövite dikes with thicknesses ranging from a few centimetres to 30 m. The larger dikes are associated with mixed silicate-carbonate rocks (hollaites, etc.) in fragments and in diffuse streaks; they are always foliated (flow structure). The smaller dikes consist of nearly pure white sövite exhibiting sharp contacts towards the country rocks. Vestiges of crushing or boudinage-like flow lines are seen in many places.

The dikes have on the whole the same circular strike as the main sövite complex, and more or less concentric dips. They may be compared to cone sheets, but are not as regular as the sövite cone sheets at Alnö, and do not dip towards a single well-defined focus. The larger dikes, together with the flow structure of the main sövite body, seem to indicate a poorly defined focus at a depth of 2000–3000 m below the present surface.

Table VII demonstrates that the sövites of Fen are very similar, chemically, to the carbonated lavas of Katwe; the table also shows that lavas may have a

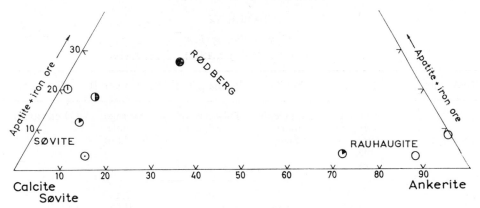

Fig. 4 Simplified mineral associations of analysed samples of sövite, rauhaugite and rödberg. The ratio between the white and black segments of the circles indicates the proportion apatite: iron ore in the rock samples. The four minerals presented in the diagram: calcite, ankerite, apatite, iron ore (= magnetite + hematite) make up, on an average, more than 90% of the rocks.

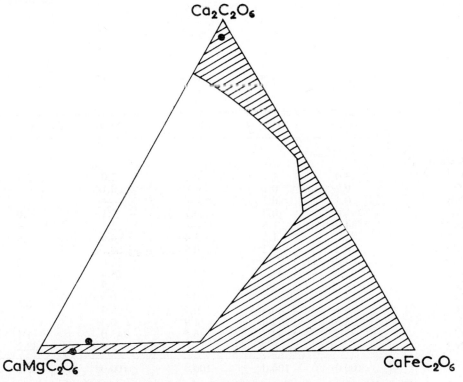

Fig. 5 Composition of calcite and ankerite in the Fen carbonatites. The area of solid solutions at 600°C is indicated by hatching.

I

TABLE VI

Carbonatites of Fen

(after Brögger, 1921)

Rock name:	Sövite	Sövite	Rauhaugite I	Rauhaugite II	Rödberg
Locality:	Average sample Hydro's quarry Söve	Cappelen's quarry Söve	Dike SW of Söve	Average sample Rauhaug[1]	Fen mines
SiO_2	3.36	2.00	0.89	2.22	4.15
TiO_2	0.30	0.19	—	0.15	
ZrO_2	—	—	—	—	} 2.65
Nb_2O_5	0.80	0.82	—	0.07	
Al_2O_3	1.69	0.66	0.76	2.01	
Fe_2O_3	6.13	2.44	0.06	1.99	
FeO	2.99	2.06	3.51	6.23	} 31.90
MnO	0.31	0.29	0.67	0.90	
MgO	3.10	2.25	16.88	9.40	5.40
CaO	44.35	48.72	31.49	30.24	28.65
BaO	0.10	0.04	0.03	5.47	
Na_2O	0.04	0.02	0.05	0.26	} not determined
K_2O	0.50	0.32	0.11	0.31	
P_2O_5	3.26	3.38	2.83	1.00	1.25
CO_2	32.80	36.22	42.88	35.96	ca 25[2]
SO_3	0.06	0.02		2.86	
H_2O-	(0.14)	(0.10)	—	(0.11)	} ca 1[2]
H_2O+	0.16	0.10	tr	0.15	
F	0.28	0.29	0.08	0.15	
Cl	0.02	0.02	0.07	—	
S	0.42	0.51	0.07	0.52	
	100.81	100.45	100.38	100.00	ca 100
Cation %					
Si	3.0	1.7	0.7	2.0	3.9
Ti	0.2	0.1	—	0.1	
Nb	0.3	0.3	—	—	
Al	1.8	0.7	0.7	2.1	3.0
Fe^{3+}	4.0	1.6	—	1.3	
Fe^{2+}	2.4	1.5	2.4	4.4	} 22.6
Mn	0.2	0.2	0.5	0.7	
Mg	4.0	2.9	20.1	12.6	7.6
Ca	41.7	45.2	27.0	28.4	29.1
Ba	—	—	—	1.9	
Na	—	—	0.1	0.5	
K	0.6	0.4	0.1	0.4	} 0.5
P	2.5	2.6	1.9	0.7	
C	39.3	42.8	46.5	43.0	1·1
S^{6+}				1.9	32.2
	100.0	100.0	100.0	100.0	100.0

[1] Averaged by Saether (1957).   [2] Given by Saether (1957).

high content of sodium carbonate which, if it was present in the sövite magma, could have been responsible for fenitization and later metasomatic activities.

Sövite from the type locality is a marble-like rock with up to 95 per cent calcite. The average quarried rock at Söve assays as follows (Björlykke, 1953):

Calcite	67.0	Pyrite	1.0
Apatite	7.7	Silicates	22.0
Magnetite, hematite	2.0	Miscellaneous	0.3

The silicates (see Table III) are phlogopite, amphibole and some aegirine. At other localities biotite, often altered to chlorite, is the chief silicate mineral. In some places microcline, albite, and more rarely quartz are found. Sericite may occur pseudomorphic after nepheline. Magnetite has exsolved ilmenite; it contains TiO_2 3.0 per cent, V 0.4 per cent. Apatite is a fluorapatite.

Constant constituents are barite, and a pyrochlore rich in niobium (= koppite). Brögger's analysis of koppite, from Söve, later modified by Björlykke (1934), can be recalculated to the formula: $(NaCa)_2(NbTa)_2O_6(OH)$:

Fe	0.46		
Mg	0.11		
Ca	1.00	1.97	
Na	0.40		O 6.02
Ti	0.08		(OH) (1.00)[a]
Nb	1.72		
Ta	0.08	1.93	
(La, Ce, etc.)	0.05		

[a] This leaves 1.73 per cent H_2O not accounted for by the formula.

However, the pyrochlore minerals in sövite vary in colour from colourless to red, brown and black, and they are usually zoned. The composition varies accordingly. A series of chemical analyses show the following ranges (Björlykke and Svinndal, 1960):

Nb_2O_5	...	58–72%	FeO	...	1.0–20%
Ta_2O_5	...	0.5–2%	CaO	...	0.5–20%
TiO_2	...	0.5–6%	ThO_2 + Rare Earths		0.5–20%

At Cappelen mine, uranium-rich pyrochlore (U_3O_5 = 15–20 per cent) corresponding to ellsworthite is found.

Additional minerals, only occasionally present are zoisite, fluorite, topaz, corundum, zircon, rutile and columbite pseudomorphic after pyrochlore (see Aubert, 1947).

Sövite from the type locality is rather coarse-grained with calcite 2–4 mm across, and euhedral crystals of magnetite and koppite attaining 5 mm. At other places the grain size is less, 0.5–1 mm for calcite, but again magnetite, koppite and apatite are in large crystals.

Sövite, even without macroscopically visible schistosity, exhibits a clear

TABLE VII
Sövite compared with carbonatite lavas

Rock type:	Sövite	Carbonated Katungite	Natro-Carbonatite
Locality:	Cappelen's quarry Fen (Brögger, 1921)	Katwe (Holmes, 1956)	Oldoinyo L'engai (Dawson, 1962b)
SiO_2	2.00	5.62	tr.
TiO_2	0.19	0.53	0.10
Nb_2O_5	0.82	—	—
Al_2O_3	0.66	1.29	0.08
Fe_2O_3	2.44	2.84	0.26
FeO	2.06	1.94	
MnO	0.29	0.46	0.04
MgO	2.25	1.46	0.49
CaO	48.72	46.88	12.74
BaO	0.04	0.75	0.95
SrO	—	0.39	1.24
Na_2O	0.02	0.40	29.53
K_2O	0.32	0.64	7.58
P_2O_5	3.38	1.96	0.83
CO_2	36.22	33.02	31.75
SO_3	0.02	0.48	2.00
H_2O^-	0.10	0.38	8.59
H_2O^+	0.10	1.19	
F	0.29	—	2.69
Cl	0.02	0.04	3.86
S	0.51	—	—
	100.45	100.27	102.73
Mol. %			
$CaCO_3$	81.4	79.4[a]	19.6
$MgCO_3$	4.2	4.0	—
Na_2CO_3		1.2	67.6
K_2CO_3		1.2	6.0
Rest	14.4[b]	14.2[c]	6.8[d]

[a] Includes carbonates of Ba, Sr, Mn.
[b] Mainly silicates.
[c] Mainly phosphates and silicates.
[d] Mainly hydrated salts.

although incomplete regulation of the calcite axes. Three types of petrofabrics can be seen:

1. S–tectonics with a maximum of calcite axes round the pole of the macroscopically visible planar structure.
2. B–tectonics with the calcite axes sub-parallel to an approximately vertical plane perpendicular to the planar structure.
3. Maximum of calcite (and biotite) axes along the surface of a conc whose axis of rotation is parallel to the supposed tectonic *b*-axis.

All three types occur in tectonically deformed marble and indicate, either that sövite was intruded in the solid state, or was subsequently recrystallized by plastic flow. Similar structural patterns are described from the Shawa complex (Johnson, 1961).

Rauhaugite

Saether (1957) distinguishes between type I and type II.

Type I is a white, marble-like rock which weathers yellowish. Ankerite comprises 95 per cent of the rock (Fig. 4) the other minerals being as normal for sövite. It also has the same fabric as sövite. Carbonatites transitional between rauhaugite and sövite do occur, but in subordinate amounts. Brögger's statement that the two types were not transitional is, therefore, only approximately correct.

Type II is yellowish-white or grey and becomes rusty on weathered surfaces. Ankerite is the most abundant mineral (Fig. 4). The commonest non-carbonate minerals are chlorite with smaller amounts of biotite evenly distributed as dark dust, or collected in irregular spots and veins. Magnetite occurs in a similar way and may locally, together with apatite, attain high concentrations; it contains Ti 0.2 per cent, V 0.2 per cent, Mn 1 per cent. Hematite and pyrite are common. Quartz, albite, microcline and particularly barite, may occur in minute clusters and veins. Fluorite occasionally occurs in the same way. At a single locality near Fen farm the rock has a bluish tinge from finely dispersed fluorite. Periclase and a mineral of the melilite group have been identified.

Rauhaugite II occurs as an irregular core of the sub-circular carbonatite body without definite borders to the surrounding rocks. On the north side there is a broad metasomatic transitional zone between it and fenite. It typically passes into damkjernite by gradual transitions.

Dikes and veins of rauhaugite are common. v. Eckermann (1948) introduced the name beforsite for dikes of the same composition in Alnö. In the Fen area there is no reason for using a special name for the dike rocks, as the rock in the rauhaugite dikes does not differ from rauhaugite in the main body.

On the whole the rauhaugite dikes have the same mode of occurrence as the sövite dikes with which they occur. They are, though irregular in detail, parallel to the margins and flow lines of the main sövite body.

Rödberg

Rödberg (= Red Rock) is an old miners' term for a red, fine-grained, carbonate-hematite rock occurring mainly in the eastern part of the Fen complex. This rock is known only from Fen.

The carbonate grains are irregular 0.01–1 mm across; hematite is present as small tablets, 0.003–0.01 mm, in places poicilitically included in calcite crystals. In thin sections the rock is seen to be completely studded with reddish dust. Hematite regularly makes up 20–50 per cent of the rock. Minor constituents are chlorite, apatite and magnetite; accessory minerals are quartz, albite and barite. There is a regular content of niobium (0.05–0.5%), but the source mineral is not known.

In rödberg, as in rauhaugite, there are exogenic 'relics' of gneiss, and of the Fen rocks. Towards damkjernite there is a metasomatic transition zone, but the contact with rauhaugite is knife-sharp, although irregular and curved. The radioactivity of the rock is high with Th 0.2 per cent and cerium earths 1 per cent. The

Th-bearing minerals are hidden in very fine disseminations in the ore, and have not yet been identified.

Saether looks upon the rock as a peri-magmatic product formed at relatively shallow levels from the same magmatic solutions that produced rauhaugite at deeper levels.

Transitional Rocks

A large number of transitional rocks have been described and named by Brögger (Tables I and VIII).

Juvite is a foyaite with calcite and rather a lot of feldspar.

TABLE VIII

Transitional rocks of Fen

(after Brögger, 1921)

Rock name:	Juvite	Kamperite	Tveitåsite	Hollaite	Kåsenite
Locality:	Juvet	Kamperhaug	Tveitåsen	Holla Church	Kåsene
SiO_2	51.41	51.04	48.46	35.86	17.26
TiO_2	0.47	0.63	1.64	2.51	0.57
ZrO_2	0.04	0.06	0.05	0.04	0.03
Al_2O_3	20.41	17.17	3.08	3.54	2.83
Fe_2O	1.08	1.12	5.97	7.26	2.10
FeO	1.55	6.25	7.43	6.90	3.20
MnO	0.06	0.18	0.42	0.52	0.20
MgO	0.10	4.17	5.57	4.92	2.00
CaO	4.27	3.00	18.27	25.35	40.73
BaO	0.05	0.48	0.06	0.03	0.02
Na_2O	6.67	2.27	3.03	2.21	1.57
K_2O	8.21	10.16	1.59	1.16	0.83
P_2O_5	0.36	0.89	2.34	1.76	2.89
CO_2	3.04	0.11	1.12	6.99	25.06
H_2O^-	(0.19)	(0.08)	(0.19)	(0.08)	(0.17)
H_2O^+	2.01	2.12	0.44	0.38	0.21
F	0.02	0.07	0.20	0.15	0.20
Cl	—	—	0.02	0.01	0.02
S	0.27	0.11	0.34	0.48	0.25
	100.21	99.83	100.03	100.15	100.14
Cation %					
Si	46.3	48.1	46.3	34.2	15.3
Ti	0.3	0.5	1.2	1.8	0.4
Zr	—	—	—	—	—
Al	21.6	19.1	3.5	4.0	2.9
Fe^{3+}	0.8	0.8	4.4	5.2	1.4
Fe^{2+}	1.5	4.9	6.5	5.5	2.4
Mn	0.1	0.2	0.4	0.4	0.2
Mg	0.2	5.9	8.0	7.0	2.6
Ca	4.1	3.1	18.7	26.0	38.6
Ba	—	0.2	—	—	—
Na	11.6	4.1	5.6	4.0	2.7
K	9.5	12.2	1.9	1.4	1.0
P	0.3	0.7	1.9	1.4	2.2
C	3.7	0.2	1.6	9.1	30.3
	100.0	100.0	100.0	100.0	100.0

Tveitåsite is a shonkinite with microcline perthite and aegirine-augite. It may be regarded as a variety of fenite.

Kamperite is a dike rock related to minette with feldspar and biotite.

Hollaite and kåsenite are pyroxene sövite or sövitic melteigites. They differ from the rocks of the ijolite–melteigite series only in the amount of calcite. Veins of pegmatitic feldspar-pyroxene sövite were called hollaite pegmatite by Brögger.

TABLE IX

Damkjernite of Fen compared with African kimberlites

| | Weight % | | | | Molecular equivalent norms | | | |
	1	2	3	4		1	2	3	4
SiO_2	31.86	35.8	36.58	31.80	Or	6.1	19.3	3.0	18.5
TiO_2	1.82	2.8	2.67	1.40	Ab	9.8	7.2	2.5	—
ZrO_2	0.02	0.02	—	—	An	12.4	16.8	18.7	—
Al_2O_3	8.26	11.6	7.15	3.41	Ne	2.0	2.3	—	—
Fe_2O_3	6.27	5.0	6.69	5.19	Ac	—	—	—	2.8
FeO	4.18	6.7	4.99	3.48	En	—	—	19.9	5.9
MnO	0.27	0.22	0.34	—	Di	2.6	6.1	9.8	—
MgO	19.03	10.2	22.55	24.69	Ol	36.6	21.1	0.9	42.4
CaO	14.61	13.8	6.05	10.04	Mt	5.9	5.1	4.8	4.4
BaO	0.07	0.13	—	—	Il	2.5	4.0	5.2	1.8
Na_2O	1.50	1.24	0.28	0.29	Hm	—	—	1.9	—
K_2O	2.04	3.5	0.47	4.32	Py	0.8	0.8	—	—
P_2O_5	1.36	1.0	0.38	1.49	Ap	2.6	2.1	0.8	4.3
CO_2	7.59	6.0	—	7.65	Cc	18.7	15.1	—	14.3
SO_3	—	0.06	—	—	$MgCO_3$	—	—	—	5.7
H_2O^-	(0.17)	(0.17)	3.31	0.67					
H_2O^+	0.43	1.6	8.51	5.59					
Cl	0.01	0.01	—	—					
F	0.12	0.1	—	—					
S	0.31	0.30	—	—					
	99.92	100.25	99.96	99.98		100.0	100.0	100.0	100.0

1. Damkjernite, Damtjern, Fen (Brögger, 1921).
2. Damkjernite, Fen. Average of four localities (Brögger, 1921 averaged by Saether, 1957).
3. Basaltic kimberlite, Thaba Putsoa pipe, Basutoland (Dawson, 1962a, p. 551).
4. Micaceous kimberlite, Lion Hill dike, South Africa (Wagner, 1914, p. 110).

Ringite and ringite pegmatite are high in calcite and contain in addition 10–30 per cent aegirine-augite and 10–30 per cent feldspar (albite and microcline perthite).

The transitional rocks are poorly defined and pass into each other and into fenite imperceptibly. They are also transitional into sövite and into kimberlite.

Hydrothermal-metasomatic alterations are conspicuous. Nepheline goes into aggregates of albite, muscovite and chlorite, often studded with small grains of epidote. Prehnite and zeolite (probably natrolite) are occasionally formed.

At a more advanced stage of the metasomatism the outlines of the nephelines are affected. Pyroxene is also attacked and altered into aggregates of biotite or chlorite and calcite. Brögger described two occurrences of damourite (compact aggregates of muscovite) which he regarded as altered nepheline rocks. Eventually muscovite also disappears, and the rock is now transformed into a biotite-calcite or a chlorite-calcite rock. At this advanced stage of metasomatism and recrystallization great exchange of substance has taken place. The recrystallization progresses with a rather sharp front into the rock with preserved igneous structure, and behind this front all traces of the original structure are obliterated. Fenite is also affected and changed into an aggregate of calcite, biotite and feldspar.

Damkjernite–Kimberlite

Kimberlitic pipes, breccias, dikes and irregular intrusions are regularly associated with carbonatite circular complexes all over the world. In the Fen area Brögger described the kimberlitic rocks as damkjernite.

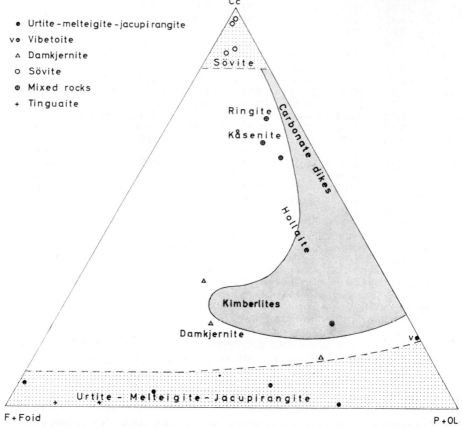

Legend:
- Urtite - melteigite - jacupirangite
- ∨• Vibetoite
- ∆ Damkjernite
- ○ Sövite
- ⊕ Mixed rocks
- + Tinguaite

Fig. 6 Graphical illustration of the mineralogical composition of the rocks of the Fen complex compared to kimberlites and carbonated dikes of South Africa (shaded area) after Holmes (1956).

Damkjernites are dark porphyritic rocks; phenocrysts of biotite (1–5 cm long) are most common, but hornblende, pyroxene and olivine also occur. The phenocrysts are typically rounded, bent and broken.

The chemical analyses displayed in Table IX and plotted in Fig. 6 show the relations to kimberlite.

Biotite exhibits hexagonal outlines, and seems to be homogeneous. Hornblende is a light brown barkevikite often corroded and coated by a green amphibole which also occurs in the groundmass. Blue amphibole makes up the outermost rim. Pyroxene is a light green diopside with shells of violet titanaugite or aegirine-augite. Magnesian orthopyroxene occurs locally. Olivine is magnesian (Fo_{85}), but often altered into serpentine. Magnetite, nepheline and feldspar are abundant. Calcite is partly primary, but also secondary (metasomatic); locally it attains high concentrations.

Fig. 7   Damkjernite breccia with inclusions showing the effect of rounding and polishing, probably due to gas coring. The ruler is 30 cm long. Orekås, east shore of Norsjö (photo Bergstöl).

The groundmass is made up of pyroxene, amphibole, biotite, magnetite and nepheline-pseudomorphs in a matrix of feldspar and calcite. Accessories are apatite (up to 6 per cent), ilmenite, chromite, picotite, pyrite, sphene and melanite. Inclusions are:

1.   Exogenic fragments of gneiss, fenite, urtite–jacupirangite, sövite or rauhaugite. In certain damkjernite breccias they are so numerous that the damkjernite itself is quite subordinate.
2.   Endogenic fragments of peridotite, pyroxenite, hornblendite (OBP-series of Holmes, see p. 250). The fragments are frequently surrounded by an aureole of damkjernite conferring a nodular structure upon the rock.

Inclusions of both types may be angular, but in places they exhibit remarkably well-rounded spheroidal shapes as if they were ground in a mill (see Fig. 7). Similar rounded pebbles are pictured by Dawson (1962a), whose conclusion was that kimberlite is the result of interaction between inclusions of forsterite, enstatite, diopside and ilmenite in a fluid rich in water, carbon dioxide, alkalies, lime and, in some cases, silica. This conclusion seems equally valid for the damkjernites of Fen.

Emplacement

The rocks adjacent to the damkjernite pipes are hardly metamorphosed, nor are they visibly brecciated or shattered. The contacts are conspicuously clean and sharp.[1]

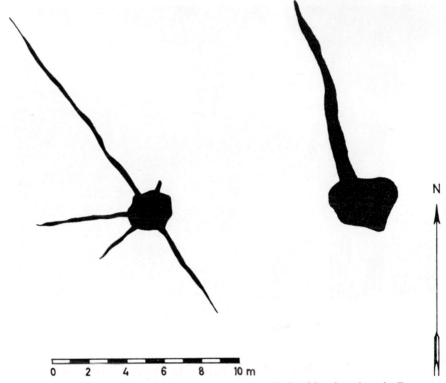

N

0	2	4	6	8	10 m

Fig. 8   Schematic cross-sections of two small damkjernite pipes in Pre-cambrian gneiss, east coast of Norsjö.

Around some of the small damkjernite pipes (diameters of about 2 m) thin radial veins or 'rays' cut the surrounding gneiss for distances of 10–12 m (Fig. 8). The manner of emplacement of damkjernite was not explosion-like; rather it seems to have been by a mechanism of gas coring. The location of the individual pipes was governed by an existing fissure pattern. (See pp. 227 and 228.)

Related to damkjernite are the mineralogically and chemically highly variable silicate-carbonate rocks such as Brögger called hollaite, kåsenite, ringite. Again the alnöitic dikes of v. Eckermann (1958), and the carbonate dikes of Holmes

[1] This statement needs modification in the case of damkjernite intruding the silicate and carbonate rocks of the Fen circular complex. The contacts are here often (subsequently?) metasomatically altered, and transitional rock types have developed.

(1936) are closely related. Kimberlites of similar composition have been described by Dawson (1962a) from Basutoland, and by Williams (1933) from the Orange Free State.

Tinguaites

Tinguaite dikes and patches abound in the Precambrian gneiss-granite adjacent to the Fen area. They have been studied particularly by Bergstöl to whom we are obliged for the following information.

Table X

Tinguaite and garnetiferous phonolite from Fen

Rock type	Tinguaite Valebö (Brögger, 1932)	Tinguaite Holla (Bergstöl, in prep.)	Garnetiferous phonolite, Holla (Bergstöl, in prep.)
SiO_2	52.60	54.40	41.06
TiO_2	0.44	0.54	1.45
Al_2O_3	20.78	21.28	17.16
De_2O_3	2.57	2.44	6.56
FeO	2.00	1.25	1.54
MnO	0.20	0.25	0.40
MgO	0.34	0.58	1.65
CaO	1.68	1.00	13.75
BaO	0.15	—	—
Na_2O	9.12	10.45	1.85
K_2O	7.07	5.15	6.55
P_2O_5	0.07	0.10	0.72
CO_2	0.32	0.41	6.08
Cl	0.27	—	—
H_2O	2.34	2.54	1.10
	99.95	100.39	99.87
Cation %			
Si	47.5	48.4	38.3
Ti	0.3	0.4	1.1
Al	22.0	22.2	18.9
Fe'''	1.7	1.6	4.6
Fe''	1.5	0.9	1.2
Mn	0.2	0.2	0.3
Mg	0.5	0.8	2.3
Ca	1.6	1.0	13.8
Ba	0.1	—	—
Na	16.0	18.0	3.4
K	8.1	5.9	7.8
P	0.1	0.1	0.6
C	0.4	0.5	7.7
	100.0	100.0	100.0

Tinguaites are intruded as large and small dikes, as patches, and as discordant elongate or irregular bodies. The dikes are mostly composite with a light reddish selvage varying in width from 1 mm to 10 cm. They occur in great numbers in the neighbourhood of Fen, but more remote areas of the gneiss terrane are also thickly intruded. Up to 10 km from Fen tinguaites are frequently to be seen. Tinguaite is a nepheline syenite porphyry with a grey-green groundmass and phenocrysts of alkali feldspar, nepheline, some biotite and pyroxene. The

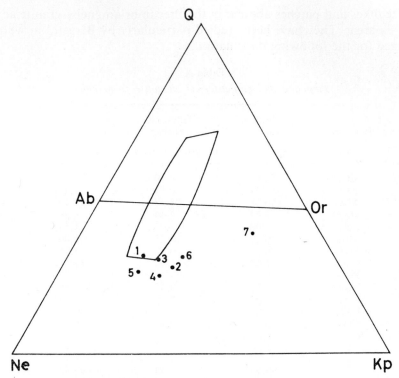

Fig. 9 Position of tinguaites in petrogeny's residual system. The low-
temperature trough is indicated after Bowen.
1. Tinguaite, Lundebruene, Fen. (Bergstöl, in prep.).
2. Tinguaite, Valebö. (Brögger, 1932).
3. Tinguaite, Hedrum, Oslo area. (Brögger, 1933).
4. Ijolite-tinguaite, Fen. (Brögger, 1921).
5. Tinguaite, Alnö. (v. Eckermann, 1948a).
6. Tinguaite, Alnö. (v. Eckermann, 1948a).
7. Garnetiferous phonolite, Lundebruene, Fen. (Bergstöl, in prep.).

groundmass consists of feldspar laths, nepheline, aegerine needles and an iso-tropic matrix which is believed to be sodalite. The phenocrysts of alkali feldspar are optically monoclinic, but x-ray studies show that they are triclinic with Δ values in the range 0.80–0.90.

The phenocrysts of nepheline are partly fresh but rimmed by cancrinite and analcite, partly altered into muscovite with 1M-structure. The red selvage con-sists mainly of alkali feldspar.

Chemical analyses are given in Table X, and plotted in Fig. 9.

The tinguaites are older than the rocks of the Fen circular complex. Xenoliths of tinguaite are found in damkjernitic plugs and breccias a damkjernite dike is also seen to cut a tinguaite body (Fig. 10).

A garnetiferous phonolite dike is found about 1 km SW of Fen. It is 5 m wide striking NW for about 100 m. It carries about 5 per cent of a black titaniferous garnet (melanite) of the same type found in melteigite ($a_0 = 12.094$ Å).

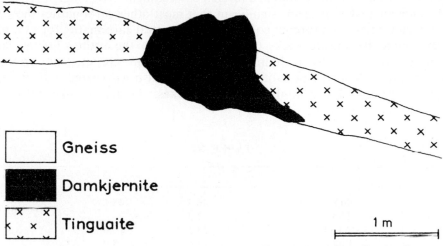

Fig. 10 Damkjernite plug penetrating a dike of tinguaite. Sprakevik, east shore of Norsjö.

The remainder of the rock is made up of calcite, altered phenocrysts of nepheline, and a small amount of biotite, in a groundmass of feldspar, chloritized aegirite and a little nepheline.

PETROGENESIS

The formation of the Fen rocks has been variously stated as:

  1. Metasomatic formation of all rocks including the urtite–ijolite–melteigite series.
  2. Magmatic origin of all rocks.

The problem is a difficult one and only a few of the principal considerations can be discussed here.

First of all, carbonatite lavas are now known. They have been described by v. Knorring and DuBois (1961), Dawson (1962*a, b*, this vol. pp. 155–167), DuBois *et al.* (1963) and Guest (1963). These papers include descriptions of lavas that are principally sodium carbonate. Sahama (1962) stated that carbon dioxide plays an important role in the lavas of Mount Nyiragongo (compare Chaigneau *et al.* 1960) and supports the suggestion by Meyer (1958) that the existence of a carbonatite melt in various African volcanoes indicates differentiation of an ijolitic parent magma towards carbonate lava (see Table VIII).

Experimental studies of carbonate and carbonate-silicate systems by Wyllie and Tuttle (1959, 1960, 1962), Koster van Groos and Wyllie (1963) and Wyllie (this vol., pp. 309-350) have established the existence of simplified carbonatite melts at pressures as low as 27b and temperatures below 600°C. It has been established that calcite can crystallize from melts having a wide variety of compositions and along with many of the minerals found in carbonatite complexes.

Assuming a magmatic origin for the Fen rocks there remains the problem of why they appear in a small vent in a foreign environment. Although it is difficult to provide an answer it seems significant that most other carbonatites show the same peculiarities: in a foreign country rock a central carbonatite forms a plug about which the silicate rocks (often belonging to the urtite – ijolite – jacupirangite series, but also including peridotite, serpentinite, etc.) are arranged concentrically. Most carbonatite complexes are also associated with faulting and brecciation and with kimberlite–alnöite dikes. Tinguaitic dikes also seem to be universally present.

TABLE XI

	1	2
SiO_2	46.3	46.1
TiO_2	2.3	—
Al_2O_3	13.1	13.0
Fe_2O_3	11.6	8.0
FeO	—	—
MgO	6.1	6.3
CaO	12.9	26.5
Alkalies	6.8	—
P_2O_2	1.0	—

1. Damkjernite plug. Sanna SW of Fen (recalculated free of H_2O and CO_2).
2. Garnetiferous skarn (hornfels of class 9) Gjellebekk, Oslo. (Goldschmidt, 1911).

The origin of the carbonates is unknown. In most places there is little direct evidence of thick limestone beds at depth and in the Fen area it is improbable that any exist. It has often been assumed, therefore, that carbon dioxide ± lime are derived from magmas at great depth.

We favour the suggestion by Holmes (1950) that carbonatite magma can assimilate granite. Waters (1955) rejected this and argued that kimberlite (and katungite lava) is produced by partial melting of metamorphic-plutonic rocks formed by biotitization and uralization of normal orogenic serpentinites. We fail to see, however, what becomes of the carbonatites in this hypothesis. To us the reaction between granitic rocks and carbonatites is important and whichever was molten during the reaction is less important than the fact that reaction took place to produce a skarn. Holmes looks upon the peridotites, glimmerites and pyroxenites (which he calls the OBP series and which in part belong to the kimberlite-like rocks, alnöites, ouachitites, etc., and to the katungite lavas) as skarn rocks.

It is well known that reaction skarns in limestone contacts are radically different both chemically and mineralogically from either parent rock. v. Eckermann (1950) compared the mineral assemblages at Alnö with skarns in Fennoscandian limestones. Unfortunately he gives no analyses, but there appears to be great chemical similarity. In Table XI a garnetiferous skarn from the Oslo contact metamorphic area is compared with a kimberlite.

The concentration of certain elements in carbonatites is of the kind often seen in skarn; for example, titanium is often high. It is of interest to note that in

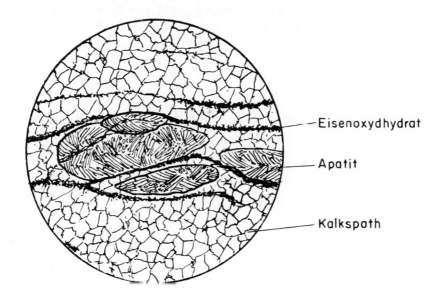

Fig. 11   Sövite with drops consisting of randomly oriented apatite. Drawing by Brögger (1921), p. 239, who writes: "The illustration gives only an approximate idea of the structure; actually the number of the apatite needles in each drop is much higher than shown in the figure" (translated from German).

brickets of calcite and gabbro pressed together under a temperature gradient in a laboratory furnace titanium migrates and accumulates at the gabbro-calcite contact.

The habit of apatite crystals in certain sövite dikes suggests magmatic origin of the carbonate. Brögger (1921) described sövite dikes 10–100 cm wide with flow-oriented ellipsoidal drops of apatite arranged in parallel rows. These drops are built of a large number of acicular needles arranged in all directions; each needle is about 0.02 mm thick. Similar textures were found by Wyllie, Cox and Biggar (1962) in the system $CaO-CaF_2-P_2O_5-H_2O-CO_2$. Apatite in equilibrium with melt or vapour forms equant stubby prisms while apatite that crystallized from the liquid during quenching has acicular habit. The texture is very similar to the Fen rocks. Brögger's illustration is reproduced as Fig. 11 and may be compared with those of Wyllie *et al.*

Melilite occurs very rarely at Fen, in contrast to Alnö and many other carbonatites. Saether (1957) reported its 'occasional' presence in rauhaugite that he believed had formed by carbonatization at 300–500°C of silicate rocks, mainly damkjernite. However, it has been found by Harker and Tuttle (1956) and by Christie (1961) that melilite is stable only above 500–700°C depending on the partial pressure of CO_2, H_2O, etc. Wyllie (this vol., p. 309) finds it stable down to at least 575°C. At lower temperatures it decomposes into hydrogarnet and other silicates and at 500°C this decomposition is very rapid. It seems inescapable, then, that the melilite-bearing rocks could not have crystallized much below 600°C and that melilite became unstable during cooling and was largely

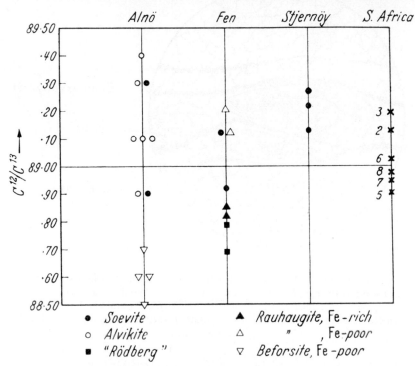

Fig. 12 Diagram showing the distribution of the carbon isotope ratios. The samples from Alnö, Fen and Stjernøy are after v. Eckermann *et al.* (1952). The African occurrences (x) are after Holmes (1956) and are marked according to the numbers used by him.

destroyed. Only occasionally did it survive as relics in some rauhaugite. It has already been mentioned that the composition of feldspars in the fenites indicate crystallization at not less than 650°C.

Isotopic data by v. Eckermann *et al.* (1942) and by Baertschi (1957) on Fen rocks are given in Fig. 12. Values for strontium and barium analyses are given in Table XII, and in Table XIII apatite analyses are given which agree with Brasseur *et al.* (1961) that apatites from carbonatites have a Sr/Mn ratio of about 50 compared to about 0.2 for apatites from other rocks.

These results are in agreement with the well-established geochemical characteristics of carbonatite complexes and make it highly improbable that the Fen carbonatite could be a metasomatically altered Precambrian limestone.

The sequence of the Fen rocks is difficult to establish. Observations from other areas indicate no rules; the carbonatites may be younger or older than the silicate rocks. This should not be surprising, for the carbonatite magmas cannot be assumed to have crystallized as a series of minerals which were stable from

TABLE XII

Abundances of strontium and barium in some carbonate rocks

	1	2	3	4	5	6	7	8	9
SrO %	0.84	0.73	0.51	0.45	0.63	1.0	0.006	0.47	0.16
BaO %	0.08	0.07	0.06	0.04	0.06	0.07	0.006	0.02	0.44

1–5. Sövites from Fen: 1. Hydro quarry; 2. Tuftestollen; 3. Tufte; 4. Cappelen quarry; 5. Average of the four sövites; 6. Sövite from Spitzkop (Holmes, 1956); 7. Limestone of the Transvaal system (Holmes, 1956); 8. Rauhaugite from Ringsevja, Fen; 9. Rödberg from Tuftestollen, Fen. The Fen sövites have traces of Y_2O_3, but less than 0.01 %; rödberg has 0.01 %, Spitzkop has 0.015 %, and the Transvaal limestone has less than 30 ppm Y_2O_3.

the start. As early as 1933 Daly emphasized that in such gas-rich solutions, auto-pneumatolysis and autometasomatic replacement of early minerals must have been active. Hence the arguments of Bowen and others against the magmatic origin are not conclusive. One would expect that the primary features of the rocks, structurally, mineralogically and geochemically would be partly obliterated, or even completely destroyed by late metasomatic processes.

TABLE XIII

Abundances of some minor elements in apatite

	In sövite Fen (Bergstöl)	In sövite Lueshe (Brasseur)	Average apatites[a] (Brasseur)
SrO %	0.44	1.0	0.02–0.06
BaO %	0.40	0.40	0.04
Y_2O_3	0.02	n.d.	n.d.
MnO %	0.02	0.02	0.1–0.3

[a] Apatites from pegmatites and greisen.

Typical to the Fen area and to similar ring complexes is the existence of relatively large amounts of pure carbonatites. From Fen various mixed carbonate-silicate rocks are also known (kåsenite, hollaite, etc., and the kimberlite dikes and pipes) but in amount they are subordinate; in many similar occurrences all but the kimberlites are almost unknown. Thus, on the one hand there are series of silicate rocks such as the urtite–ijolite–melteigite series that is easily explained as formed by a cooling magma undergoing fractional crystallization, while, on the other hand, there are carbonatites such as sövite which is a monomineralic rock and by no means can be regarded as a product of fractional crystallization.

This contrast is borne out by Fig. 6, which reflects the general conditions in all occurrences. The dominant rock types are concentrated along the base of the triangle, and in the apex; in between there is very little.

These contrasted rock types are in contact with each other, are in the same vent and are, generally speaking, contemporaneous. Thus they seem to be cogenetic and from the same magma chamber.

It is, indeed, difficult to see how one of these two types could develop from the other through magmatic differentiation. It is therefore possible that they represent immiscible portions of the same magma or that they correspond to a liquid portion (the silicate rocks) in equilibrium with a 'fluid' portion, i.e. a supercritical (?) gas phase (the carbonatites). (See Koster van Groos and Wyllie, 1963; Wyllie, this vol., pp. 309-350).

In the case of the latter alternative we may imagine a deep-seated reservoir containing a liquid magma capped by a fluid phase. The internal (hydrostatic) pressure would be high, and an explosion may ensue as is known to have happened at Alnö. At Fen the evidence is not so clear, but there is every reason to believe that the development was rather similar. Carbonatites and peralkalic rocks thus formed would be sharply separated.

A gravimetric survey indicates that the Fen circular complex consists of a heavy plug probably of kimberlitic material (specific gravity = 3.10) capped by a thin layer (some hundred metres thick) of carbonatites and light silicate rocks (Ramberg, 1964).

It may also happen that the high pressure would cause only a slight yielding of the roof. Then the fluid phase would become agitated, boiling would start, and the uprushing gas streams would penetrate into narrow cracks. The further general development of this process was convincingly explained by Cloos (1941) in the case of the formation of the Swabian tuff pipes: the cracks are persistently widened by the erosive powers of the rising gas-particle streams, until massive blocks of rock become isolated and engulfed. Reynolds' (1954, 1956) studies make it reasonable that the gas-particle mixture within which the blocks sink resemble the expanded fluidized beds of industry: the major blocks with a specific gravity greater than that of the fluidized system would subside as if in quicksand. The fluidized matter would, in part, intrude the country rock, giving rise to dikes, plugs and breccias of a great variety of mixed carbonate-silicate rocks (alnöite, kimberlite, etc.).

It appears, therefore, that fluidization and gas coring are the main processes responsible for the formation of the circular carbonatite complexes with their variety of dikes, breccias and subsidiary plugs.

REFERENCES

Aubert, F., 1947, Identifisering av de Nb–Ta– förende mineraler i sövit og forsök på deres magnetiske separasjon: *Tidsskr. Kjemi, Bergvesen*, v. **7**, pp. 169–171.

Baertschi, P., 1957, Messungen und Deutung relativer Haufigkeits variationen von O^{18} und C^{13} in Karbonatgesteinen und Mineralien: *Schweiz. Min. Petr. Mitt.*, v. **37**, pp. 73–152.

Barth, T. F. W., 1963, The composition of nepheline: *Schweiz. Min. Petr. Mitt.* (Parker vol.), v. **43**, pp. 153–164.

Bergstöl, S., 1960, *Undersokelse av bergartene rundt Fensfeltet:* Unpublished dissertation, University of Oslo.

Bergstöl, S., in prep., Tinguaite dikes related to the Fen circular complex.

Bergstöl, S. and Svinndal, S., 1960, The carbonatite and the peralkaline rocks of the Fen area: Geology of Norway, *Norges Geol. Unders*, No. **208**, pp. 99–105.

Björlykke, H., 1934, Norwegische Mikrolithmineralien: *Norsk Geol. Tidsskr.*, v. **14**, pp. 145–161.

Björlykke, H., 1953, Utnytting av sövemalm: *Tidsskr. Kjemi Bergvesen*, v. **13**, pp. 47–48.

Björlykke, H., 1955, The niobium deposits at Söve, southern Norway: *Min. Journ.*, v. **244**, pp. 412–413.

Björlykke, H. and Svinndal, S., 1960, The carbonatite and the peralkaline rocks of the Fen area. Mining and exploration work. Geology of Norway: *Norges Geol. Unders*, No. **208**, pp. 105–110.

Bowen, N. L., 1924, The Fen area in Telemark, Norway: *Am. Jour. Sci.*, v. **8**, pp. 1–11.

Bowen, N. L., 1926, The carbonate rocks of the Fen area in Norway: *Am. Jour. Sci.*, v. **12**, pp. 499–502; translated into German: *Centralblatt f. Min. A.*, No. 8 pp. 241–245.

Brasseur, H., Herman, P. and Hubaux, A., 1962, Apatites de l'est du Congo et du Ruanda: *Ann. Soc. Géol. Belgique*, **85**, Bull. No. **2**, pp. 61–85.

Brauns, A. and Brauns, R., 1925, Ein Carbonatit aus dem Laacher Seegebiet: *Centralblatt f. Min. A.*, pp. 97–101.

Brauns, R., 1926, Primärer Calcit in Tiefengesteinen oder Verdrängung der Silikate durch Calcit? *Centralblatt f. Min. A.*, No. **1**, pp. 1–8.

Brögger, W. C., 1921, Die Eruptivgesteine des Kristianiagebietes. IV. Das Fengebiet in Telemark Norwegen: *Norsk. Vidensk. Selsk. Skr. I, Math. Naturv kl.*, No. **9**, Oslo.

Brögger, W. C., 1932, Die Eruptivgesteine des Oslogebeties. VI. Uber Verschiedene Ganggesteine des Oslogebietes: *Norsk. Vidensk. Selsk. Skr. I, Math. Naturv kl.*, No. **7**, Oslo.

Bugge, A., 1928, En forkastning i det syd-norske grunnfjell: *Norges Geol. Unders*, No. **130**.

Chaignau, M., Tagieff, H. and Fabre, R., 1960. Composition des gaz volcaniques du lac de lave permanent du Nyira-gongo (Congo): *C.R. Acad. Clerm.–Ferrand*, v. **250**, p. 2482–2485, *Centre National De Volcanologie*, No. **3**.

Christie, O. H. J., 1961, On the sub-solidus relations of silicates. I. The lower breakdown temperature at the akermanite gehlenite mixed crystal series at moderate water pressure: *Norsk Geol. Tidsskr.*, v. **41**, pp. 255–269.

Cloos, H., 1941, Bau und Tatigkeit von Tuffschloten: *Geol. Rundschau*, v. **32**, pp. 709–800.

Daly, R. A., 1933, *Igneous Rocks and The Depth of The Earth*, New York, McGraw-Hill.

Dawson, J. B., 1962a, Basutoland kimberlites: *Geol. Soc. America Bull.*, v. **73**, pp. 545–559.

Dawson, J. B., 1962b, Sodium carbonate lavas from Oldoinyo Lengai, Tanganyika: *Nature*, v. **195**, pp. 1075–1076.

DuBois, C. G. B., Furst, J., Guest, N. J., Jennings, D. J., 1963, Fresh natro carbonatite lava from Oldoinyo L'Engai: *Nature*, v. **197**, pp. 445–446.

v. Eckermann, H., 1948a, The genesis of the Alnö alkaline rocks: *Int. Geol. Congr., 18th sess*, Pt. 2, pp. 46–48.

v. Eckermann, H., 1948b, The alkaline district of Alnö Island: *Sverig. Geol. Unders., Ser. Ca*, No. **36**.

v. Eckermann, H., 1950, A comparison between the parageneses of Fenoscandian limestone contact minerals and those of the Alnö alkaline rocks, associated with carbonatites: *Mineralog. Mag.*, v. **29**, pp. 304–312.

v. Eckermann, H., 1952, The distribution of barium and strontium in the rocks and minerals of the syenitic and alkaline rocks of Alnö Island: *Arkiv. f. Mineral Geol.*, v. **1**, pp. 367–375.

v. Eckermann, H., 1958. The alkaline and carbonatitic dikes of the Alnö formation on the mainland north-west of Alnö Island: *Kgl. Svenska Vetensk.–Akad. Handl., Ser. 4*, v. **7**, No. **2**.

v. Eckermann, H., 1961, The petrogenesis of the Alnö alkaline rocks: *Geol. Inst. Uppsala Bull.*, v. **40**, pp. 25–36.

v. Eckermann, H., Ubisch, H. von and Wickman, F. E., 1952, A preliminary investigation into the isotopic composition of carbon from alkaline intrusions: *Geochim. et Cosmochim Acta*, v. **2**, pp. 207–210.

v. Eckermann, H., and Wickman, F. E., 1956, A preliminary determination of the maximum age of the Alnö rocks: *Geol. Fören. Förh.*, v. **78**, pp. 122–124.

Faul, H., Elmore, P. L. D. and Brannock, W. W., 1959, Age of the Fen Carbonatite (Norway) and its relation to the intrusives of the Oslo Region: *Geochim. et Cosmochim Acta*, v. **17**, pp. 153–156.

Goldschmidt, V. M., 1918, Et hittil ukjendt omraade av alkali-bergarter: *Vid. akad. Forh. Kristiania*, p. 20 (Abstract)

Goldsmith, J. R., Graf, D. L., Witters, J. and Northrop, D. A., 1962, Studies in the system $CaCO_3$–$MgCO_3$–$FeCO_3$: *Jour. Geol.*, v. **70**, pp. 659–688.

Harker, R. I. and Tuttle, F., 1956, The lower limit of stability of akermanite: *Am. Jour. Sci.*, v. **254**, pp. 468–478.

Higazy, R. A., 1954, Trace elements of volcanic and ultrabasic potassic rocks of southwestern Uganda and adjoining part of the Belgian Congo: *Geol. Soc. America Bull.*, v. **65**, pp. 39–70.

Högbom, A. E., 1895, Über das Nephelinsyenitgebiet auf der Insel Alnö: *Geol. För. Förh.*, v. **17**, pp. 100–160, 214–256.

Holmes, A., 1936, A contribution to the petrology of kimberlite and its inclusions: *Geol. Soc. S. Africa Trans.*, v. **39**, pp. 379–427

Holmes, A., 1950, Petrogenesis of katungite and its associates: *Am. Mineralogist*, v. **35**, pp. 772–792.

Holmes, A., 1956, The ejectamenta of Katwe crater, south-west Uganda: *Verh. Konink. Nederland Geol. Mijnbouw Genootschap, Geol. ser.*, v. **16**, (Brouwer vol.), pp. 139–166.

Johnson, R. L., 1961, The geology of Dorowa and Shawa carbonatite complexes, Southern Rhodesia: *Geol. Soc. S. Africa Trans.*, v. **44**, pp. 101–145.

King, B. C., and Sutherland, D. S., 1960, Alkaline rocks of eastern and southern Africa parts I–III: *Science Progress*, v. **48**, pp. 298–321, 504–524, 709–720.

Kley, W. and Schmidlin, P., in Neumann, H., 1960, Apparent ages of Norwegian minerals and rocks: *Norsk. Geol. Tidsskr.*, v. **40**, pp. 173–191.

Knorring, O. von and DuBois, C. G. B., 1961, Carbonatitic lava from Fort Portal area in Western Uganda. *Nature*, v. **192**, pp. 1064–1065.

Koster van Groos, A. F. and Wyllie, P. J., 1963, Experimental data bearing on the role of liquid immiscibility in the genesis of carbonatites: *Nature*, v. **199**, pp. 801–802.

Meyer, A., 1958, Carbonatites—quelques grands traits: *C.C.T.A.* Theme 7, Carbonatites, No. **44**, pp. 295–301.

Meyer, A. and Bethune, P. De., 1958, La carbonatite Lueshe (kivu): *Congo Belge Ser. Geol., Bull.* **8**, Fasc. 5.

Neumann, H. and Rosenquist, I., 1940, On the red fluorescent calcite from the Fen area near Ulefoss: *Norsk Geol. Tidsskr.*, v. **20**, pp. 267–268.

Pecora, W. T., 1956, Carbonatites: A review: *Geol. Soc. America Bull.*, v. **67**, pp. 1537–1556.

Ramberg, I. B., 1964, Preliminary results of gravimetric investigations in the Fen area: *Norsk Geol. Tidsskr.*, v. **44**, pp. 431–434.

Ramberg, I. B., and Barth, T. F. W., in press, Eocambrian volcanism in Southern Norway: *Norsk Geol. Tidsskr.*

Reynolds, D., 1954, Fluidization as a geological process and its bearing on the problem of intrusive granites: *Am. Jour. Sci.*, v. **252**, pp. 577–613.

Reynolds, D., 1956, Calderas and ring-complexes: *Verh. Konink. Nederland Geol. Mijnbouw Genootschap, Geol. ser.*, v. **16**, (Brouwer vol.), pp. 355–379.

Saether, E., 1948a, On the genesis of peralkaline rock provinces: *Int. Geol. Congr., 18th sess.*, Pt. **2**, pp. 123–130.

Saether, E., 1948b, Forelöpig meddelelse om resultater av undersökelser i Fensfeltet. *Norsk Geol. Tidsskr.*, (1947), pp. 66–73.

Saether, E., 1957, The alkaline rock province of the Fen area in southern Norway. *Det. Kgl. Norske Vid. Selsk. Skr.*, No. **1.**

Sahama, T. G., 1962, Petrology of Mt. Nyiragongo: *Edinburgh Geol. Soc. Trans.*, v. **19,** pp. 1–28.

Wagner, P. A., 1914, The diamond fields of southern Africa: *The Transvaal Leader* Johannesburg.

Waters, A. C., 1955, Volcanic rocks and the tectonic cycle, in Crust of the Earth: *Geol. Soc. America. Spec. Paper* **62,** p. 703.

Werenskiold, W., 1910, Om Öst-Telemarken: *Norges Geol. Unders.*, v. **53,** p. 47.

Wyllie, P. J., Cox, K. G. and Biggar, G. M., 1962, The habit of apatite in synthetic systems and igneous rocks. *Jour. Petrology*, v. **3,** pp. 238–242.

Wyllie, P. J. and Tuttle, O. F., 1960, The system $CaO-CO_2-H_2O$ and the origin of carbonatites. *Jour. Petrology*, **1,** pp. 1–46.

Wyllie, P. J. and Tuttle, O. F., 1962, Carbonate lavas: *Nature*, v. **194,** p. 1269.

Part II
Fenitization

D. McKIE

Fenitization

INTRODUCTION

Brögger in his memoir on Fen (1921, p. 156) gave the name 'fenite' to a group of rocks, originally of approximately granitic composition, metasomatically altered towards an alkali-syenitic composition by solutions whose source he presumed to be the ijolite-melteigite magma. He regarded the associated melanocratic tveitåsites as contaminated magmatic rocks, but v. Eckermann (1948, p. 27) has shown that comparable rocks are metasomatic at Alnö. The term fenitization has, with the passage of time, acquired a wider meaning than Brögger originally gave it, and as generally used today embraces the whole pattern of widespread metasomatism of rocks of varied composition in the immediate environs of carbonatite complexes. Such is the proper use of a name for a metasomatic process tending to give rise to a local equilibrium product, the composition of which is determined by the chemical potentials of the mobile components in the metasomatizing solution and by the concentrations of the inert components, if any, in the rock undergoing metasomatism.

The development of fenites in some carbonatite complexes in the absence of significant intrusion of magmas of the ijolite-melteigite suite, forces the conclusion that the metasomatism must be related to carbonatite magma rather than to an alkaline silicate magma. The distinction may not however be significant if carbonatite magma is merely a highly volatile residual fraction of an alkaline silicate magma, but the provision of large volumes of metasomatizing solutions may be expected to be more particularly a property of the volatile fraction than of the coexisting relatively involatile silicate fraction.

The occurrence of rocks described as fenites at Norra Kärr and other alkaline intrusions from which carbonatites are conspicuously absent in outcrop is not inconsistent with the preferred definition of fenitization, although it represents an exception to the normal association. Fenites are normally associated with, and alkaline intrusions of a certain type are common associates of, carbonatite complexes; the association of recognizable fenites with such alkaline intrusions in the absence of carbonatite may merely imply that occasionally the volatile carbonate-rich magmatic fraction was not fixed at the currently exposed level or that it may not have been a volumetrically significant entity.

In the following pages a comparative account is given of the bulk compositional adjustment towards local equilibrium of the rocks surrounding a number of carbonatite intrusions. There follows a study of the sequence of mineral phase assemblages in fenitization at various localities, and in conclusion an analysis of the essential features and mechanism of fenitization is attempted.

THE CHEMISTRY OF FENITIZATION

Detailed chemical studies of the changes in rock composition during fenitization have been made at Alnö by v. Eckermann (1948) and at Spitzkop by Strauss and Truter (1950). Frequent comparison will be made between these and Oldonyo Dili, a carbonatite in the Northern Province of Tanganyika, whose 2 sq miles of fenite outcrop have been newly studied with twelve rock analyses, seven analyses of ferromagnesian minerals, and a number of feldspar analyses. Less adequate chemical data are available for Fen (Brögger, 1921; Saether, 1957), Chishanya in Rhodesia (Swift, 1952), Tweerivier in the Transvaal (Fockema, 1952), Tundulu and Nkalonje in Malawi (Dixey, Campbell Smith and Bissett, 1955), Nguala in Tanganyika, and Norra Kärr in Sweden (Adamson, 1944).

In selecting a variation diagram to display the significant features of a metasomatic process, without introducing spurious effects, the physical conditions under which the process operates have to be considered. The persistence of original textures, at least in the early stages, and the lack of new compressive structures suggest that fenitization may have occurred at approximately constant volume. The evidence is not good, but it seems unlikely that any change in volume has been large. If constant volume conditions obtained, a plot in terms of atoms per unit volume would be most suitable. However, it would be difficult to use such a plot comparatively, because most of the fenite analyses in the literature are not accompanied by specific gravity data. The influence of the variation of elements of relatively high atomic weight, such as Fe, on the weight percentages of the light elements would make weight percentage variation diagrams unsatisfactory also. Molecular variation diagrams overcome this difficulty, but they imply that the total number of oxide molecules in the rock remains constant; such an assumption is clearly invalid where redox reactions are involved. The assumption that the oxygen content of a rock remains constant is probably close to the truth for redox processes and may apply to some hydration–dehydration reactions. Since a great many solid–solid reactions involve the persistence of a crude oxygen framework, the assumption of constant oxygen content is probably the best that can conveniently be made; it may indeed be better than an assumption of constant volume, since minor volume changes may be associated with change in cation co-ordination within an approximately persistent oxygen framework. The close relationship between concentration per unit volume of rock and cationic concentration referred to a fixed number of anions in a zone of fenitization is illustrated for the Oldonyo Dili fenites by the two lowest rows of Table I, where the specific gravity (G) and the volume (V) in $Å^3$, per 100 anions are shown for each analysed fenite. For the country rock and the fenites of the main series analyses, 1–10, the mean volume per 100 anions is 2091 $Å^3$ with a standard deviation of 31 $Å^3$, representing constancy within $\pm 1.5\%$; moreover the variation of V with Si concentration displays no definite trend through the series and is quite irregular.

The Standard Cell of Barth (1952, p. 82) expresses the atomic proportions of cations combined with 160 oxygen anions. Barth's reason for choosing the figure

160 does not seem compelling and therefore fenite analyses have been recalculated here (Tables II, IV–VII) in terms of numbers of cations combined with 100 anions (O, OH, F). Since Si always decreases with progress of fenitization at the occurrences for which data are available, other cations are plotted against Si in the variation diagrams; the units on the graphs are number of cations per 100 anions. The Si scale is expanded by a factor of 2 relative to the scale for the other cations to give a wider spread; the distortion introduced is inconsiderable.

One of the principal sources of data for this chapter is the Oldonyo Dili carbonatite, of which no description has yet been published. A brief account of the main features of the complex must therefore be interposed here; a comprehensive account of the Oldonyo Dili carbonatite is in preparation.

Oldonyo Dili was recognized as a carbonatite complex in 1954 by N. J. Guest, who in the following year prepared a geological sketch-map and wrote a brief account of the geology as an unpublished report of the Geological Survey of Tanganyika. During the field seasons of 1957 and 1958 a more accurate outcrop map and a detailed topographical base map were made by a field party of Goldfields of South Africa Ltd. under the direction of Dr. A. F. Cluver[1].

Oldonyo Dili lies on the high plateau close to the western scarp of the Gregory Rift at 3° 25'S, 35° 40'E, near the southernmost limit of the Neogene volcanic field of Northern Tanganyika and central Kenya. It is deeply eroded, displaying a relief of only 1000 ft, and would appear to be considerably older than the plateau lavas, trachytes and alkali basalts, which approach its western, northern and eastern sides and are contemporaneous with the later phases of the Oldeani and Ngorongoro volcanoes. No relics occur of effusive rocks related to the earlier period of vulcanicity, which may be Miocene (like the Kavirondo Gulf carbonatites in Kenya, where the extent of erosion is similar), or even as early as Cretaceous.

The complex consists of a considerable number of small sövite bodies intruded into a fenitized area, two miles long and one mile across. The sövite intrusions (Fig. 1) are mostly subarcuate in outcrop and have steeply dipping contacts conformable with their strongly displayed gently curving, steeply dipping mineral banding. Sövite intrudes rocks fenitized to varying degrees and outcrops close to the outer limit of fenitization especially in the south and the west. The country rocks outside the fenitized area are Archaean gneisses of the Usagaran System (Precambrian), principally biotite gneisses with ribs of amphibolite and occasional simple pegmatites and quartz veins. The sövotes frequently enclose xenoliths of fenite along their margins; a xenolith has been analysed and is discussed further below. The marginal zone of the sövites normally carries an appreciable content of accessory aegirine-augite, brown biotite and occasionally alkali-amphibole. Fenite xenoliths are rimmed by brown or green biotite. The major constituent (60–96%) of all the sövite specimens examined is calcite; dolomite and ankeritic carbonates do not apparently occur at Oldonyo Dili. Common accessory minerals in the sövites are pyrochlore (in small yellow

[1] I must here express my indebtedness to Goldfields of South Africa Ltd. and particularly to Dr. Cluver for the invitation to examine the petrology of Oldonyo Dili, which I visited in April 1957, and for permission to reproduce the fenite-sövite and the fenite-gneiss boundaries from their map.

TABLE I[a]

Chemical analyses of fenites from Oldonyo Dili

	1	2	3	4	5	6	7	8	9	10	11	12
SiO_2	74.82	73.75	71.85	67.91	66.54	60.14	59.49	60.54	58.13	59.42	53.15	55.21
Al_2O_3	14.60	13.89	15.27	15.80	13.30	12.39	13.02	15.82	12.43	16.28	4.32	15.17
Fe_2O_3	0.30	0.74	0.72	2.27	3.46	9.75	9.11	6.04	10.42	5.88	15.70	6.07
FeO	0.76	0.37	1.07	0.39	0.67	0.83	0.63	0.91	0.70	0.55	5.09	2.11
MgO	0.16	0.17	0.49	0.57	0.80	1.07	1.17	0.63	1.12	1.09	2.47	2.23
CaO	0.81	1.05	2.17	1.41	2.43	2.16	2.70	2.84	1.98	2.66	8.51	3.06
Na_2O	3.36	4.31	5.59	6.22	6.28	8.01	6.34	9.26	6.23	7.90	8.13	5.93
K_2O	5.03	4.85	2.53	3.86	4.95	4.35	6.57	2.35	7.10	3.51	0.79	5.83
H_2O+	0.34	0.57	0.36	0.83	0.47	0.18	0.36	0.45	0.69	1.11	0.28	1.02
H_2O-	0.04	0.04	0.05	0.30	0.02	0.07	0.09	0.19	0.16	0.50	0.11	0.32
TiO_2	0.13	0.09	0.23	0.25	0.26	0.43	0.43	0.41	0.58	0.49	0.87	0.60
P_2O_5	0.04	0.04	0.09	0.08	0.09	0.32	0.16	0.30	0.49	0.59	0.46	0.14
MnO	0.03	0.02	0.03	0.16	0.19	0.07	0.37	0.11	0.14	0.22	0.42	0.10
CO_2	nd	nd	nd	nd	1.05	nd	nd	0.22	nd	0.31	nd	1.62
Total	100.42	100.09	100.45	100.05	100.51	99.77	100.44	100.07	100.17	100.51	100.30	99.41
G	2.622	2.581	2.640	2.627	2.678	2.750	2.860	2.716	2.747	2.758	3.101	2.664
V	2059	2101	2060	2097	2087	2124	2057	2105	2148	2067	2008	2170

G: specific gravity. V: volume in $Å^3$ per 100 anions. nd: not determined. D. McKie, anal.

Field numbers are given in parentheses in the key below.

1. Granitic gneiss with biotite and garnet (D499).
2. Quartz-bearing aegirine magnesioarfvedsonite fenite (D513).
3. Quartz-bearing magnesioarfvedsonite fenite (D553/5).
4. Quartz-bearing aegirine magnesioarfvedsonite fenite (D515).
5. Quartz-bearing aegirine magnesioarfvedsonite fenite (D497).
6. Aegirine magnesioarfvedsonite fenite (D507).
7. Aegirine magnesioarfvedsonite fenite (D625).
8. Aegirine fenite (D592).
9. Aegirine magnesioarfvedsonite fenite (D620A).
10. Aegirine magnesioarfvedsonite fenite (D622).
11. Aegirine-augite fenite (D503).
12. Aegirine fenite xenolith (D426).

[a] Locations of the specimens are shown by numbers in Fig. 1 (p. 265).

octahedra and cube-octahedra), magnetite, limonite, quartz, apatite and barite. Fluorite and opaline silica occur rarely. There is no apparent regularity in the distribution of the various accessory mineral assemblages over the many sövite bodies.

Sövite dikes occur at several localities within the Oldonyo Dili complex and one outcrops between the easternmost limit of fenitization and the rift escarpment. Two silicate dikes have been recognized; one is a tinguaite and the other an alvikitic alnöite.

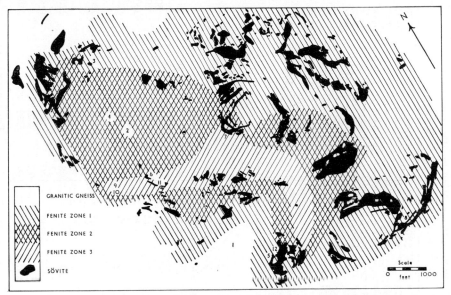

Fig. 1. Geological map of Oldonyo Dili. The outer margin of zone 1 represents the first appearance of aegirine or magnesioarfvedsonite; that of zone 2 the complete disappearance of biotite; and that of zone 3 the complete disappearance of quartz and microcline-microperthite.

The chemical compositions of twelve Oldonyo Dili fenites are presented as oxide weight percentages in Table I and as cationic concentrations per 100 anions in Table II. The main series of fenites, analyses 2–10, are presumed to be the products of fenitization of the dominant country rock at Oldonyo Dili, a granitic gneiss represented by analysis 1. The principal chemical changes during fenitization are displayed in Fig. 2 and examined statistically in Table VIII. The first column of Table VIII shows the correlation coefficient r_{12} for each cationic concentration with Si concentration; r_{12} is defined by the equation

$$r_{12} = \frac{\sum(X_{Si} - \bar{x}_{Si})(X_R - \bar{x}_R)}{+\sqrt{\sum(X_{Si} - \bar{x}_{Si})^2 \cdot \sum(X_R - \bar{x}_R)^2}},$$

where X_{Si} and X_R are the cationic concentrations of Si and the cation R respectively in each analysis of Table II, $\bar{x}_{Si}$ and $\bar{x}_R$ are the corresponding means, and the sum is taken over analyses 1–10. All correlation coefficients are negative,

TABLE II

Compositions of fenites from Oldonyo Dili in cations per 100 oxygen anions

	1	2	3	4	5	6	7	8	9	10	11	12
Si	40.34	40.07	39.00	37.50	37.10	35.30	34.94	34.69	34.34	33.80	33.08	32.32
Al	9.28	8.90	9.77	10.28	8.74	8.57	9.01	10.68	8.65	10.91	3.17	10.46
Fe^{3+}	0.12	0.30	0.29	0.94	1.45	4.31	4.02	2.60	4.63	2.51	7.35	2.67
Fe^{2+}	0.34	0.17	0.49	0.18	0.31	0.41	0.31	0.44	0.34	0.26	2.65	1.03
Mg	0.13	0.14	0.40	0.47	0.66	0.93	1.02	0.54	0.99	0.92	2.29	1.94
Ca	0.47	0.61	1.26	0.83	1.45	1.36	1.70	1.74	1.25	1.62	5.68	1.69
Na	3.51	4.54	5.88	6.65	6.78	9.11	7.22	10.28	7.13	8.71	9.80	6.73
K	3.46	3.36	1.75	2.72	3.52	3.26	4.92	1.71	5.35	2.55	0.63	4.35
H	1.22	2.06	1.30	3.06	1.75	0.71	1.41	1.72	2.72	4.21	1.15	3.98
Ti	0.05	0.04	0.09	0.10	0.11	0.19	0.19	0.18	0.26	0.21	0.41	0.26
P	0.02	0.02	0.04	0.04	0.04	0.16	0.08	0.14	0.25	0.29	0.24	0.07
Mn	0.01	0.01	0.01	0.08	0.09	0.04	0.18	0.06	0.07	0.11	0.22	0.05
C	—	—	—	—	0.80	—	0.18	0.17	—	0.24	—	1.29

The columns are numbered as in Table I

TABLE III

Trace elements in fenites from Oldonyo Dili and Ngualla

	1	2	3	4	5	6	7	8	9	10	11	12	Ng
Ga	25	22	14	25	20	35	22	22	22	22	50	20	5
Cr	4	—	5	6	4	8	12	5	12	5	50	140	—
V	—	10	20	40	25	320	90	130	250	90	200	140	14
Li	50	3	5	25	20	3	8	1	2	8	3	110	10
Ni	—	—	2	12	—	4	2	4	7	3	12	55	—
Co	—	—	—	—	—	—	—	—	—	—	—	12	—
Zr	50	100	120	220	100	450	165	450	320	320	1000	100	120
Y	18	—	15	15	10	—	15	15	10	10	—	10	15
La	55	—	—	220	—	220	220	120	100	65	—	40	65
Sr	100	220	400	1200	700	—	250	500	1000	1000	220	1600	180
Pb	45	—	46	45	45	370	—	12	12	—	—	15	32
Ba	370	800	700	1600	800	320	700	700	440	700	125	1600	2200
Rb	500	150	12	100	320	250	440	12	440	18	—	320	45
N	—	—	45	—	50	250	150	460	220	150	250	—	32

Concentrations are given in ppm. A dash indicates concentration below the limit of sensitivity. The numbering of the columns corresponds to that in Table I, 11 being the melanocratic fenite and 12 the fenite xenolith; Ng is the fenite from Ngualla (analysis on p. 275).

but only those for Mg and Ti have the high negative value indicative of close antipathetic variation with Si. The irregularity of the variation is clearly considerable and a more fruitful approach is through the slope and the standard error of

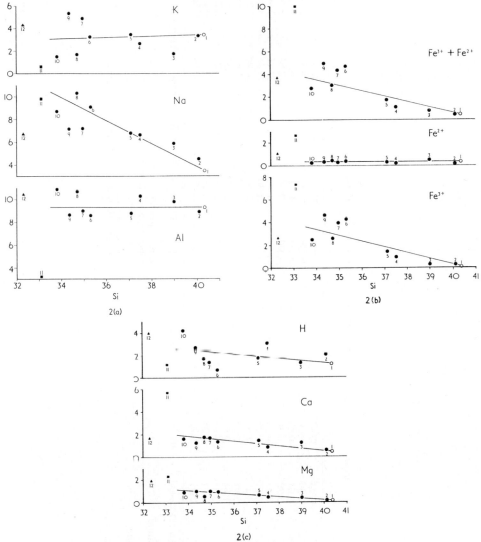

Fig. 2. Variation of the major elements in fenitization at Oldonyo Dili.
Numbers refer to the columns of Tables I and II.

the slope of the straight line fitted by least squares to the concentration data on the assumption that the concentration of the cation R is the dependent variable with respect to Si concentration. The slope b is then given by

$$b = \frac{\Sigma(X_{Si} - \bar{x}_{Si})(X_R - \bar{x}_R)}{\Sigma(X_{Si} - \bar{x}_{Si})^2}$$

TABLE IV

Compositions of country rocks from Alnö Island in cations per 100 oxygen anions

	1	2	3	4	5	6	7	8	9	10
Si	40.38	39.64	39.45	38.31	36.91	38.01	37.13	38.60	36.89	34.85
Al	9.03	9.30	9.16	9.57	10.13	10.06	10.49	9.04	9.87	9.81
Fe^{3+}	0.26	0.07	0.88	0.19	0.34	0.08	0.23	0.22	0.09	0.53
Fe^{2+}	0.22	0.80	0.46	1.56	2.43	2.00	2.00	1.87	2.63	2.29
Mg	0.24	0.53	0.52	1.43	2.03	1.61	1.70	1.78	2.15	2.96
Ca	0.40	0.77	0.29	1.25	1.26	0.97	1.30	1.47	1.45	3.30
Na	2.50	3.45	1.67	3.03	2.60	3.12	2.56	2.53	4.05	3.20
K	4.90	3.08	5.30	3.18	3.38	3.18	2.72	1.89	1.63	1.18
H	0.54	1.64	0.92	1.36	3.02	1.29	2.22	1.64	2.53	6.18
Ti	—	0.06	—	0.15	0.08	0.12	0.18	0.25	0.27	0.29
P	0.16	0.14	0.25	0.15	0.03	0.05	0.21	0.09	0.14	0.14
Mn	0.09	0.01	0.23	0.02	0.01	0.03	0.05	0.03	0.04	0.06

The compositions have been calculated from the anlyses of v. Eckermann (1948, pp. 21–25); the numbering of the columns corresponds to the numbering of the analyses.

1. White aplitic Harnö granite.
2. Harnö granite.
3. Red aplitic Harnö granite.
4. Bergefors granite.
5. Bergefors granite-gneiss.
6. Gneiss-granite from Boräng.
7. Gneiss-granite from the east coast.
8. Biotite-schist.
9. Archaean schist.
10. Metabasitic (dioritic) fragment in migmatite.

TABLE V

Compositions of fenites from Alnö Island in cations per 100 (O, F, S) anions

	11	12	13	14	15	16	17	18	19	20
Si	35.72	35.60	34.41	34.13	33.92	33.20	31.78	30.04	28.90	30.41
Al	9.57	11.57	11.28	10.57	8.97	12.09	11.46	8.10	13.15	12.49
Fe^{3+}	2.32	0.55	1.05	0.71	1.67	0.94	2.34	2.75	1.47	1.41
Fe^{2+}	0.82	0.39	0.74	2.06	2.18	1.04	0.92	1.92	1.16	1.04
Mg	1.49	0.48	1.46	2.08	2.22	1.42	0.26	2.22	0.74	1.22
Ca	4.18	1.26	2.51	3.03	3.67	3.37	2.21	6.00	4.81	2.48
Na	2.99	4.93	8.52	5.18	4.42	4.24	7.08	3.10	3.17	5.25
K	3.13	6.18	2.52	3.99	4.67	5.99	4.39	5.73	5.25	5.12
H	1.11	1.18	2.90	2.63	2.65	2.40	6.12	2.87	1.62	9.51
Ti	0.12	0.23	0.17	0.20	0.30	0.26	0.13	0.05	0.12	0.14
P	0.14	0.16	0.24	0.08	0.12	0.27	—	0.47	0.53	0.21
Mn	0.05	0.03	0.05	0.09	0.11	0.06	0.05	0.19	0.06	0.12
C		0.66		0.50	0.60	0.26	1.60	3.08	3.45	1.37
Ba		0.10	0.01	0.07	0.04	0.07	0.05	0.04		
F		0.07				0.11				
S		0.24		0.13	0.33		0.62	0.17		0.08

The compositions have been calculated from the analyses of v. Eckermann (1948, pp. 35–39); the numbering of the columns corresponds to the numbering of the analyses.

11. Fenite.
12. Syenitic fenite.
13. Syenitic fenite.
14. Syenitic fenite.
15. Syenitic fenite.

16. Pulaskitic fenite.
17. Alkorthositic fenite.
18. Fenite.
19. Fenite.
20. Fenite.

K

and its standard error by

$$\text{S.E. } (b) = \sqrt{\frac{\sum(X_R - \bar{x}_R)^2 - b^2\sum(X_{Si} - \bar{x}_{Si})^2}{(N-2)\sum(X_{Si} - \bar{x}_{Si})^2}}$$

where N is the number of analyses considered, i.e. $N = 10$. Small standard errors correspond in general to high negative values of r_{12}; r_{12} however gives no measure of the magnitude of the slope. The values of b in the fourth column of Table VIII indicate that the principal changes are a large decrease in silicon content accompanied by rather smaller increases in sodium and ferric iron concentrations. All other chemical changes are relatively small; Mg, Ca, Ti, P and Mn clearly increase slightly, but for Al, Fe^{2+}, K and H, although the slopes are all negative, the standard error is such that their real relationship may be constancy, a slight increase or a slight decrease in concentration. Strong correlation and relatively small standard error are scarcely to be expected in metasomatism, itself an inhomogeneous process, of a rock as inhomogeneous as granitic gneiss is prone to be. Hydrogen content is irregularly variable and is probably too much dependent on secondary processes to be interpretable in terms of fenitization. The CO_2 content of the three rocks for which it was determined is related to the crystallization of patches of calcite, which cannot be regarded as an essential concomitant of fenitization.

The relationship of analyses 11 and 12 to the main series of fenites will be discussed later in terms of their mineralogy. At this stage it is proper to point out however that analysis 11 belongs to a dark aegirine-augite–plagioclase rock, characterized by very low Al, low Si and K, high Mg, and very high Fe and Ca contents, probably a product of fenitization of a plagioclase amphibolite. Analysis 12 is of a xenolith of fenite from the marginal zone of one of the sövite bodies; it is characterized by low Si and Na contents and appears to represent a fairly low-grade fenite which has reacted to some extent with carbonatite magma.

For the optical spectrographic determination of trace elements in the Oldonyo Dili fenites I am indebted to Dr. S. R. Nockolds. In the main series of fenites, Table III columns 1–10, concentration increases as fenitization proceeds for V, Zr, La, Sr, Ba and Nb, all of which, except vanadium, are elements characteristically concentrated in the accessory minerals of sövites. The concentration of Ba in most cases exceeds, but is occasionally less than that of Sr. The elements Ga, Cr, Ni and Y vary irregularly or remain constant in concentration. Li and Pb decrease, while Rb is markedly variable in concentration and may decrease with progressive fenitization.

v. Eckermann (1948) lists ten analyses of country rocks occurring in the immediate environs of Alnö and ten analyses of fenites derived from them. The analyses, recalculated in cations per 100 oxygen ions, are set out in Tables IV and V respectively. The data are displayed, together with those for Oldonyo Dili and Spitzkop, on Fig. 3, and examined statistically in the second and fifth columns of Table VIII. The correlation coefficient of cationic concentration with silicon concentration fails to reach a high negative value for any of the cations determined in the Alnö rocks; one contributory factor must be the wide variation in composition displayed by the granites, granite-gneisses, and biotite-schists that are the country rocks, and another the relatively high calcite content of some of the fenites. The values of b, however, indicate that the principal accompaniments of the large decrease in Si concentration, of similar magnitutude to that at Oldonyo

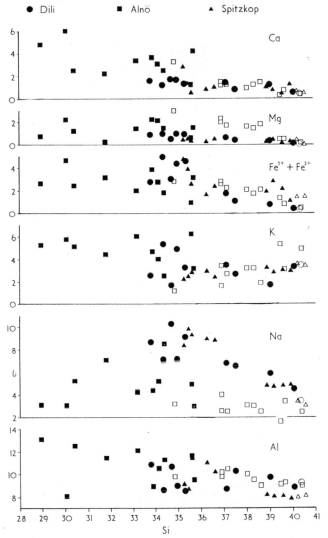

Fig. 3. Comparison of the variation of major elements in fenitization at Oldonyo Dili, Alnö and Spitzkop. Solid symbols: fenites. Hollow symbols: country rocks.

Dili, are definite, although smaller, increases in Ca, H, Na, Al, K and Fe^{3+} concentrations in that order of magnitude. The increase in Ca concentration is closely related to crystallization of calcite in the fenites, but the increase in concentration of the other cations is clearly attributable to the process of fenitization. Mn appears to increase in concentration slightly and Mg, Ti, Fe^{2+} and P

TABLE VI

Compositions of fenites from Spitzkop in cations per 100 oxygen anions

	F	E	D	C	B	A	J	K	I	H	G
Si	40.55	40.18	39.91	39.54	36.61	35.59	39.17	38.86	36.25	35.46	35.23
Al	8.12	7.96	7.84	8.08	10.22	11.44	8.04	8.22	11.00	8.72	9.08
Fe^{3+}	0.36	0.72	1.08	1.60	1.42	2.00	0.98	0.30	1.36	3.38	2.58
Fe^{2+}	1.09	0.72	—	0.53	0.95	0.55	1.82	1.62	0.28	0.49	2.15
Mg	0.02	0.46	0.24	0.13	0.49	0.39	0.43	0.25	0.25	0.52	0.42
Ca	0.48	0.69	1.24	0.46	1.02	0.48	0.73	1.01	0.78	1.37	2.80
Na	3.04	3.40	4.90	4.78	8.80	9.32	4.70	4.82	8.94	9.82	8.34
K	3.38	3.54	2.94	3.02	2.42	2.80	2.80	3.18	2.88	2.44	2.20
H	1.46	1.82	1.10	2.18	1.88	1.86	1.54	1.84	1.50	1.16	0.98
Ti	0.15	0.09	0.04	0.10	0.11	0.11	0.19	0.25	0.13	0.40	0.22
P	0.06	—	0.28	0.02	0.01	0.01	0.08	0.46	0.28	0.40	0.12
Mn	0.15	0.02	0.04	0.04	0.04	0.02	0.04	0.05	0.03	0.10	0.16
C	—	0.08									—

The compositions have been calculated from the analyses of Strauss and Truter (1950); the labelling of the columns corresponds to the labelling of the analyses.

F. Bushveld granophyre } country rocks.
E. Bushveld Main granite }
D. Granophyre } affected by long range albitization.
C. Granite }
B. Red quartz syenite } products of first (red) fenitization.
A. Cellular red umptekite }
J. Amphibole-bearing soda granite
K. Amphibole-bearing soda granite
I. Pyroxene-bearing umptekite (fine) } products of second (white) fenitization.
H. Pyroxene-bearing umptekite (coarse)
G. Pyroxene-bearing umptekite (fine)

are constant within the limits of the standard error of the slope *b*. These conclusions are in general accord with those of v. Eckermann except in two important respects. v. Eckermann considered that Na was lost and Al remained constant during fenitization at Alnö; it seems difficult however to avoid the conclusion that both elements have increased in concentration.

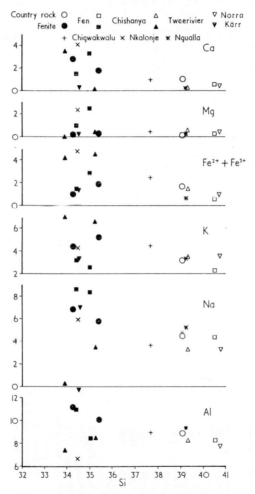

Fig. 4. The variation of major elements in fenitization at several localities for which few analyses are available.

The two analyses of country rocks and the nine analyses of fenites from Spitzkop, Sekukuniland, Eastern Transvaal given by Strauss and Truter (1950) have been similarly recalculated and are set down in Table VI, and examined statistically in Table VIII. The decrease in Si to the inner umptekite boundary at Spitzkop is slightly less than the decrease at Oldonyo Dili, and is accompanied by a very strong increase in Na concentration, by significant increases in Al and Fe^{3+}, by a smaller increase in Ca, by possible small increases in Mg and Ti, by

TABLE VII

Composition of fenites from several localities in cations per 100 oxygen anions

	O	II	I	A	C	B	F80	F247	F244	Ch	Nk	Ng	NK-1	NK-36
Si	39.05	35.41	34.26	40.48	35.02	34.40	39.29	35.26	33.92	37.66	34.43	39.19	40.75	34.53
Al	8.91	10.09	11.17	8.31	8.49	11.01	8.28	8.53	7.42	9.02	6.72	9.41	7.82	13.99
Fe^{3+}	0.95	1.37	0.46	0.11	2.29	1.26	0.79	4.09	3.70	1.87	3.72	0.59	0.39	0.62
Fe^{2+}	0.72	0.50	0.49	0.50	0.58	0.22	0.75	0.45	0.49	0.59	1.05	0.12	0.61	1.11
Mg	0.21	0.34	0.16	0.33	2.51	0.96	0.59	0.37	—	0.54	2.39	0.31	0.43	0.24
Ca	1.07	1.84	2.78	0.59	3.29	1.54	0.34	0.20	3.49	0.98	4.11	0.31	0.49	0.32
Na	4.53	5.80	6.84	4.39	8.41	8.64	3.29	3.50	0.33	3.70	6.02	5.30	3.34	7.05
K	3.23	5.20	4.42	2.29	2.64	3.18	3.46	6.63	6.99	4.54	4.29	3.44	3.56	3.35
H	1.33	1.56	0.90	2.59	0.62	2.71	3.89	6.21	3.18	0.94	0.79	2.47	1.77	2.80
Ti	0.17	0.19	0.05	0.06	0.16	0.14	0.10	0.47	0.47	0.65	0.30	0.09	0.10	0.08
P	0.01	0.03	0.24	0.03	0.29	0.07	0.03	0.10	0.16	0.14	0.28	0.03	0.03	0.03
Mn	0.03	0.05	0.05	0.01	0.10	0.04	0.01	0.06	0.03	0.02	0.30	0.02	0.03	0.01
C	0.08	1.25	1.89	0.07	0.21	1.16	0.27	0.06	2.45	—	0.39	—	—	0.25
Ba	—	0.03	0.01	—	—	—	—	—	—	—	—	—	0.01	—

O   Archean gneiss, Holla farm, Fen (Brögger, 1921, p. 8).
II   Fenite, Melteig, Fen (Brögger, 1921, p. 158).
I   Fenite, Melteig, Fen (Brögger, 1921, p. 158).
A   Gneissic granite, Sabi River, north east of Chishanya (Swift, 1952, p. 350).
C   Melancratic syenite (fenite), Chishanya (Swift, 1952, p. 350).
B   Leucocratic syenite (fenite), Chishanya (Swift, 1952, p. 350).
F80   Granite, Kareesloot, near Tweerivier (Fockema, 1952, p. 158).
F247 Femic quartz-syenite (fenite), Tweerivier (Fockema, 1952, p. 168).
F244 Potash-rich quartz-syenite (fenite), Tweerivier (Fockema, 1942, p. 168).
Ch   Altered pyroxene-granite or granulite (fenite), Chigwakwalu Hill, Tundulu (Dixey et al., 1955, p. 55).
Nk   Feldspar-pyroxene rock, crest of Nkalonje Hill (Dixey et al., 1955, p. 55).
Ng   Quartz-aegirine-magnesioarfvedsonite-fenite, Ngualla, Tanganyika.
NK-1 Red Växiö granite, 20 km south east from Norra Kärr, Sweden (Adamson, 1944, p. 120).
NK-36 Aegirine-fenite, 1 metre from contact, Norra Kärr, Sweden (Adamson, 1944, p. 222).

apparent constancy of H, P and Mn, and by a definite decrease in K concentration. Strauss and Truter were able to distinguish three successive stages in the fenitization at Spitzkop, in the last of which the behaviour of Na and Al was reversed, but their conclusions about the overall elementary gains and losses were much the same as those derived here.

The compositions of fenites from some other localities for which rather fewer chemical data are available are shown in Table VII and plotted on Fig. 4. At Fen the two analysed fenites (Brögger, 1921) show clear increases relative to the analysed gneiss in Al, Na and K, approximate constancy of Fe and Mg, and increase in Ca only as calcite; Si is the only element that clearly decreases. Of the minor elements, P increases, Mn remains approximately constant, and the behaviour of Ti is uncertain.

For Chishanya in Rhodesia the data shown on Fig. 4, derived from the analyses of Swift (1952), indicate that decrease in Si is accompanied by a large increase in Na and rather small increases in Fe and Mg; Ca increases probably only as calcite. The behaviour of Al and K is uncertain. The minor elements Ti, P and Mn all appear to increase.

Fockema (1952) pointed out that in the area of fenitization around the confluence of the Elands and Crocodile Rivers in the Transvaal, referred to subsequently by the name of the farm Tweerivier for brevity, the fenites have been affected by subsequent alteration which has converted their ferromagnesian minerals entirely into chlorite and iron-rich ochre. The conclusions drawn from Fig. 4 may, consequently, be unreliable. Decrease in Si is accompanied by marked increases in Fe and K, constancy of Mg, and apparent decreases in Al and Na; the decreases may however be attributed to subsequent leaching of aegirine. Ca increases significantly only as calcite. The minor elements Ti, P, and Mn increase.

Also plotted on Fig. 4 are the compositional data, derived from a new analysis of a fenite from Ngualla in southern Tanganyika. The composition of the Ngualla fenite in oxide weight percentages is SiO_2, 71.91; Al_2O_3, 14.65; Fe_2O_3, 1.43; FeO, 0.26; MgO, 0.38; CaO, 0.53; Na_2O, 5.02; K_2O, 4.95; H_2O^+, 0.68; H_2O^-, 0.09; TiO_2, 0.22; P_2O_5, 0.05; MnO, 0.05; total 100.22; its cationic constitution per 100 anions is shown in the tenth column of Table VII. The rock is composed of saussuritized phenocrysts of twinned plagioclase in a fine-grained groundmass of quartz and potash feldspar; small grains of aegirine are disseminated through the groundmass. Small quartz veins and aegirine-arfvedsonite veins traverse the texture and in the latter arfvedsonite is particularly developed where they intersect large plagioclase crystals. In bulk composition the Ngualla fenite resembles fenite 3 from Oldonyo Dili (Table II) and the white fenite J from Spitzkop (Table VI), and it would appear to represent an early stage in the fenitization of the principal country rock surrounding the carbonatite intrusion, the so-called porphyry complex, none of the members of which has been analysed.

The composition of two fenites of the Chilwa series, one from Chigwakwalu Hill, Tundulu and the other from Nkalonje are plotted on Fig. 4. No conclusions can be drawn about the elementary gains and losses involved in their formation.

They have been included merely to show that they are not anomalous in composition.

The development of fenites at Norra Kärr in the absence of associated sövitic intrusion has been discussed by Adamson (1944) in the light of two chemical

TABLE VIII

Statistical analysis of the variation in concentration of the major elements relative to Si concentration at Oldonyo Dili, Alnö and Spitzkop

	r_{12}			$-b$		
	Ol. Dili	Alnö	Spitzkop	Ol. Dili	Alnö	Spitzkop
Al	−0.2170	−0.5605	−0.7466	0.078±.123	0.224±.078	0.464±.138
Fe^{3+}	−0.8636	−0.7264	−0.7910	0.617±.128	0.181±.040	0.351±.091
Fe^{2+}	−0.1661	−0.0716	−0.0732	0.007±.015	0.016±.053	0.024±.107
Mg	−0.9035	−0.1428	−0.5629	0.125±.021	0.033±.053	0.043±.021
Ca	−0.8317	−0.8175	−0.4964	0.153±.036	0.380±.063	0.158±.092
Na	−0.8674	−0.4505	−0.9690	0.728±.148	0.225±.105	1.190±.101
K	−0.2071	−0.4081	−0.8163	0.101±.168	0.183±.096	−0.159±.037
OH	−0.3577	−0.5531	−0.2721	0.153±.141	0.362±.129	−0.049±.058
Ti	−0.9543	−0.1958	−0.4388	0.029±.003	0.005±.006	0.021±.014
P	−0.8340	−0.0045	−0.1598	0.034±.008	0.000±.018	0.013±.026
Mn	−0.6700	−0.2377	−0.1497	0.015±.006	0.004±.004	0.004±.008

analyses, one of a granite from beyond the outer limit of fenitization and the other of a fenite from close to the grennaite boundary. The corresponding cationic concentrations are shown in the last two columns of Table VII and plotted on Fig. 4. Decrease in Si is clearly accompanied by considerable increases in the concentration of Al, Fe and Na. The unexpected decrease in Mg may be more apparent than real and a consequence of the variability of the Växiö granite,

TABLE IX

Elementary gains and losses in fenitization

	Si	Al	Fe	Mg	Ca	Na	K	H	Ti	P	Mn
Ol. Dili	− − −	(±)	+ +	+	+	+ +	±	±	(+)	(+)	(+)
Alnö	− − −	+	+	(±)	+ +	+	+	+ +	(±)	(±)	(±)
Spitzkop	− − −	+ +	+ +	(⊦)	+	+ + +	−	(±)	(+)	(±)	(±)
Fen	− − −	+	±	±	+	+	+		?±	+	±
Chishanya	− − −	?+	+	+	+	+	?+		+	+	+
Tweerivier	− − −	?−	+	±	+	?−	+		+	+	+
Chilwa Is.	− − −	+	+			+	+		+		
Norra Kärr	− − −	+	+	−	±	+	±		±	±	±

Some quantitative expression is given to changes at Oldonyo Dili, Alnö and Spitzkop based on the values of $-b$ shown in Table VIII: $+ + + > 0.9$, $+ + > 0.3$, $(+) < 0.1$, $±$ sense of change uncertain, $(±)$ sense of small change uncertain. The interpretation for Chilwa Island is that of Garson and Campbell Smith (1958) rather than that of Campbell Smith (1956); for the other complexes the interpretations are based on re-study of the analyses and differ in detail from those of the original descriptions.

to which Adamson draws attention. In its essential features, however, fenitization at Norra Kärr in no way differs from that in the environs of any sövite intrusion.

The conclusions derived from examination of Table VIII and Figs. 2–4 are summarized in Table IX. In general, fenitization involves a large decrease in Si (implicit in the construction of the figures) and large increases in Na and Fe concentrations; Al tends to increase, but may remain constant; K tends to increase or remain constant except at Spitzkop; Mg tends to remain constant, but may increase; and Ca tends to increase principally as calcite. The minor constituent elements Ti, Mn and P, tend to increase or remain constant. The

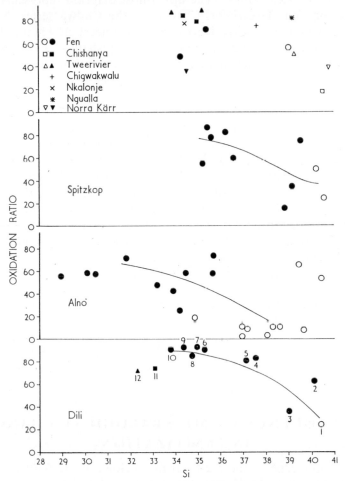

Fig. 5. Comparison of the variation of oxidation ratio, O.R. $= 100\ Fe^{3+}/$
$(Fe^{3+}+Fe^{2+})$, in fenitization at various localities.

interpretation put on their chemical and petrographic data by the original authors differs significantly from the present interpretation only in the behaviour of Na at Alnö. The anomalous pattern of elementary gains and losses at Tweerivier must be ascribed, at least in part, to subsequent alteration of dark minerals.

The oxidizing character of the fenitizing solutions at all the complexes under detailed examination is shown by the graphs of Fig. 5. There the oxidation ratio of iron, defined as O.R. $= 100\ Fe^{3+}/(Fe^{3+}+Fe^{2+})$, where Fe^{3+} and Fe^{2+} are concentrations in atomic units, is plotted against the concentration of silicon in atoms per 100 anions, representing degree of fenitization. The three lower diagrams of Fig. 5 indicate that oxidation increases to a very high level as fenitization proceeds at Oldonyo Dili, to a rather lower level at Alnö, and to a high level at Spitzkop, although for the last occurrence considerable scatter is exhibited by the plotted points. The uppermost diagram represents what data are available for Fen, Tweerivier, Chishanya, the Chilwa series, Ngualla and Norra Kärr. At Fen and Norra Kärr it remains uncertain whether fenitization has occurred under oxidizing conditions. At Chishanya strong oxidation is demonstrated. At Tweerivier apparently strong oxidation must be ascribed in part to subsequent alteration of ferromagnesian minerals to iron-rich ochre and chlorite. The isolated fenite analyses available for Chigwakwalu, Nkalonje and Ngualla correspond to high oxidation ratios.

The marked increase in oxidation ratio during fenitization is not so much due to the oxidation of Fe^{2+} *in situ* as to the influx of solutions carrying a considerable content of iron largely as Fe^{3+}, as the data displayed on Fig. 2 for Oldonyo Dili clearly show. The fenitizing solutions must have acquired high concentrations of Fe^{3+} at source in the carbonatite magma chamber and during their subsequent passage through the surrounding gneisses their content of dissolved iron must have been maintained largely in the ferric state. The dissociation constants of H_2O and of CO_2 are closely similar; either will provide a highly oxidizing environment for iron silicates and oxides (Darken and Gurry, 1945; Muan, 1958). The oxidation that leads characteristically to the formation of acmitic pyroxenes and of soda-ferric-amphiboles in fenitization cannot therefore be attributed solely to the presence of CO_2 in the fenitizing solutions; simple aqueous solutions would be comparably oxidizing. The essential requirement would appear to be the absence of reducing agents such as H_2 or CO from the carbonatite magma system; it is significant that the iron and manganese minerals of the sövites generally, and therefore the carbonatite magma itself, are commonly highly oxidized.

THE SEQUENCE OF MINERALOGICAL CHANGES IN FENITIZATION

Quantitative knowledge of the chemical mineralogy of the fenites has hitherto been severely restricted. This comparative study is therefore based on new work on the Oldonyo Dili fenites; what data are available for other zones of fenitization are then discussed in the light of the results for Oldonyo Dili. The mineralogy and petrography of each of the analysed fenites are first described and in later paragraphs the composition and behaviour of each major constituent mineral is discussed in a wider context.

The only analysed country rock from Oldonyo Dili (analysis 1)[1] is a granitic gneiss composed of approximately equal amounts of microcline-microperthite and quartz, rather less oligoclase-albite, biotite and some pink garnet. The

---

[1] In the sequel each Oldonyo Dili fenite will be referred to by the number of its analysis in Tables II and III.

TABLE X

Chemical analyses of ferromagnesian minerals from Oldonyo Dili

Weight percentages

	Bt-1	Bt-3	Am-3	Am-6	Px-6	Px-11	Px-12
SiO_2	34.65	37.33	51.47	52.71	51.64	51.17	51.53
Al_2O_3	16.88	14.93	2.63	3.13	1.57	1.40	1.87
Fe_2O_3	5.09	3.52	9.04	9.50	26.02	19.21	27.75
FeO	21.80	19.35	12.82	7.41	2.09	6.68	1.26
MnO	0.30	0.22	0.22	0.79	0.13	0.44	0.17
MgO	4.22	7.81	6.83	11.19	1.57	2.96	1.36
TiO_2	3.55	3.21	3.04	0.56	1.00	0.79	1.55
CaO	0.20	0.10	1.05	2.22	3.75	9.32	3.01
Na_2O	0.12	0.34	7.81	8.35	11.17	7.78	11.33
K_2O	9.16	9.25	2.48	1.97	0.40	0.15	0.30
BaO	0.04	0.08	nd	nil	nil	nil	nil
Li_2O	0.04	0.06	nd	0.02	nil	nil	nil
Rb_2O	0.33	0.08	nd	nil	nil	nil	nil
F	nd	0.82	nd	1.50	nd	nd	nd
H_2O+	3.18	3.23	2.20	1.16	nd	nd	nd
H_2O-	0.36	nil	0.19	0.01	0.37	nil	0.04
	99.92	100.33	99.78	100.18	99.71	99.90	100.17
$O=F$		0.34		0.49			
		99.99		99.69			
Unit-cell contents							
Si	5.47	5.73	7.67	7.71	7.93	7.89	7.85
Al ⎰	2.53	2.27	0.33	0.29	0.07	0.11	0.15
⎱	0.61	0.43	0.13	0.25	0.21	0.14	0.18
Fe^{3+}	0.61	0.41	1.01	1.05	3.01	2.23	3.18
Fe^{2+}	2.88	2.49	1.60	0.91	0.27	0.86	0.16
Mn	0.04	0.03	0.03	0.10	0.02	0.06	0.02
Mg	0.99	1.79	1.52	2.44	0.36	0.68	0.31
Ti	0.42	0.37	0.34	0.06	0.12	0.09	0.18
Ca	0.03	0.02	0.17	0.35	0.62	1.54	0.49
Na	0.04	0.10	2.26	2.37	3.33	2.32	3.34
K	1.85	1.81	0.47	0.37	0.08	0.03	0.06
Ba	—	—	—	—	—	—	—
Li	0.03	0.04	—	0.01	—	—	—
Rb	0.03	—	—	—	—	—	—
F	—	0.40	—	0.70	—	—	—
OH	3.35	3.31	2.19	1.13	—	—	—
O	20.65	20.29	21.81	22.17	24.00	24.00	24.00

The unit-cell or fractional unit-cell contents are calculated for each mineral to 24(O,OH,F).

nd = not determined.

BaO, Li_2O, Rb_2O were determined spectrographically.

Bt-1   Biotite from granitic gneiss (analysis 1 of Table I). D. McKie, anal.

Bt-3   Biotite from quartz–bearing magnesioarfvedsonite–fenite (analysis 3 of Table I). J. H. Scoon, anal.

Am-3   Magnesioarfvedsonite from quartz–bearing fenite (analysis 3 of Table I). J. H. Scoon, anal. The small quantity of material available was inadequate for the determination of F.

Am-6   Magnesioarfvedsonite from quartz-free aegirine-magnesioarfvedsonite-fenite (analysis 6 of Table I). J. H. Scoon, anal. F determined spectrographically.

Px-6   Aegirine from quartz-free aegirine-magnesioarfvedsonite-fenite (analysis 6 of Table I). D. McKie, anal.

Px-11   Aegirine-augite from melanocratic quartz-free fenite (analysis 11 of Table I). D. McKie, anal.

Px-12   Aegirine from fenite xenolith (analysis 12 of Table I). D. McKie, anal.

potassium feldspar is a microcline-microperthite composed[1] of microcline with albite exsolution lamellae, each phase displaying twinning on the albite law; the bulk composition of the microperthite is approximately Or_{89} (by flame photometric analysis of a separated concentrate) and the composition of the microcline lamellae is near Or_{94}. Quartz is typically slightly strained. The oligoclase-albite has a composition near $Or_1Ab_{85}An_{14}$ and is commonly twinned on the albite law; in contrast to the microperthite, which is always slightly sericitized, the plagioclase is quite fresh. Biotite is strongly pleochroic, with α light brown, β and γ nearly opaque, and has an iron-rich composition, shown in column Bt-1 of Table X, characterized by 2.5 aluminium ions in 4-fold co-ordination and by a deficiency of cations on the 6-fold sites, 5.55 instead of 6.00 in a unit-cell with 24 anions. Garnet is pale pink and rather sporadic in the granitic gneiss; it has not been seen in any of the fenites.

In the earliest observed stage of fenitization, fenite 3, quartz remains in a strained condition and microcline microperthite (Or_{94}) persists. In addition to twinned oligoclase untwinned albite, which may be metasomatic, is present. The microperthite is again composed of albite-twinned microcline with a relatively small content of albite-twinned albite lamellae. Magnesioarfvedsonite[2] has developed in fine-grained aggregates and groups of very thin needles along the cleavages and edges of biotite grains (Fig. 6). Biotite here has α yellow-brown, and β, γ dark red-brown; its composition, set down in column Bt–3 of Table X, is rather more magnesian and correspondingly poorer in iron, but otherwise not dissimilar to that of the biotite in the granitic gneiss. The composition of the magnesioarfvedsonite is shown in column Am–3 of Table X; it is characterized by approximately equal contents of Mg^{2+} and Fe^{2+} and by almost complete substitution of Fe^{3+} for Al^{3+} on 6-fold sites. An oscillation photograph of a thin acicular grain of magnesioarfvedsonite displayed sharp powder lines and no single crystal reflections; the absence alike of spottiness and of line broadening indicates a grain size in the range 1–0.1 μ. Alteration of biotite to magnesioarfvedsonite takes place within the biotite grains along cleavages and at biotite-quartz and biotite-microperthite contacts, but not at biotite-plagioclase contacts. The alteration of biotite, however, involves loss of Al and K and gain of Si; it occurs at contacts with quartz and microperthite not for reasons of ease of cation transfer, but because the solubility of quartz and microperthite, in contrast to the stability of oligoclase-albite, in the metasomatizing solutions provides room for the deposition of magnesioarfvedsonite as well as the essential supply of Si. The ultrafine grain size of the magnesioarfvedsonite is testimony of a facile alteration process, the product of which has been preserved in this low-grade fenite, never exposed to conditions favourable to subsequent recrystallization to coarser grain size.

The next stage is represented by fenite 2. Quartz has become unstrained and is here more abundant than in the analysed gneiss. Fenite 2 may be derived from a

---

[1] The examination of the feldspars by single crystal and powder x-ray techniques and by electron probe analysis is described in detail in a subsequent paragraph. All feldspar compositions quoted in the course of petrographic description are by electron probe analysis.

[2] The nomenclature of Deer, Howie, and Zussman (1962) is used for amphiboles and pyroxenes.

more siliceous gneiss and in contrast fenite 3 may be derived from a gneiss poorer in quartz and more calcic than the analysed granite-gneiss. Twinned oligoclase-albite is common and an optically homogeneous orthoclase cryptoperthite makes its appearance in quantity. Quartz grains are occasionally rounded and apparently replaced by feldspar. The rock is veined with closely matted, finely

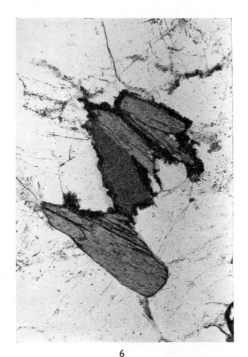

6   7

Fig. 6. Fenite 3, Oldonyo Dili. The replacement of biotite by magnesio-arfvedsonite occurs at the interfaces with quartz and microcline-micro-perthite, but not with the two albite grains which form the upper corners of the figure. Plane polarized light, × 60.

Fig. 7. Fenite 2, Oldonyo Dili. Aegirine is restricted to a vein of felted acicular crystals. Coarse bladed magnesioarvedsonite appears within the vein in the upper left hand corner of the figure. Plane polarized light, × 25.

acicular aegirine often intergrown with blades of magnesioarfvedsonite (Fig. 7). The absence of biotite may be due to an originally small or zero content of biotite, since fenite 4 still contains relics of biotite although it is much poorer in Si and richer in Na and Fe.

Fenite 4 contains twinned plagioclase and some microperthite, but most of its feldspar is orthoclase cryptoperthite. Plagioclase is of two kinds, an oligoclase with a composition near An_{22} and an effectively pure albite ($An_{<1}$). Quartz, unstrained, shows evidence of replacement by feldspar. The few grains of ragged biotite that remain are all associated with magnesioarfvedsonite, although the alteration is not so intimate as in fenite 3. Veins of matted aegirine needles, often with a central zone of bladed magnesioarfvedsonite, traverse the rock. Radiating groups of aegirine needles and magnesioarfvedsonite blades are disseminated through the rock.

Fenite 5 is abnormal in that it contains patches of calcite; it has apparently been affected either during or after fenitization by solutions capable of precipitating calcite, solutions that should probably be regarded as distinct from the fenitizing solutions, which do not normally deposit carbonates. Twinned albite $(Or_{<1}An_{<1})$ is abundant and replacement of microcline-microperthite marginally

8   9

Fig. 8. Fenite 5, Oldonyo Dili. Alteration of microcline-microperthite to orthoclase-cryptoperthite is apparent at the bottom and at the top of the figure, the centre of which is occupied by a vein of felted acicular aegirine. Crossed polars, × 50.

Fig. 9. Fenite xenolith 12, Oldonyo Dili. Relics of coarse red-brown biotite are intimately associated with finer yellow-brown biotite and with aegirine. Plane polarized light, × 60.

by orthoclase-cryptoperthite has occurred (Fig. 8). Orthoclase-cryptoperthite also occurs as small grains in close association with aegirine. In a rimmed grain the microcline-microperthite core was found to have a composition near $Or_{89}Ab_{11}An_{<1}$ and the cryptoperthitic margin a similar composition near $Or_{90}Ab_{10}An_{<1}$. Analysis of an isolated orthoclase cryptoperthite grain yielded a composition near $Or_{86}Ab_{14}An_{<1}$. Unstrained quartz is common. Aegirine occurs in veins and in radiating groups of stout prisms margined by blades of magnesioarfvedsonite. Calcite and quartz appear in drop-like intergrowths and aegirine grows in patches of calcite. This is the last fenite of the main series in which quartz is present.

At the stage represented by fenite 6 Si has decreased very considerably, quartz has disappeared entirely, and microcline-microperthite has been wholly replaced by orthoclase-cryptoperthite. Twinned albite ($Or_{<1}An_{<1}$) is present. Aegirine, mostly coarser than in earlier stages, is distributed abundantly throughout the rock; its composition, shown in column Px-6 of Table X, is dominantly acmitic and corresponds in essence to $Ac_{78}Jd_6Di_9Hd_7$. Magnesioarfvedsonite, in radiating groups of coarse blades, occurs independently of aegirine; its composition, shown in column Am-6 of Table X, clearly identifies it as a magnesioarfvedsonite. The striking contrast in composition between the coexisting amphibole and pyroxene are the relative enrichment in Fe^{3+} and corresponding impoverishment in Fe^{2+} and Mg^{2+} in the aegirine. The grains of magnesioarfvedsonite, unlike those in fenite 3, are shown by c-axis oscillation photographs to be properly single crystals.

Fenite 7 is of similar composition, is quartz-free, and contains only occasional relict kernels of microcline-microperthite within orthoclase-cryptoperthite. The x-ray diffraction pattern of the cryptoperthite displays strong sharp reflections of orthoclase accompanied by a relatively weak pattern of albite-twinned albite; with a composition close to $Or_{86}Ab_{14}An_{<1}$, it is conspicuously more sodic than its progenitor, the microcline-microperthite of composition near $Or_{94}Ab_6An_{<1}$. Twinned albite ($Or_{<1}An_{<1}$) is abundant. Patches of finely granular orthoclase-cryptoperthite occur intergrown with aegirine. Coarse blades of magnesioarfvedsonite are present and aegirine is distributed in abundance throughout the rock. A feature of this stage of fenitization is that aegirine is no longer largely confined to veins, but forms an essential constituent of the texture of the rocks. A few small patches of calcite and occasional prisms of apatite are noticeable.

In fenite 8 the twinned albite and the orthoclase-cryptoperthite grains both tend to be sericitized centrally and to have clear rims. Microperthite, which occurs in small bulk, appears not to be relict, but the product of local exsolution during cooling; it has not been examined in detail. Aegirine is disseminated throughout the rock (Fig. 9) and is coarser than in earlier stages. Magnesioarfvedsonite is absent.

The dominant feldspar in fenite 9 is orthoclase-cryptoperthite near $Or_{85}Ab_{15}An_{<1}$; it displays patchy extinction, but no lamellar exsolution. Twinned albite is present only in small amount. Aegirine occurs as large patches and veins of matted needles. Magnesioarfvedsonite is present, in small amount and only locally, as coarse blades within the aegirine mats; small aegirine needles occur within the magnesioarfvedsonite blades and may be indicative of alteration of the latter with gain in Na, loss of Mg, and oxidation of Fe^{2+}. Apatite is fairly common on the margins of aegirine patches.

Fenite 10, although it would appear compositionally to be the most advanced of the main series, shows some petrographic resemblances to earlier stages. Abundant fine-grained aegirine encloses and is margined by magnesioarfvedsonite, which thus appears here again to have crystallized, at least in part, later than aegirine and to show no sign of alteration to aegirine. The absence of quartz and of microcline-microperthite clearly establish fenite 10 in an advanced stage of fenitization; the dominant feldspar is orthoclase-cryptoperthite and is accompanied by twinned albite.

Fenite 11 is compositionally and mineralogically clearly not of the main series. The dominant feldspar is untwinned and of composition near $Or_1Ab_{99}An_{<1}$; a small amount of twinned albite of similar composition also occurs. Occasional grains of a sericitized potassium feldspar are present; electron probe examination gives compositions near $Or_{64}Ab_{36}An_{<1}$, but it is uncertain to what extent the sericitization is responsible for the apparently low potassium content. The abundant coarse pyroxene is distinguished from the aegirine of the fenites of the main series by its oblique extinction. Its composition, shown in column Px-11 of Table X, is markedly calcic and corresponds to an aegirine-augite near $Ac_{56}Jd_4Di_{17}Hd_{23}$ in harmony with the high Ca and Fe content of the rock. On compositional grounds it has already been suggested that fenite 11 is a product of the fenitization of one of the small plagioclase-amphibolite bodies that are distributed sporadically through the granitic gneiss surrounding Oldonyo Dili. These are composed of hornblende, andesine, quartz, and occasionally augite; apatite is always a relatively abundant accessory. All the available specimens were insufficiently homogeneous or too weathered to be suitable for chemical analysis. If the suggested derivation of this fenite is right, it implies the replacement of intermediate plagioclase by albite, complete solution of quartz, and the replacement of hornblende by aegirine-augite. None of these processes is to be seen in an uncompleted state. That calcium should have entered the pyroxene structure in quantity while the associated feldspar is very nearly calcium-free requires comment. It is evident from the study of the main series of fenites that the stable feldspars are albite and orthoclase-cryptoperthite near Or_{85}, but it would scarcely be expected that so relatively calcic a rock would contain virtually calcium-free feldspars. The retention of calcium in the pyroxene may well have a structural explanation; the initial alteration of hornblende to augite would require little transfer of cations, except perhaps the solution of Ca^{2+}, and it might be supposed that with progressive fenitization early formed augite would become aegirine-augite and perhaps eventually, at a stage later than that represented here, aegirine. It is difficult to escape the conclusion either that fenite 11 is in a transitional state, as indeed are most of the fenites studied, between its progenitor and a fenite in complete equilibrium with the fenitizing solutions under the physical conditions operative at its site, or that it has been subjected to metasomatism by solutions of anomalous composition. The latter possibility is inherently less acceptable, but too little has been seen of the fenitization of plagioclase-amphibolites for a firm decision to be reached; in support of the former possibility is the apparent disequilibrium distribution of calcium between the feldspar and pyroxene phases.

The fenite xenolith, analysis 12, is conspicuously impoverished in Si and Na and has a low oxidation ratio relative to the main series fenites. It is composed of twinned oligoclase-albite and orthoclase-cryptoperthite, with abundant red-brown biotite enveloped in a mosaic of pale yellow-brown biotite and felted acicular aegirine (Fig. 9); radiating groups of aegirine needles are distributed through the rock and calcite forms small irregular patches. The composition of the aegirine, set down in column Px-12 of Table X, corresponds essentially to $Ac_{87}Di_8Hd_5$ and is conspicuously more sodic than that of fenite 6. The rock appears to have been in an early stage of fenitization, since its aegirine content is small, when it was invaded by carbonatite magma. The complete solution of quartz and the crystallization of biotite are perhaps better regarded as con-sequences of reaction with the carbonatite liquid than as fenitization phenomena; the marginal zones of sövite bodies are usually free of primary quartz and frequently pale yellow-brown or strongly pleochroic red-brown biotites of similar appearance. The impoverishment of Na^+ and Fe^{3+} relative to Si can be interpreted as a consequence of the replacement of quartz by calcite instead of by aegirine as in a normal fenite.

TABLE XI

Chemical and crystallographic data for feldspars from Oldonyo Dili

| Fenite No. | K-feldspar | | Na-feldspar | |
	Structure type	Composition	Composition	ψ
1	M	$Or_{94}Ab_6An_{<1}$	$Or_1Ab_{85}An_{14}$	1.302 ± 0.025
3	M	$Or_{94}Ab_6An_{<1}$	$Or_1Ab_{82}An_{17}$*	1.428 ± 0.042
4	(M)+(O)		$Or_{<1}Ab_{99}An_{<1}$	1.137 ± 0.021
			$Or_{<1}Ab_{78}An_{22}$	
5	$(M)^1$	$Or_{89}Ab_{11}An_{<1}$	$Or_{<1}Ab_{99}An_{<1}$	1.096 ± 0.021
	$(O)^1$	$Or_{90}Ab_{10}An_{<1}$		
	(O)	$Or_{86}Ab_{14}An_{<1}$		
6	O		$Or_{<1}Ab_{99}An_{<1}$	1.057 ± 0.013
7	O	$Or_{86}Ab_{14}An_{<1}$	$Or_{<1}Ab_{99}An_{<1}$	1.056 ± 0.010
9	O	$Or_{85}Ab_{15}An_{<1}$		
10	O			
11	O		$Or_1Ab_{99}An_{<1}$	1.064 ± 0.024

M = microcline-microperthite.
O = orthoclase-cryptoperthite.
$\psi = 2\theta_{1\bar{3}1} - 2\theta_{131}$ for CuKα
* approximate composition derived from flame photometric analysis of plagioclase concentrate.
( ) Optical determination only.
$(M)^1$, $(O)^1$ core and rim respectively.

Before concluding this account of the sequence of mineralogical changes in fenitization at Oldonyo Dili some account must be given of the examination of the feldspars. The relevant observational data are shown in Table XI.

The compositions of selected sodic and potassic feldspars have been determined through the courtesy of Dr. J. V. P. Long by electron probe analysis on polished thin-sections. Madagascar orthoclase of composition $Or_{88.08}$, determined by flame photometry by Mr. J. H. Scoon, was used as a standard for potassium, and wollastonite was used as the calcium standard; sodium was estimated by difference. The results of the determinations are shown in Table XI as weight percentages of end-members. Estimated standard deviations are for potash feldspars $\pm 3\%$, for Or in plagioclase $\pm < 1\%$, for An in oligoclase-albite $\pm 2\%$ and for An in albite $\pm < 1\%$.

As an indicator of the structural state of the plagioclases the separation of the 131 and 1$\bar{3}$1 peaks on a diffractometer trace taken with CuKα radiation was measured, the plagioclase concentrates for diffractometry being obtained from finely ground material by centrifugal separation in methylene iodide diluted with carbon tetrachloride. The diffractometer was run four times over each pair of peaks. The mean value of the parameter $\psi = 2\theta_{1\bar{3}1} - 2\theta_{131}$ and its standard error are shown for each specimen in the right-hand column of Table XI, from which it is evident that the oligoclase-albite of the parent granitic gneiss and the fenitic albite lie close to the limiting line of lowest structural state (Smith, 1956). In qualitative terms the structural state of the fenitic albites, corresponding to that of pegmatitic and granitic plagioclases, is indicative of either low temperature of crystallization or adjustment by slow cooling to structural equilibrium at low temperatures.

The crystallography of the potassium feldspars of six of the analysed fenites has been examined by the standard b-axis oscillation technique of Smith and MacKenzie (1955); diffraction patterns were recorded for two crystals from each rock. The microcline-microperthite of the granitic gneiss displays a strong albite-twinned microcline pattern, each twin-related pair of reflections being joined by a relatively weak streak; a weak pattern of albite-twinned albite is also present. Although neither crystal gives very sharp reflections the reciprocal lattice parameters have been estimated as α^* 90°27', γ^* 91°59' (each to an accuracy of about $\pm$ 3'), quite close to those of specimen 4639 of Smith and MacKenzie (1959) and approaching maximum microcline. One of the microcline-microperthite crystals from fenite 3 yields a similar diffraction pattern; the other has relatively diffuse albite-twinned microcline merging into sharp orthoclase reflections, which may be interpreted as indicative of partial transformation to the monoclinic polymorph. All the other potassium feldspars examined, from fenites 6, 7, 9 and 10, have $-2V \sim 45°$ and yield strong, sharp orthoclase diffraction patterns accompanied by relatively weak patterns of albite-twinned albite; in some crystals row line streaks are centred on the orthoclase intensity maxima, a common feature of orthoclase diffraction patterns (Smith and McKenzie, 1959). Attention has already been drawn to the difference in composition between the microcline Or_{94} and the orthoclase Or_{86} in these rocks and, if MacKenzie's (1954) view that microcline can tolerate only a small sodium content is accepted, it follows that the microcline of the granitic gneiss could not have become more sodic to reach equilibrium in the continued presence of the highly sodic fenitizing solutions, but had to transform, as it is observed to have done, to more sodic orthoclase.

Little need be added here to what has already been said about the ferromagnesian minerals. The two analysed biotites are similar in composition except for the rather higher Mg/Fe in Bt-3 relative to Bt-1. Both magnesioarfvedsonites are of quite ordinary composition (cf. Deer, Howie and Zussman, 1962) and differ from one another significantly only in the higher Mg/Fe of Am-3 relative to Am-6. The two analysed aegirines are closely similar and indeed there is no optical evidence that the aegirines of the main series of fenites vary much in composition; the aegirine-augite, Px-11, of the basic fenite is less completely oxidized and has of course a higher calcium content.

No evidence of exsolution has been revealed in a number of c-axis oscillation

TABLE XII

Trace element concentrations in ferromagnesian minerals from Oldonyo Dili

	Gneiss 1	Bt-1	Fenite 3	Bt-3	Fenite 6	Am-6	Px-6	Fenite 11	Px-11	Fenite xenolith 12	Px-12
Ga	25	50	14	35	35	5	25	50	20	20	22
Cr	4	22	5	45	8	5	22	50	60	140	400
V	—	90	20	100	320	65	450	200	450	140	450
Li	50	200	5	320	3	100	8	3	4	110	20
Ni	—	15	2	22	4	10	3	12	12	55	28
Co	—	18	—	22	—	—	—	—	—	12	—
Zr	50	220	120	—	450	100	800	1000	550	100	450
Y	18	10	15	—	—	—	—	—	—	10	—
La	55	—	—	—	—	—	—	—	—	40	—
Sr	100	—	400	—	220	30	25	220	220	1600	25
Pb	45	—	46	—	—	—	—	—	—	15	—
Ba	370	370	700	800	370	45	50	125	20	1600	50
Rb	500	3000	12	700	320	15	—	—	—	320	—
Nb	—	340	45	—	250	—	160	250	—	—	160

Concentrations are given in ppm. A dash indicates concentration below the limit of sensitivity.

photographs taken of aegirines and magnesioarfvedsonites from the Oldonyo Dili fenites; all the analysed specimens have been so examined.

Trace element concentrations in the analysed minerals are shown in Table XII, where they are compared with those of the host rocks. The determinations were very kindly made for me by Dr. S. R. Nockolds. In the biotite of the granitic gneiss, Bt-1, enrichment in Li, Rb and Nb are notable; it is interesting that this biotite from outside the fenite zone should be enriched like the rocks of the carbonatite complex itself in niobium. The relict biotite in the low grade fenite 3 displays a similar pattern of trace element concentrations, except for Rb, which, although of lower absolute concentration, is more strongly enriched relative to the bulk rock, and Nb, which is below the limit of sensitivity. The magnesio-arfvedsonite of fenite 3 was not available in adequate quantity for trace element analysis. In the higher grade fenite 6 aegirine is conspicuously enriched in V and Zr relative to both magnesioarfvedsonite and whole rock; the high Li content of the magnesioarfvedsonite is notable. The aegirine-augite of the basic fenite 11 differs in its trace elements from the main series aegirine Px-6 only in its relatively high Sr content. The aegirine, Px-12, of the fenite xenolith is notable for its surprisingly high Cr content, which reflects the overall enrichment of the xenolith in Cr.

The oxidation ratio $(100Fe^{3+}/(Fe^{3+} + Fe^{2+}))$ in the ferromagnesian minerals rises steadily from biotite (Bt-1 18, Bt-3 14) through magnesioarfvedsonite (Am-3 39, Am-6 54) to aegirine (Px-6 92, Px-12 95) in the fenites of the main series, reflecting the essential oxidizing nature of the fenitization process. The marked difference in oxidation ratio between the coexisting amphibole and aegirine in fenite 6 is notable.

In summary then the sequence of mineralogical changes in fenitization at Oldonyo Dili begins with the alteration of biotite to magnesioarfvedsonite, either preceded or followed by the crystallization of aegirine and subordinate-magnesioarfvedsonite in narrow veinlets. At an early stage also microcline-microperthite near Or_{94} begins to be replaced by orthoclase-cryptoperthite near Or_{86}. Quartz then loses its strain shadowing and aegirine and magnesioarfved-sonite begin to grow, although not as pseudomorphs, in the room left by solution of quartz. Quartz probably starts to dissolve at the beginning of the fenitization process, but the decrease in quartz content does not become marked until this stage. The replacement of microcline-microperthite by more sodic orthoclase-cryptoperthite and the solution of quartz reach completion more or less simul-taneously; aegirine is now very abundantly and magnesioarfvedsonite abundantly distributed throughout the rock. Little of the original texture remains, although foliation is discernible even in the most advanced fenites in hand specimen and in the field. In the later stages inconclusive evidence points to the replacement of magnesioarfvedsonite by aegirine. Throughout the fenitization process plagio-clase appears to be decreasing slowly in amount; the oligoclase-albite, near An_{14}, of the granitic gneiss and low grade fenites is effectively replaced by albite and in part apparently by aegirine and orthoclase-cryptoperthite, but the manner of its replacement cannot be clearly seen. The final product is an orthoclase-cryptoperthite—aegirine rock with subordinate albite and magnesioarfvedsonite and accessory apatite. Each newly formed mineral species is of approximately constant composition throughout the main series of fenites and has evidently crystallized at a composition in equilibrium with the fenitizing solutions under the conditions operative at the site of its growth; such conditions have clearly not varied much from place to place during the process. Fenitization appears to have taken place at Oldonyo Dili, as elsewhere, before the onset of carbonatite intrusion or in the early stages of intrusion at the observable level of exposure.

At Alnö the range of composition of the country rocks is greater and the course of fenitization more variable. Von Eckermann (1948) distinguished six successive zones in the fenites: (1) thermal shock zone, (2) quartz-syenitic zone, (3) syenitic zone, (4) alkaline fenites, outer zone of nephelinization, (5) alkaline ultra-fenites, (6) rheomorphic fenites. The Oldonyo Dili fenites are comparable only with the first three of the Alnö zones. In the thermal shock zone quartz becomes granulated and strained. In the next zone quartz begins to dissolve and microcline to untwin; simultaneously microcline and albite become slightly sericitized by hydration and reddened by oxidation and exsolution of their small iron content as hematite. At this stage also soda-orthoclase, ranging in composition from Or_{70} to Or_{75} and not sericitized, crystallizes with calcite in cracks in quartz grains. At the inner margin of zone (3) quartz and microcline have been wholly replaced by homogeneous soda-orthoclase. Such is the course of fenitization of the Harnö pegmatite, originally a microcline-quartz-albite assemblage; the mineralogical changes are essentially similar to those observed among the light minerals at Oldonyo Dili, except that at Alnö sericitization of microcline and albite has developed further. More sodic pegmatites in contrast lose Na to produce likewise a soda-orthoclase between Or_{70} and Or_{75} in adjustment towards equilibrium with the metasomatizing solutions. In less acid rocks aegirine-augite begins to replace quartz in zone (2), the necessary cations being supplied by reaction of albite, biotite, and quartz, in the proportions $1:1:17.6$, with the solutions. The aegirine-augite here is much poorer in sodium and Fe^{3+} than that at Oldonyo Dili and varies in composition with the composition of the rock. Von Eckermann quotes no analyses, but mentions the limits Fe_2O_3, 5.57–12.06%, (Fe,Mn)O, 5.72–7.52%; $(Na,K)_2O$, 0.84–3.13%; (cf. Table X). The development of pyroxene ceases when the entire quartz content of the rock has been consumed. Excess biotite may remain to react at a later stage with albite to produce montmorillonite and more pyroxene; hydration more or less simultaneously begins to convert the remaining albite to natrolite. In those members of the migmatite complex richest in Fe and Mg pyroxene formation stops, not for lack of Si, but because all the available Na has entered the pyroxene structure; then, under highly oxidizing conditions, melanite forms. Nowhere apparently in the first three zones does alkali-amphibole develop in the Alnö fenites; in this respect, in the reaction of biotite with albite rather than with microcline-microperthite, in the subsequent development of natrolite and melanite, and in the composition of the pyroxene the behaviour of the ferro-magnesian minerals differs from that at Oldonyo Dili.

The processes of formation of the red and white fenites at Spitzkop are more closely comparable to the sequence of changes recorded at Oldonyo Dili. The country rocks at Spitzkop are coarse-grained Bushveld Main granite and finer-grained Bushveld granophyre, which retain their distinction of grain size during fenitization as far as the inner boundary of the white fenites. In the earliest stages, according to Strauss and Truter (1950), quartz, hornblende, biotite and magnetite reacted with solutions poor in Si and rich in Na, Al, Fe^{3+} and possibly CO_2 to deposit aegirine and alkali-amphibole in the room of the dissolved quartz and dark minerals, and to produce solutions rich in Si, Al and Na, which albitized the surrounding terrain of granite and granophyre over a zone as much as half a mile wide. In the early stages also perthite become turbid and a little new albite crystallized. The resulting 'red' fenite is described as a cellular umptekite composed of microperthite, oligoclase, albite, quartz, aegirine, alkali-amphibole and cavities filled with red ochre; the subsequent decomposition of aegirine and alkali-amphibole is presumed to account for the occurrence of the ochre-filled cavities. In the next stage, attributed to a second later fenitization affecting granite, granophyre and red fenite, the replacement of quartz by dark blue fibrous soda-amphibole continued and was accompanied by the crystallization of apatite. As the fenitization proceeded the blue amphibole decomposed to magnetite and larger grains of a soda-amphibole with pleochroism from pale brown to deep brownish-green. Of the original mafic minerals only a few shreds of biotite persisted through this stage. Simultaneously the original turbid perthite was mantled by albite and then gradually replaced by coarse clear microcline-perthite; new perthite also entered some of the space left by solution of quartz. The product of fenitization at this stage is composed of microcline-perthite, albite, soda-amphibole, magnetite, accessory zircon (recrystallized), apatite, sphene and relics of quartz and biotite. In the final stage quartz dissolved completely and soda-amphibole was altered to green soda-pyroxene, the resulting 'white' fenite being a pyroxene-umptekite composed of microcline-perthite, aegirine-augite (about 20%), albite, sphene, apatite and magnetite. Quartz veins in the Bushveld granophyre were converted to albite veins within the zone of white fenites, confirming by analogy that quartz was in part replaced by albite in the granite-derived fenites. No mineral analyses are quoted by Strauss and Truter, and it is therefore impossible to make a detailed assessment of the elementary exchanges implied by the observed mineralogical changes. The similarities to Oldonyo Dili are marked, but at Spitzkop the new feldspar is apparently microcline-perthite, although the evidence is not quite conclusive, instead of orthoclase-cryptoperthite, and soda-pyroxene does not appear until quartz has disappeared; the conversion of soda-amphibole to soda-pyroxene at a late stage, suspected at Oldonyo Dili, is here demonstrated clearly. Closer to the intrusion centre a suite of nepheline bearing, possibly metasomatic, rocks is developed.

At Fen Saether (1957), following Brögger (1921), was able to demonstrate a fairly clear sequence of reactions during fenitization. In the first stage the biotite in the granitic gneiss or the iron-rich amphibole in the more basic country rocks abstracted Na from the metasomatizing solutions to produce aegirine-augite and soda-amphibole; the new minerals crystallized more or less in the place of the original dark minerals, but not as pseudomorphs.

Saether quotes spectrographic analyses of biotite from a gneiss and of aegirine-augite from a fenite. The biotite, with unit cell contents approximately $K_{1.8}Na_{0.2}Mg_{1.5}Mn_{0.06}Fe_{3.4}Ti_{0.2}Al_{3.0}Si_{5.6}O_{20.4}(OH)_{3.6}$, is similar to, but more magnesian than that in the gneiss at Oldonyo Dili (Bt-1, Table X). The aegirine-augite corresponds to $Ac_{47}Di_{18}Hd_{27}En_3Fs_5$ and is less sodic even than the pyroxene from the basic fenite 11 at Oldonyo Dili, though apparently richer in aegirine than the partially analysed Alnö pyroxenes. The conversion of biotite to aegirine-augite required addition of Si, Na and some Mg, while release of Al, Fe, K and Ca to the solutions apparently took place; however soda-amphibole, of which no analysis was made, crystallized simultaneously and its crystallization may well have affected the elementary exchange between solution and the solid state. Saether considers that quartz did not begin to dissolve until the third stage, but it would seem likely that the supply of Si required for the alteration of biotite was provided here, as elsewhere, by solution of quartz. In the second stage of fenitization, in part overlapping the first stage, the homogeneous potassium feldspar of the gneiss became perthitized at constant composition and oligoclase was altered to albite and calcite. In the third stage quartz and albite were completely replaced by a hypothetical dominantly potassic single phase feldspar, which subsequently exsolved; here Saether differs from Brögger in proposing an overall accession of K as well as Na during fenitization and particularly at this stage. In the third stage also aegirine-augite replaced soda-amphibole, as at Spitzkop and possibly at Oldonyo Dili. While the interpretation of this reaction remains uncertain, it would seem more likely that it might occur in response to rising temperature than as a consequence of approach towards compositional equilibrium with solution. In the fourth and final stage partial melting was presumed by Saether to have produced pulaskitic fenite composed of aegirine-augite, homogeneous soda-potash-feldspar, and usually some nepheline (later altered to muscovite). The occurrence of a homogeneous alkali feldspar merely implies however that the temperature exceeded that of the solvus at the appropriate composition and pressure; partial melting need not be postulated. In the alteration of biotite to soda-pyroxene and soda-amphibole Fen resembles Oldonyo Dili, although Saether makes no mention of any subsequent introduction of soda-pyroxene. The development of a single-phase soda-potash-feldspar in the final product and the comparative stability of perthitic alkali feldspars in the early stages are similar too; early exsolution is not observed at Oldonyo Dili because the microcline of the gneiss is already microperthitic.

Swift (1952), has distinguished three stages in the fenitization of granitic gneiss, composed of quartz, microcline, oligoclase-albite and biotite at Chishanya; his paper contains no mineral analyses. Initially quartz recrystallized as smaller grains and was partly replaced by green amphibole. In the second stage patches of soda-amphibole and albite developed, presumably at the expense of quartz; simultaneously biotite exsolved magnetite dust and was partly altered to soda-amphibole, titanomagnetite was partially altered to sphene, and the original microcline and plagioclase became turbid. In the third and final stage quartz was entirely replaced by soda-pyroxene and albite, amphibole was altered to soda-pyroxene, and microcline was replaced by orthoclase; apatite in association with aegirine, and calcite in association with albite became plentiful; ragged flakes of biotite, more reddish in colour than the granitic biotite, persisted throughout this stage. In the replacement of biotite by soda-amphibole, beginning fairly early, Chishanya resembles Oldonyo Dili, and in the conversion of microcline-microperthite to single phase orthoclase, presumably sodic, it resembles Alnö and Oldonyo Dili. In the persistence of some biotite to a late stage however and in the lateness of the appearance of soda-pyroxene Chishanya differs from other areas of fenitization.

Fockema (1952), was unable to present a detailed picture of the course of fenitization at Tweerivier because the ferromagnesian minerals have there always been replaced, presumably at quite a late stage in the development of the complex, by chlorite and ochre. He was able however to recognize an initial stage of quartz granulation as at Alnö. His second stage is characterized by veins of iron oxide and chlorite (after aegirine?) and partial solution of quartz, with redeposition as chert within fractures in feldspar grains. In the third stage the replacement of quartz by ferromagnesian minerals, now altered, begins and is carried to completion in the fourth stage. The difficulty of distinguishing between the mineralogical changes that occurred during fenitization and subsequent alteration would rob any comparative comment on Tweerivier of significance.

At Chilwa Island also the course of fenitization is not clear; there the pattern is complicated by the possibility of successive episodes of fenitization and by a considerable degree of variation in country rock types. Garson and Campbell Smith (1958), were however able to recognize an outer shock zone with fractures infilled with orthoclase, aegirine-augite, and biotite and some replacement of quartz by orthoclase and aegirine-augite in the body of the fractured rock. Exsolution apparently occurs in alkali feldspars at an early stage as at Fen. At a later stage aegirine replaces quartz, drawing Na from solution, and clear orthoclase replaces turbid alkali feldspars. The end product appears to be an orthoclase-aegirine rock with some plagioclase near Ab_{90}; however, there is some evidence for the alteration of soda-pyroxene to soda-amphibole in the later stages, a reversal of the sequence observed elsewhere. Another curious feature of the Chilwa Island fenites is the occurrence of yellowish soda-pyroxenes, supposedly close to end-member acmite.

Dixey, Campbell Smith and Bisset (1937, revised 1955), described the metasomatism of gneisses about other carbonatitic diatremes in Malawi towards fenites composed of orthoclase or microperthite, soda-pyroxene, and sometimes quartz. They described the occurrence of blue soda-amphibole as well as soda-pyroxene. Their collection was not, however, complete enough to enable them to make a detailed interpretation of the processes involved in fenitization around the vents.

At Norra Kärr, where there is no associated intrusion of sövite, Adamson (1944), distinguished four stages in the fenitization of the Växiö granite, the essential constituent phases of which are quartz (undulose), microcline-perthite, albite (sericitized) and biotite. In the first stage, at about 100 m from the grennaite contact, microcline recrystallizes with diminution in size of the albitic lamellae, and quartz dissolves and is in part reprecipitated as oriented blebs within microcline grains. At about 30 m from the contact no quartz remains, initially turbid albite has recrystallized *in situ* to fresh albite-twinned albite (optically $Ab_{92}An_8$), and aggregates of smaller albite grains crystallize in the room of quartz. In the third stage, at about 10 m from the contact, microcline begins to be rimmed, and may eventually be entirely replaced, by albite in parallel orientation. Close to the contact the bulk of the feldspar is antiperthitic, with microcline lamellae in an albitic host, and only at this late stage does biotite begin to be converted to aegirine and small independent aegirine grains appear in the rock. In the formation of antiperthitic feldspars at high grade and in the lateness of the reaction of biotite the fenitization of the Växiö granite at Norra Kärr is exceptional.

CONCLUSION

In conclusion it may be said that, although the course of fenitization differs in detail at the several localities for which data are available, the general pattern is that of a sodium-ferric-metasomatism in which large amounts of silicon go into solution and variable amounts of aluminium, potassium and calcium become fixed in the minerals of the fenites. The metasomatizing solutions may well have been of broadly similar composition at all fenite occurrences; that Si content has been used as the reference variable and thus as the sole indicator of grade of fenitization in Figs. 2–5 is undoubtedly in part responsible for the scatter of the plotted points of the high-grade fenites. The interaction of the solutions with the rocks through which they passed, and the consequent element-ary gains and losses will have been dependent on the original modal composition of the rocks and on the chemical composition and structural state of their constituent minerals. The sequence of mineralogical changes in rocks of broadly granitic composition through the zones of progressive fenitization, that is zones of increasing temperature exposed to decreasingly modified solutions, leads ultimately towards a rock composed of orthoclase-cryptoperthite and soda-pyroxene with some albite and soda-amphibole.

The detailed mechanism of the fenitization process and the conditions under which it operated are by no means clear; only the broad outlines are discernible. In particular there is a need for close petrological study under conditions of good field exposure of the response of rocks of varied composition to fenitization. The proper understanding of the physical chemistry of fenitic metasomatism clearly requires further chemical study of bulk compositions and chemical and crystallographic study of mineralogical transformations at successive stages of fenitization at a number of occurrences.

Acknowledgements. My warmest thanks are due to Professor C. E. Tilley and Dr. S. R. Nockolds for many stimulating conversations on the problems of carbonatite complexes, to Goldfields of South Africa Limited and Dr. A. F. Cluver for permission to reproduce boundaries from their map of Oldonyo Dili, to Dr. C. H. Kelsey for her help in computing, to Dr. J. V. P. Long for the electron probe analyses of feldspars, to Dr. S. R. Nockolds for spectrographic trace element determinations, and to Mr. J. H. Scoon for several chemical analyses of minerals.

REFERENCES

Adamson, O. J., 1944, The Petrology of the Norra-Karr district: *Geol. För. Förh.* v. **66**, pp. 113–255.

Barth, T. F. W., 1952, *Theoretical Petrology:* New York, Wiley.

Brögger, W. C., 1921, Die Eruptivgesteine des Kristianiagebietes, IV., Das Fengebiet in Telemark: *Norsk. Vidensk. Selsk. Skrifter.* I, *Math. Naturv. Kl.*, (1920), No. **9**, pp. 1–408.

Darken, L. S. and Gurry, R. W., 1945, The system iron-oxygen. I. The Wustite field and related equilibria: *Jour. American Chem. Soc.*, v. **67**, pp. 1398–1412.

Deer, W. A., Howie, R. A. and Zussman, J., 1962, *Rock-forming minerals:* London, Longmans.

Dixey, F., Smith, W. C. and Bissett, C. B., 1937, The Chilwa series of Southern Nyasaland: *Nyasaland Geol. Surv. Bull.* **5**, (revised 1955).

v. Eckermann, H., 1948, The alkaline district of Alnö Island: *Sveriges. Geol. Undersök.*, *Ser. Ca.* No. **36**.

Fockema, R. A. P., 1952, The geology of the area around the confluence of the Elands and Crocodile Rivers: *Geol. Soc. S. Africa Trans.*, v. **55**, pp. 155–171.

Garson, M. S. and Smith, W. C., 1958, Chilwa Island: *Nyasaland Geol. Surv. Mem.* **1**.

MacKenzie, W. S., 1954, The orthoclase-microcline inversion: *Mineralog. Mag.*, v. **30**, pp. 354–366.

Muan, A., 1958, Phase equilibria at high temperature in oxide systems involving changes in oxidation states: *Am. Jour. Sci.*, v. **256**, pp. 171–207.

Saether, E., 1957, The alkaline rock province of the Fen Area in Southern Norway: *Norsk. Vidensk. Selsk. Skrifter*, No. **1**.

Smith, J. V., 1956, The powder patterns and lattice parameters of plagioclase feldspars. I. The soda-rich plagioclases: *Mineralog. Mag.*, v. **31**, pp. 47–68.

Smith, J. V. and MacKenzie, W. S., 1955, The alkali feldspars: II. A simple x-ray technique for the study of alkali feldspars: *Am. Minerologist*, v. **40**, pp. 733–747.

Smith, J. V. and MacKenzie, W. S., 1959, The alkali feldspars. V. Orthoclase and microcline perthites: *Am. Minerologist*, v. **44**, pp. 1169–1186.

Smith, W. C., 1956, A review of some problems of African carbonatites: *Geol. Soc. London Quart. Jour.*, v. **112**, pp. 189–220.

Strauss, C. A. and Truter, F. A., 1950, The alkali complex at Spitzkop, Sekukuniland, Eastern Transvaal: *Geol. Soc. S. Africa Trans.*, v. **53**, pp. 81–125.

Swift, W. H., 1952, The geology of Chishanya, Buhera District, Southern Rhodesia: *Edinburgh Geol. Soc. Trans.*, v. **15**, pp. 346–359.

W. J. VERWOERD

Fenitization of Basic Igneous Rocks[1]

INTRODUCTION

Of all known carbonatites about 90 per cent are situated in areas of Archean granite or gneiss. This is not too surprising in view of the well-established association of alkaline complexes with the stable continental shields. As a result of this association, nearly all descriptions of the contact metasomatic effects observed around carbonatite and/or nepheline syenite complexes apply to syenitic rocks similar to the leucocratic type originally described by Brögger (1921) under the name 'fenite'. It is even true of some complexes not emplaced in gneiss or granite: thus Baker (1953) traced five stages in the development of typical fenite from feldspathic sandstone at Kikonde in the Mount Jombo alkaline complex (Kenya). Similar effects have been observed by the author in the case of the poorly exposed Glenover carbonatite which was emplaced in feldspathic quartzite of the Loskop System (Transvaal). Although hesitating to call them fenites, Meyer and Bethune (1960) describe the formation of albite– and albite–microcline–aegirine–soda-hornblende rocks by soda meta-somatism from pelitic metasediments of garnet grade around the Lueshe carbonatite (Congo). Ordinary contact metamorphic effects including recrystal-lization and development of biotite were observed in folded Palaeozoic sediments around the Magnet Cove carbonatite-alkaline complex (Erickson and Blade, 1963).

The following carbonatites are also situated in non-granitic environments but fenitization of the country rock, if present, is imperfectly known:

> Jacupiranga: mica schist and granodiorite (Leonardos, 1956)
> Araxà: phyllite and quartzite (Leonardos, 1956)
> Rocky Boy: Cretaceous and Tertiary sediments (Pecora, 1956)
> Mrima: sandstone and shale of Karroo System (Triassic) (Baker, 1953)
> Muambe[2]: shale, grit, sandstone, basalt (Dias, 1961).

Only two carbonatite occurrences in an environment of basic igneous rocks seem to have been recorded before: at Magnet Heights, Sekhukhuneland, Transvaal (Strauss and Truter, 1951b) and on the island of Stjernøy, Finnmark, northern Norway (Heier, 1961; Strand, 1952). The latter is an irregular body of biotite-sovite containing up to about 10 per cent apatite. It is situated in the

---

[1] Published under South African Government Printer's copyright Authority No. 3084 of Nov. 2nd, 1962.
[2] Dixey et al. (1937) make passing reference to 'fenitized Karroo rocks, both sediments and lavas', around Muambe.

Seiland petrographic province dominated by gabbro, which may or may not be genetically related to the carbonatite. Strand (1952) found no evidence of metasomatic changes in the silicate rocks included by or adjacent to the carbonatite, but Heier (1961) believes that the emplacement of the carbonatite was accompanied by gaseous H_2O and CO_2 that altered the gabbro to hornblendite. Lack of alkalies explains the absence of fenitization effects. At Magnet Heights a thin beforsite dike cuts through gabbro, magnetitite and albitite without any apparent effect on the country rock. Next to the Nemegosenda alkaline complex in Canada, fenitization of a small gabbro mass resulted in ijolitized breccia (Parsons, 1961).

The gabbro and metagabbro intrusives of the Bancroft area, eastern Ontario, may also be mentioned here. The process of nephelinization which affected limestone, amphibolite and paragneiss in this area has been related to 'genuine feldspathoid intrusives of magmatic origin' (Tilley, 1958; Tilley and Gittins, 1961) and can therefore be regarded, perhaps, as a fenitization phenomenon. According to Hewitt and James (1956) the nephelinization is post-gabbro in age, but no fenitization effects have been observed in gabbro, even where it is enveloped by nepheline-bearing gneiss and marble, e.g. at Egan Chute. Perhaps the opposite is true in adjacent Faraday township where 'the Faraday metagabbro is injected and partially replaced by nepheline' (Hewitt and James, 1956, p. 29).

At least five occurrences where the fenitization of basic rocks can be demonstrated are known in southern Africa. Two of these have been studied by the author while the others are briefly summarized from the available literature.

NOMENCLATURE

When v. Eckermann (1948) proposed to extend the meaning of fenite to include all products of contact metasomatism induced by alkaline intrusions and carbonatites, irrespective of composition, he clearly recognized the possibility that such products may be formed in rocks with compositions vastly different from granite. Among the basic rocks that suffered metasomatic effects analogous to fenitization in southern Africa are basalt, dolerite, gabbro, anorthosite and fayalite diorite. v. Eckermann's proposal to call all these altered rocks fenite has been adopted, but a need for further qualification according to composition is felt. This difficulty was met by v. Eckermann by coining such terms as alkorthositic fenite, syenitic fenite, foyaitic fenite and melteigitic fenite. Such a procedure can be followed only in cases where an igneous rock with a corresponding composition is known and named but this is not always the case. Soda-hornblende–gabbro and aegirine-cancrinite-plagioclase rock for instance, occur only as fenites (e.g. Goudini, Transvaal). The mere use of the adjective 'fenitized' in front of the parent rock name is inadequate, for two reasons:

(*a*) More than one type of fenite may result from the same parent during different stages of fenitization (e.g. Alnö, Goudini).

(*b*) A single type of fenite may be derived from various rocks, e.g. granite and feldspathic sandstone.

Brögger (1921) introduced the term tveitäsite for mesotype to melanocratic aegirine-augite–feldspar rocks formed in part by fenitization and in part by assimilation of granite in ijolite magma. This term has not been generally adopted even for the type locality (Saether, 1957) and, although referring to dark peralkaline rock, is quite inapplicable to fenitized gabbro or dolerite as described in this chapter. Mathias (1956) preferred to use the general designation 'melano-cratic fenite' but also proposed the terms basalt fenite, gabbro fenite (for a rock with the composition of theralite), foyaite fenite, syenite fenite and tinguaite fenite. This usage is inconsistent because it refers to the composition of the parent in some instances and to that of the product in others.

Since fenites are metamorphic rocks the creation of new names for varieties is unjustified, and for the same reason the direct application of igneous rock names like umptekite or syenite to fenites is inadmissible. The only solution seems to be the rather cumbersome method generally used for naming metamorphic rocks, viz. the enumeration of principal mineral constituents as a prefix to fenite, e.g. microperthite–aegirine fenite (Fen, Spitzkop), soda-orthoclase fenite (Alnö), soda-hornblende–labradorite fenite (Goudini). However, in many cases, e.g. theralitic fenite, v. Eckermann's style is to be preferred for brevity.

DOROWA, TUNDULU, DERDEPOORT

Fenitization of dolerite at Dorowa, Rhodesia, has been described by Johnson (1961 and pp. 205–224). At its northern end the zone of fenitized granite around the Dorowa ijolite-carbonatite complex comes in contact with a poorly exposed, decomposed dolerite sheet. Fresh samples of drill core show that the dolerite 'is cut by biotite-apatite veins 3–5 mm in width, within about 5 mm of which the dolerite is visibly altered and lighter in colour'. A subordinate constituent of the veinlets is yellow-green amphibole with $Z: c = 32°$. The alteration of the dolerite involves replacement of cloudy andesine (An_{45}) by zeolites and calcite, the conversion of colourless augite to a mosaic of aegirine-augite with $X: c = 20°$, partial replacement of iron ore by sphene and an increase of biotite, both in amount and grain size.

From these data it appears as if the fenitization of the dolerite was mainly characterized by the introduction of potash, soda, lime, iron and phosphate coupled with the abstraction of silica, i.e. essentially similar effects to those encountered in the granite except, perhaps, for a greater enrichment in potash.

At Tundulu, Garson (1962) also describes fenitized dolerite. Minute veins are filled with calcite and orthoclase, and bordered by thin replacement flakes of muscovite. Pyroxenes are replaced by riebeckite and eventually by aegirine-augite and aegirine. Original brown hornblende is changed to riebeckite. Plagioclase becomes turbid and filled with calcite inclusions, often accompanied by slightly clearer rims of albite. Reddish brown biotite appears in some of the most highly fenitized dolerites at the expense of original ferromagnesian con-stituents.

The breccia pipe and associated carbonatite at Derdepoort near Pretoria also caused a limited amount of alteration in an adjacent diabase sill belonging to the

Bushveld Complex. The considerably decomposed rock contains pink patches of alkali feldspar and chlorite pseudomorphs after amphibole prisms. It is furthermore traversed by microscopic veinlets consisting of blue soda-amphibole tufts, apatite and calcite.

MESSUM

The Messum igneous complex is one of the great volcano-plutons of South West Africa. The only carbonatite present is a single vein 5 ft wide in the core of the complex (Mathias, 1956), yet extensive fenitization of agglomerate and tuff around a central intrusive mass of foyaite has taken place and this process also affected more resistant pre-foyaite basic rocks which occur as xenoliths, dikes or sheets, both in foyaite and the surrounding aureole. The fenitization of the pyroclastics proceeded beyond v. Eckermann's 'saturation point' to the production of metasomatic foyaite.

According to Mathias (1956) the following stages in the fenitization of basalt, dolerite and gabbro may be distinguished:

(*a*) Replacement of augite by zoned amphibole (hastingsite), except in the case of gabbro where the pyroxene remains unchanged up to stage (d); increase in albite content of plagioclase.

(*b*) Introduction of perthitic alkali feldspar, often replacing sodic plagioclase.

(*c*) Introduction of nepheline, clearly replacing plagioclase, with accessory sodalite and analcite.

(*d*) Increase in proportion of orthoclase, nepheline and ferrohastingsite until basic xenoliths are reduced to mafic streaks in foyaite.

Augite, especially in fenitized basalt, shows clear evidence of replacement, the sequence of changes being as follows: augite →pale green slightly sodic augite (occasionally developed) →magnesiohastingsite →femaghastingsite →ferrohastingsite. Aegirine-augite is uncommon in these rocks. Olivine, present in gabbro and as an accessory in dolerite, is a normal magnesian type (Fa_{20}–Fa_{30}) and shows no change during fenitization.

In order to get a quantitative idea of the chemical changes involved in the metasomatism of both extrusive and intrusive basic rocks at Messum, Barth standard cells of fenitized basalt and theralitic fenitized gabbro were calculated, utilizing analyses G11 and G9e respectively, from Mathias (1956). These are given in Table 1[1]. Some difficulty was experienced in deciding which analyses of unchanged rocks to use for comparison. The only basalts that have escaped alteration and were suitable for analysis belong to the peripheral zone of the complex; among these four petrographic types have been distinguished. Because bronzite basalt (L14) is the youngest in the sequence and has virtually the same alkali content as the tholeitic type (designated as rare), it is considered to be

---

[1] Editor's note: These are calculated on the basis of 160 anions and are, therefore, not directly comparable with those of McKie (Tables II, IV–VII, pp. 266, 268–269, 272, 274) which are calculated on the basis of 100 anions.

nearest in composition to the core basalts; however, the latter are still younger because the core zone has been interpreted as a subsided remnant of the summit of the 'Messum volcano' (Korn and Martin, 1954). The choice of bronzite

TABLE I

Chemical analyses of Messum rocks

(From Mathias, 1956)

	L14	G11	T58	G9e
SiO_2	52.26	46.86	47.15	46.26
Al_2O_3	15.03	18.29	18.51	16.38
Fe_2O_3	2.22	1.58	2.73	2.30
FeO	7.29	7.19	6.75	6.84
MnO	0.18	0.23	0.15	0.18
MgO	6.23	6.13	9.80	9.84
CaO	9.26	8.74	9.70	10.52
Na_2O	2.04	4.28	2.46	3.61
K_2O	1.44	2.33	0.52	1.60
TiO_2	1.03	1.22	0.83	1.20
P_2O_5	0.15	0.43	0.15	0.10
CO_2	1.42	0.66	0.13	—
H_2O^+	1.29	1.64	0.85	0.68
Total:	99.84	99.58	99.73	99.51
Standard cell contents:				
Si^{4+}	48.6	44.6	44.8	44.9
Al^{3+}	16.5	20.5	20.7	18.8
Fe^{3+}	1.6	1.1	1.9	1.7
Fe^{2+}	5.7	5.7	5.4	5.6
Mn^{2+}	0.2	0.2	0.1	0.1
Mg^{2+}	8.6	8.7	13.9	14.2
Ca^{2+}	9.2	8.9	9.9	10.9
Na^+	3.7	7.9	4.6	6.8
K^+	1.7	2.8	0.7	2.0
Ti^{4+}	0.7	0.9	0.6	0.9
P^{5+}	0.1	0.3	0.1	0.1
C^{4+}	1.8	0.9	0.2	0
OH^-	8.0	10.4	5.4	4.4
Total cations:	98.4	102.5	102.9	106.0

L14: Bronzite basalt of peripheral volcanic phase, Messum.
G11: Basalt fenite of core zone, Messum.
T58: Hypersthene microgabbro of intrusive phase, Messum.
G9e: Gabbro fenite of core zone, Messum.

basalt is also justified by the correspondence in average anorthite content of its plagioclase (An_{60}) with that of the unzoned phenocrysts in the core basalts. Similarly, fenitized gabbro is compared with unfenitized hypersthene microgabbro (Analysis T58) rather than with olivine eucrite lower down; a satisfactory correspondence in the composition of plagioclase and the presence of biotite is obtained but the olivine in the hypersthene microgabbro is slightly too rich in iron (Fa_{35}) while there is no orthopyroxene in the theralitic fenite. The calculations are therefore only approximations.

In Fig. 1 a diagrammatic representation of the direction and amount of transfer of elements during the fenitization of basic rocks is given on the basis of the number of ions per standard cell. The method assumes that the transformations were isovolumetric, i.e. (O + OH) remained constant. It should perhaps be emphasized that the fenitization at Messum took place in an open system, mainly within porous pyroclastic rocks and that *PTX* conditions must have been very different from those in sub-volcanic provinces like Spitzkop (Korn and

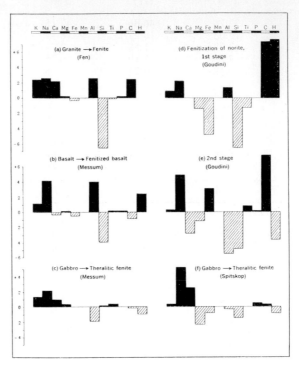

Fig. 1. Fenitization diagrams. Addition (black) and subtraction (diagonal ruling) of elements during fenitization are given in number of atoms per standard cell of 160 oxygen atoms.

Martin, 1954) or Alnö. However, there seems to be no reason to conclude that the fenitization of the basic rocks under discussion did not take place at constant volume. The fenitization diagram of Messum basalt shows that a net addition of 6.5 ions and a total migration of 17.9 ions per standard cell were involved; Na, Al, OH and a lesser amount of K were added and mainly Si abstracted. There is a remarkable similarity between this diagram and the one representing fenitization of granite at the type locality of Fen. (Figures calculated by Saether, 1957). An even smaller substance transfer (2.1 ions net addition) is necessary to convert hypersthene microgabbro to theralitic fenite by addition of Na, K, Ca and subtraction of Al, OH. A notable feature in the latter instance is that Fe, Si seem to have remained constant.

GOUDINI

A straightforward example of the fenitization of norite is provided at Goudini, Transvaal. The assemblage of carbonatized volcanics is briefly described elsewhere in this volume (p. 450). It was emplaced on the margin of an ultrabasic portion of the Bushveld Complex and is adjoined by pyroxenite (bronzitite), anorthosite, harzburgite and norite. Unfortunately these rocks are hidden from view except along the north west contact of the volcano where a narrow strip of norite showing evidence of fenitization is exposed against volcanic breccia. Most of the fragments in the breccia at this locality also consist of fenitized norite. The extent of the fenitized aureole cannot be determined owing to lack of outcrops. It seems likely, however, that fenitization may have been restricted to the vicinity of the metacarbonatite area in the north west quarter of the volcano.

Anorthosite which was enveloped by pyroclastic rocks exhibits merely brecciation, saussuritization of the plagioclase and alteration of interstitial pyroxene to chlorite, carbonate and pumpellyite. These changes indicate low-grade metamorphism rather than any form of fenitization.

The unaltered norite is fairly typical of the chilled floor phase of the Bushveld Complex and consists of plagioclase laths (An_{70}), ophitically intergrown with orthopyroxene (bronzite) and subordinate diallage. The first signs of fenitization are turbidity (incipient hydration) in the feldspar and the development of lenticular blue soda-hornblende veinlets along cleavage directions of clinopyroxene (Fig. 2). This is followed by fracturing, the fractured rock being traversed by innumerable cracks filled with soda-hornblende and carbonate. Next to the amphibole veins, all pyroxene has been replaced and feldspar is rendered opaque. The alteration of pyroxene commences along grain boundaries and cleavages. It is accompanied by the liberation of iron ore and crystallization of dolomite while the blue amphibole often grades marginally into chlorite. Interstitial patches and veinlets of soda-hornblende have spherulitic structure, locally containing minute blebs of an unidentified pinkish mineral with very low refractive index.

Among several possible reactions up to this stage, the following equation may serve as an example, although analyses indicate the abstraction not only of Si but of Mg, Fe and Ti as well:

$$5 \, Ca \, (Mg \, Fe) \, Si_2O + Na_2O + H_2O + 10 \, CO_2 + 3O_2 \rightarrow$$

augite

$$Na_2Fe_3^{2+} \, Fe_2^{3+} \, (OH)_2 \, Si_8O_{22} + 5 \, Ca \, Mg \, (CO_3)_2 + 2 \, SiO_2$$

riebeckite   dolomite

A more advanced stage of fenitization due to closer proximity to the volcanic centre is represented by certain outcrops of norite-bearing breccia. Here the pyroxenes and most of the groundmass between the fragments are altered to

L

fine-grained, massive green aegirine while the feldspars have acquired a reddish tinge. In thin section the plagioclase shows little hydration but has been extensively replaced by cancrinite and calcite. The cancrinite occurs as ramifying veinlets with a fibrous structure and often contains granular carbonate strung out in the middle of the veinlets (see Fig. 3). Apatite in the form of idio-morphic prisms, often grouped in clusters, is disseminated throughout the feldspar areas. Red ferruginous dust is especially concentrated around the apatite. The formation of aegirine and cancrinite may be explained by the following equations, in which calcite should be substituted for dolomite if the abstraction of Mg is taken into account:

$$4Ca(Mg, Fe)Si_2O_6 + 2Na_2O + 8CO_2 + 3O_2 \rightarrow 4Na\,Fe\,Si_2O_6 + 4Ca\,Mg\,(CO_3)_2$$

$$\underbrace{}_{\text{augite}} \qquad\qquad\qquad \underbrace{}_{\text{acmite}} \quad \underbrace{}_{\text{dolomite}}$$

$$2Na\,Al\,Si_3O_8 + 2Ca\,Al_2Si_2O_8 + 2\,H_2O + 2\,Na_2O + 2\,CO_2 + O_2 \rightarrow$$

$$\underbrace{}_{\text{albite}} \quad \underbrace{}_{\text{anorthite}}$$

$$2\,Na_2Ca[CO_3(OH)_2]Si_3Al_3O_{12} + 4\,SiO_2$$

$$\underbrace{\phantom{2\,Na_2Ca[CO_3(OH)_2]Si_3Al_3O_{12}}}_{\text{cancrinite}}$$

The transfer of elements during the fenitization at Goudini can be followed quantitatively in Fig. 1 (d), (e). An analysis of unaltered norite from the imme-diate vicinity is not available for comparison but the use of a previously published analysis of the floor phase at Zilikaatsnek in the Pretoria-Brits area is justified by the close petrographic correspondence between the two localities. It is note-worthy that a net addition of 3.6 ions per standard cell would account for the differences between unaltered norite and aegirine-cancrinite fenite. As expected a marked increase of Na, CO_3 and OH is indicated during the first stage while further amounts of Na, CO_3, Fe and Ti were added during the second stage. It seems likely that Fe and Ti which were driven out during the first stage migrated inwards and were incorporated again as the process of fenitization advanced. In the second stage higher temperature conditions resulted in dehydration, while Al, Ca and Mg were abstracted in addition to silica. The removal of Ca and Mg finds a parallel in the second stage of fenitization from syenitic to pula-skitic fenite at Dorowa (Johnson, 1961). The fenitization at Goudini differs from that at most other localities in the prominent part played by CO_3 ions, as could be expected from the carbonatization of the adjacent, closely related volcanics. These processes must have operated under near-surface conditions essentially similar to those that controlled the fenitization at Messum.

SPITZKOP

Among the saturated and undersaturated rocks of the Spitzkop alkaline complex Strauss and Truter (1951a) described a suite consisting of theralite, anorthositic

Fig. 2. Incipient fenitization of norite at Goudini. Turbid plagioclase adjoining clinopyroxene with a thin blue soda-hornblende rim. Lenticular soda-hornblende veinlets penetrate the clinopyroxene along cleavage directions. Plane polarized light, × 123.

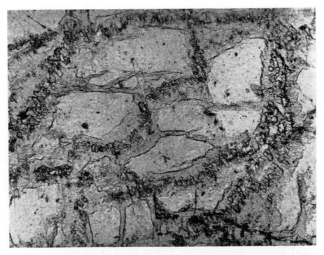

Fig. 3. Second stage of fenitization at Goudini. Clear plagioclase remnants, partly replaced by ramifying veinlets of cancrinite carrying dolomite strings. Plane polarized light, × 125.

theralite, magnetite theralite and fayalite diorite. They interpreted these rocks as fenites occupying a continuous arcuate zone within the outer ring of syenitic fenite from which they were supposedly derived. As an alternative in the case of the banded and foliated types (but not the fayalite diorite), these authors suggest that the rocks may be truly magmatic intrusives genetically related to the ijolite and foyaite, while admitting that they 'somewhat resemble the gabbros of the Bushveld Complex'.

For a variety of reasons Strauss and Truter's interpretations are regarded as untenable. The basic rocks all show abundant fenitization as is evident from the petrographic descriptions, summarized and slightly amended below (from Strauss and Truter). If the effects of subsequent impregnation by alkaline solutions are disregarded, each of these rock types corresponds exactly to its counterpart in the Main Zone and Upper Zone of the Bushveld Complex nearby. It is concluded that they occur as xenoliths in the ijolite which forms the main plug of the alkaline complex.

(*a*) The fayalite diorite differs petrographically from fayalite diorite at Bloedrivier, 22 miles south west of Spitzkop (Lombaard, 1950) in the following respects: fayalite occurs as ragged relics surrounded and penetrated by aegirine-augite and magnetite; brown soda-amphibole with $2V(-) = 45°$ and very strong absorption (ferrohastingsite?) is present, often as reaction rims around clino-pyroxene; anorthoclase $(2V(-) = 54°)$ occurs as vein-like streaks and encloses the other minerals poikilitically; fractures filled with blue soda-hornblende (riebeckite?) traverse the rock south of Spitzkop (hill) in all directions. All these relations reflect metasomatic changes due to introduction of alkalies.

Unfortunately the Bushveld fayalite diorites have not been analysed and even if some of them were, a close correspondence with Spitzkop may not be obtained in view of their highly variable composition. It can be shown, however, that Strauss and Truter's postulated transformation of white pyroxene fenite to fenitized fayalite diorite would involve vast amounts of substance transfer viz. the addition of Ca, Fe, OH and removal of K, Na, Al and Si, bearing no resemblance to known fenitization processes beyond the stage of syenitic fenite.

(*b*) Interesting textural relations which may be ascribed to fenitization also characterize the 'theralite'. The usual constituents of olivine gabbro are present (augite, bytownite, chrysolite and bronzite) and the following sodium-bearing minerals as well: pargasite, aegirine-augite, nepheline, scapolite and secondary natrolite. Augite is always mantled by sodic amphibole (pargasite, $2V(+) = 79°$ $Z: c = 27°$), either in optical continuity or as a fine-grained aggregate. This is surrounded in turn, by a delicate vermicular intergrowth of aegirine-augite in nepheline (see Fig. 4) which invariably intervenes between the mafic minerals and replacement remnants of perfectly fresh plagioclase. A similar texture consisting, however, of vermiform nepheline in a plagioclase host from the Bancroft area has been ascribed by Tilley (1958) to metasomatism. Nepheline also occurs as independent anhedral patches in the 'theralite'. Isolated grains of scapolite are sometimes strung out along cleavage cracks in plagioclase.

Where magnetite is present in the theralitic fenite and anorthosite, double reaction rims similar to those around pyroxene are found between magnetite and

Fig. 4. Theralitic fenite, Spitzkop alkaline complex. Augite (top right) with darker pargasite rim, separated from plagioclase (left) by vermicular intergrowth of nepheline and aegirine-augite. Plane polarized light, × 123.

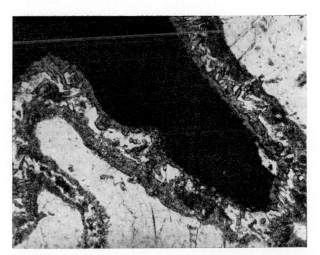

Fig. 5. Magnetite-rich theralitic fenite, Spitzkop alkaline complex. Successive zones of barkevikite, nepheline and vermicular nepheline-aegirine-augite intergrowth between magnetite and plagioclase. Plane polarized light, × 125.

plagioclase. In this case the soda amphibole is more iron-rich (barkevikite according to Strauss and Truter, 1951a) and usually appears in the form of radiating prisms (Fig. 5).

The chemical composition of the 'theralite' may be compared in the usual way with that of Main Zone gabbro 10 miles north of Magnet Heights. Figure 1 (f) proves that the transformation of gabbro to 'theralite' would be possible by the net addition of 3 ions per standard cell and a total migration of 14.6. The changes that are involved (addition of Na and Ca with lesser amounts of K, P and CO_3) are typical of fenitization processes, although abstraction of Si is quantitatively less important than in acid rocks. Mg, Fe and Al were abstracted instead, as at Goudini. It follows that although the fenitization of granite and gabbro at Spitzkop have certain features in common, especially enrichment in soda, the actual changes were governed by the original composition of the rock.

(c) Mottled anorthosite which occurs interlayered with the theralitic fenite shows analogous fenitization of the dark minerals. Plagioclase (An_{65}) is replaced to a larger extent by scapolite (mizzonite, $N_o = 1.586$), associated in some cross-cutting veinlets with secondary albite. Nepheline is mainly present in vermicular intergrowth with aegirine-augite but also as disseminated specks in plagioclase. Natrolite veinlets with fibrous structure cut through all the other constituents.

Finally, reaction rims are absent from the nephelinized biotite pyroxenite which is therefore regarded as an integral part of the Spitzkop Complex.

SWARTBOOISDRIF

The unique setting of the carbonatite and nepheline syenite intrusions near Swartbooisdrif, South West Africa, viz. in anorthosite of the Kunene basic complex, leads one to expect peculiar fenitization effects, if present. Mr. D. K. Toerien (private communication) believes that the remarkable development of sodalite and cancrinite in the carbonatite dikes is due to the fenitization of nepheline syenite and anorthosite inclusions. Sodalite seems to replace alkali feldspar preferentially while cancrinite develops at the expense of plagioclase. The country rock of the nepheline syenite plug shows surprisingly little alteration, but xenoliths of anorthosite in it are partly or wholly replaced by cancrinite. The intrusion of the second group of carbonatite dikes was accompanied by more intensive contact effects than the nepheline syenite: magnetite-rich anorthosite passes over into pure magnetite-cancrinite and magnetite-cancrinite-sodalite rock as the carbonatite is approached. The transformation of basic plagioclase to cancrinite involves the introduction of Na, CO_3 and OH and the removal of Si, a process compatible with fenitization at other localities.

CONCLUSIONS

Chemically, the fenitization of acid and basic rocks is essentially the same process characterized by enrichment in alkalies. The abstraction of silica is less pronounced in basic rocks and is often accompanied by removal of iron and magnesium. Calcium and aluminium play a variable role in both classes of rocks.

The addition of large amounts of carbonate ions at Goudini (and Swartbooisdrif?) appears to be exceptional; perhaps a distinction is necessary between fenitization directly associated with alkaline intrusives, as at Spitzkop, and fenitization which accompanies the carbonatite phase.

The mineralogical changes during fenitization are controlled by the original composition of the rock and by physico-chemical conditions, to some extent dependent on distance from eruptive centre. Thus in the absence of quartz and biotite, either feldspar (Messum) or pyroxene (Goudini) may be attacked first. The usual minerals of other fenites are also developed in fenitized basic rocks, viz. sodic amphiboles (though often richer in iron), aegirine-augite, aegirine, alkali feldspars and nepheline. Cancrinite, sodalite and scapolite may now be added to the list. The development of cancrinite as a product of fenitization at Goudini and Swartbooisdrif may cause doubts about the primary nature of the cancrinite described by Meyer and Bethune (1960) in the 'busorite' associated with the Lueshe carbonatite, Congo; there is no apparent reason why cancrinite should form only at the expense of basic plagioclase during fenitization.

REFERENCES

Baker, B. H., 1953, The alkaline igneous complex at Jombo: *Kenya Geol. Surv., Rep.* **24**.
Brögger, W. C., 1921, Die Eruptivgesteine des Kristianiagebietes. IV. Das Fengebiet in Telemark, Norwegen: *Vidensk. Selsk. Skrifter I. Math. Nat. Kl.*, (1920), No. **9**.
Dias, M. B., 1961, Geologia do Monte Muambe: *Bol. Estud. Serv. Geol.*, Lourenço Marques, Mozambique, No. **27**, pp. 37–88.
Dixey, F., Smith, W. C. and Bisset, C. B., 1937, revd. 1955, The Chilwa series of Southern Nyasaland: *Nyasaland Geol. Surv., Bull.* **5**.
v. Eckermann, H., 1948, The alkaline district of Alnö Island: *Sveriges Geol. Unders. Ser. Ca*, **36**.
Erickson, R. L. and Blade, L. V., 1963, Geochemistry and Petrology of the alkalic igneous complex at Magnet Cove, Arkansas: *U.S. Geol. Survey, Prof. Paper* **425**.
Garson, M. S., 1962, The Tundulu carbonatite ring complex in Southern Nyasaland: *Nyasaland Geol. Surv., Mem.* **2**.
Heier, K. S., 1961, Layered gabbro, hornblendite, carbonatite and nepheline syenite on Stjernöy, North Norway: *Norsk. Geol. Tidskr.*, v. **41**, pp. 109–155.
Hewitt, D. F. and James, W., 1956, Geology of Dungannon and Mayo Townships: *Ontario Dept. Mines*, 64th *Ann. Rept.*, v. **64**, pt. 8, 1955.
Johnson, R. L., 1961, The Geology of the Dorowa and Shawa carbonatite complexes, Southern Rhodesia: *Geol. Soc. S. Africa Trans.*, v. **64**, pp. 101–145.
Korn, H. and Martin, H., 1954, The Messum igneous complex in South West Africa: *Geol. Soc. S. Africa Trans.*, v. **57**, pp. 83–122.
Leonardos, O. H., 1956, Carbonatitos com apatita e pirocloro: *Dept. Nac. Prod. Min., Minis. da Agricultura*, Rio de Janeiro, *Avulso* **8**, pp. 7–30.
Lombaard, A. F., 1950, Die geologie van die Bosveldkompleks langs Bloedrivier: *Geol. Soc. S. Africa Trans.*, v. **52**, p. 343.
Mathias, M., 1956, The petrology of the Messum igneous complex, South West Africa: *Geol. Soc. S. Africa Trans.*, v. **59**, pp. 23–58.
Meyer, A. and Bethune, P. de, 1960, The Lueshe carbonatite (Kivu, Belgian Congo): *Internat. Geol. Congr.*, 21st sess., pt. 13, pp. 304–309.
Parsons, G. E., 1961, Niobium-bearing complexes east of Lake Superior: *Ontario Dept. Mines, Geol. Rept.*, **3**.
Pecora, W. T., 1956, Carbonatites: A review: *Geol. Soc. America Bull.*, v. **67**, pp. 1537–1556.

Saether, E., 1957, The alkaline rock province of the Fen area in Southern Norway: *Det. Kongl. Norsk. Vidensk. Selsk. Skrifter*, No. 1.

Strand, T., 1952, Biotittsövit på Stjernöy, Vest Finnmark: *Norges Geol. Unders. Arbok*, v. **183**, pp. 10–21.

Strauss, C. A. and Truter, F. C., 1951a, The alkali complex at Spitzkop, Sekukuniland, Eastern Transvaal: *Geol. Soc. S. Africa Trans.*, v. **53**, pp. 81–125.

Strauss, C. A. and Truter, F. C., 1951b, Post-Bushveld ultrabasic, alkali and carbonatite eruptives at Magnet Heights, Sekukuniland, Eastern Transvaal: *Geol. Soc. S. Africa Trans.*, v. **53**, pp. 169–190.

Tilley, C. E., 1958, Problems of alkali rock genesis: *Geol. Soc. London Quart. Jour.*, v. **113**, pp. 323–360.

Tilley, C. E. and Gittins, J., 1961, Igneous nepheline-bearing rocks of the Haliburton-Bancroft Province of Ontario: *Jour. Petrology*, v. **2**, pp. 38–48.

Part III

Experimental Studies

P. J. WYLLIE

Experimental Studies of Carbonatite Problems: The Origin and Differentiation of Carbonatite Magmas

INTRODUCTION

The experimental data reported by Wyllie and Tuttle (1960a, b) confirm that melts with a variety of compositions can precipitate calcite through a wide pressure range and through a wide temperature interval, and that these melts persist down to temperatures of the order of 600°C, which agrees reasonably well with temperatures inferred for the emplacement of natural carbonatites. This is regarded as verification for the magmatic origin of carbonatites where the field relationships are consistent with magmatic origin. However, neither the experimental data nor the field and petrographic studies provide reliable estimates of the compositions of natural carbonatite magmas at the time of intrusion. This is clear from the variety of hypotheses to be found in the geological literature as well as in the earlier chapters of this book. The composition and nature of a carbonatite magma depends upon the processes involved in its formation. In this chapter are described the results of experiments designed to elucidate the petrogenic relationships among carbonatite magmas and the alkaline igneous rocks associated with carbonatites in the field, and to test various hypotheses of origin which have been proposed on the basis of petrological studies and inferences. In addition to results related to these central objectives, the phase relationships in some of the systems studied illustrate several ways in which the crystallization of carbonatite magmas could proceed, and they indicate that some of the observed sequences of emplacement of carbonatites could be explained by differentiation processes occurring within a crystallizing carbonatite magma.

Most of the material in this chapter represents a progress report of an extended programme at the Pennsylvania State University which has been supported by the National Science Foundation since 1961 (Grant No. NSF-G-19588). This support is gratefully acknowledged. Thanks are due also to the Department of Scientific and Industrial Research for its support of the work in systems containing P_2O_5 which was conducted at Leeds University between 1959 and 1962. The chapter covers research completed by September 1963.

Crystallization of carbonatite magmas

It is possible to trace paths of crystallization in the ternary system $CaO-CO_2-H_2O$ (Wyllie and Tuttle, 1960a), but when other components are added there are too many variables involved for satisfactory treatment of this kind. The phase relationships of interest in these studies involve crystalline phases, liquids (fused salts containing dissolved volatile components) which are extremely fluid and reactive, and vapours (H_2O- and CO_2-rich fluid phases containing a small proportion of dissolved solids). The vapour phase in systems which include alkalis as components may contain much larger proportions of solids, and in parts of these systems there may be continuous solubility relationships between the liquids and the vapours, corresponding to complete compositional transition between the magmas and the low temperature hydrothermal or 'carbothermal' solutions. Despite the complexities in the phase relationships it is possible to demonstrate, in a general way if not in detail, how the paths of crystallization and the nature of the crystalline phases being precipitated from the liquids are affected by changes in temperature, in pressure, and in the compositions of coexisting vapour phases. In natural occurrences of carbonatites all of these variables may be included among the regional factors which exert independent, external controls on the behaviour of a carbonatite magma.

Differentiation of carbonatite magmas

Many carbonatite masses exhibit inhomogeneities on both large and small scales indicating the operation of differentiation processes. It has already been established (Wyllie and Tuttle, 1960a, b) that the synthetic carbonatite magmas are extremely fluid, and that crystal settling occurs within a few minutes. This would provide abundant opportunities for the separation of magma batches or accumulated crystal fractions of different compositions from a carbonatite magma, and such separation would be facilitated by the repeated explosive activity which appears to be an essential part of the history of many carbonatite complexes.

The Chilwa Island complex provides examples of both large and small scale differentiation (p. 52). Evidence for large scale differentiation is offered by the successive intrusion of calcitic sövite, ankeritic sövite, and finally sideritic carbonatites. On a smaller scale, the segregation of minerals is illustrated by the development of apatite-rich bands and lenses in the carbonatite. Phase relationships in the systems $CaO-MgO-CO_2-H_2O$ and $CaO-CaF_2-P_2O_5-CO_2-H_2O$ have been studied to see whether crystallization differentiation in the synthetic carbonatite magmas is capable of reproducing the natural differentiation products occurring in the examples cited.

Hypotheses for the origin of carbonatite magmas

The experimental results described in this chapter have some bearing on four of the hypotheses which have been proposed for the origin of magmatic carbonatites:

(1) Carbonatite magmas are residual melts derived from carbonated alkali peridotite magmas.

(2) Carbonatite magmas are primary. In 1948, v. Eckermann suggested that a primary carbonatite magma might be extremely rich in alkali carbonates, with the alkalis being responsible for fenitization and the development of some of the associated alkaline igneous rocks.

(3) Carbonatite magmas represent an immiscible liquid fraction which has separated from a parent, ultrabasic or basic magma.

(4) Magmatic carbonatite is formed at a late stage in the crystallization of a peralkaline magma as a precipitation product of alkali-alkaline earth exchange reactions. Tomkeieff (1961) postulated that sodium carbonate within the magma reacted with 'shadow mineral molecules' to produce reactions of the type:

$$CaAl_2Si_2O_8 + Na_2CO_3 \rightleftharpoons NaAlSiO_4 + CaCO_3$$
$$\text{anorthite} \qquad\qquad\qquad \text{nepheline} \quad \text{calcite}$$

These hypotheses have been proposed on the basis of field and petrological investigations, and the experiments described have been designed to test the feasibility of these processes.

Experimental approaches

Three approaches have been adopted in the investigation of the phase relationships in systems more complex than $CaO-CO_2-H_2O$. The first is to study the phase relationships in a series of quaternary systems where one component has been added to the ternary system. Results obtained in systems with MgO and P_2O_5, respectively, as the fourth component provide some insight into differentiation processes in carbonatite magmas. The system with SiO_2 as the fourth component is the simplest system combining silicate minerals and the synthetic carbonatite of the ternary system, and this forms an important basis for interpretation of the phase relationships in the more complex silicate-carbonate systems.

The second approach is to add to the ternary system silicate minerals such as feldspars, nepheline, pyroxenes and olivine. These systems contain five or six components and it is therefore impossible to follow paths of crystallization even under isothermal isobaric conditions. However, information of three kinds can be determined directly from the phase fields intersected by selected composition joins through the systems: (1) the solubility of the 'silicate component' in the synthetic carbonatite magma, (2) the depression of the liquidus and solidus temperatures caused by solution of the silicate, and (3) the nature of the primary crystalline phases occurring on the liquidus rising from the minimum temperature on the liquidus. Investigation of the system $CaO-MgO-SiO_2-CO_2-H_2O$ has been started in this way; this system includes synthetic carbonatite magmas and liquid compositions corresponding to ultrabasic magmas. The 'mineral components' orthoclase, albite and nepheline have been added to the synthetic carbonatite magmas in the composition join $CaCO_3-Ca(OH)_2-H_2O$ in order to determine the nature of the reactions occurring in systems containing both alkalis and the alkaline earth oxide, CaO.

The third approach is to start with silicate 'mineral components' and to add to these an excess of alkalis in the form of carbonates. Experimental determination of the phase fields intersected by joins through the tetrahedron $CaAl_2Si_2O_8$–$NaAlSi_3O_8$–Na_2CO_3–H_2O not only provides a more direct study of the exchange reactions than that outlined under the second approach, but also provides information about the relationships between a silicate magma and a hypothetical alkali carbonate magma.

The initial experimental work in each system was completed at a pressure of 1 kb, and significant relationships or reactions encountered at this pressure are then followed through a range of pressures. Table I is a key for the abbreviations used in this chapter.

TABLE I

Abbreviations used for phases in figures and text

V	Vapour	CAp	$Ca_{10}CO_3P_6O_{24}$	Mo	Monticellite
L	Liquid	QZ	Quartz	En	Enstatite
CC	Calcite	Wo	Wollastonite	Fo	Forsterite
CH	Portlandite	Ra	Rankinite	Ab	Albite
Do (Dol)	Dolomite	C_2S	Ca_2SiO_4	An	Anorthite
MC	Magnesite	C_3S	Ca_3SiO_5	Pl	Plagioclase
MH	Brucite	Sp	Spurrite	Ne	Nepheline
P	Periclase	Ch	Calciochondrodite	NC	Sodium Carbonate
CF	Fluorite	Di	Diopside	No	Noselite
HAp	Hydroxylapatite	Ak	Akermanite	Can	Cancrinite
FAp	Fluorapatite	Me (Mel)	Melilite	Kb	Kilobar(s)

THE SYSTEM $CaO–MgO–CO_2–H_2O$

When MgO is added as a fourth component to the system $CaO–CO_2–H_2O$, the minerals periclase, brucite, magnesite and dolomite are added to portlandite and calcite. Wyllie and Tuttle began investigation of the quaternary system in 1958 with the intention of finding out whether liquids in the system could precipitate first calcite and then dolomite. However, problems of interpretation were encountered and the experimental study still awaits completion. The preliminary experimental data available provided the basis for a theoretical analysis of the system (Wyllie, unpublished manuscript), and the results which are outlined below may be applied to the crystallization and differentiation of carbonatite magmas. Marcello Carapezza, a visitor from the University of Bologna, has recently completed some reconnaissance runs in the system aimed at testing the theoretical analysis.

Decarbonation reactions and liquidus relationships

The upper temperature stability limits of brucite, magnesite and dolomite in the systems bounding the quaternary system are given in Fig. 1 by the experimentally determined dissociation reactions. The curve for the reaction of calcite and quartz to form wollastonite (Harker and Tuttle, 1956) is given for comparison. The melting relationships in the system $CaO–CO_2–H_2O$ are given by the two solid curves involving a liquid phase. The lower curve, E_1, corresponds to the ternary eutectic where melting begins in the system.

Wyllie and Tuttle (1960b) found in their preliminary work at 1 kb pressure that only a small amount of MgO was soluble in the ternary liquid (probably less than 5 wt %), and that the quaternary eutectic, E_2, where melting begins, occurred at 620°C, 25°C lower than in the ternary system. The dashed curve E_2 in Fig. 1 is an estimate for the quaternary eutectic reaction, located 25°C below the ternary eutectic reaction E_1. Carapezza (personal communication) has recently confirmed that the reaction curve lies between 590°C and 610°C at 4 kb pressure.

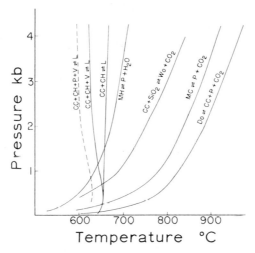

Fig. 1. The system $CaO-MgO-CO_2-H_2O$. For abbreviations see Table I. Univariant reactions with one silicate reaction for comparison. E_1 is the minimum liquidus temperature in the system $CaO-CO_2-H_2O$, and E_2 is the same for the quaternary system (see Fig. 2). In the reaction, E_2, periclase is replaced by brucite and then dolomite at successively higher pressures (see Fig. 5). After Harker and Tuttle (1955, 1956), Goldsmith and Heard (1961), Roy and Roy (1957), Wyllie and Tuttle (1960a), and Raynor and Wyllie (unpublished).

It will be shown in the following discussion that the magnesian phase involved in the eutectic reaction E_2 may be periclase, or brucite, or dolomite, depending upon the pressure. At 1 kb pressure, Wyllie and Tuttle (1960b) found no magnesite or dolomite on the liquidus nor in subsolidus runs, and they were unable to establish criteria for the recognition of primary brucite as distinct from brucite quenched from the liquid phase, or produced from periclase during a quench. The change from periclase to brucite occurs at a pressure very close to 1 kb, and at 500 b pressure, periclase is certainly stable rather than brucite.

Figure 2 shows schematically the quaternary liquidus phase relationships at 500 b pressure, and the same arrangement persists up to about 1 kb pressure where brucite must appear on the liquidus. From the field boundaries limiting the primary phase fields for portlandite and calcite there rises a steep liquidus surface with periclase as the primary phase. The liquidus surface bounded by the front field boundaries in Fig. 2 (including E_1 and E_2) is the vapour-saturated surface giving the compositions of liquids saturated with the volatile components CO_2 and H_2O. These liquids coexist with crystalline phases and a vapour phase with compositions on the vaporus surface, which is essentially the join CO_2–H_2O. As the liquid composition changes from the carbonate to the hydrate side of the tetrahedron, so does the vapour phase composition change from CO_2 to H_2O. The vapour phases in equilibrium with the eutectic liquids E_1 and E_2 are very rich in H_2O, and poor in CO_2. This is why neither

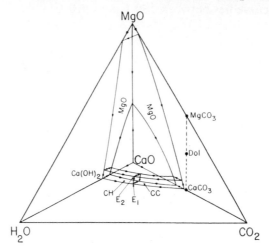

Fig. 2. The system CaO–MgO–CO_2–H_2O. For abbreviations see Table I. Schematic liquidus field boundaries and primary phase volumes at 500 b pressure.

magnesite nor dolomite appears on the liquidus at this pressure, despite the fact that the eutectic reaction curve E_2 lies well within the stability fields for these minerals (Fig. 1). In order to appreciate the effect of vapour phase composition on the stability fields of dolomite and magnesite and to compare these stability fields with the liquidus relationships, it is necessary to use a diagram in which the vapour phase composition is represented. The petrogenetic model (Wyllie, 1962) has proved useful for this purpose.

Composition of vapours: The petrogenetic model

Figure 3 illustrates schematically an isobaric section through the petrogenetic model for the quaternary system at a pressure of 500 b. Only reactions or assemblages involving a vapour phase are shown on the diagram, and the horizontal axis gives the composition of the vapour phase in each assemblage at various temperatures. Univariant reactions are represented by points, and the lines represent the intersections of divariant reaction surfaces with the isobaric section. Figure 3A is drawn approximately to scale, and the relationships near the H_2O composition cannot be distinguished. Figures 3B and 3C are enlarged to illustrate two ways in which the sub-solidus reaction curves could intersect. In subsequent discussions, only the arrangement in Fig. 3B will be considered.

The arrangement of the two ternary liquidus reactions (isobaric field boundaries) meeting at the ternary eutectic E_1 is based on experimental data (Wyllie
and Tuttle, 1960a; Fig. 10B for 1 kb pressure). In the presence of CO_2 at 500 b
pressure, calcite melts at about 1240°C (Wyllie and Tuttle, 1960a, Fig. 14).
When the vapour phase is diluted with H_2O the melting temperature is lowered,
and when the vapour phase contains more than about 80 wt% of H_2O the
melting temperature decreases markedly for each slight increase in H_2O content.

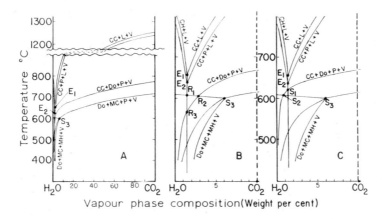

Fig. 3. The system $CaO-MgO-CO_2-H_2O$. For abbreviations see Table I.
Schematic isobaric section through the petrogenetic model at 500 b pressure. *A.* Approximately to scale; relationships near the H_2O axis are not
distinguishable. *B* and *C.* Alternative arrangements for reactions near
the H_2O axis.

This reaction curve meets the portlandite melting curve (isobaric field boundary)
at E_1, at 645°C, where the vapour phase composition is very rich in H_2O. The
liquidus field boundaries on the vapour-saturated liquidus surface for the
quaternary system (Fig. 2) involve the additional phase periclase. These boundaries are represented by the curves located approximately 25°C below
the ternary curves in Fig. 3, and they meet at the quaternary eutectic
E_2. Below E_2 there extends a curve for the sub-solidus assemblage,
CC + CH + P + V.

The arrangement of the sub-solidus reaction curves meeting at S_3 (Fig. 3) is
based on results from the system $MgO-CO_2-H_2O$ (Walter, Wyllie and Tuttle,
1962, Fig. 6). The three reactions which involve the dissociation of magnesite,
the dissociation of brucite, and the conversion of magnesite to brucite have been
illustrated in a 1 kb isobaric section through the petrogenetic model by Wyllie
(1962, Fig. 3). Their positions within the petrogenetic model are changed only
slightly by the presence of dolomite as an additional phase. The assemblage
Do + MC + P + V represents the dissociation of magnesite, in the presence of
dolomite, and the reaction curve therefore extends from the point for the dissociation of magnesite in the presence of pure CO_2, to lower temperatures as the vapour

phase is diluted with H_2O. At S_3, this meets the similar curve for the dissociation of brucite, and extending to lower temperatures from this point is a curve for the conversion of brucite to magnesite, in the presence of dolomite. The fourth curve extending to lower temperatures from S_3 is necessitated by the presence of dolomite, but this need not concern us in the present discussion. The temperature and the vapour phase composition for S_3 have been determined experimentally by Walter, Wyllie and Tuttle (1962) at pressures of 1 and 4 kb.

In the presence of CO_2 at 500 b pressure, dolomite dissociates at a temperature about 60°C higher than magnesite (Fig. 1), and in Fig. 3 the reaction curve for the dissociation of dolomite in the quaternary system has therefore been placed about 60°C higher than that for the dissociation of magnesite (in the presence of dolomite). This curve crosses that for the dissociation of brucite at the univariant point R_2 (Fig. 3B). Other univariant sub-solidus reactions are represented by the points R_1 and R_3, where the dissociation reaction curves intersect the sub-solidus curve below the eutectic E_2.

Figure 3 shows that although liquid, dolomite and magnesite are simultaneously stable through a limited temperature range at 500 b pressure, these phases cannot coexist because each phase assemblage is in equilibrium with a vapour phase of different composition. In the presence of an aqueous vapour with the composition of the vapour in equilibrium with liquids near the eutectic E_2, dolomite and magnesite, as well as brucite, are stable only at temperatures lower than that of the eutectic E_2.

An isothermal line can be drawn through Fig. 3A in such a way that it intersects the curves for the quaternary assemblages $CH + P + L + V$, $CC + P + L + V$, $CC + Do + P + V$, and $Do + MC + P + V$. The points of intersection give the compositions of the vapour phase in each assemblage at 500 b pressure and at the temperature of the isothermal line. Since the compositions of the crystalline phases are known (neglecting solid solution for the present), and the liquid composition is known approximately, a knowledge of the vapour phase composition provides sufficient information for the construction of a schematic isobaric isothermal phase diagram for the quaternary system. Figure 4 illustrates such a diagram for 1 kb pressure and 770°C; these conditions were selected because the vapour phase compositions are better known experimentally at 1 kb pressure than the approximate values for 500 b given in Fig. 3. The four-phase tetrahedron for $CH + P + L + V$ has been omitted for simplicity.

Figure 4 shows that the four-phase tetrahedron involving liquid, $CC + P + L + V_1$, is separated from the four-phase tetrahedron involving dolomite, $CC + Do + P + V_2$, by the three-phase space $CC + P + V_{1-2}$. The plane $CC–P–V_1$ is a barrier separating the liquid from the large stability fields for dolomite and magnesite. With decreasing temperature, the vapour phases V_1, V_2 and V_3 all change composition towards H_2O. It can be seen from Fig. 3 that in a given temperature interval V_2 and V_3 change composition far more than does V_1, so that V_2 and V_3 approach V_1 in composition. At 500 b pressure (Fig. 3) and at 1 kb pressure (Wyllie and Tuttle, preliminary results) the liquid is consumed in a eutectic reaction (E_2) before V_2 overtakes V_1 so that dolomite cannot reach the liquidus. However, at higher pressures, V_2 does overtake the

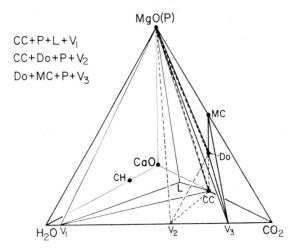

Fig. 4. The system CaO–MgO–CO$_2$–H$_2$O. For abbreviations see Table I. Isobaric isothermal section at 1 kb pressure and 770°C showing three 4-phase tetrahedra.

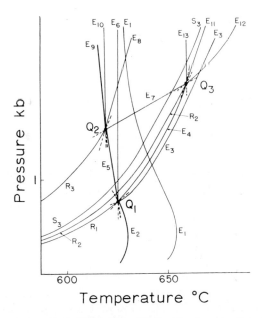

Fig. 5. The system CaO–MgO–CO$_2$–H$_2$O. For key to the reactions see Table II. Schematic univariant reactions around invariant points Q. The reactions E involve a liquid phase, whereas R and S are sub-solidus. The heavy line through Q_1 and Q_2 gives the beginning of melting (equivalent to E_2 in Fig. 1).

vapour phase of a four-phase tetrahedron involving a liquid phase, and then dolomite does have a stability field on the liquidus.

The effect of pressure

Figure 1 shows that the temperatures of the univariant melting reactions involving a vapour phase decrease slightly with increasing pressure. The temperatures of the univariant dissociation reactions, on the other hand, increase appreciably with increasing pressure. In isobaric sections through the petrogenetic model at increasing pressures, therefore, the divariant sub-solidus reaction curves will move upwards in the section until they intersect the liquidus reaction curves which simultaneously are moving downwards. It can be seen in Fig. 3B that as the pressure is increased above 500 b, the divariant curve for the dissociation of brucite, $R_1R_2S_3$, will intersect the solidus at E_2, and then move to higher temperatures; brucite will then be stable on the liquidus. At a higher pressure, the divariant curve for the dissociation of dolomite, R_2R_3, will in turn intersect the solidus producing a stability field for dolomite on the liquidus. These changes are illustrated in detail in Figs. 5 and 6.

Figure 5 is a schematic PT projection for the quaternary system which is based on the available experimental data, a qualitative consideration of the effect of pressure on the reactions in the petrogenetic model (Figs. 3 and 6), and the application of Schreinemaker's principles for the invariant points Q_1, Q_2 and Q_3. The univariant reaction curves labelled E refer to reactions including a liquid phase, and the sub-solidus reaction curves are labelled R or S. Table II lists the phase assemblages for each reaction.

TABLE II

Key to invariant and univariant assemblages in Figure 5. There are eight phases involved: calcite (CC), portlandite (CH), dolomite (Do), magnesite (MC), brucite (MH), periclase (P), liquid (L) and vapour (V).

Q_1 — CC + CH + MH + P + L + V	E_4 — CC + MH + P + L + V
Q_2 — CC + CH + Do + MH + L + V	E_5 — CC + CH + MH + L + V
Q_3 — CC + Do + MH + P + L + V	E_6 — CC + CH + MH + P + L
R_1 — CC + CH + MH + P + V	E_7 — CC + Do + MH + L + V
R_2 — CC + Do + MH + P + V	E_8 — CH + Do + MH + L + V
R_3 — CC + CH + Do + MH + V	E_9 — CC + CH + Do + L + V
S_3 — Do + MC + MH + P + V	E_{10} — CC + CH + Do + MH + L
E_1 — CC + CH + L + V	E_{11} — Do + MH + P + L + V
E_2 — CC + CH + P + L + V	E_{12} — CC + Do + P + L + V
E_3 — CH + MH + P + L + V	E_{13} — CC + Do + MH + P + L

The three reactions R_1, R_2 and S_3 lie at temperatures just below the dissociation curve for brucite (Figs. 1 and 3B). The reaction E_1 is the eutectic melting reaction in the ternary system CaO–CO_2–H_2O (Figs. 1 and 3B). The heavy line corresponds to the dashed line E_2 in Fig. 1, representing the quaternary eutectic melting reaction. In Fig. 5, this is divided into three portions by the invariant points Q_1 and Q_2, each portion corresponding to the stability range of a different magnesian phase in the assemblage: E_2 represents the assemblage CC + CH + P + L + V,

E_5 the assemblage $CC + CH + MH + L + V$, and E_9 the assemblage $CC + CH + Do + L + V$.

Figure 6 provides a key to the reactions plotted in Fig. 5. Figure 6A is reproduced from Fig. 3B, an isobaric section through the petrogenetic model at 500 b pressure. The curve mm represents the upper stability limit of brucite, and dd represents the upper stability limit of dolomite. The invariant point Q_1 is generated at a pressure in the region of 1 kb when R_1 meets E_2, as shown in Fig. 5.

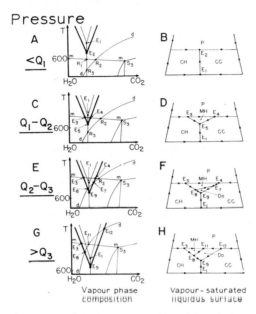

Fig. 6. The system $CaO-MgO-CO_2-H_2O$. For abbreviations see Table I. mm is the upper temperature stability limit of brucite, and *dd* is the same for dolomite. The heavy lines give the temperature of beginning of melting in the presence of each vapour phase composition. Schematic diagrams illustrating the effect of increasing pressure on the phases stable on the vapour-saturated liquidus surface. Compare the right-hand diagrams with Fig. 2, and the left-hand diagrams (isobaric sections through the petrogenetic model) with Fig. 3. The univariant reactions E, R and S are illustrated in Fig. 5 and tabulated in Table II.

Four reaction curves extend to higher pressures above Q_1, each including brucite and liquid in the phase assemblage. The vapour-absent reaction (E_6, Fig. 5) is not represented in the petrogenetic model, Fig. 6C.

At a higher pressure, the reaction R_3 meets the quaternary eutectic E_5 as shown in Fig. 5 (see also Fig. 6C). Above this pressure, dolomite becomes stable on the liquidus below the univariant reactions E_7 and E_8 (Fig. 6E). The pressure of the invariant point Q_2 depends upon the position of the reaction R_3. In Fig. 3B and 6A, at 500 b pressure, R_3 is located not too far below S_3. However, it is difficult to estimate its true position because the dolomite reaction curve dd in Fig. 6A is very steep in this part of the diagram. It can be seen in Fig. 5 that if R_3 is located at lower temperatures, higher pressures will be required before the curve R_3 intersects the curve E_5 at the invariant point Q_2. Recent reconnaissance studies by Carapezza (personal communication) suggest that the reaction E_5 may persist at least to a pressure of 4 kb. The third invariant point, Q_3, is generated when the reactions E_4, E_7 and R_2 become coincident (see Figs. 5 and 6E).

Another invariant point may be generated at a very high pressure when the reactions S_3 and E_{11} become coincident. The composition of the vapour phase involved in the reaction S_3 becomes richer in H_2O with increasing pressure. It contains 94 wt% of H_2O at 1 kb, and 96 wt% of H_2O at 4 kb (Walter, Wyllie and Tuttle, 1962, Fig. 6), but since the vapour phase in the reaction E_{11} probably contains at least 98 or 99 wt% of H_2O, considerably higher pressures would be required before the reaction curves would intersect. Above this hypothetical invariant point, magnesite would have a field of stability on the liquidus.

The right-hand diagrams in Fig. 6 illustrate schematically the primary crystalline phases on the vapour-saturated liquidus surface of the quaternary system at various pressures. Figure 6B corresponds to the situation illustrated in Fig. 2, where periclase, portlandite and calcite are the only crystalline phases stable in equilibrium with liquids and vapours. Figure 6D illustrates the appearance of brucite on the vapour-saturated liquidus surface, and Fig. 6F shows the field for dolomite. With increasing pressure, the dolomite field expands until it separates the field for brucite from the calcite field. The stability fields for brucite and dolomite in equilibrium with liquid extend towards CaO from the vapour-saturated liquidus surface, just as the fields for portlandite and calcite do in Fig. 2. If magnesite does become stable on the liquidus, its stability field would replace the peritectic E_{11} in Fig. 6H.

The phase assemblages at the univariant point and divariant curves in the petrogenetic model diagrams can be read directly from the diagrams showing the liquidus surface. For example, the univariant assemblage E_5 in Fig. 6C consists of L + V plus the three crystalline phases CC + CH + MH occurring around the point E_5 in Fig. 6D. The divariant assemblage between E_4 and E_5 in Fig. 6C consists of L + V plus the two crystalline phases CC + MH occurring on either side of the line E_4E_5 in Fig. 6D.

FeO as an additional component

Addition of iron to the system introduces the minerals siderite, ankerite and iron oxides. It also introduces problems involving oxidation states and a vapour phase of more complex composition than CO_2 + H_2O, which makes both experimental and theoretical analysis of the system difficult. However, it is known that siderite dissociates at much lower temperatures than magnesite and dolomite. At 1 kb pressure, for example, magnesite dissociates at 820°C (Fig. 1), whereas siderite dissociates at a temperature near 450°C (preliminary, unpublished results of Raynor and Wyllie obtained with ferrous oxalate in sealed capsules). The dissociation temperature is very dependent upon the oxygen fugacity in the system (French and Eugster, 1963). The isobaric dissociation curve for siderite in the petrogenetic model (with the vapour phase components other than CO_2 being plotted jointly as 'H_2O') would thus be located well below the corresponding curves for magnesite and dolomite shown in Figs. 3 and 6. Therefore, much higher pressures would be required for the siderite dissociation curve to reach the solidus in the system, and only then could siderite become stable on the liquidus. A moderate amount of FeO in the system would probably lead to the precipitation of ankerite rather than dolomite in the appropriate pressure range. Any excess of iron above that soluble in ankerite would probably be precipitated as iron oxides through a wide pressure range, and only at very high pressures would the precipitation of siderite from the liquid be possible.

Processes of crystallization and differentiation

Crystallization may proceed in this system as a result of changes in temperature, changes in pressure, and changes in the composition of the vapour phase in equilibrium with the liquid. The path of crystallization, and the sequence of minerals precipitated, is therefore dependent upon several variables. The effects of each of these must be considered in turn, although it is unlikely in nature that only one of them would be changing during crystallization.

At sufficiently high, constant pressure, Fig. 6H shows that for a liquid coexisting with a vapour and precipitating initially calcite, the calcite would be joined at a lower temperature by one of the phases periclase, dolomite or portlandite. With fractional crystallization the final liquid at E_9 would precipitate calcite, dolomite and portlandite. Thus, under isobaric conditions, the sequence of crystallization for the carbonates is calcite, followed by calcite plus dolomite.

Since explosive activity is an important feature of carbonatite complexes, pressure variations may play as significant a role in the crystallization of carbonatites as temperature variations. Consider a liquid on the primary field for calcite in Fig. 6H, near to the field boundary $E_{12}E_9$, coexisting with calcite and vapour. An increase of pressure causes the size of the dolomite field to increase, and the field boundary could therefore cross the liquid composition, placing the liquid in the primary phase field of dolomite. If equilibrium is maintained, the calcite crystals in the original liquid would be converted to dolomite. The situation is complex, because an increase in pressure also causes a decrease in liquidus temperatures. However, Fig. 6 confirms that the same liquid composition could precipitate calcite at lower pressures, and dolomite at higher pressures, with no significant change in temperature or vapour phase composition.

It is very probable that the vapour phase composition in natural carbonatites would not be controlled entirely by the crystallizing magma, but in part, at least, by the regional conditions. Consider a liquid on the field boundary $E_{12}E_9$ in Fig. 6H, coexisting with calcite, dolomite and vapour. If the vapour phase composition is enriched in H_2O under isobaric isothermal conditions, and if equilibrium is maintained, Fig. 6G shows that the calcite would dissolve, and the liquid composition would move across the dolomite field, with the dolomite dissolving. Conversely, if the vapour phase were enriched in CO_2 under isobaric, isothermal conditions, the liquid would crystallize completely, leaving an assemblage of calcite and dolomite.

The final liquid produced by fractional crystallization of synthetic carbonatite magmas in this system, as in other related systems, always precipitates hydrous minerals such as portlandite. Portlandite has not been reported from carbonatites. It is possible that the extremely H_2O-rich composition of the vapour phase in equilibrium with the final liquids (e.g. E_9 in Fig. 6G) may rarely be attained in natural occurrences because of the restraints imposed by the regional controls. If there is a regional limit for the maximum H_2O content of vapours, this could cause the carbonatite magmas to crystallize completely to carbonates, with all H_2O being given off to the vapour phase. For example, crystallization could be completed at some point on the field boundary $E_{12}E_9$ in Fig. 6H, before the vapour phase composition reached E_9 (Fig. 6G). For this to occur, there would have to be a rather sensitive regional control on the vapour phase composition, because the temperature of the solidus in Fig. 6G (the heavy line) is clearly very sensitive to small changes in vapour phase composition.

Figure 5 indicates that the occurrence of dolomite in a carbonatite requires that the magma crystallized above a certain pressure, Q_2. The pressure can be located experimentally in this simple system, but its value in a more complex system would be lowered because the solidus temperature would be lowered by the presence of additional components. Movement of the heavy line in Fig. 5 to lower temperatures would cause its point of intersection with R_3, the point Q_2, to move to lower pressures.

Conditions in this relatively simple system are too complex for any detailed exposition of how differentiation might occur to be at all meaningful. However, it may be pointed out that several of the crystallization sequences occurring in the system $CaO-MgO-FeO-CO_2-H_2O$ conform to the intrusion sequences deduced in natural complexes. Isobaric crystallization yields sequences of mineral assemblages, whereas sequences produced by changes in pressure, as well as by external changes in the vapour phase composition, tend to provide monomineralic sequences. It is reasonable to conclude, therefore, that synthetic carbonatite magmas are capable of yielding a series of differentiates during crystallization which are similar to the sequences occurring in natural carbonatites.

THE SYSTEM $CaO-CaF_2-P_2O_5-CO_2-H_2O$

Apatite is a ubiquitous accessory mineral in carbonatites, and it may become highly concentrated in bands and lenses. The behaviour of apatite in synthetic carbonatite magmas has been studied experimentally by G. M. Biggar (1962), who determined the solid-liquid-vapour phase relationships in parts of the systems $CaO-CaF_2-P_2O_5-H_2O$ and $CaO-P_2O_5-CO_2-H_2O$ (Fig. 7) for his Ph.D. degree at the University of Leeds. The results were presented orally in 1962 (Biggar and Wyllie, 1962), and some possible applications of the work have been published (Wyllie, Cox and Biggar, 1962). The main results of the study, extracted from manuscripts in preparation by Biggar and Wyllie, are outlined below.

Figure 7 shows the two quaternary systems which were investigated, and the inner tetrahedra marked by the heavy lines show the composition ranges of starting mixtures which were used. The phase relationships at 1 kb pressure are illustrated in these sub-tetrahedra in Fig. 8. The phase relationships do not change significantly within the pressure range 500 b to 4 kb. Temperatures shown in Figs. 8 and 9 were measured experimentally, except for those enclosed in parentheses, which were estimated.

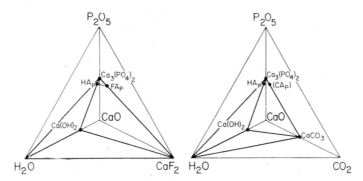

Fig. 7. The systems $CaO-CaF_2-P_2O_5-H_2O$ and $CaO-P_2O_5-CO_2-H_2O$. For abbreviations see Table I. The heavy lines enclose the range of starting compositions used.

CaO–CaF₂–P₂O₅–H₂O

Figure 8 shows the liquidus field boundaries in the quaternary system $Ca(OH)_2-CaF_2-Ca_3(PO_4)_2-H_2O$ at 1 kb pressure. The join $Ca(OH)_2-CaF_2-Ca_3(PO_4)_2$ is a ternary eutectic system at this pressure, and only a few weight percent of $Ca_3(PO_4)_2$ is soluble in the low temperature liquid on the join

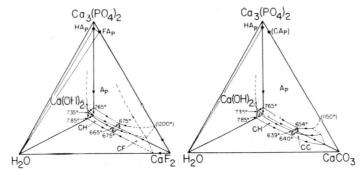

Fig. 8. Part of the systems $CaO-CaF_2-P_2O_5-H_2O$ and $CaO-P_2O_5-$ CO_2-H_2O. For abbreviations see Table I. Liquidus field boundaries and primary phase volumes at a pressure of 1 kb. Temperatures in parentheses were estimated.

$Ca(OH)_2-CaF_2$. The liquidus surface with apatite as a primary phase rises steeply from the ternary eutectic at 675°C. In the presence of H_2O, the phase relationships are very similar. A few percent of H_2O dissolves in the ternary liquids, depressing the liquidus temperature by small amounts. The eutectic at 665°C is the minimum liquidus temperature in the system, and this liquid coexists with fluorite, portlandite, apatite (composition 55 hydroxylapatite,

45 fluorapatite, weight percent), and a vapour phase composed essentially of H_2O.

$CaO-P_2O_5-CO_2-H_2O$

Liquidus field boundaries within the composition join $CaCO_3-Ca(OH)_2-Ca_3(PO_4)_2-H_2O$ at 1 kb pressure are illustrated in Fig. 8. This join is not a quaternary system because calcite melts incongruently, and the vapour phase coexisting with the liquids has compositions varying between H_2O and CO_2. The join $CaCO_3-Ca(OH)_2$ does not remain binary above about 950°C, which causes the liquidus field boundaries to leave this composition tetrahedron near $CaCO_3$. Hydroxylapatite occurs in the system, and no definite evidence for the formation of a carbonatapatite was obtained.

Despite these differences from the fluorite system, the general pattern of the phase relationships is very similar. Only a few weight percent of $Ca_3(PO_4)_2$ is soluble in the synthetic carbonatite magma near the join $CaCO_3-Ca(OH)_2$, and the primary field for apatite rises steeply from the quaternary eutectic at 639°C on the vapour-saturated liquidus surface. The liquid at the eutectic coexists with calcite, portlandite, apatite (mainly hydroxylapatite, with possibly some carbonatapatite of unknown composition in solid solution), and a vapour phase composed of $H_2O + CO_2$ which is very rich in H_2O.

$Ca_3(PO_4)_2-CaF_2-CaCO_3-Ca(OH)_2$

Figure 9 illustrates schematically the liquidus phase relationships in this system at a pressure of 1 kb. It is based on results for the system $CaCO_3-Ca(OH)_2-CaF_2$ (Gittins and Tuttle, 1964) and the results shown in Fig. 8. No vapour phase is

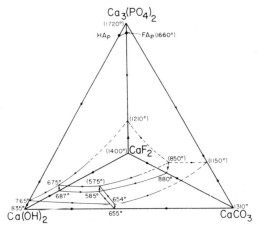

Fig. 9. Part of the system $CaO-CaF_2-P_2O_5-CO_2-H_2O$. For abbreviations see Table I. Liquidus field boundaries and primary phase volumes at a pressure of 1 kb. Temperatures in parentheses were estimated.

represented in the diagram, but because calcite melts incongruently at this pressure there is a vapour rich in CO_2 in part of the system. The quaternary eutectic liquid, at an estimated temperature of 575°C, coexists with apatite, calcite, fluorite and portlandite. Addition of H_2O to the system would not change the relationships significantly; a few wt% of H_2O would dissolve in the liquid causing liquidus temperatures to be depressed slightly (compare Fig. 8).

Figures 8 and 9 show that the presence of a small percentage of P_2O_5 in a synthetic carbonatite magma is sufficient to produce apatite as a crystalline phase on the liquidus. The diagrams also show that calcite and apatite can be precipitated simultaneously from a synthetic carbonatite magma through a wide temperature range, and Biggar (1962) has shown that these relationships persist through a wide pressure range.

Apatite crystals coexisting in equilibrium with liquid or vapour were small and equant, whereas those precipitated from a melt during a rapid quench formed acicular prisms exhibiting a variety of parallel and skeletal growths (Wyllie, Cox and Biggar, 1962). Liquids in the system are extremely fluid. It was observed that even the long apatite needles precipitated from the liquid during a quench tended to settle towards the bottom of the capsule containing the charge.

Segregation of apatite in carbonatites

The experimental data establish the facts that a carbonatite magma containing initially more than a few percent of P_2O_5 would begin to precipitate apatite before calcite, and that calcite and apatite could be co-precipitated through a wide temperature interval. The synthetic carbonatite magmas are very fluid, and crystal settling occurs with both calcite and apatite. Given a carbonatite magma precipitating these minerals, there is a good chance that partial segregation of the minerals could occur as a result of crystal settling during quiet periods. With the onset of explosive activity, producing movement within the magma column, any accumulations of apatite-rich mixtures would become streaked out forming bands parallel to the flow structures in the crystallizing magma. There is little difficulty in accounting for the observed flow banding and segregation of apatite on the basis of a magmatic carbonatite intrusion.

Detailed examination of apatites in carbonatites might be worth while. For example, material enclosed by dendritic or skeletal apatites could provide information about the composition of the magma from which the apatites crystallized. This might be one of the most promising places to seek portlandite and other hydrated phases which are readily altered to carbonates by migrating CO_2.

THE SYSTEM CaO–SiO_2–CO_2–H_2O

This system contains high temperature silicate liquids as well as the low temperature synthetic carbonatite magmas, and the phase relationships provide a basis for interpretation of the more complex systems, described in later sections, which include some of the additional components required to bring the composition of the silicate liquids closer to the composition of silicate magmas. Phase relationships at liquidus temperatures in the presence of excess vapour have been determined at a pressure of 1 kb, and the results have been presented orally (Haas and Wyllie, 1963). A detailed manuscript is in preparation, and studies at higher pressures are under way.

The vapour-saturated liquidus surface

Figure 10 is a schematic diagram showing the position of the vapour-saturated liquidus surface, ABCD, which gives the compositions of liquids coexisting with crystalline phases and with vapours on the vaporous surface extending between CO_2 and H_2O. The vaporous surface will be treated as the line $CO_2–H_2O$ in subsequent discussions, since the vapour phase at 1 kb pressure contains only a small proportion of dissolved solids. The vapour-saturated liquidus surface lies close to the composition plane $Ca_2SiO_4–CaCO_3–Ca(OH)_2$ at 1 kb pressure, and intersects it along the line MON. Crystalline phases encountered in the portion of the system studied all lie on this composition plane; they are dicalcium silicate, spurrite,

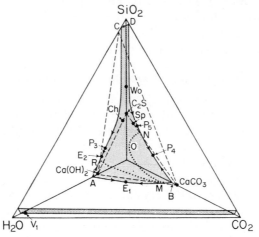

Fig. 10. The system $CaO–SiO_2–CO_2–H_2O$. For abbreviations see Table I. A schematic isobaric tetrahedron for 1 kb pressure. The large shaded area represents the vapour-saturated liquidus surface, and the small area represents the vaporous surface.

calciochondrodite, calcite and portlandite. Phase relationships on the lower part of the liquidus surface are therefore almost ternary, and it is convenient to project the liquidus surface on to the composition plane $Ca_2SiO_4–CaCO_3–Ca(OH)_2$. The results are shown in Fig. 11. Hydrous phases other than portlandite and calciochondrodite were not encountered in this study, but from the available data (Roy, 1958) it seems possible that phases 'Y' and 'Z' in the system $CaO–SiO_2–H_2O$ could have stability fields as primary phases on the quaternary liquidus at 1 kb pressure.

Extending from the ternary eutectics and peritectics E_1, E_2, P_3, P_4 and P_5, whose positions are shown shematically in Fig. 10 and in projection in Fig. 11, there are quaternary liquidus field boundaries giving the compositions of liquids coexisting with two crystalline phases and a vapour phase. These meet in the quaternary peritectics and eutectic P_8, P_7 and E_6, represented in projection in Fig. 11. The ternary eutectic liquid E_1 coexists with the vapour V_1 (Fig. 10) which contains only a very small proportion of CO_2. It can be shown on theoretical grounds, although it was not proved experimentally, that the vapours

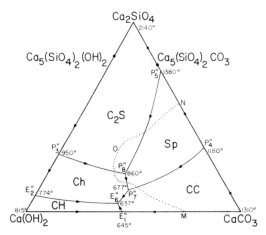

Fig. 11. The system CaO–SiO$_2$–CO$_2$–H$_2$O. For abbreviations see Table I. Liquidus field boundaries and primary phase fields for 1 kb pressure projected from the vapour-saturated liquidus surface (Fig. 10) on to the plane Ca$_2$SiO$_4$–CaCO$_3$–Ca(OH)$_2$.

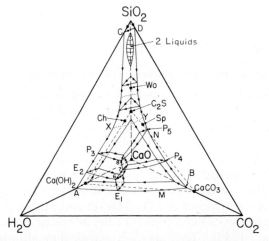

Fig. 12. The system CaO–SiO$_2$–CO$_2$–H$_2$O. For abbreviations see Table I. Schematic liquidus field boundaries and primary phase volumes at 1 kb pressure. Compare Fig. 11. The dotted line XY represents the intersection of the vapour-saturated liquidus surface with the plane C$_2$S–CO$_2$–H$_2$O.

coexisting with the quaternary peritectic and eutectic liquids also have compositions close to V_1.

From the results shown in Fig. 11, and from what is known of the bounding binary and ternary systems, it is possible to deduce the general phase relationships for the whole system. The result is illustrated in Fig. 12, which is somewhat distorted in order to show the isobaric liquidus field boundaries at 1 kb pressure. Figure 11 is a key to the primary phase volumes in the lower part of Fig. 12. The phase relationships above the composition Ca_2SiO_4 are reasonable estimates based on known experimental data for the systems $CaO-SiO_2$ and SiO_2-H_2O. It is assumed that the two-liquid field does not reach the vapour-saturated liquidus surface. This is probably true for the system $CaO-SiO_2-H_2O$, but possibly not for the system $CaO-SiO_2-CO_2$. The small liquidus volume for rankinite has been omitted for simplicity (see Fig. 21 for part of the rankinite field).

The plane $Ca_2SiO_4-CO_2-H_2O$ intersects the vapour-saturated liquidus surface in the line XY, which is a temperature maximum corresponding to the melting of Ca_2SiO_4 in the presence of a vapour phase. Silicate liquids with compositions above this thermal barrier yield on crystallization only silicate minerals and vapours, whereas liquids with compositions below this line yield a residual melt corresponding to the synthetic carbonatite magma. At temperatures below 860°C at 1 kb pressure the residual liquid precipitates spurrite, calciochondrodite, calcite and portlandite, as illustrated in Fig. 11.

It is of interest to note that although there is a large field for spurrite on the liquidus, extending down to temperatures of 677°C at 1 kb pressure, wollastonite has no stability field on the liquidus below the thermal barrier XY in Fig. 12, despite the fact that in carbonate dissociation sequences, wollastonite is normally regarded as a low temperature mineral compared to spurrite. However, it can be shown that at higher pressures wollastonite does appear on the low temperature liquidus between the fields for spurrite and calcite. In order to illustrate how dissociation reactions become involved with liquidus reactions it is necessary to use a diagram showing the vapour phase compositions.

Composition of vapours: The petrogenetic model

Figure 13 is an isobaric section through the petrogenetic model for the system at 1 kb pressure, showing divariant curves for one liquidus and for one sub-solidus reaction. The upper curve extending to the ternary eutectic E_1 was measured experimentally by Wyllie and Tuttle (1960a, Fig. 10B), and it gives the compositions of the vapour phase in equilibrium with liquids on the field boundary BE_1 in Fig. 12. The position of the lower curve was calculated by Haas (unpublished) using the available data for the formation of spurrite from calcite and wollastonite in the presence of CO_2 (Harker and Tuttle, 1957). The probable intervention of a narrow stability zone for tilleyite has been ignored in the present discussion (Harker, 1959). This diagram shows that although wollastonite is stable in the presence of CO_2 to temperatures well above the eutectic E_1, its upper stability temperature limit lies below E_1 when the assemblage involves an aqueous vapour phase. Thus, the low temperature assemblage is not stable on

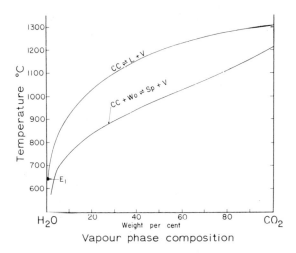

Fig. 13. The system $CaO-SiO_2-CO_2-H_2O$. For abbreviations see Table I. Isobaric section through the petrogenetic model at 1 kb pressure. The upper reaction curve gives the experimentally located position of the ternary field boundary BE_1 in Fig. 12. The lower reaction curve shows the calculated position of a quaternary sub-solidus reaction. This figure shows the proper scale for the schematic Figs. 14, 15 and 16 which follow.

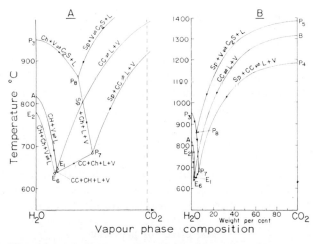

Fig. 14. The system $CaO-SiO_2-CO_2-H_2O$. For abbreviations see Table I. Schematic isobaric section through the petrogenetic model at 1 kb pressure showing liquidus relationships. Lettering corresponds to that in Fig. 11. For correct scale see Fig. 13. *A* is an enlarged version of the relationships near H_2O in *B*.

the liquidus of the system at this pressure, whereas the high temperature assemblage, spurrite + vapour, is stable with the liquids. With increasing pressure, however, the dissociation reaction moves upwards through the section until it intersects the liquidus curves producing a stability field for wollastonite on the liquidus.

Details of the liquidus and sub-solidus relationships in the petrogenetic model are shown in Figs. 14 (liquidus) and 15 (sub-solidus). These figures are schematic, being distorted near the H_2O composition in order to show the various reaction curves. The true scale is indicated by the curves in Fig. 13. The lettering of the peritectics and eutectics corresponds to the lettering in Figs. 10, 11 and 12.

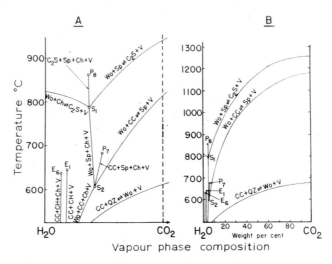

Fig. 15. The system $CaO-SiO_2-CO_2-H_2O$. For abbreviations see Table I. Schematic isobaric section through the petrogenetic model at 1 kb pressure showing sub-solidus relationships. Lettering and scale corresponds to that in Fig. 14.

Figure 14 shows the liquidus field boundaries on the vapour-saturated liquidus surface for the system (Figs. 11 and 12). The sub-solidus assemblages in Fig. 15 are of two types. From each peritectic or eutectic on the vapour-saturated liquidus surface, one sub-solidus assemblage (including a vapour phase) extends to lower temperatures; these are intersected by decarbonation reaction curves extending from the CO_2 axis, or by dehydration reaction curves extending from the H_2O axis. The more important of these dissociation reactions are shown schematically, and the points of intersection, S_1 and S_2, represent univariant assemblages. The temperatures of S_1 and S_2 are not known.

The effect of pressure

The effect of increasing pressure on these reactions is summarized in Fig. 16, which shows a series of schematic isobaric sections through the petrogenetic model. Figures 16A and 16D correspond to Figs. 15 and 14, respectively. With increasing pressure the temperatures of the liquidus reactions decrease slightly, whereas the temperatures of the dissociation reactions increase appreciably. The univariant reactions S_1 and S_2 therefore move upwards towards P_8 and P_7. At pressure P_2 in Fig. 16B, S_2 reaches P_7 at an invariant point where the six phases Wo + CC + Sp + Ch + L + V coexist. Four other univariant reactions in addition to S_2 and P_7 must extend from the invariant point, and these are shown in the schematic PT projection of Fig. 17. One of these (V), is a

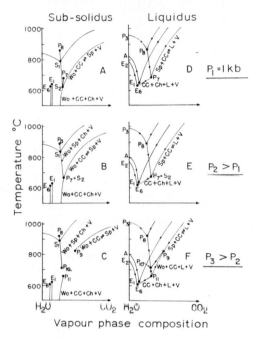

Fig. 16. The system $CaO–SiO_2–CO_2–H_2O$. For abbreviations see Table I. Schematic isobaric sections through the petrogenetic model showing the effect of increasing pressure. Lettering corresponds to that in Figs. 11, 17 and 18. *A* and *D* correspond to Figs. 15 and 14, respectively. *B* and *E* at pressure P_2 represent conditions at the invariant point in Fig. 17. *C* and *D* at pressure P_3 represent conditions above the invariant point in Fig. 17. The projected liquidus relationships are shown in Fig. 18.

reaction without a vapour phase, and therefore it does not appear in the petrogetic model. The other three reactions involve a liquid phase as well as a vapour, and they extend to higher pressures above the invariant point in Fig. 17. They are represented in Figs. 16C and 16F by the quaternary peritectics P_9, P_{10} and P_{11}.

It can be seen from Fig. 17 that wollastonite occurs in equilibrium with the low temperature liquids of the system only at pressures greater than the invariant point. Furthermore, it appears from Fig. 17 that the pressure at the invariant point would be not much greater than 1 kb. However, if the position of S_2 actually occurs at temperatures appreciably lower than indicated in Figs. 15 and 16A, then the intersection of S_2 and P_7 at the invariant point in Fig. 17 would not occur until much higher pressures.

The effect of these changes on the vapour-saturated liquidus surface is shown

M

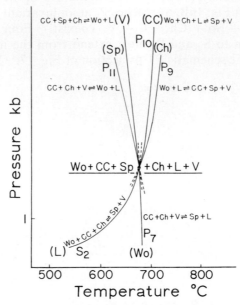

Fig. 17. The system CaO–SiO$_2$–CO$_2$–H$_2$O. For abbreviations see Table I. Schematic PT projection showing the invariant point above which wollastonite becomes stable on the liquidus. See Fig. 18.

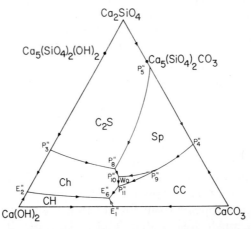

Fig. 18. The system CaO–SiO$_2$–CO$_2$–H$_2$O. Pressure >1 kb, for abbreviations see Table I. Schematic liquidus field boundaries and primary phase fields for pressure P$_3$ (see Fig. 15) projected from the vapour-saturated liquidus surface (Fig. 10) on to the plane Ca$_2$SiO$_4$–CaCO$_3$–Ca(OH)$_2$. Compare Fig. 11.

in Fig. 18, which is a projection similar to Fig. 11. The peritectic P_7 (P_7'' in the projection of Fig. 11) has been replaced by three peritectics P_9, P_{10} and P_{11} whose projections in Fig. 18 are connected by three field boundaries outlining a field for the primary crystallization of wollastonite. The size of the wollastonite field increases with increasing pressure as the temperatures of P_9 and P_{10} increase (Fig. 17).

It is interesting to note that at a pressure somewhat higher than P_3 in Fig. 16, coincidence of the univariant points S_1 and P_8 would produce another invariant point with the development of a second triangular field for primary wollastonite replacing the invariant point P_8'' in Fig. 18. Similarly, if the decarbonation reactions involving tilleyite and rankinite had been included in the analysis started in Fig. 15, fields for primary tilleyite and for rankinite would appear on the liquidus in the region of P_{11} and P_8 respectively.

Conclusions

Only a few weight percent of SiO_2 is soluble in the synthetic carbonatite magma, and from the minimum liquidus temperature at E_6 there rises a fairly steep liquidus surface with hydrated or carbonated minerals as primary phases (Figs. 11 and 12). Calciochondrodite is not yet known in nature, and spurrite has not been reported from a carbonatite (to the best of my knowledge). The intervention of the wollastonite field between the fields for spurrite and calcite at higher pressures (Fig. 18) is therefore of particular interest, because wollastonite does occur in many alkaline-carbonatite complexes. Figure 18 shows that wollastonite and calcite may be coprecipitated from a synthetic carbonatite magma, the temperature range of coprecipitation increasing with increasing pressure. Figure 17 shows that if wollastonite occurs in a magmatic carbonatite, the magma must have crystallized above a minimum pressure represented by the invariant point in this simple system. The presence of additional components would displace the melting curve to lower temperatures, which would bring the stability of wollastonite on the liquidus down to lower pressures. The results in this system indicate that only silicate magmas originally undersaturated in SiO_2 (compositions below XY in Fig. 12) can yield residual melts capable of precipitating calcite, that is, carbonatite magmas.

THE SYSTEM $CaO–MgO–SiO_2–CO_2–H_2O$

Addition of MgO to the system just described introduces several other silicate minerals which are found in carbonatites and associated igneous rocks, as well as providing liquids with compositions approaching the ultrabasic magmas which have been proposed as the parents of these rocks. Work completed so far has been limited to the system $CaO–MgO–SiO_2–H_2O$. However, from what is known of the system $CaO–SiO_2–CO_2–H_2O$ it appears that $Ca(OH)_2$ serves as a reasonable model for mixtures composed of $Ca(OH)_2$ and $CaCO_3$, and liquids with compositions near $Ca(OH)_2$ in the hydrous system therefore serve as proxies for the synthetic carbonatite magma.

$CaO–MgO–SiO_2–H_2O$

Figure 19 shows the compositions of the minerals occurring in this system, and the positions of the two composition joins so far investigated (the heavy lines). The phase fields intersected by parts of these joins at 1 kb pressure are illustrated

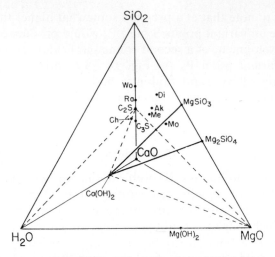

Fig. 19. The system $CaO–MgO–SiO_2–H_2O$. For abbreviations see Table I. The two heavy lines are the composition joins studied. They intersect the dashed compatibility tetrahedron $C_2S–MgO–Ca(OH)_2–H_2O$.

in Fig. 20 (Franz and Wyllie, 1963). The vertical lines labelled $C_2S + P + V$ in Fig. 20 represent the intersections of the two composition joins with the side of the dashed compatibility tetrahedron in Fig. 19. The solidus within this compatibility tetrahedron is at 725°C. Only a few wt % of enstatite or of

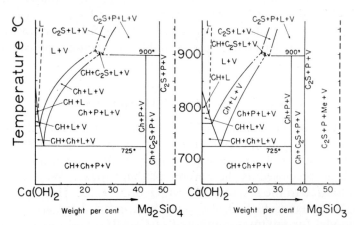

Fig. 20. The system $CaO–MgO–SiO_2–H_2O$. For abbreviations see Table I. Preliminary diagram showing the phase fields intersected at 1 kb pressure by the joins $Ca(OH)_2–Mg_2SiO_4$ and $Ca(OH)_2–MgSiO_3$ (Fig. 19).

forsterite are soluble in the portlandite liquid, and from the lowest points on the liquidus intersections there rises a steep liquidus surface with calciochondrodite as a primary phase below 900°C, and with dicalcium silicate as a primary phase at higher temperatures. These phase relationships are similar to the liquidus relationships determined in the system $CaO-SiO_2-H_2O$ (Fig. 11), except that, at temperatures just below the liquidus, periclase appears as an additional phase in Fig. 20.

Figure 21 shows schematically, for 1 kb pressure, the positions of the liquidus field boundaries in the bounding ternary systems which include H_2O as a component. The field boundaries for $CaO-SiO_2-H_2O$ are taken from Fig. 12, and

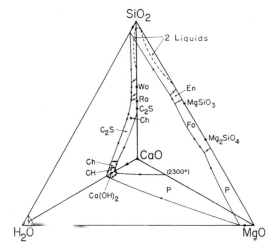

Fig. 21. The system $CaO-MgO-SiO_2-H_2O$. For abbreviations see Table I. Schematic liquidus field boundaries at 1 kb pressure for the ternary systems $CaO-MgO-H_2O$ (Fig. 2), $CaO-SiO_2-H_2O$ (Fig. 12) and $MgO-SiO_2-H_2O$.

the field for rankinite has been included. Those for the system $CaO-MgO-H_2O$ are taken from Fig. 2. Those for $MgO-SiO_2-H_2O$ are schematic, based on the reasonable assumption that H_2O under pressure dissolves in the liquids of the binary system $MgO-SiO_2$, depressing the liquidus temperatures, but not affecting the phase relationships significantly. It is assumed that the two-liquid field disappears before the H_2O-saturated liquidus field boundary is reached. The H_2O-saturated liquidus field boundaries in Fig. 21 form the three edges of the H_2O-saturated liquidus surface for the quaternary system.

The primary phases and liquidus field boundaries on the H_2O-saturated liquidus surface are shown in Fig. 22. The general arrangement of the phase fields on this surface is similar to that for the dry system $CaO-MgO-SiO_2$. A small percentage of H_2O dissolves in the liquids of the dry system, depressing the liquidus temperatures but probably causing few significant changes in the phase relationships except towards the portlandite corner of the surface. It is assumed that the two-liquid field does not reach the H_2O-saturated surface (see Fig. 21). It can be seen in Fig. 21 that the primary phase volume for CaO is screened from the H_2O-saturated surface by primary phase volumes for periclase, portlandite, calciochondrodite and dicalcium silicate. The positions in Fig. 22 of the primary phase fields for portlandite and calciochondrodite, and the positions of the peritectic at 900°C and the eutectic at 725°C, are based on the experimental data shown in Fig. 20. This part of Fig. 22 has been expanded slightly in order to show the phase relationhips. The temperatures in parentheses are estimated.

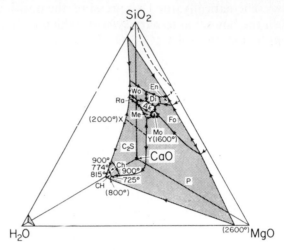

Fig. 22. The system $CaO–MgO–SiO_2–H_2O$. For abbreviations see Table I. Schematic field boundaries and primary phase fields on the vapour-saturated liquidus surface (shaded: compare Fig. 21) at 1 kb pressure. The phase relationships on the lower left part of the surface are based on the results shown in Fig. 20; they are slightly expanded from true scale. Temperatures in parentheses are estimated. XY is part of a temperature maximum on the vapour-saturated liquidus surface corresponding to the line of intersection of the surface with the plane $Ca_2SiO_4–MgO–H_2O$.

The plane $MgO–C_2S–H_2O$ forms one side of the dashed compatibility tetra-hedron in Fig. 19, and this plane intersects the H_2O-saturated surface along a line, part of which is the dashed line XY in Fig. 22. This line is a temperature maximum on the liquidus, corresponding to the temperature maximum along $C_2S–MgO$ in the dry ternary system, and it acts as a thermal barrier. Parent liquids with compositions above XY (extended towards MgO) cannot yield low temperature residual liquids precipitating the hydrated phases.

$CaO–MgO–SiO_2–CO_2$

From what is known of the systems $CaO–SiO_2–CO_2–H_2O$ (Figs. 11 and 12), and $CaO–MgO–CO_2$ (Fig. 2) it can be concluded that the CO_2-saturated liquidus surface for the system $CaO–MgO–SiO_2–CO_2$ would be similar to that for the hydrous system in Fig. 22, with less vapour dissolved in the liquids, with higher liquidus temperatures, possibly with part or all of the two-liquid field extending to the CO_2-saturated surface, and, most important, with a primary phase field for calcite replacing the portlandite field, and with a more extensive primary phase field for spurrite replacing the calciochondrodite field. Liquidus temperatures in the carbonate corner of the surface would be appreciably higher, with the quaternary peritectic and eutectic temperatures being perhaps of the order of 1300°C and 1100°C, respectively (compare Fig. 11). A compatibility tetrahedron corresponding to that illustrated in Fig. 19 would still be present, and the temperature maximum corresponding to XY (extended towards MgO) would also persist as a thermal barrier. Parent liquids with compositions above XY would therefore be unable to produce residual liquids capable of precipitating the carbonated phases spurrite and calcite.

$CaO-MgO-SiO_2-CO_2-H_2O$

Figure 22 can also serve as a model for the five-component system $CaO-MgO-SiO_2-CO_2-H_2O$ at 1 kb pressure, with the two volatiles CO_2 and H_2O represented by the same corner of the tetrahedron, and the liquids represented in terms of the components CaO, MgO, SiO_2, and percentage of total dissolved volatiles. For liquids above XY, the general arrangement of the silicate phase fields on the projected surface for the quinary vapour-saturated liquidus would be similar to that shown in Fig. 22. The liquids would contain dissolved CO_2 and H_2O, and would coexist with a vapour phase whose composition varies between H_2O and CO_2. However, the situation becomes more complex for liquids below XY, because the primary phases on the liquidus change as the vapour composition changes from H_2O towards CO_2, and here the quinary liquidus relationships cannot be projected on to the surface in Fig. 22. However, the surface can still represent the quinary liquidus in terms of CaO, MgO, SiO_2 and total dissolved volatiles. Near the compositions portlandite and calcite on the CaO-volatile join, the liquids would persist to lower temperatures than those indicated in Fig. 22, precipitating spurrite and calcite, in addition to calciochondrodite and portlandite, as indicated in Fig. 11, with these phases co-existing with periclase, as indicated in Figs. 2 and 22. Brucite would appear instead of periclase when the liquidus temperature becomes less than about 630°C.

A temperature maximum equivalent to XY (extended towards MgO) would persist in the 5-component system (see Fig. 12 for $CaO-SiO_2-CO_2-H_2O$, Fig. 22 for $CaO-MgO-SiO_2-H_2O$ and for $CaO-MgO-SiO_2-CO_2$, with the differences noted above). At 1 kb pressure, the parent liquids in this system with compositions above XY (Fig. 22), precipitating minerals such as olivine, pyroxene, monticellite and melilite (akermanite), could not yield residual liquids precipitating the carbonated and hydrated phases below XY. The temperature maximum XY acts as a barrier separating the high temperature silicate liquids, corresponding to ultrabasic magmas, from the low temperature synthetic carbonatite magmas.

Effect of pressure

The temperature maximum across the dicalcium silicate liquidus, corresponding to XY in Fig. 22, is a very prominent feature. It is unlikely that even very high pressures, in the presence of volatile components, could be effective in destroying this thermal barrier.

It has been shown that at higher pressures in the system $CaO–MgO–CO_2–H_2O$ dolomite would appear as an additional mineral stable on the synthetic carbonatite liquidus (Fig. 6). Similarly, at higher pressures in the system $CaO–SiO_2–CO_2–H_2O$, wollastonite becomes stable on the synthetic carbonatite liquidus. Thus, at higher pressures, dolomite and wollastonite would appear on the low temperature liquidus in the five-component system. As already mentioned, the minimum pressures for the stabilities of dolomite (Fig. 5) and wollastonite (Fig. 17) in the simple systems are lowered by the presence of additional components.

There are a number of dissociation reactions in the system $CaO–MgO–SiO_2–CO_2$ which involve silicate minerals, as well as the carbonated phases calcite, dolomite and spurrite. When the effect of H_2O on these dissociation reactions is considered in the petrogenetic model, it can be seen that several of the divariant dissociation curves would intersect the vapour-saturated liquidus curves for the system, in the same way that dissociation reactions and liquidus curves intersect in Figs. 3, 6, 15 and 16. This gives rise to the possible appearance of minerals such as forsterite, pyroxenes, monticellite and akermanite on the low temperature synthetic carbonatite liquidus (below XY in Fig. 22), as well as on the high temperature silicate liquidus (above XY in Fig. 22). Both theoretical analysis and experimental tests along these lines are under way.

Conclusions

The above considerations lead to the conclusion that at 1 kb pressure and, indeed, through a wide range of pressures, high temperature silicate liquids precipitating originally minerals such as olivine, pyroxene, melilite and monticellite (liquids with compositions above XY extended towards MgO in Fig. 22) are incapable of yielding low temperature residual melts which precipitate carbonated and hydrated phases. On the basis of this evidence, therefore, it appears to be unlikely that a carbonated peridotite magma could yield a carbonatite magma by crystallization differentiation. However, the parent magma envisaged by proponents of this hypothesis is a carbonated alkali peridotite magma and, as shown in the next section, the addition of mineral components such as nepheline *might* provide alternative crystallization paths which by-pass the thermal barrier and lead to low temperature liquids.

The presence of calcite in ultramafic igneous rocks has been generally attributed to late stage alteration. However, it now appears possible for mineral assemblages involving olivine, pyroxene, monticellite, melilite, dolomite and calcite to be precipitated simultaneously from magmas at low to moderate temperatures (in the range 600°C–800°C). The silicate phases appear on the portion of the synthetic carbonatite liquidus where the temperature is rising steeply above the minimum liquidus temperature (for example, compare Figs. 11 and 18 for wollastonite). It is therefore probable that the proportion of silicate minerals to carbonated and hydrated minerals would be small, and the crystalline product would perhaps bear little resemblance to a peridotite. Nevertheless, these results suggest that some 'altered' ultramafic rocks may, in fact, represent primary crystallization from a magma rich in CO_2 and H_2O.

It may be noted that, at 4 kb pressure, serpentine is stable at temperatures a little above 500°C, and the lowest liquidus temperature in the system $CaO-MgO-CO_2-H_2O$ is 600°C (Fig. 1). Addition of SiO_2, required to give serpentine, would lower the liquidus temperature further, and addition of other components such as FeO would contribute to the lowering. Thus, we are not too far away from the condition where serpentine could be a primary crystalline phase in carbonatite magmas.

If this condition could be reached experimentally, a small amount of serpentine (and other minerals) would be in equilibrium with a large amount of CaO-rich liquid. This recalls the fact that lime metasomatism is often connected with serpentinite and ultramafic intrusions. Unfortunately, the proportions of serpentine and CaO-rich liquid in these systems are wrong for this to be a reasonable explanation for magmatic serpentinites. Furthermore, although it would probably be possible to bridge the temperature gap of 100°C (between 600°C and 500°C) by adding selected components (e.g. alkalis), it would be very difficult to do this by adding components with compositions appropriate for serpentinites and other ultramafic rocks. There is therefore a composition gap as well as a temperature gap.

THE SYSTEM $CaO-Na_2O-Al_2O_3-SiO_2-CO_2-H_2O$: PART I

Figure 23 is a composition tetrahedron for the system $CaO-Na_2O-Al_2O_3-SiO_2$, which contains a representative of the basic oxides (CaO) and the alkalis (Na_2O). The significance of phase relationships in such systems in connection with the origin of carbonatites has already been emphasized. However, in order to bring the system into reasonable conformity with carbonatite compositions it is

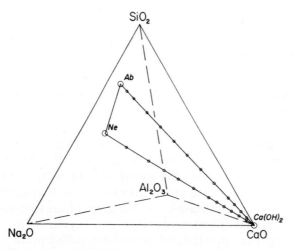

Fig. 23. The system $CaO-Na_2O-Al_2O_3-SiO_2-H_2O$. For abbreviations see Table I. The composition joins Ab–Ca(OH)$_2$ and Ne–Ca(OH)$_2$.

necessary to add CO_2 and H_2O as components, and a six-component system is difficult to handle, both theoretically and experimentally. One way to tackle such a system is to consider the phase relationships in the four-component system illustrated *in the presence of CO_2 and H_2O under pressure*. Another way is to plot empirically the phase fields intersected by the composition joins selected for study; usually, the compositions of vapours, liquid and many of the crystalline phases do not lie on the selected joins at all. Results obtained in two joins in Fig. 23 (Ab–Ca(OH)$_2$–H$_2$O and Ne–Ca(OH)$_2$–H$_2$O) have been presented (Watkinson and Wyllie, 1963).

Ab–Ca(OH)$_2$–H$_2$O

Figure 24 shows the phase fields intersected at 1 kb pressure by the portlandite end of this join in the presence of 25 weight per cent H_2O. A vapour phase is present in addition to the phases listed. Only about 2.5 wt% of Ab is soluble

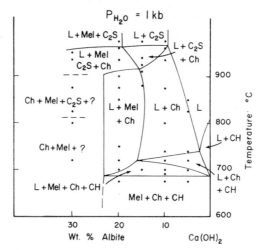

Fig. 24. The system CaO–Na$_2$O–Al$_2$O$_3$–SiO$_2$–H$_2$O. For abbreviations see Table 1. Preliminary diagram showing the phase fields intersected at kb pressure by the join Ca(OH)$_2$–Ab in the presence of 25 wt% H$_2$O. A vapour phase is present in addition to the phases listed.

in the low temperature portlandite liquid, and from the minimum liquidus temperature there rises a steep liquidus surface with calciochondrodite as a primary phase. Above 950°C, this is replaced by dicalcium silicate. At temperatures just above the solidus, and for compositions richer in albite, these crystalline phases are joined by a soda-bearing melilite. The liquidus relationships are comparable with those for the systems CaO–SiO$_2$–H$_2$O (Fig. 11), and CaO–MgO–SiO$_2$–H$_2$O (Fig. 20), and it may be concluded that the liquidus with dicalcium silicate as primary phase rises to a temperature maximum corresponding to the thermal barrier encountered in previous systems.

For compositions near portlandite the solidus temperature is 685°C, but for mixtures containing more than about 25 wt% Ab, another compatibility region is entered and the solidus temperature jumps to about 900°C. Plagioclase feldspar appears as a stable phase in this join only for starting mixtures containing more than about 65 wt% of Ab, and it is unstable in contact with the synthetic carbonatite magma. Similarly, orthoclase is unstable in contact with the synthetic carbonatite magma (Watkinson, unpublished). In both systems, melilite is stable rather than feldspar.

Ne–Ca(OH)$_2$–H$_2$O

Figure 25 shows the phase fields intersected at 1 kb pressure by the portlandite end of this join in the presence of 25 wt% H$_2$O. A vapour phase is present in addition to the phases listed. Nepheline is more soluble in the portlandite

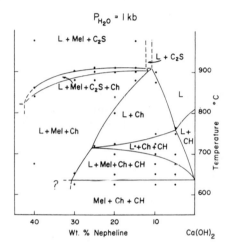

Fig. 25. The system CaO–Na$_2$O–Al$_2$O$_3$–SiO$_2$–H$_2$O. For abbreviations see Table I. Preliminary diagram showing the phase fields intersected at 1 kb pressure by the join Ca(OH)$_2$–Ne in the presence of 25 wt% H$_2$O. A vapour phase is present in addition to the phases listed.

liquid than albite, and the solidus temperature near portlandite is also lower. The portlandite end of the join intersects the same phase fields intersected by the albite join, but the fields are of rather different shape, and they extend further towards the silicate 'component'. The steep liquidus with dicalcium silicate as a primary phase suggests that in this join also, a temperature maximum or thermal barrier occurs on the liquidus for primary dicalcium silicate.

There is a difference between the relationships encountered in this join and those on the albite join. In the albite join, the field for Mel + Ch + L + V is bounded below by a small 5-phase field lying just above the solidus, and it is bounded laterally by a vertical line separating it from phase assemblages containing no liquid. In the nepheline join, the intersected field for Mel + Ch + L + V extends much further towards nepheline and, so far, it has not been possible to locate a solidus terminating the field below. Charges containing 40% and 50% nepheline when quenched from temperatures of about 550°C contain material which is sticky and ductile. These charges are quite different from the crystalline material obtained in corresponding parts of the albite join. Our present interpretation, which is only tentative, is that the charges concerned contain a liquid phase enriched in soda, and probably also in silica, compared to the composition of the starting mixtures. This low temperature liquid probably occurs on the nepheline side of the thermal barrier extending across the liquidus for dicalcium silicate. Liquids rich in soda and silica might exhibit continuous solubility relationships with a coexisting aqueous phase, and if this is the situation, then interpretation of the results with the experimental technique employed is difficult.

$Ab-Ne-CaCO_3-Ca(OH)_2-H_2O$

Watkinson (unpublished) is continuing these studies by adding Ab and Ne separately to mixtures of $CaCO_3-Ca(OH)_2$ in the presence of 25 wt % H_2O at 1 kb pressure. The liquidus surface rising from the low temperature synthetic carbonatite magma in both joins is similar to that for the system $CaO-SiO_2-CO_2-H_2O$ (Figs. 11 and 12). Below the liquidus, phase assemblages involving melilite and liquid are intersected by a very wide range of compositions within the composition join $Ab-Ne-CaCO_3-Ca(OH)_2-H_2O$, and melilite is stable on both sides of the inferred temperature maximum extending across the liquidus for primary dicalcium silicate. The vapour phase in this system contains dissolved Na_2O, and although no solubility measurements have been made, it seems likely that such a vapour phase could be responsible for some of the fenitization occurring around natural carbonatites.

Phase relationships involving the peculiar low temperature 'liquid' encountered in the join $Ne-Ca(OH)_2-H_2O$ are being examined with $CaCO_3$ as an additional component. If these liquids do represent residual melts enriched in soda and silica, addition of $CaCO_3$ to the starting mixtures in Fig. 25 makes available CO_2 for the residual liquid, which could lead to the precipitation of Na_2CO_3, or to exchange reactions involving the precipitation of calcite and further enrichment of the liquids in alkalis. In order to estimate what happens in this part of the system, it will be necessary to investigate the phase relationships in the system $Na_2O-SiO_2-CO_2-H_2O$ through a range of temperatures and pressures.

In the join $Ab-Ne-CaCO_3-Ca(OH)_2-H_2O$ there appear to be two low temperature residual liquids. One is the synthetic carbonatite magma composed essentially of $CaCO_3$ and $Ca(OH)_2$, which is apparently separated by a thermal barrier from parent silicate-rich liquids precipitating either plagioclase feldspar or nepheline. The other is a low temperature liquid which appears on the nepheline joins but not on the albite joins, and which is possibly enriched in soda and silica. The phase fields involved are adjacent to fields including portlandite and calciochondrodite as crystalline phases (Fig. 25) and, by analogy with $CaO-SiO_2-CO_2-H_2O$ (Fig. 11), they may be adjacent also to fields including spurrite and calcite as crystalline phases. This suggests that there might be an alternative crystallization path, by-passing the thermal barrier, which yields residual liquids capable of precipitating calcite, but enriched simultaneously in alkalis and silica. Obviously, much experimental work remains to be completed before these complex phase relationships can be worked out, and before this tentative interpretation can be adequately tested.

Conclusions

Our preliminary conclusion is that parent liquids precipitating plagioclase feldspar in this six-component system cannot yield residual liquids corresponding to carbonatite magmas. However, parent liquids precipitating nepheline might yield low temperature liquids, capable of precipitating calcite, which are simultaneously enriched in alkalis and silica. If these liquids correspond to carbonatite magmas, they are rather different from the $CaCO_3$–$Ca(OH)_2$ compositions which have been described previously as synthetic carbonatite magmas. The liquids involved may exhibit continuous solubility relationships with the vapour phase, and comparable magmas would therefore be transformed continuously into hydrothermal or 'carbothermal' solutions. Solutions of this kind, as well as the vapour phase in other parts of the system, could be responsible for fenitization.

The differences between the phase relationships for compositions involving albite on the one hand, and nepheline on the other hand, confirm the conclusion already apparent from field and petrological studies; namely, that it is the alkaline magmas, undersaturated in silica, which are genetically associated with carbonatites. It would be interesting to determine experimentally the effect of adding nepheline as a 'mineral component' to the system CaO–MgO–SiO_2–CO_2–H_2O (see Fig. 22 and accompanying discussion), but this would produce a seven component system!

The possible development of an alkali-rich residual liquid in the join Ne–$Ca(OH)_2$–H_2O (Fig. 25) leads us to examine the phase relationships in systems containing alkali carbonates as 'mineral components'.

THE SYSTEM CaO–Na_2O–Al_2O_3–SiO_2–CO_2–H_2O: PART II

The effects of excess alkalis on the phase relationships in silicate-carbonate systems are being investigated by studying the phase fields intersected by composition joins through the system CaO–Na_2O–Al_2O_3–SiO_2 (Fig. 23) in the presence of CO_2 and H_2O under pressure. The CO_2 has been added as the 'mineral component' Na_2CO_3, and various percentages of H_2O have been added to mixtures on the join $NaAlSi_3O_8(Ab)$–$CaAl_2Si_2O_8(An)$–Na_2CO_3 (Fig. 26). Preliminary results have been presented orally (Koster van Groos and Wyllie, 1963a), and a brief note has been published (Koster van Groos and Wyllie, 1963b).

Ab–Na_2CO_3–H_2O

The phase fields intersected by this join in the presence of 10 wt% H_2O at 1 kb pressure (Fig. 26) are illustrated in the preliminary Fig. 27. In the presence of excess water at this pressure albite melts at 910°C. Addition of sodium carbonate lowers the saturated liquidus temperature to 730°C, with the solution of about 18 wt% of Na_2CO_3 (expressed in terms of anhydrous components) in the liquid. This liquid quenches to form a homogeneous glass. At temperatures above 750°C (for this pressure and for this composition join) there exists a wide miscibility gap between the silicate liquid (L_1) and a liquid containing at least

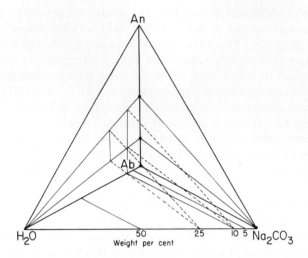

Fig. 26, The system $CaO-Na_2O-Al_2O_3-SiO_2-CO_2-H_2O$. For abbreviations see Table I. Composition joins expressed in terms of the 'mineral components' albite, anorthite and Na_2CO_3, together with various proportions of H_2O.

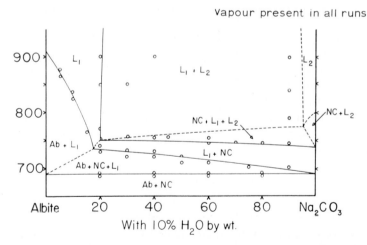

Fig. 27. The system $Na_2O-Al_2O_3-SiO_2-CO_2-H_2O$. For abbreviations see Table I. Preliminary diagram showing the phase fields intersected at 1 kb pressure by the join $Ab-Na_2CO_3$ in the presence of 10 wt% H_2O (see Fig. 26). Cancrinite and noselite are also present in parts of the diagram. Albite is *not* a stable phase right across the diagram: it is replaced by cancrinite.

90 wt % of $Na_2CO_3(L_2)$. The second liquid does not quench to a glass. The solidus temperature is 690°C. The join $Ab-Na_2CO_3-H_2O$ is not a ternary system, because the vapour phase in many parts of the join contains CO_2 as well as H_2O. Phases belonging to the cancrinite family and the noselite family are encountered in parts of the join, but their distribution has not yet been established. The stability field of albite is limited by the cancrinite formation (compare Fig. 29).

Charges quenched from the two-liquid field consist of mixtures of the silicate glass (L_1), and aggregates of sodium carbonate which crystallized from the

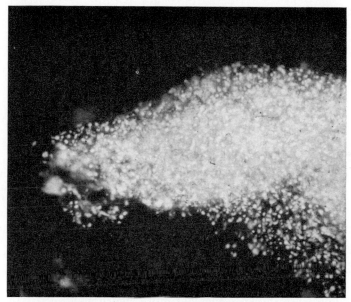

Fig. 28. The system $Na_2O-Al_2O_3-SiO_2-CO_2-H_2O$. Photomicrograph of immersion oil mount of a crushed charge from the field $L_1 + L_2$ in Fig. 27 (nicols crossed). The isotropic silicate glass is crowded with small spheres composed of sodium carbonate crystal aggregates.

carbonate liquid (L_2) during the quench. Partial separation of the two liquids on a gross scale is observed in most runs, and Fig. 28 illustrates the separation of the two liquids on a finer scale. This is a photomicrograph of crushed fragments in immersion oil, with the nicols crossed. The silicate glass is isotropic, but a large glassy fragment is outlined approximately by the distribution of birefringent specks which represent the original globules of carbonate-rich liquid in the silicate liquid. These have crystallized to fine-grained aggregates of sodium carbonate during the quench. Their spherical shape can be seen where their density is least, towards the thin edges of the glass fragment.

$Ab_{80}An_{20}-Na_2CO_3-H_2O$

The phase fields intersected by this join in the presence of 10 wt % H_2O at 1 kb pressure are rather complex, and before considering them in detail the phase relationships are compared with the albite join in Fig. 29, in order to see the major changes produced by the addition of the anorthite component. The two-liquid field is still intersected by the plagioclase join, although it is somewhat narrower, and the fields for the silicate liquid and the carbonate liquid are correspondingly wider. The solidus temperature at the silicate end of the section is hardly changed. The stability field of feldspar, which is shaded, is limited in the plagioclase join by the formation of a cancrinite of unknown composition. Other phases which appear are a mineral with the noselite structure, wollastonite

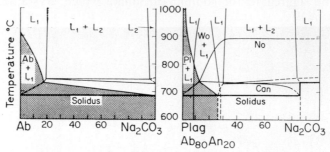

With 10 weight per cent H_2O

Fig. 29. The system $CaO–Na_2O–Al_2O_3–SiO_2–H_2O$. For abbreviations see Table I. Preliminary diagram comparing the phase fields intersected at 1 kb pressure by the composition joins $Ab–Na_2CO_3$ (Fig. 27) and plagioclase $(Ab_{80}An_{20})–Na_2CO_3$ (Fig. 30) in the presence of 10 wt % H_2O (see Fig. 26). Albite or plagioclase feldspar is stable only in the shaded areas. The albite stability field is significantly less extensive than indicated.

and calcite. The distribution of cancrinite and noselite in the albite join has not yet been established, but it is known that albite is *not* stable all the way across the diagram.

The phase fields are shown somewhat more clearly in Fig. 30. In most parts of this composition join the phase relationships can be considered only in terms of the six-component system; for simplicity, therefore, many of the phase fields intersected have not been labelled, and none has been labelled completely. A vapour phase, containing CO_2 as well as H_2O and dissolved solids, is present in all fields. A small proportion of calcite is stable in most fields on the join. Wollastonite appears in small amounts within the boundaries indicated. Cancrinite is abundant below about 725°C across most of the join. This is replaced by the noselite-mineral above the line 'Can' in Fig. 29. The noselite-mineral is stable up to the line at 900°C ('No' in Fig. 29), but its upper temperature stability limit is lowered abruptly in the silicate liquid field, L_1, until it meets the upper boundary for the cancrinite-bearing field.

It is worth emphasizing the fact that the two liquids L_1 and L_2 in Figs. 27, 29 and 30 are true melts. They coexist with a third fluid phase called here a vapour, which is a dense aqueous solution containing some CO_2, a small proportion of dissolved silicate and an unknown proportion of dissolved sodium carbonate. In some parts of the system there may be continuous solubility relationships between a soda-rich liquid and the vapour phase, but in the pressure, temperature and composition range of the present investigation the existence of two liquid phases and a vapour phase appears to be established. This points to the complexities of the phase relationships in natural carbonatite systems, where alkalis may play an important role.

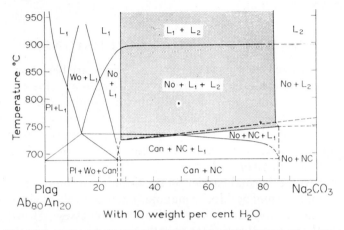

Fig. 30. The system $CaO–Na_2O–Al_2O_3–SiO_2–CO_2–H_2O$. For abbreviations see Table I. Preliminary diagram showing the phase fields intersected at 1 kb pressure by the join plagioclase ($Ab_{80}An_{20}$)–Na_2CO_3 in the presence of 10 wt% H_2O (see Fig. 26). Two liquids coexist only in the shaded area.

In their reference to preliminary data from this plagioclase join, Koster van Groos and Wyllie (1963b) reported that nepheline was one of the new phases produced. This has not been confirmed, but there is now evidence from the join $Ab_{50}An_{50}$–Na_2CO_3 H_2O that nepheline may have a stability field below the solidus.

Conclusions

Although much experimental work remains to be completed in this complex system, the results obtained do draw attention to the possible role of liquid immiscibility in the genesis of carbonatites and associated igneous rocks. It is difficult to understand how a deep-seated primary magma composed largely of alkali carbonates could be generated in the mantle of the earth, and it is difficult to understand how such a magma could persist until it reached a high level in the earth's crust without the occurrence of almost complete reaction with the silicates of the crust. The lava flows composed essentially of carbonates of sodium and calcium which were erupted recently from Oldonyo Lengai in Tanganyika, whatever their origin, managed to reach the surface without becoming contaminated by silicates (Dawson, 1962; this vol. p. 155). An immiscibility relationship between an alkali carbonate magma and the silicates is a possible explanation. Further experimental studies are required to test v. Eckermann's proposal that carbonatite magmas represent an immiscible fraction from a melilite-basalt magma, but at least it has been established that liquid immiscibility does exist between silicate and carbonate melts.

Addition of Na_2CO_3 to hydrated plagioclase feldspar melts appears to produce alkali–alkaline earth exchange reactions of the type predicted by Tomkeieff (1961). Calcite is produced as a primary phase, albeit in small amounts, and there is evidence for the formation of nepheline as well, in the sub-solidus region of the $Ab_{50}An_{50}$ join.

SUMMARY AND CONCLUSIONS

It should be emphasized that many of the conclusions are based on the preliminary experimental data available by October 1963, and they serve only as working hypotheses. In this summary, the experimental results will be extrapolated directly to natural occurrences by using the terms 'silicate magmas' and 'carbonatite magmas' instead of the correct terms 'silicate liquids with compositions approaching those of silicate magmas', and 'liquids with compositions approaching possible carbonatite magmas'.

There is a persistent thermal barrier on the liquidus of the systems investigated which suggests that normal peridotite magmas are incapable of yielding a residual lime-rich carbonatite magma by crystallization processes. However, there is some evidence that crystallization of an alkali peridotite magma might yield a residual alkali-rich carbonatite magma. Carbonatite magmas of this kind may exhibit continuous transition into hydrothermal or 'carbothermal' solutions. These solutions, as well as the vapour phase which may be given off from the magma at higher temperatures, could provide an adequate source of alkalis for fenitization.

Liquid immiscibility exists between some silicate magmas and alkali carbonate magmas, which indicates that the separation of a derivative carbonatite magma as an immiscible liquid fraction from a parent peridotite magma may be possible. This fact also provides support for the hypothesis that a primary alkali carbonate magma could form and persist without significant contamination by silicates until conditions (composition, temperature or pressure) were reached where the immiscibility relationship ceased to exist.

There is some evidence to support the hypothesis that alkali-alkaline earth exchange reactions occurring within peralkaline mafic or ultramafic magmas can yield carbonatite as a precipitate while simultaneously the magma is enriched in feldspathoidal components, but the amount of calcite precipitated in the range of compositions used so far is very small.

Physical conditions for the equilibrium coexistence of alkali feldspars and calcite have not been found, despite the fact that these minerals are associated in some carbonatites. There appears to be little possibility for the coprecipitation of these minerals from a lime-rich carbonatite magma; melts rich in alkali and lime carbonates as well as alkali feldspars have not yet been studied.

Differentiation processes occurring during the crystallization of carbonatite magmas rich in lime, magnesia, and iron could produce the sequence of carbonatite intrusion observed at some carbonatite complexes. Changes in temperature, in pressure, and in external (regional) vapour phase composition may all play an important role in crystallization processes. The composition of the carbonate minerals being precipitated from a carbonatite magma is pressure dependent: for many initial compositions, low pressures favour the development of carbonatites rich in calcite, and increasing pressure tends to favour the formation of dolomite or ankerite, with siderite forming only at the highest pressures. Crystallization differentiation in magmatic carbonatites provides a ready explanation for the development of bands and lenses of carbonatite rich in apatite.

Finally, it may be concluded that although the experimental data described in this chapter cannot be used to prove that any particular petrological process does occur, they do confirm that many of the features observed in carbonatite complexes can be explained in terms of carbonatite magmas, and they confirm that many processes and products are possible during the development and crystallization of carbonatite magmas. The geological history of an alkaline complex containing carbonatites is undoubtedly complicated, probably with different processes occurring simultaneously and in succession. Repeated intrusions of a fluid, reactive, volatile-charged carbonatite magma may be followed by differentiation, the action of vapours and solutions given off by the crystallizing carbonatite or emanating from greater depths, metasomatism occurring within and around the complex, and the development of explosion breccias with concomitant changes in pressure on the magma at greater depth. Superimposed on the effects of these processes may be the effects of remobilization, plastic flow, later metamorphism, shearing and recrystallization. Reconstruction of the history of each carbonatite complex is the responsibility of the geologists studying them in the field, and the function of the experimental petrologists is to provide a foundation of reasonable possibilities for sound reconstruction, and to test where possible, the hypotheses which are made. The results outlined in this chapter have taken a few steps in this direction.

REFERENCES

Biggar, G. M., 1962, High pressure–high temperature phase equilibrium studies in the system $CaO–CaF_2–P_2O_5–H_2O–CO_2$ with special reference to the apatites: Ph.D. dissertation, Leeds University, England.

Biggar, G. M. and Wyllie, P. J., 1962, Solid–liquid–vapour phase relationships at high pressures in parts of the system $CaO–CaF_2–CO_2–H_2O–P_2O_5$ [Abstract]: *Jour. Geophys. Res.*, v. **67**, pp. 3542–3543,

Dawson, J. B., 1962, The geology of Oldoinyo Lengai: *Bull. volcanol.*, v. **24**, pp. 349–387.

v. Eckermann, H., 1948, The alkaline district of Alnö Island: *Sverig. Geol. Undersök. Ser. Ca*, No. **36**.

Franz, G. W. and Wyllie, P. J., 1963, Phase relationships in portions of the joins $Mg_2SiO_4–Ca(OH)_2$ and $MgSiO_3–Ca(OH)_2$ at 1 kilobar pressure [Abstract]: *Interim Proc. Geol. Soc. America, Ann. Meeting, New York*.

French, B. M. and Eugster, H. P., 1963, Stability of siderite, $FeCO_3$ [Abstract]: *Geol. Soc. America Spec. Paper* **73**, p. 155.

Gittins, J. and Tuttle, O. F., 1964, The system $CaF_2–Ca(OH)_2–CaCO_3$: *Am. Jour. Sci.*, v. **262**, pp. 66–75.

Goldsmith, J. R. and Heard, H. C., 1961, Sub-solidus phase relationships in the system $CaCO_3–MgCO_3$: *Jour. Geology*, v. **69**, pp. 45–74.

Haas, J. L. and Wyllie, P. J., 1963, The system $CaO–SiO_2–CO_2–H_2O$. I. Melting relationships in the presence of excess vapour [Abstract]: *Am. Geophys. Union Trans.*, v. **44**, p. 117.

Harker, R. I., 1959, The synthesis and stability of tilleyite, $Ca_5Si_2O_7(CO_3)_2$: *Am. Jour. Sci.*, v. **257**, pp. 656–667.

Harker, R. I. and Tuttle, O. F., 1955, Studies in the system $CaO–MgO–CO_2$. Part I. The thermal dissociation of calcite, dolomite and magnesite: *Am. Jour. Sci.*, v. **253**, pp. 209–224.

Harker, R. I. and Tuttle, O. F., 1956, Experimental data on the P_{CO2}–T curve for the reaction: calcite + quartz = wollastonite + carbon dioxide: *Am. Jour. Sci.*, v. **254**, pp. 239–256.

Harker, R. I. and Tuttle, O. F., 1957, Synthesis of spurrite and the reaction wollastonite + calcite spurrite + carbon dioxide: *Am. Jour. Sci.*, v. **255**, pp. 226–234.

Koster van Groos, A. F. and Wyllie, P. J., 1963a, The system $CaO–Na_2O–Al_2O_3–SiO_2–CO_2–H_2O$. II. The join $NaAlSi_3O_8–Na_2CO_3–H_2O$ (10 weight%) [Abstract]: *Am. Geophys. Union Trans.*, v. **44**, p. 117.

Koster van Groos, A. F. and Wyllie, P. J., 1963b, Experimental data bearing on the role of liquid immiscibility in the genesis of carbonatites: *Nature*, v. **199**, pp. 801–802.

Roy, D. M., 1958, The system $CaO–Al_2O_3–SiO_2–H_2O$. IV. Phase equilibria in the high-lime portion of the system $CaO–SiO_2–H_2O$: *Am. Mineralogist*, v. **43**, pp. 1009–1028.

Roy, D. M. and Roy, R., 1957, A re-determination of equilibria in the system $MgO–H_2O$ and comments on earlier work: *Am. Jour. Sci.*, v. **255**, pp. 574–583.

Tomkeieff, S. I., 1961, Alkalic ultrabasic rocks and carbonatites in the U.S.S.R.: *Int. Geol. Rev.*, v. **3**, pp. 739–758.

Walter, L. S., Wyllie, P. J. and Tuttle, O. F., 1962, The system $MgO–CO_2–H_2O$ at high pressures and temperatures: *Jour. Petrology*, v. **3**, pp. 49–64.

Watkinson, D. H. and Wyllie, P. J., 1963, The system $CaO–Na_2O–Al_2O_3–SiO_2–CO_2–H_2O$. I. The joins $NaAlSi_3O_8–Ca(OH)_2–H_2O$ and $NaAlSiO_4–Ca(OH)_2–H_2O$. [Abstract]: *Am. Geophys. Union Trans.*, v. **44**, p. 117.

Wyllie, P. J., 1962, The petrogenic model, an extension of Bowen's petrogenetic grid: *Geol. Mag.*, v. **99**, pp. 558–569.

Wyllie, P. J., Cox, K. G. and Biggar, G. M., 1962, The habit of apatite in synthetic and igneous systems: *Jour. Petrology*, v. **3**, pp. 238–243.

Wyllie, P. J. and Tuttle, O. F., 1960a, The system $CaO–CO_2–H_2O$ and the origin of carbonatites: *Jour. Petrology*, v. **1**, pp. 1–96.

Wyllie, P. J. and Tuttle, O. F., 1960b, Experimental verification for the magmatic origin of carbonatites: *Int. Geol. Gongr.*, *21st sess.*, pt. 13, pp. 310–318.

More recent papers relevant to this chapter may be found in the References at the end of the book under Franz, Franz and Wyllie, Koster van Groos and Wyllie, Watkinson, Wyllie, Wyllie and Biggar, Wyllie and Haas, Wyllie and Raynor.

F. J. KUELLMER, A. P. VISOCKY and O. F. TUTTLE

Preliminary Survey of the System Barite-Calcite-Fluorite at 500 Bars

INTRODUCTION

The present study was the outgrowth of a general discussion of carbonatites, followed by consideration of mineral associations in several New Mexico mining districts. Barite-calcite-fluorite veins in many ore districts are believed to be related in a physico-chemical sense to carbonatite magmas in a manner analogous to the relationship between silicate magmas and quartz, pegmatite, and aplite veins. Thus a study of the melting relations in the system $BaSO_4$–$CaCO_3$–CaF_2 with and without water appeared to be desirable. The addition of water to this system produced dissociation and the system is one of higher order (Ricci, 1951, p. 9) i.e. not quaternary. When water was added as portlandite, however, the system remained quaternary and dissociation was not observed. The following abbreviations will be used: barite (B), calcite (CC), fluorite (CF), portlandite (CH).

EXPERIMENTAL PROCEDURES

The method used follows closely the procedure described in greater detail by Wyllie and Tuttle (1960). Starting materials were 'Baker Analysed' reagent-grade CaF_2 (fluorite), $BaSO_4$ (barite), $Ca(OH)_2$ (portlandite) and $CaCO_3$ (calcite), which were dried by storing in a desiccator, weighed to the desired proportions and mixed in a mechanical shaker. Once the various dry compositions were prepared they were kept in stoppered vials. In general, because the relative humidity in Socorro is so low, no special drying was necessary. Accuracy of the proportions of the materials comprising the dry mixtures is limited primarily by the homogeneity of the mixed product. The consistent results produced by a single sample or adjacent samples and the weighing accuracy suggest that the compositional accuracy was well within 1 per cent.

Those samples containing water were prepared immediately before use by adding a known weight of prepared dry mixture to a capsule containing a known weight of water. Numerous tests were made of the rate of water loss by evapora tion during preparation of a hydrous sample; these demonstrated no appreciable loss during the first fifteen minutes after the opened capsule was filled with water.

353

As the preparation time prior to sealing the capsule was considerably shorter than ten minutes, it is believed that no significant amount of water was lost. Because of the small amount of sample used, the water content of the hydrous compositions has an accuracy of only $\pm$ 3 per cent throughout most of the compositional range, and $\pm$ 5 per cent at a water content greater than 90 per cent or less than 10 per cent.

Samples of known compositions were sealed in gold or platinum capsules which were then placed in a water-filled, pressure vessel (stellite cold-seal bombs; see Tuttle, 1949) and heated to the desired temperature. Temperatures were measured with a chromel-alumel thermocouple and are believed accurate to $\pm$ 5°C. Pressure was attained primarily by expansion of the water during heating with some additional pressure applied by means of a small hand-pump. The pressure of the runs could not be controlled exactly, so that although the pressure was accurate to $\pm$ 100 lb/in^2, runs were made where the pressure deviated from 500 b by as much as 35 b. Presumably the gauge pressure was a close measure of the total pressure on the sample, assuming that the thin-walled collapsible capsule had no appreciable strength. The duration of most runs was from 15 to 20 minutes, after which the pressure vessel was removed from the furnace and quenched by immersion in cold water. During the quenching interval, the pressure returned to atmospheric pressure slightly more rapidly than the bomb temperature reached room temperature, which appears to have caused a minor dissociation of calcite to form portlandite in some of the hydrous runs. Six runs were made at the Pennsylvania State University using equipment which maintained the pressure during the quenching interval, and for another six the pressure was maintained above 275 b by using a two-man quenching technique, in which one person maintained as high a pressure as possible during quenching by vigorous operation of the small hand-pump.

After the runs the samples were examined under the petrographic microscope, with additional verification of the phases by means of x-ray powder diffraction for about twenty five samples. As the liquids present at the temperature and pressure of the run could not be quenched to a glass, textural criteria were used to establish the presence of a liquid phase and to identify the solid phases present. Primary calcite formed small clear rhombohedral-shaped crystals with sharp or subrounded edges and coigns. Many of the calcite crystals displayed a corroded or dusty appearance which, under high magnification, suggests abundant small cavities or gas bubbles at or near the surface of the grain. Barite formed small, clear, euhedral crystals showing a pseudo-hexagonal or rectangular cross-section; most crystals had a small gas cavity at the centre which may have been a centre of nucleation. Fluorite formed round or spheroidal crystals with no development of crystal faces. The presence of liquid, was revealed by a very fine-grained intergrowth of one or more solid phases which in most instances had a dendritic, fibrous, or radial texture. Some of the hydrous runs, in addition, showed a glass. In summary, the textural criteria are identical to that used in distinguishing matrix from phenocrysts in ordinary igneous petrography. Phenocrysts represent the primary solid phase or phases, whereas the matrix represents the primary liquid phase which crystallized during the quench.

TABLE I

Results of quenching experiments on the system: Barite-Calcite-Fluorite at 500 b

Temp. °C	CaCO$_3$	BaSO$_4$	CaF$_2$	Results[a]	Temp. °C	CaCO$_3$	BaSO$_4$	CaF$_2$	Results[a]
1057		70	30	B, L	932	40	25	35	L
,,		65	35	L	,,	40	15	45	CF, L
,,		60	40	CF, L	,,	55		45	CF, L
1047		60	40	CF, L	,,	55	30	15	L
,,		65	35	B, L	,,	62	14	24	L
1040		60	40	CF, L	,,	65	10	25	L
,,		65	35	B, L	,,	65	15	20	CC, L
1035		70	30	B, L	,,	70	5	25	CC, L
1032		55	45	B, CF, L$_t$	,,	70		30	CC, L
,,		65	35	B, CF, L$_t$	,,	60	25	15	CC, L
,,		55	45	B, CF	,,	65	20	15	CC, L
1017	60	40		L	,,	67.5	26	6.5	CC, L
,,	57.5	42.5		B, L	,,	70	25	5	B, CC, L
1012	57.5	42.5		B, L	,,	65	30	5	B, CC, L
,,	60	40		CC, L	,,	60	30	10	CC, L
1007	60	40		B, CC, L$_t$	910	57	5	38	CF, L
,,	55	45		B, CC, L$_t$	,,	54	9	37	CF, L
997	57.5	42.5		B, CC	,,	53	15	32	L
,,	60	40		B, CC	,,	60	5	35	L
957	70		30	L	,,	65	5	30	L
,,	65	10	25	L	,,	62	14	24	L
,,	65	15	20	L	,,	55	25	20	L
,,	60	25	15	L	,,	50	15	35	L
,,	30	35	35	L	,,	40	25	35	CF, L
,,	25	42	33	L	,,	35	30	35	CF, L
,,	23	44	33	L	,,	30	35	35	B, CF, L
,,	35	25	40	CF, L	,,	35.5	35.5	29	B, CF, L
,,	26.5	37	36.5	CF, L	,,	35	40	25	B, L
,,	35	40	25	L	,,	49	35	16	B, L
,,	45	38	17	B, L	,,	45	45	10	B, CC, L
,,	17	43	40	B, CF, L	,,	55	30	15	B, CC, L
,,	17.5	47.5	35	B, CF, L	,,	60	25	15	B, CC, L
,,	20	48	32	B, CF, L	,,	70	20	10	B, CC, L
,,	45	45	10	B, L	,,	65	20	15	B$_t$, CC, L
,,	45	50	5	B, L	,,	75	15	10	CC, L
,,	50	45	5	B, L	,,	50	30	20	B, L
,,	50	47	3	B, CC, L	,,	45	22.5	32.5	CF$_t$, L
,,	53	40	7	B, L	886	65		35	L
,,	55	40	5	B, CC, L	,,	64	2	34	L
,,	65	30	5	CC, L	,,	59.5	11	29.5	L
,,	65	20	15	CC, L	,,	56	13.5	30.5	CF, L
,,	70	15	15	CC, L	,,	51	21	28	L
,,	69	10	21	CC, L	,,	47	24	29	L
,,	75	5	20	CC, L	,,	23.3	23.3	53.4	L
,,	60	35	5	CC, L	,,	39.4	30.3	30.3	CF, L
932	20	55	25	B, CF, L	,,	35	30	35	CF, L
,,	25	42	33	B, CF, L	,,	45	22.5	32.5	CF, L
,,	15	70	15	B, L	,,	50	19	31	CF, L
,,	30	40.1	30	B, L	,,	60	5	35	CF, L
,,	27	37	36	CF, L	,,	60		40	CF, L
,,	35.5	35.5	29	L	,,	70		30	CC, L
,,	35	40	25	B, L	,,	35.5	35.5	29	B, CF, L
,,	35	30	35	L	,,	35	40	25	B, L
,,	45	38	17	B, L	,,	40	35	25	B, L
,,	43	36	21	L	,,	50	30	20	B, L
,,	49	35	16	L	,,	55	25	20	B, CC, L
,,	55	35	10	B, L	,,	57	21.5	21.5	CC, L
,,	10	45	45	B, L	,,	65	20	15	B, CC, L
,,	53	40	7	B, CC, L	,,	70	15	15	CC, L
,,	35	25	40	CF, L	,,	65	15	20	CC, L

Temp. °C	Composition wt.% CaCO₃	BaSO₄	CaF₂	Resultsª	Temp. °C	Composition wt.% CaCO₃	BaSO₄	CaF₂	Resultsª
886	59	17	24	CC, L	861	39.4	30.3	30.3	B, CF, L
„	65	5	30	CC, L	840	69.2	10.3	20.5	CC, L
„	63	4	33	CC, L	„	65	15	20	CC, L
„	45	27.5	27.5	L	„	56.2	13.4	30.4	CC, CF, L
873	60		40	CC, CF, Lt	„	56.4	16.3	27.3	CC, L
867	65		35	CC, CF	„	53.2	20.4	26.4	L
861	63	4	33	CC, CF, L	„	51	21	28	CF, L
„	61	8	31	CC, L	„	47	24	29	CF, L
„	59.5	11	29.5	CC, L	„	45	27.5	27.5	B, CF, L
„	60	5	35	CC, CF, L	„	43	36	21	B, L
„	56	13.5	30.5	CF, L	„	48	27.5	24.5	B, L
„	55	12.5	32.5	CF, L	„	53.4	23.3	23.3	B. CC, L
„	53.2	20.4	26.4	L	„	49	25	26	L
„	51	21	28	CF, L	„	45	30	25	B, CF, L
„	53.4	23.3	23.3	L	830	53	18	29	CC. CF. L
„	48	27.5	24.5	B, L	„	56.4	16.3	27.3	CC, CF, L
„	45	27.5	27.5	L	„	53.2	20.4	26.4	CC, L
„	58.4	17.2	24.4	CC, L	„	51	21	28	CF, L
„	70	5	25	CC, L	„	47	24	29	CF, L
„	65	15	20	CC, L	„	47	25.5	27.5	B CF L
„	70	15	15	CC, L	„	51	26	23	B. CC, L
„	55	25	20	B, CC, L	„	53.4	23.3	23.3	B. CC, L
„	50	30	20	B, CC, L	„	48	27.5	24.5	B, L
„	43	36	21	B, L	828	53.2	20.4	26.4	CC, L
„	40	35	25	B, L	818	53.2	20.4	26.4	CC, B, CF
„	35	40	25	B, CF, L	812	53.2	20.4	26.4	CC, B. CF
„	40	25	35	CF, L	808	53.2	20.4	26.4	CC, B, CF
„	35	25	40	CF, L					

ª B = barite, CC = calcite, CF = fluorite, L = liquid, t = trace

The total number of experimental determinations was more than 400. Most of the prepared mixes have compositions which lie within that part of the ternary diagram (Fig. 1) covered by the solid-line isotherms. The total number of prepared compositions is about 140, spread out at 5 per cent intervals through the central part of the ternary diagram, except that near the eutectic and towards the calcite apex many of the mixes are separated by a 2.5 per cent compositional interval. The maximum temperature attained was 1057°C. All the dashed isotherms in Fig. 1 are schematic.

EXPERIMENTAL DATA

The system Barite-Calcite-Fluorite

Experimental data on the anhydrous system are presented in Table I and illustrated in Fig. 1. In a strict sense this system is not ternary at high temperatures in compositions near calcite because of the incongruent decomposition of calcite. Such decomposition does not appear to be important for the barite and fluorite components, but if it were, it would increase the number of components needed to describe the system. Dissociation was not a problem in the present study because a vapour phase did not appear on the liquidus near the ternary eutectic nor along any of the field boundaries leading to the binary eutectics.

The melting points for the end members of the ternary diagram (Fig. 1) were not determined for this investigation but are taken from data of Silverman, Morey and Rossini (1943) for fluorite and barite, and from Wyllie and Tuttle (1960, p. 36) in which the *PT* curves allow one to estimate the incongruent melting of calcite at 500 b. The melting points used for barite and fluorite are uncorrected for pressure differences. None of these, however, will affect that part of the ternary diagram containing the solid-line isotherms.

With the foregoing limitations in mind, the melting relations are those of a simple ternary eutectic system with no detectable solid solution of the end

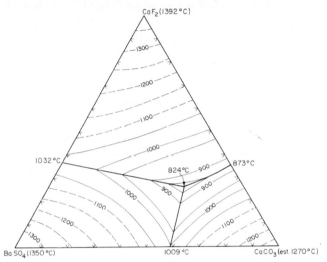

Fig. 1. Ternary isobaric diagram for the system barite-calcite-fluorite at 500 b. The dashed isotherms represent interpolations between the experimental data and the estimated melting points of the pure end-members. The ternary eutectic temperature is 824°C.

members. Barite, calcite and fluorite were the only primary solid phases identified under the microscope. X-ray study of the products revealed that all discernible reflections are a result of nothing other than barite, calcite or fluorite and that the various spacings are identical, within the limits of error, to those of the original starting materials. Several of the most intense aragonite reflections were noted in powder films of the more $CaCO_3$-rich mixes but were completely absent in the same compositions after the runs.

TABLE II

Eutectic temperatures and compositions located within the system:
Barite-Calcite-Fluorite at 500 b

Temp. °C	Composition wt. %			Symbol Fig. 3
	barite	calcite	fluorite	
824	22.0	52.0	26.0	E_1
1009	41.0	59.0	0	e_3
873	0	64.5	35.5	e_1
1032	63.0	0	37.0	e_2

The temperature and composition of the binary eutectics, and the ternary eutectic are given in Table II. Note that the binary eutectic (Fig. 1) along the calcite-fluorite join is only about 50°C higher than the ternary eutectic.

Crystal settling was a common feature of many of the charges. As would be expected, the effectiveness of the gravitational differentiation of primary solid phases and liquid is proportional to the relative densities of the various solids. Barite, in most runs, was concentrated at the bottom of the charge. In runs containing only barite and a large proportion of liquid, fractionation was so extreme that careless sampling of the products could easily have led to errors in identification. Fluorite showed a lesser tendency to accumulate by gravity settling; this effect was most marked in charges in which fluorite was the primary phase. Calcite showed no evidence of gravitational concentration, but showed a very marked tendency to form large crystals.

Effect of adding water

The addition of water to the system at 500 b total pressure lowers the temperature of beginning of melting drastically, but a vapour phase is produced giving five phases: barite, calcite, fluorite, liquid and vapour. As this assemblage was

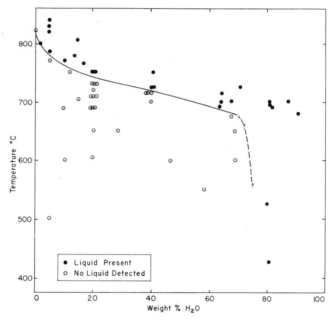

Fig. 2. Effect of adding water to the B–CC–CF system. The approximate temperature at which a liquid phase first appears as a result of dissociation, plotted as a function of water content. This is not a binary system.

observed over a range of temperatures at this pressure the system cannot be quaternary. Five phases in a quaternary system are univariant and should coexist at one temperature only for a given pressure. Experimental evidence is thus conclusive that the system is of higher order (Ricci, 1951, p. 9).

TABLE III

Results of quenching experiments on the system: Barite-Calcite-Fluorite-Portlandite at 500 b

Temp. °C	$CaCO_3$	$BaSO_4$	CaF_2	$Ca(OH)_2$	Results[a]
800		30		70	L
775		30		70	B, L
,,		25		75	L
,,		20		80	CH, L
760		30		70	B, CH
,,		25		75	B, CH
,,		20		80	B, CH
700			30	70	CH, L
700			35	65	CF, L
690			30	70	CH, L
690			35	65	CF, L
685			10	90	CH, L, CFt
684			26	74	CF, CH, L
684			35	65	CF, CH, L
680			30	70	CF, CH
670	45			55	L
660	45			55	L
660	50			50	CC, L
,,	40			60	CH, L
650	45			55	CC, CH
680		10	25	65	CH, L
,,		10	30	60	CF, L
,,		15	20	65	B, CH, L
,,		15	25	60	L
,,		15	30	55	CF, L
,,		20	20	60	B, CH, L
,,		20	25	55	B, L
,,		20	30	50	B, CF, L
,,		25	25	50	B, CF, L
,,		25	20	55	B, L
,,		30	15	55	B, CH, L
670		10	25	65	CF, CH, L
,,		10	30	60	CF, CH, L
,,		15	25	60	B, CH, L
,,		15	30	55	CF, L
,,		20	25	55	B. L
,,		30	20	50	B, CH, L
660		15	25	60	B, CF, CH
650	35	10		55	CH, L
,,	35	15		50	B, CH, L
,,	35	20		45	B. L
,,	40	10		50	CH, L
,,	40	13		43	B, L
,,	40	20		40	B, CC, L
,,	45	5		50	CC, L
,,	45	10		45	CC, L
,,	45	15		40	B, CC, L
640	35	10		55	CC, CH, L
,,	35	15		50	B, CH, L
,,	35	20		45	B, L
,,	35	25		40	B, L
,,	40	20		40	B, CC, L
,,	40	15		45	B, L, CC
,,	40	10		50	CC, CH, L
,,	45	5		50	CC, CH, L
,,	45	10		45	CC, CH, L
,,	45	15		40	CC, B, L
635	40	15		45	CC, B, CH
600	35		25	40	CC, CF, L
,,	30		25	45	CF, CH, L
600	45		20	35	CC, CF, L
,,	40		20	40	CC, CF, L
,,	35		20	45	CF, L
,,	30		20	50	CF, CH, L
,,	45		15	40	CC, L
,,	40		15	45	CC, L
,,	35		15	50	CH, L
,,	30		15	55	CH, L
,,	40		10	50	CC, CH, L
,,	35		10	55	CC, CH, L
590	45		15	40	CC, L
,,	40		15	45	CC, CHt, L
585	30		15	55	CC, CH, L
,,	35		15	50	CC, CH, L
,,	40		15	45	CC, CH, L
,,	45		15	40	CC, L
580	45		15	40	CC, CF, CH
575	35		20	45	CC, CF, CH
590	40	10	10	40	B, CC, CH, L
590	30	10	20	40	B, CF, CH, L
585	31	12	17	40	B, CF, CH, L
,,	25	10	25	40	B, CF, CH, L
,,	25	25	10	40	B, CC, CH, L
,,	35	10	15	40	B, CC, CH, L
,,	25	5	30	40	CF, CH, L
,,	33	6	21	40	CF, CH, L
,,	37	6	18	39	CC, CF, L
,,	33	9	18	40	B, CF, CH, L
,,	33	12	15	40	B, CH, L
,,	36	3	21	40	CC, CF, CH, L
,,	39	3	18	40	CC, CF, CH, L
,,	39	6	15	40	CC, L
,,	42	6	12	40	B, CC, CH, L
,,	35	8	17	40	B, CC, CF, L
595	33	8	14	45	B, CH, L
,,	36	5	14	45	CH, L
,,	30	11	14	45	B, CH, L
,,	30	8	17	45	B, CH, L
,,	30	6	19	45	CF, CH, L
,,	34	6	15	45	CH, CFt, L
,,	32	7	16	45	CH, CFt, L
,,	29	8	18	45	CF, CH, L
,,	33	11	11	45	B, CC, CH, L
,,	36	8	11	45	B, CC, CH, L
,,	38	6	11	45	CC, CH, L
590	28	11	16	45	CF, B, CH, L
585	33	6	16	45	CF, CC, CH, L
,,	33	8	14	45	B, CF, CH, L
,,	34	6	15	45	CF, CC, CH, L
,,	36	5	14	45	CC, CH, L
,,	32	7	16	45	B, CF, CH, L
,,	31	9	15	45	B, CF, CH, L
,,	33	11	11	45	B, CC, CH, L
,,	38	6	11	45	CC, CH, L
,,	36	8	11	45	B, CC, CH, L
580	34	6	15	45	B, CC, CH, L, CFt
578	36	8	11	45	B, CC, CH, L
575	36	8	11	45	B, CC, CF, CH
570	36	8	11	45	B, CC, CF, CH

[a] B = barite, CC = calcite, CF = fluorite, CH = portlandite, L = liquid, and t = trace

As experimental investigations of the phase relations in a five or six component system are prohibitively difficult, no attempt was made to study the system in detail. However, some observations of geological interest were made. Addition of water produces no textural changes in the primary solid phases. Grain size and habit remain the same in the wet or dry systems. If 20% water is added to a mixture near the ternary eutectic the quenched runs were observed to contain some liquid at temperatures as low as 750°C (Fig. 2). This same mixture showed no evidence of a liquid phase at 730°C. If 40% water is added, liquid could be detected at temperatures as low as 725°C. The addition of 60% water gave runs in which a quenched liquid was observed at 690°C. With 80% water in the runs no lower temperature limit was found for the existence of quenched liquid. However, the amount of quenched liquid after runs at 80% water and 425°C (the lowest run temperature) was very small. The existence of a liquid as well as a vapour at such low temperatures is probably the result of dissociation of one or

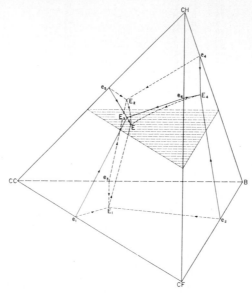

Fig. 3. Isobaric polythermal projection of the B–CC–CF–CH system showing freezing point relations at 500 b. The eutectic points are indicated by
the letter 'E', or 'e' with appropriate subscripts and may be identified by
referring to Tables II and IV. Lines connecting the eutectic points are
schematic boundary curves. The arrows indicate the direction of decreasing temperature. The shaded plane indicates the 42% portlandite plane
which contains the quaternary eutectic point (E).

more of the solid phases making up the mixtures. No primary portlandite was found in any of the hydrous runs. This fact, which accords with data of Wyllie and Tuttle (1960, p. 25, Fig. 8), suggests that dissociation of either fluorite or barite (and most likely barite) may be responsible for the low-temperature liquid phase.

The system Barite-Calcite-Fluorite-Portlandite

When portlandite, $Ca(OH)_2$, is added the system is quaternary except at high temperatures near the calcite apex. No vapour phase appeared in any of the runs made in the quaternary system. Adding portlandite as a fourth component produced three additional binary joins, and three new ternary systems. Data for these systems are listed in Table III and the eutectic compositions and tempera-tures in Table IV. Portlandite formed rounded transparent plates, which con-tained abundant small inclusions or cavities.

The quaternary eutectic is 576°C ($\pm$ 5) and a composition of $B_8CC_{35}CF_{15}CH_{42}$

TABLE IV

Eutectic temperatures and compositions located within the system:
Barite-Calcite-Fluorite-Portlandite at 500 b

Temp. °C	Composition wt.%				Symbol Fig. 3
	barite	calcite	fluorite	portlandite	
765	26	0	0	74	e_1
655	0	45	0	55	e_5
684	0	0	32	68	e_6
637	18	39	0	48	E_2
582	0	34	18	48	E_3
662	14	0	27	59	E_4
576	8	35	15	42	E

(Fig. 3). Comparison of ternary calcite-fluorite-portlandite and quaternary barite-calcite-fluorite-portlandite systems (see E_3 and E in Table IV), shows that the quaternary eutectic temperature is only very slightly lower than the ternary calcite-fluorite-portlandite eutectic. Although the difference is close to the precision of the determinations, samples from both systems which were run simultaneously demonstrate that the 6–10° difference is real and in the expected direction. Further, if the quaternary eutectic composition is recalculated on a barite-free basis, it differs only slightly from that of the ternary calcite-fluorite-portlandite eutectic composition.

Data from Gittins and Tuttle (1964) on the ternary calcite-fluorite-portlandite system at 1000 b may be compared with data here (Table V). Note that the eutectic temperatures given here are slightly higher, except for the calcite-fluorite binary eutectic, and that the ternary eutectic composition is shifted very slightly towards the portlandite apex with no significant change in fluorite content. According to Wyllie and Tuttle (1960) the incongruent melting of calcite and the congruent melting of portlandite should occur at a lower temperature when the pressure decreases from 1000 to 500 b. The slight difference between these two sets of measurements may well be explicable as a result of differences in sample preparation, and in the average relative humidity of Socorro, New Mexico, and State College, Pennsylvania.

TABLE V

Comparison of eutectic temperatures and compositions in the CC–CF–CH system at 500 and 1000 b.

Pressure b	Temp. °C	Composition wt.%			Source
		$CaCO_3$	CaF_2	$Ca(OH)_2$	
500	873	64	36	0	This report
1000	880	64	36	0	Gittins and Tuttle
500	684	0	32	68	This report
1000	670	0	31	69	Gittins and Tuttle
500	655	45	0	55	This report
1000	653	44	0	56	Gittins and Tuttle
500	582	34	18	48	This report
1000	575	38	17	45	Gittins and Tuttle

Above 600°C an unidentified phase appeared with the quenched liquid. It was not found in runs made at temperatures below the quaternary eutectic. The properties are: a habit and appearance similar to primary portlandite, a higher interference colour than portlandite basal plates (first order red in contrast to isotropy), one index of refraction is about 1.545, and another is 1.540 (estimated). Because of its habit and index it may be a barium oxide hydrate or a solid solution intermediate between portlandite and some barium oxide compound. Inasmuch as this phase is not found at or below the eutectic temperature, and all known barium oxides (hydrated) melt at lower temperatures, it is believed to represent a quenched liquid rather than a primary phase. Further study to identify this phase is in progress.

Although the barite-calcite-fluorite-water system is extremely complex and not completely understood, an interesting comparison may be made between the effect of adding H_2O rather than $Ca(OH)_2$ to the anhydrous system. Both lower the minimum temperature at which a liquid may exist. The addition of portlandite to the system does not produce detectable dissociation and as there is no solid solution, the barite-calcite-fluorite eutectic is lowered in temperature to a quaternary eutectic at 576°C. By adding water, dissociation occurs, the number of components is increased, and the temperature at which a liquid first appears may range over a four hundred degree interval.

GEOLOGICAL CONSIDERATIONS

Perhaps the most important feature of the experimental study is the relatively low temperature at which a liquid can coexist with calcite, barite or fluorite— at least 300° below the beginning of melting of granite at 500 b pressure and about 200° below the beginning of melting in the system $CaO–H_2O–CO_2$. This temperature is well within the range believed to be representative of the carbonatites and their lavas. The addition of alkalis will lower the temperature of the beginning of melting drastically and because of the high solubility of alkali carbonates in water at atmospheric pressure and room temperature it is very probable that liquids carrying a high concentration of calcite, barite and fluorite could exist at all temperatures between the quaternary eutectic temperature and room temperature. In other words, we may expect to have all gradations between carbonatite magmas and carbonatite hydrothermal solutions, in one case producing carbonatite dikes and in the other producing calcite-barite-fluorite veins.

Examples of dikes of barite-calcite-fluorite have been described by v. Eckermann from the Alnö district (1948, p. 82). The dikes range in thickness from one to three metres with a central core rich in barite while the outer margins (about 10 cm width) contain 40% barite, 40% calcite and 20% fluorite. The proportions of barite, calcite and fluorite are not constant but this is not surprising considering the low viscosity of the melts. In the experimental study barite always settled to the bottom of the charge when there was appreciable liquid present. Fluorite also commonly segregated at the bottom of the charge.

There is little doubt of the magmatic origin of the barite and fluorite-bearing cone sheets of the Alnö region of Sweden. The dikes have been described in detail by v. Eckermann (1958) and have many features characteristic of magmatic dikes including 'sometimes almost glassy chilled contacts' (v. Eckermann, 1958, p. 51). The dikes also have well developed flow banding with acicular crystals aligned parallel to the flow direction. The barite and fluorite content of the dikes is highly variable; one analysed fluorite-bearing dike has a calculated modal analysis with 81.9% fluorite and a barite-rich dike has a central zone containing 96.6–99.6% modal barite. The present authors suggest that the variable fluorite and barite content of the dikes is a result of gravitational differentiation in the highly fluid carbonatite magma.

Although barite-calcite-fluorite assemblages may be found as dikes intimately associated with carbonatites and may owe their origin to magmatic processes, the common occurrence of this assemblage is as low temperature vein fillings undoubtedly representing hydrothermal emplacement. Is there any relation between the dikes and veins? Do they have a common carbonatite parent?

In some districts the mineralogy of barite-calcite-fluorite vein deposits is similar to carbonatite assemblages. For example, the Gallinas bastnaesite deposit in New Mexico carries abundant barite, fluorite and calcite (Griswold, 1959). Here the rare earth content strongly suggests carbonatite affinities although the deposit has many characteristics of hydrothermal emplacement. At Mountain Pass, California (Olson, *et al.*, 1954) there are associated veins which probably represent hydrothermal introduction of barite, calcite and fluorite, but the main bastnaesite deposit has carbonatite mineralogy and may well represent magmatic emplacement.

In the Hansonburg District, Socorro County, New Mexico (Kottlowski, 1953; Kopicki, 1962), on the other hand, the hydrothermal veins of barite, calcite and fluorite have no associated rare earth minerals which would suggest carbonatite affinity. Fluorspar deposits of the south-east Zuni Mountains, New Mexico (Rothrock, *et al.*, 1946, p. 178) as well as numerous other barite-fluorite occurrences (Clippinger, 1949) commonly have a barite-calcite-fluorite assemblage along with other minerals of hydrothermal origin. On the basis of the experimental data, such hydrothermal veins should not differ fundamentally from magmatic carbonatites, and yet the rare earth content suggests a completely different origin. One might suggest a deep-seated origin and differentiation process for normal carbonatites, and a local melting of calcareous sediments by Tertiary porphyries to produce the abundant barite-calcite-fluorite vein assemblages. Unfortunately when most field occurrences of barite-calcite-fluorite assemblages were being studied, little credence was given to the magmatic origin of carbonatites. Further, many of the barite-calcite-fluorite assemblages in New Mexico occur in regions of minor alkaline intrusions, which also have received little petrographic study. Additional work now in progress may contribute to a better understanding of these relationships.

SUMMARY

Disregarding the incongruent melting of calcite, the melting relations of barite-calcite-fluorite at 500 b are those of a simple ternary eutectic system. Binary eutectics were found at $1032°C$ ($B_{63}CF_{37}$ weight percent), $1009°C$ ($B_{41}CC_{59}$), and $873°C$ ($CC_{64.5}CF_{35.5}$). The ternary eutectic is at $824°C$ with a composition of $B_{22}CC_{52}CF_{26}$. Adding water to the system lowers the barite-calcite-fluorite eutectic but because of dissociation, presumably in the liquid and vapour phases, the system is not quaternary. A quench phase indicating melting has been observed at temperatures as low as $425°C$ in water-rich mixtures.

The addition of water as $Ca(OH)_2$, (portlandite) to this system generates a univariant curve which originates at the ternary $B_{22}CC_{52}CF_{26}$ isobaric eutectic and moves into the quaternary system where it terminates at a quaternary isobaric eutectic at the composition $B_8CC_{35}CF_{15}CH_{12}$ at $576°C$. In connection with the study of this quaternary system the following binary eutectics were found: $CC_{45}CH_{55}$ at $655°C$; $CF_{32}CH_{68}$ at $684°C$; and $B_{26}CH_{74}$ at $765°C$. Ternary eutectics were also found at $B_{18}CC_{39}CH_{48}$ at $637°C$; $CC_{34}CF_{18}CH_{48}$ at $582°C$; and $B_{14}CF_{27}CH_{59}$ at $662°C$.

Melting relations within this system provide additional verification for the magmatic origin of carbonatites. A variable volatile content accompanied by fractional crystallization could have a considerable effect on the paragenetic sequence of many barite-calcite-fluorite dikes associated with carbonatites as well as hydrothermal veins containing barite, calcite and fluorite.

REFERENCES

Clippinger, D. M., 1949, Barite of New Mexico: *New Mex. Bur. Mines and Min. Res.*, *Circ.* **21**.

v. Eckermann, H., 1948, The alkaline district of Alnö Island: *Severig. Geol. Undersök. Ser. Ca*, No. **36**.

v. Eckermann, H., 1958, The alkaline and carbonatitic dikes of the Alnö formation on the mainland north-west of Alnö Island: *Kungl. Vetenskap Akademiens Handl., Fjörde serien.*, v. **7**.

Gittins, J. and Tuttle, O. F., 1964, The system CuF_2–$CaCO_3$–$Ca(OH)_2$ at 1000b: *Am. Jour. Sci.*, v. **262**, pp. 66–75.

Griswold, G. B., 1959, The Mineral deposits of Lincoln County, New Mexico: *New Mex. Bur. Mines and Min. Res., Bull.* **67**.

Kopicki, R. J., 1962, Geology and ore deposits of the northern part of the Hansonburg District, Bingham, New Mexico: *M. S. Thesis, New. Mex. Inst. Min. and Tech.*

Kottlowski, F. E., 1953, Geology and ore deposits of a part of the Hansonburg Mining District, Socorro County, New Mexico: *New Mex. Bur. Mines and Min. Res., Circ.* **23**.

Olson, J. C., Shawe, D. R., Pray, L. C. and Sharp, W. N., 1954, Rare earth mineral deposits of the Mountain Pass District, San Bernardino Co., California: *U.S. Geol. Surv., Prof. Paper* **261**.

Ricci, J. E., 1951, The phase rule and heterogeneous equilibrium: *New York, D. Van Nostrand Co.*

Rothrock, H. E., Johnson, C. H. and Hahn, A. D., 1946, Fluorspar resources of New Mexico: *New Mex. Bur. Mines and Min. Res., Bull.* **21**.

Silverman, A., Morey, G. W. and Rossini, F. D., 1943, Data on Chemicals for Ceramic use: *Bull. Nat. Research Council*, No. **107**.

Tuttle, O. F., 1949, Two pressure vessels for silicate–water studies: *Geol. Soc. Am. Bull.*, v. **60**, p. 1727.

Wyllie, P. J. and Tuttle, O. F., 1960, The system CaO–CO_2–H_2O and the origin of carbonatites: *Jour. Petrology*, v. **1**, pp. 1–46.

J. L. POWELL, P. M. HURLEY and H. W. FAIRBAIRN

The Strontium Isotopic Composition and Origin of Carbonatites[1]

INTRODUCTION

Recent developments in isotope geology indicate that certain radiogenic isotopes such as ^{87}Sr can be used as tracers in geologic processes. In the present investigation this concept is applied to the origin of carbonatites. Previous reports of the isotopic composition of strontium in carbonatites include a summary account of this work (Powell, Hurley and Fairbairn, 1962) and an article by Hamilton and Deans (1963) dealing with carbonatites from Africa.

Strontium possesses four naturally occurring stable isotopes of mass 84, 86, 87 and 88. ^{87}Sr is also the daughter of ^{87}Rb. Therefore the abundance of ^{87}Sr, expressed by the $^{87}Sr/^{86}Sr$ ratio, increases in any system containing rubidium in proportion to the Rb/Sr ratio of the system.

Faure and Hurley (1963) have shown that the $^{87}Sr/^{86}Sr$ ratio in the source regions of basalt magma is relatively constant. They found the $^{87}Sr/^{86}Sr$ ratios of 25 basalts to vary from approximately 0.702 to 0.707. Rocks usually found in the sial, including sedimentary carbonate rocks, in general have higher $^{87}Sr/^{86}Sr$ ratios (Gast, 1960; Faure and Hurley, 1963). If carbonatites are xenoliths of limestone their $^{87}Sr/^{86}Sr$ ratios, if not altered by diffusion of ^{87}Sr, should resemble those of limestones. If the rocks of the carbonatite-alkalic rock association are formed by partial melting of sialic material, their $^{87}Sr/^{86}Sr$ ratios should be higher than those of basalts. If, on the other hand, they are derived from the same source region as basalt magma their $^{87}Sr/^{86}Sr$ ratios should fall within the basalt range. In addition, if carbonatites are comagmatic with the alkalic rocks with which they occur the $^{87}Sr/^{86}Sr$ ratios of the carbonatites from individual complexes will be identical to those of the associated alkalic rocks.

EXPERIMENTAL METHOD

The experimental techniques have been described in detail by Powell (1962) and are similar to those reported by Faure and Hurley (1963). A brief description of the method follows.

Whole-rock samples were ground either in a pre-contaminated steel percussion mortar or in a Pica Blender Mill and 0.5–1 gm taken for analysis. Carbonate

[1] M.I.T. Age Studies No. 40.

samples were dissolved in pyrex beakers with $2N$ vycor-distilled HCl; silicate samples were dissolved in platinum dishes with a 2.5:1 mixture of HF and $HClO_4$. Strontium was separated on an ion exchange column with Dowex 50W–X8 resin and $2N$ vycor-distilled HCl as the eluant. The progress of strontium on the column was monitored by the addition of a small amount of radioactive ^{85}Sr to the sample. In most cases the carbonate rocks and calcium-rich silicate rocks were passed through the ion-exchange column twice to insure adequate separation of strontium from calcium. Two blank runs gave an average of 0.26 μgm of strontium per analysis. Since carbonatites contain an average of from 0.5–2% strontium oxide by weight (Pecora, 1956) this blank is insignificant.

Samples were mounted as strontium nitrate on tantalum filaments that had previously been heated in the mass spectrometer until they were observed to be free from rubidium and strontium at a temperature higher than that to be employed during the run. The instrument used is a 6-in radius, 60° sector mass spectrometer employing a single-filament surface ionization source, magnetic sweeping, a single collector and a vibrating reed electrometer. Operating pressures were in general less than 4×10^{-6} mm Hg.

When stable strontium emission had been obtained and no ^{85}Rb peak was visible, over 70 consecutive scans of the strontium mass range were recorded. The intensity of strontium emission generally increased throughout the course of the run. The position of the base line for each scan was checked by allowing the instrument to sweep below the ^{86}Sr peak and above the ^{88}Sr peak. After the run had been completed base lines were drawn and the peak heights measured to the nearest 0.01 in. The peak heights were summed in sets of six and isotopic ratios calculated for each set. The final average ratios were calculated from the individual ratios of each set. An instrumental precision error in the form of the standard deviation of the mean $^{87}Sr/^{86}Sr$ ratio was calculated from the isotopic ratios obtained from each set of six scans and was used to judge the relative quality of each run. For the analyses reported herein the instrumental precision error varies from 0.04%–0.12%.

In this work the ratio of $^{86}Sr/^{88}Sr$ was assumed to be constant, and in any measurement the deviation of the recorded ratio of $^{86}Sr/^{88}Sr$ from this constant was used to normalize the recorded value of $^{87}Sr/^{86}Sr$. The value assumed for the ratio of $^{86}Sr/^{88}Sr$ was 0.1194, which was the average found for the instrument described above during the period in which the analyses reported here were made. The effectiveness of this process of normalization in reducing experimental error has been demonstrated by Faure and Hurley (1963).

Periodic analyses of a standard strontium carbonate reagent produced by Eimer and Amend Chemicals (lot 492327) permitted comparison of our results with those of other laboratories and enabled us to calculate the precision of the analytical technique. The results of these analyses are compared in Table I with those reported by other investigators.

The $^{87}Sr/^{86}Sr$ ratio of the standard which we obtained is about 0.003 units higher than the value more recently reported by Hurley, *et al.* (1963). Re-analysis with improved instrumentation of certain of the carbonatite samples confirms that the $^{87}Sr/^{86}Sr$ ratios which we measured differed systematically from the true values by an amount which was constant within the analytical precision. Therefore a correction of $- 0.0030$ has been applied to each of the $^{87}Sr/^{86}Sr$ ratios. These values supersede those previously reported by Powell, Hurley and Fairbairn (1962). An identical correction has been applied with the authors' consent to the data reported by Faure and Hurley (1963) to which frequent reference is made. It should be emphasized that since the conclusions reported here are based on differences between the $^{87}Sr/^{86}Sr$ ratios of certain rock types and not on the absolute values of individual isotopic ratios they are unaffected by this correction.

TABLE I

Isotopic composition of strontium in reagents manufactured by Eimer and Amend Chemicals

Material analysed	$^{86}Sr/^{88}Sr$	$^{87}Sr/^{86}Sr$	Reference
Sr metal	0.1194 ± 0.0012	0.712 ± 0.007	Nier, 1938, p. 277
SrCO$_3$. Average of 6 analyses	0.1195 ± 0.0003	0.711 ± 0.004	Aldrich, *et al.*, 1953, p. 458
SrCO$_3$, lot 492327	0.1196	0.712	Herzog, *et al.*, 1953, p. 462
SrCO$_3$, lot 492327 Average of 18 analyses in 21 months	0.1194 ± 0.0001	0.7116 ± 0.0004[a]	This work
SrCO$_3$, lot 492327		$0.708-0.709$[a]	Hurley, *et al.*, 1963

[a] Normalized to $^{86}Sr/^{88}Sr = 0.1194$ (see text).

The standard deviation of a single analysis of the $^{87}Sr/^{86}Sr$ ratio calculated from 18 analyses of the standard is ± 0.0015, or about 0.2%. Therefore a conservative estimate of the precision of measurement of the $^{87}Sr/^{86}Sr$ ratio in our work is ± 0.002, or about 0.3%.

RESULTS

Strontium isotopic ratios in sedimentary carbonate rocks

The isotopic composition of strontium in sedimentary carbonate rocks is of particular interest to this investigation. The data are summarized in Table II. With the exception of the very old Bulawayan limestone the $^{87}Sr/^{86}Sr$ ratios in sedimentary carbonate rocks vary from 0.707–0.711. The data of Hamilton and Deans (1963) and Hedge and Walthall (1963) have not been included in Table II because of small differences in the results obtained by the Oxford, U.S. Geological Survey, and M.I.T. groups on an inter-laboratory strontium standard. Inclusion of their data would not in any way affect the conclusions reached in this paper.

Study of a limestone xenolith

In order to interpret correctly the $^{87}Sr/^{86}Sr$ ratios of carbonatites it was necessary to learn whether diffusion of ^{87}Sr can change the ratio of a limestone xenolith to that of the magma which encloses it. If this is possible, the $^{87}Sr/^{86}Sr$ ratios

TABLE II

Isotopic composition of strontium in sedimentary carbonate rocks

Sample number	Rock type and locality	Reference	$^{86}Sr/^{88}Sr$	$(^{87}Sr/^{86}Sr)^a$corr
C4317 C4543	Madison ls., Montana	This work	0.1189	0.7087 ±0.001
C4588	Trenton ls., Que.	This work	0.1196	0.7090 ±0.001
C4583	Grenville marble, nr. Hull, Ont.	This work	0.1195	0.7071 ±0.001
C4815	Ottertail ls., B.C.	This work	0.1192	0.7083 ±0.001
C4874	Dolomite, Transvaal	This work	0.1195	0.7099 ±0.001
	Bulawayan ls., S. Rhodesia	Gast (1960)		0.702 ±0.002
	Grenville marble, Ont.	Gast (1960)		0.707 ±0.002
	Newland ls., Belt series	Gast (1960)		0.707 ±0.002
	Ordovician ls., Texas	Gast (1960)		0.711 ±0.003
	Ordovician ls., Iswos, U.S.S.R.	Herzog and others (1958)	0.1191	0.7097[b] ±0.0015
	Grenville marble	Pinson and others (1958)	0.1195	0.708[b] ±0.002

[a] Normalized to $^{86}Sr/^{88}Sr$ = 0.1194 (see text). Values reported by Gast (1960) were originally normalized to $^{86}Sr/^{88}Sr$ = 0.1186 (Gast, oral communication, 1963).

[b] A correction of − 0.0030 has been applied to the $^{87}Sr/^{86}Sr$ ratios reported.

of carbonate rocks associated with igneous rocks cannot be used to distinguish carbonatites from limestone xenoliths.

The rocks chosen for this study were the Trenton limestone at Montreal, Quebec, and a small xenolith of this limestone enclosed in a gabbro at Mount Royal in Montreal. The xenolith was about 18 by 24 in in size, entirely surrounded by the gabbro, and completely recrystallized. Clark (1952) has shown that the temperature of the Mount Royal intrusion was sufficient to mobilize and recrystallize the Trenton limestone.

Semi-quantitative x-ray fluorescence analyses show that both the xenolith and the gabbro contain several hundred parts per million strontium, and that the gabbro has a strontium concentration approximately twice that of the xenolith. $^{87}Sr/^{86}Sr$ ratios were measured in: (1) a sample of fresh unmetamorphosed Trenton limestone from Westmount in Montreal, (2) a sample from the centre of the xenolith, and (3) a specimen of the gabbro collected about 18 in from the xenolith. The results are given in Table III.

TABLE III

$^{87}Sr/^{86}Sr$ Study of a limestone xenolith

Sample number	Rock type and locality	$^{86}Sr/^{88}Sr$	$^{87}Sr/^{86}Sr$	$(^{87}Sr/^{86}Sr)$corr
C4589a	Xenolith of Trenton ls., Mt. Royal, Que.[a]	0.1198	0.7078	0.7089
C4588	Trenton ls., Montreal, Quebec[a]	0.1193	0.7095	0.7092
R4590b	Gabbro, Mt. Royal,	0.1196	0.7041	0.7047

[a] Average of two analyses.

The Rb/Sr ratios of mafic rocks, carbonate rocks, and alkalic rocks associated with carbonatites are in general very low. Therefore the $^{87}Sr/^{86}Sr$ ratios of these rocks remain nearly constant with time because they are not affected by the decay of ^{87}Rb. Unless otherwise specified, the $^{87}Sr/^{86}Sr$ ratios reported here can be considered to be initial ratios.

This small xenolith, even though subjected to high temperatures, completely recrystallized, and surrounded by a relatively strontium-rich magma with a $^{87}Sr/^{86}Sr$ ratio of approximately 0.705, has preserved the ratio of the Trenton limestone, 0.709. Therefore no measurable diffusion of ^{87}Sr into or out of the xenolith has occurred. If diffusion of ^{87}Sr is negligible in small carbonate xenoliths it seems very unlikely that it could be important in ones the size of carbonatite bodies, which have areas measuring hundreds or thousands of square feet.

Additional experimental evidence in support of this conclusion comes from a study of the Ice River Complex, British Columbia (Powell, 1962) where calcite from a metamorphosed limestone containing abundant silicate minerals has a $^{87}Sr/^{86}Sr$ ratio typical of limestones, 0.708. The igneous rocks of the Complex had initial $^{87}Sr/^{86}Sr$ ratios of approximately 0.704.

The conclusion that the ^{87}Sr in carbonate rocks is relatively immobile is consistent with the fact that the strontium in these rocks is non-radiogenic and occupies calcium or strontium lattice sites.

$^{87}Sr/^{86}Sr$ Ratios in carbonatite-alkalic rock complexes

$^{87}Sr/^{86}Sr$ ratios were measured in both carbonatites and alkalic rocks from several individual complexes. In some cases sedimentary or metamorphic carbonate rocks occurring in the vicinity of the igneous rocks were also analysed. A description of these samples and their sources is given by Powell (1962).

Oka, Quebec

The Oka Complex contains: (1) calcite rock, (2) calcium-rich silicate rocks such as okaite and alnöite, and (3) alkalic rocks, for example, ijolite. It is believed to be part of the Monteregian petrographic province. The calcite rock is considered by some to be altered Grenville marble, although others classify it as a carbonatite.

In order to test these two alternatives the $^{87}Sr/^{86}Sr$ ratios of the calcite rock, the Grenville marble, and some of the silicate rocks of the Oka Complex were measured. The results of these analyses are given in Table IV. An average $^{87}Sr/^{86}Sr$ ratio for Grenville carbonates and celestites was calculated from the data listed in Table II and from those reported by Herzog, *et al.* (1958). A correction of -0.0030 has been applied to the latter.

The difference between the average $^{87}Sr/^{86}Sr$ ratios of the Oka calcite rock and the Grenville rocks is 0.0042 ± 0.0004. Since this difference is several times larger than its standard deviation it is highly significant. On the other hand the $^{87}Sr/^{86}Sr$ ratio of the Oka calcite rock is not measurably different from those of the silicate rocks of the complex. This evidence strongly supports the hypothesis that the Oka calcite rock is a carbonatite and that it is comagmatic with the associated silicate rocks.

TABLE IV

Strontium isotope ratios for the Oka, Quebec Complex

Sample number	Rock type	$^{86}Sr/^{88}Sr$	$^{87}Sr/^{86}Sr$	$(^{87}Sr/^{86}Sr)$ corr
C3252	Calcite rock[a]	0.1195	0.7028	0.7032
C4584				±0.0003 ($\bar{\sigma}$)
R4585	Okaite	0.1196	0.7029	0.7035
R4587	Ijolite	0.1197	0.7021	0.7029
R4586	Alnöite	0.1204	0.7015	0.7044
Average for Oka Complex		0.1198	0.7023	0.7035
	$\bar{\sigma}$		±0.0003	±0.0003
	σ		±0.0007	±0.0007
Average for 5 Grenville				0.7074
carbonates and celestites	$\bar{\sigma}$			±0.0003
	σ			±0.0006

[a] Average of three analyses, two of which were reported by Faure and Hurley (1963).

$$\sigma = \sqrt{\Sigma d^2/n - 1}, \qquad \bar{\sigma} = \sqrt{\Sigma d^2/n(n-1)}.$$

A rubidium-strontium age determination was carried out on a biotite from the Oka calcite rock (Powell, 1962). The initial $^{87}Sr/^{86}Sr$ ratio of the biotite was assumed to be 0.7032, the ratio of the calcite. A Monteregian age of 105 $\pm$ 10 million years was obtained, not a Grenville age of about 1 billion years. An earlier potassium-argon age determination on this same biotite sample had given 95 million years (Hurley, *et al.*, 1960, p. 283). The fact that concordant ages are obtained by the two methods verifies the assumption that the initial $^{87}Sr/^{86}Sr$ ratios of the calcite and the biotite were identical. This result in turn indicates that the calcite and biotite crystallized from a common magma about 100 million years ago.

Magnet Cove, Arkansas

This complex consists of a core of calcite rock surrounded by mafic and felsic feldspathoid-bearing rocks. Landes (1931), Daly (1933) and Shand (1950) considered the calcite rock to be a xenolith of limestone, although others believe it to be a carbonatite. The strontium isotopic ratios of several rocks from the complex are reported in Table V.

TABLE V

Strontium isotope ratios for the Magnet Cove, Arkansas Complex

Sample number	Rock type	$^{86}Sr/^{88}Sr$	$^{87}Sr/^{86}Sr$	$(^{87}Sr/^{86}Sr)$ corr
C4316	Carbonatite[a]	0.1191	0.7057	0.7046
R4321	Monchiquite	0.1194	0.7048	0.7048
R4360	Nepheline Syenite	0.1199	0.7020	0.7035
R4359	Jacupirangite	0.1196	0.7031	0.7037
G4535	Garnet from Ijolite	0.1191	0.7056	0.7047
Average for Magnet Cove Complex		0.1194	0.7042	0.7043
	$\bar{\sigma}$		±0.0007	±0.0003
	σ		±0.0016	±0.0006

[a] Average of two analyses.

It is apparent that the $^{87}Sr/^{86}Sr$ ratio of the carbonatite is identical within the analytical precision to those of the silicate rocks. This provides quantitative support for the hypothesis that the carbonatite and alkalic rocks are comagmatic.

Iron Hill, Colorado

Here a central mass of carbonate rock is surrounded by irregular zones of biotite pyroxenite, uncompahgrite, ijolite and nepheline syenite. Larsen (1942) concluded that the carbonate rock may have been formed by hydrothermal replacement, although later writers have described it as a carbonatite. The $^{87}Sr/^{86}Sr$ ratios of several rocks from the complex are listed in Table VI.

TABLE VI
Strontium isotope ratios for the Iron Hill, Colorado Stock

Sample number	Rock type	$^{86}Sr/^{88}Sr$	$^{87}Sr/^{86}Sr$	$(^{87}Sr/^{86}Sr)$ corr
C4811	Carbonatite[a]	0.1193	0.7049	0.7046
R4809	Pyroxenite[a]	0.1198	0.7003	0.7013
R5016	Ijolite	0.1207	0.6999	0.7037
R4810	Uncompahgrite	0.1196	0.7030	0.7036
Average for Iron Hill Complex		0.1199	0.7020	0.7033
	$\bar{\sigma}$		±0.0013	±0.0007
	σ		±0.0027	±0.0014

[a] Average of two analyses.

The ratios of the carbonatite, the uncompahgrite and the ijolite are identical within the analytical precision. The $^{87}Sr/^{86}Sr$ ratio of the pyroxenite appears to be somewhat lower than those of the other three rock types. If this apparent result were confirmed by further analyses it could be interpreted to mean that the pyroxenite is not comagmatic with the other rocks. At any rate the fact that the $^{87}Sr/^{86}Sr$ ratios of the carbonatite and two of the silicate rocks are identical within the analytical precision strongly supports the hypothesis that these rocks are comagmatic.

Spitzkop, Transvaal

The carbonate rock at the core of this complex has been interpreted by Shand (1950) as a xenolith of the underlying Transvaal dolomite. Strauss and Truter (1951) and Holmes (1958) have presented convincing evidence in support of the theory that it is a carbonatite. $^{87}Sr/^{86}Sr$ ratios have been measured in the Spitzkop carbonatite and in the Transvaal dolomite. The results are given in Table VII.

According to Higazy (1954) and Holmes (1958) the Transvaal dolomite has a strontium content of less than 5 parts per million. Therefore in view of its great age if this rock were to contain only 1 or 2 parts per million rubidium the $^{87}Sr/^{86}Sr$ ratio reported in Table VII would be somewhat higher than the initial ratio. Nevertheless it is apparent that the $^{87}Sr/^{86}Sr$ ratio in the Spitzkop carbonatite is quite different from that in the Transvaal dolomite. This is additional evidence that the carbonatite is not a xenolith of the dolomite.

TABLE VII

Strontium isotope ratios for the Spitzkop Carbonatite, Transvaal and the Transvaal Dolomite

Sample number	Rock type	$^{86}Sr/^{88}Sr$	$^{87}Sr/^{86}Sr$	$(^{87}Sr/^{86}Sr)$ corr
C4320	Carbonatite,	0.1194	0.7028	0.7028
C4844	Spitzkop, Transvaal[a]			
C4874	Dolomite, Transvaal system[a]	0.1195	0.7098	0.7099

[a] Average of two analyses.

Other carbonatites

The strontium isotopic ratios of the 17 additional carbonatites which were analysed are reported in Table VIII together with the data for the carbonatites previously discussed.

Inspection of the data listed in Table VIII reveals that only the Rocky Boy carbonatite has a $^{87}Sr/^{86}Sr$ ratio which differs significantly from the mean value. The $^{87}Sr/^{86}Sr$ ratio in this sample as determined by a triplicate analysis is 0.7057 ± 0.0005, and the mean for all 21 carbonatites is 0.7035 ± 0.0003.

TABLE VIII

Isotopic composition of strontium in carbonatites

Sample number	Locality	$^{86}Sr/^{88}Sr$	$^{87}Sr/^{86}Sr$	$(^{87}Sr/^{86}Sr)$ corr
C4314	Rocky Boy, Montana	0.1188	0.7075	0.7057 (3)
C4316	Magnet Cove, Arkansas	0.1191	0.7057	0.7046 (2)
C4811	Iron Hill, Colorado	0.1193	0.7049	0.7046 (2)
C4322	Mountain Pass, California	0.1189	0.7059	0.7044 (1)
C3252 C4584	Oka, Quebec[a]	0.1195	0.7028	0.7032 (3)
C4318	Alnö, Sweden	0.1198	0.7010	0.7022 (2)
C4319	Fen, Norway	0.1202	0.6998	0.7021 (1)
C4320 C4844	Spitzkop, South Africa	0.1194	0.7028	0.7028 (2)
C4843	Loolekop, South Africa	0.1194	0.7051	0.7051 (1)
C4873	Glenover, South Africa	0.1202	0.7015	0.7038 (1)
C4323	Premier Mine, South Africa	0.1189	0.7043	0.7028 (1)
C4816	Shawa, Rhodesia	0.1183	0.7067	0.7034 (1)
C4884	Kaluwe, Zambia	0.1193	0.7024	0.7021 (1)
C4886	Kangankunde, Malawi	0.1193	0.7019	0.7016 (1)
C4885	Chilwa Island, Malawi	0.1191	0.7050	0.7041 (1)
C4872	Chigwakwalu, Malawi	0.1190	0.7062	0.7050 (1)
C4841	Busumbu, Uganda	0.1184	0.7062	0.7032 (1)
C4842	Tororo, Uganda[b]	0.1188	0.7042	0.7025 (1)
C4324	Sukulu, Uganda	0.1196	0.7020	0.7026 (1)
C4878	Mrima, Kenya	0.1194	0.7044	0.7044 (1)
C4875	Rangwa, Kenya	0.1201	0.7023	0.7042 (1)
Average for 21 carbonatites		0.1193	0.7040	0.7035
	$\bar{\sigma}$	±0.0001	±0.0005	±0.0003
	σ	±0.0005	±0.0021	±0.0012

Figures in parentheses represent the number of independent analyses performed.
[a] Two analyses reported by Faure and Hurley (1963).
[b] Editor's note: Part of the Bukusu Complex.

This may indicate that the Rocky Boy carbonatite has not had the same origin as the others listed in Table VIII.

The value of σ calculated by giving equal weight to the $^{87}Sr/^{86}Sr$ ratios of each of the 21 carbonatites is 0.0012. This is nearly identical to the figure of 0.0015 calculated from the results of 18 analyses of the inter-laboratory standard. This emphasizes the fact that the $^{87}Sr/^{86}Sr$ ratios of the individual carbonatites, with the exception of Rocky Boy, are not measurably different from the mean value.

DISCUSSION OF THE RESULTS

Mode of emplacement of carbonatites

The strontium isotopic evidence indicates that the calcite rock at Oka, Quebec is not a xenolith of Grenville marble, and that the Spitzkop carbonatite is not a xenolith of the Transvaal dolomite.

The $^{87}Sr/^{86}Sr$ ratios of the Oka, Magnet Cove and Iron Hill carbonatites are identical within the analytical precision to those of the associated alkalic rocks. This strongly supports the conclusion that in each case the carbonatites and alkalic rocks are comagmatic.

The $^{87}Sr/^{86}Sr$ ratios of each of the 21 carbonatites analysed are lower than those of most limestones. With one exception the ratios of the individual carbonatites are not significantly different from the mean value. These facts are not compatible with the hypothesis that carbonatites are xenoliths of limestones randomly encountered by rising magmas.

In addition to the hypotheses of magmatic origin and of xenolithic origin, it has been suggested that carbonatites are formed by gas transfer or by hydrothermal replacement. Rocks formed from the same parent magma by magmatic crystallization, by gas transfer, or by hydrothermal replacement could possess identical $^{87}Sr/^{86}Sr$ ratios. Therefore the strontium isotopic evidence, although indicating that the carbonatites and associated alkalic rocks are comagmatic, does not allow a choice to be made between these three alternative modes of emplacement.

Homogeneity of source material

The value of σ, the standard deviation of a single analysis, calculated for a group of analyses gives an indication of the spread in the data. For the 21 carbonatites listed in Table VIII, σ = 0.0012 for the $^{87}Sr/^{86}Sr$ ratio, and for the 25 basalts analysed by Faure and Hurley (1963), σ = 0.0012. It is concluded that with respect to the $^{87}Sr/^{86}Sr$ ratio the homogeneity of the source material of carbonatite is similar to the homogeneity of the source material of basalt magma.

Site of Magma Generation

Faure and Hurley (1963) have found that the average $^{87}Sr/^{86}Sr$ ratio in basalts is approximately 0.705. They estimate that the average $^{87}Sr/^{86}Sr$ ratio of the sialic portion of the continental crust equals 0.722 ± 0.005. These authors propose that a rock having an initial $^{87}Sr/^{86}Sr$ ratio within the range observed in basalts can contain only insignificant amounts of remobilized older sialic material. The

$^{87}Sr/^{86}Sr$ ratios of the carbonatites listed in Table VIII fall well within the basalt range. Therefore the rocks of the carbonatite-alkalic rock association cannot have been formed by partial or complete melting of older sialic material. This indicates that the carbonatites and associated rocks are derived from a magma which originates below the sial and possibly below the Mohorovičić discontinuity, although it does not require that the carbon dioxide in carbonatites also be of sub-sialic origin.

Source of carbon dioxide

The $^{87}Sr/^{86}Sr$ data are presented in histogram form in Fig. 1. The data for carbonatites and sedimentary carbonate rocks are taken from Table VIII and Table II respectively; those for basalts were reported by Faure and Hurley (1963).

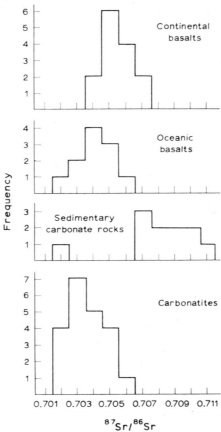

Fig. 1. Frequency distribution of $^{87}Sr/^{86}Sr$ ratios in various rock types.

The fact that the $^{87}Sr/^{86}Sr$ ratios of carbonatites are distinctly lower than those of most sedimentary carbonate rocks confirms the conclusion reached by many geologists that carbonatites are not xenoliths of limestone. It also indicates that carbonatites contain juvenile strontium which originated beneath the sial, but it does not necessarily mean that they also contain juvenile carbon dioxide. For example, the $^{87}Sr/^{86}Sr$ ratio of a carbonatite formed in the late stages of differentiation of a magma of subsialic origin which had completely assimilated a relatively small amount of limestone would be identical to or only slightly higher than that of the primary magma. A carbonatite formed in this way would contain juvenile strontium but resurgent carbon dioxide.

Carbonatites are widely distributed, and if they are formed by the process just described the primary magma involved must be one of worldwide occurrence. The most likely candidate is basalt magma, and therefore if carbonatites are produced by complete limestone assimilation their $^{87}Sr/^{86}Sr$ ratios should be identical to or slightly higher than those of basalt.

Figure 1 shows that the $^{87}Sr/^{86}Sr$ ratios of carbonatites appear to be on the average slightly lower than those of continental basalts, although the ratios of the groups overlap. The mean $^{87}Sr/^{86}Sr$ ratio of the continental basalts (includes tholeiites, olivine basalts, diabases and andesites) shown in Fig. 1 is 0.7052 $\pm$ 0.0003, and the mean for the carbonatites is 0.7035 $\pm$ 0.0003. The mean for the oceanic basalts, 0.7042 $\pm$ 0.0003, does not differ significantly from the carbonatite mean.

Additional information regarding the abundance of ^{87}Sr in mafic continental rocks is provided by Faure, *et al.* (1962), who report initial $^{87}Sr/^{86}Sr$ ratios for the Skaergaard intrusive, the Duluth gabbro, the Endion sill, the Sudbury norite, the Stillwater complex, and the Bushveld complex. The mean initial $^{87}Sr/^{86}Sr$ ratio of the rocks of these 6 intrusives is 0.7049, which may also be significantly higher than the mean ratio of the carbonatites, 0.7035.

It thus appears that the $^{87}Sr/^{86}Sr$ ratios of carbonatites are slightly lower than those of continental basalts and mafic intrusives. The validity of this apparent result must await more analyses of mafic rocks. The data presently available suggest, but do not prove, that carbonatites are not formed by complete assimilation of limestone by basaltic magmas, and therefore that they contain juvenile carbon dioxide.

Composition of source material

Most writers have proposed that the carbonatite-alkalic rock association is derived from a parent material of subsialic origin which is usually suggested to be either basalt or peridotite (kimberlite). The data obtained in this investigation support both hypotheses in that they indicate that this association is not derived from older sialic material but instead from a parent material of subsialic origin.

No data for the $^{87}Sr/^{86}Sr$ ratios of peridotites are available and therefore no comparison of carbonatite and peridotite ratios is possible at the present time. If future work confirms the tentative conclusion that the $^{87}Sr/^{86}Sr$ ratios of carbonatites are lower than those of mafic continental rocks it may then be possible to conclude that carbonatites are not differentiation products of normal basalt magma.

We suggest that the apparently lower $^{87}Sr/^{86}Sr$ ratios of the rocks of the carbonatite-alkalic rock association result from their derivation at deeper levels in the upper mantle where the Rb/Sr ratio, and therefore the $^{87}Sr/^{86}Sr$ ratio, is lower. This hypothesis is consistent with the phase equilibria evidence reported by Yoder and Tilley (1962) and with the hypothesis presented by Kushiro and Kuno (1963), both of which suggest that the more alkalic magmas are derived from greater depths than the tholeiite-type magmas. It is also consistent with geochemical evidence regarding the upward concentration of alkalis within the earth.

CONCLUSIONS

1. Study of a small, completely recrystallized xenolith of Trenton limestone enclosed in a relatively strontium-rich gabbro at Mount Royal, Quebec indicates that diffusion of ^{87}Sr in limestone xenoliths is negligible. Therefore xenoliths of limestones should retain the $^{87}Sr/^{86}Sr$ ratios characteristic of the limestones.

2. The $^{87}Sr/^{86}Sr$ ratio of the calcite rock at Oka, Quebec, is distinctly different from that of Grenville marble. A similar result was obtained for the Spitzkop carbonatite and the Transvaal dolomite. It is concluded that the Oka calcite rock is not a xenolith of Grenville marble and that the Spitzkop carbonatite is not a xenolith of Transvaal dolomite.

3. The mean $^{87}Sr/^{86}Sr$ ratio of the 21 carbonatites analysed is 0.7035 ± 0.0003 ($\bar{\sigma}$). Limestones in general have $^{87}Sr/^{86}Sr$ ratios in the range 0.707–0.711. Since diffusion of ^{87}Sr in carbonate xenoliths appears insignificant it is concluded that carbonatites are not xenoliths of limestone.

4. The $^{87}Sr/^{86}Sr$ ratio provides an empirical criterion by which carbonate rocks of intrusive appearance can be identified as carbonatites or as mobilized sedimentary or metamorphic carbonate rocks.

5. The $^{87}Sr/^{86}Sr$ ratios of carbonatites from the three complexes studied in detail are in each case identical to those of the associated alkalic rocks. This offers very strong support to the hypothesis that the carbonatites and the alkalic rocks are comagmatic, but it does not in itself tell us whether the carbon dioxide in carbonatites is juvenile or resurgent.

6. The spread in the $^{87}Sr/^{86}Sr$ ratios of the 21 carbonatites is similar to the spread observed in the ratios of basalts. It is concluded that with respect to the $^{87}Sr/^{86}Sr$ ratio the homogeneity of the source material of carbonatite is similar to the homogeneity of the source material of basalt magma.

7. The $^{87}Sr/^{86}Sr$ ratios of carbonatites are distinctly lower than those of sialic crustal materials. This indicates that the carbonatite-alkalic rock association is derived from below the sial and possibly from below the Mohorovičić discontinuity.

8. The $^{87}Sr/^{86}Sr$ ratios of carbonatites appear to be slightly lower than those of mafic continental rocks. If future work confirms this result, which is at present only tentative, it may then be possible to conclude that carbonatites are not derived from normal basalt magma by either differentiation or complete assimilation of limestone.

Acknowledgements. We wish to thank Dr. Gunter Faure who contributed materially to this investigation through his advice and constructive suggestions. Dr. Faure and Dr. Stanley Hart kindly agreed to evaluate the manuscript. The assistance of the following individuals and organizations in providing samples is gratefully acknowledged: Dr. W. T. Pecora of the United States Geological Survey; Professor Arthur Holmes; Professor Arie Poldervaart and the Department of Geology of Columbia University; Mr. Norman F. Williams, Director and Mr. Drew F. Holbrook of the Arkansas Geological & Conservation Commission; Mr. S. B. Bond and Mr. Gilles Joncas of Quebec Columbium, Ltd.; Dr. J. Gower of Kennco Explorations (Western), Ltd.; Mr. R. B. Brackin of Kennecott Copper Corporation; Dr. F. C. Truter, Director of the Geological Survey of the Republic of South Africa; the Mines and Geological Department of Kenya; the Geological Survey Department of Zambia; the Geological Survey Department of Malawi. The support of the Division of Research of the Atomic Energy Commission has made this investigation possible.

REFERENCES

Aldrich, L. T., Herzog, L. F., Doak, J. B. and Davis, G. L., 1953, Variations in strontium isotope abundances in minerals, part 1. Mass spectrometric analysis of mineral sources of strontium: *Am. Geophys. Union Trans.*, v. **34**, pp. 457–460.

Clark, T. H., 1952, Montreal area, Laval and Lachine map-areas: *Quebec Dept. Mines, Geol. Rept.* **46**.

Daly, R. A., 1933, *Igneous Rocks and The Depths of The Earth:* New York, McGraw Hill.

Faure, G. and Hurley, P. M., 1963, The isotopic composition of strontium in oceanic and continental basalts: Application to the origin of igneous rocks: *Jour. Petrology*, v. **4**, p. 31.

Faure, G., Hurley, P. M., Fairbairn, H. W. and Pinson, W. H., 1962, Isotopic compositions of strontium in continental basic intrusives: *Jour. Geophys. Research*, v. **67**, p. 3556. (Abstract only.)

Gast, P. W., 1960, Limitations on the composition of the upper mantle: *Jour. Geophys. Research*, v. **65**, pp. 1287–1297.

Hamilton, E. I. and Deans, T., 1963, Isotopic composition of strontium in some African carbonatites and limestones and in strontium minerals: *Nature*, v. **198**, pp. 776–777.

Hedge, C. E. and Walthall, F. G., 1963, Radiogenic strontium-87 as an index of geologic processes: *Science*, v. **140**, pp. 1214–1217.

Herzog, L. F., Aldrich, L. T., Holyk, W. K., Whiting, F. B. and Ahrens, L. H., 1953, Variations in strontium isotope abundances in minerals, part II. Radiogenic ^{87}Sr in biotite, feldspar, and celestite: *Am. Geophys. Union Trans.*, v. **34**, pp. 461–470.

Herzog, L. F., Pinson, W. H. and Cormier, R. F., 1958, Sediment age determination by Rb/Sr analysis of glauconite: *Am. Assoc. Petroleum Geologists Bull.*, v. **42**, pp. 717–733.

Higazy, R. A., 1954, Trace elements of volcanic ultrabasic potassic rocks of south western Uganda and adjoining part of the Belgian Congo: *Geol. Soc. America Bull.*, v. **65**, pp. 39–70.

Holmes, A., 1958, Spitzkop carbonatite, eastern Transvaal: *Geol. Soc. America Bull.*, v. **69**, pp. 1525–1526.

Hurley, P. M., *et al.*, 1960, Variations in isotopic abundances of Sr, Ca, and Ar and related topics: *Ninth Annual Progress Report for 1960, U.S.A.E.C. Contract* AT (30–1)–1381.

Hurley, P. M., Pinson, W. H., Jr. and Fairbairn, H. W., 1963, Progress report on analytical accuracy of $^{87}Sr/^{86}Sr$ measurement: *Am. Geophys. Union Trans.*, v. **44**, p. 111. (Abstract only.)

Kushiro, I. and Kuno, H., 1963, Origin of primary basalt magmas and classification of basaltic rocks: *Jour. Petrology*, v. **4**, p. 75.

Landes, K. K., 1931, A paragenetic classification of the Magnet Cove minerals: *Am. Mineralogist.*, v. **16**, pp. 313–326.

Larsen, E. S., 1942, Alkalic rocks of Iron Hill, Gunnison County, Colorado: *U.S. Geol. Surv. Prof. Paper*, **197-A**

Nier, A. O., 1938, Isotopic constitution of Sr, Ba, Bi, Tl and Hg: *Phys. Rev.*, v. **54**, pp. 275–278.

Pecora, W. T., 1956, Carbonatites: A review: *Geol. Soc. America Bull.*, v. **67**, pp. 1537–1556.

Pinson, W. H., Herzog, L. F., Fairbairn, H. W. and Cormier, R. F., 1958, Sr/Rb age study of tektites: *Geochim. et Cosmochim. Acta*, v. **14**, pp. 331–339.

Powell, J. L., 1962, *The Strontium Isotopic Composition and Origin of Carbonatites.* Ph.D. thesis, Massachusetts Institute of Technology, Cambridge, Mass.

Powell, J. L., Hurley, P. M. and Fairbairn, H. W., 1962, Isotopic composition of strontium in carbonatites: *Nature*, v. **196**, p. 1085.

Shand, S. J., 1950, *Eruptive Rocks:* London, Murby.

Strauss, C. A. and Truter, F. C., 1951, The alkali complex at Spitzkop, Sekukuniland: *Geol. Soc. S. Africa Trans.*, v. **53**, pp. 81–125.

Yoder, H. S. and Tilley, C. E., 1962, Origin of basalt magmas: An experimental study of natural and synthetic rock systems: *Jour. Petrology*, v. **3**, p. 342.

J. GITTINS

Russian Views on the Origin of Carbonatite Complexes

This attempt to summarize Russian thinking on carbonatite genesis has been prepared from the published literature and from manuscripts very kindly prepared by Borodin, Pozharitskaya and Epshtein as well as from the summary published by Tomkeieff in 1961.

The Russian position differs markedly from that of most petrologists in North America and Europe in favouring an extreme metasomatic origin whereby most of the rocks of a carbonatite complex are formed by a series of metasomatic transformations in zones surrounding an ultrabasic plug; it appears to have been influenced strongly by the number of ultrabasic alkalic-carbonatite complexes found in the Kola Peninsula, northern Siberia and Tuva (southern Siberia) and is based on Korzhinsky's theories of the differential mobility of the elements. The extent of this metasomatic argument is attested by the following quotation from Kukharenko and Dontsova (1964):

> Most investigators consider them to be pneumatolytic-hydrothermal formations arising hydrothermally by replacement of silicate rocks. The carbonatites have also been suggested to originate intrusively by the injection and subsequent crystallization of a special carbonatite magma. Those who hold this opinion . . . consider that carbonatite stocks and vein bodies (ring and radial dykes) are indeed magmatic injections.
>
> It is supposed that carbonatite melts arose while alkaline (ijolite-melteigite) magma was differentiating at depth. That such melts may exist has of late been demonstrated experimentally (Wyllie and Tuttle, 1960). But it seems improbable that they could exist in an open system under the conditions in which the sub-volcanic intrusions of alkaline-ultrabasic rocks and the carbonatites connected with them formed. . . .
>
> . . . The overwhelming majority of carbonatites replace the other rocks and not only the intrusive pyroxenites, melteigites and alkaline vein pegmatites but also the later metasomatic melilitic rocks, the apatite-forsterite magnetite ores and glimmerites and also the fenitized gneiss country rocks. Furthermore, all stages of replacement of the rocks mentioned by carbonatites may often be traced; the process starts with sporadic disseminations and thin veins of calcite in the pyroxenites and melteigites and goes on first to the production of mixed silicate-carbonate rocks and then to that of typical carbonatites containing relicts of pyroxene, magnetite, micas and other minerals.

Considerable attention is drawn to the essentially concentric arrangement of rock types and it is argued that this indicates not a comagmatic but a metasomatic origin.

The petrogenetic scheme envisaged starts with the differentiation of olivine basalt magma to produce ultrabasic rocks (dunite and pyroxenite). Juvenile solutions rich in CO_2 then react with the remaining magma saturating it and enriching it in alkalies to the extent that nepheline syenite magma is formed. Solutions derived from this magma react with the dunite or pyroxenite and generate the rocks of a carbonatite complex by a series of reactions that result in a carbonate residuum. There are slight variations between authors. For example Borodin (1957, 1958*a*, *b*, 1960) has argued that the urtite–ijolite–melteigite suite is metasomatic arising by nephelinization of the pyroxenite; aegirine replaces diopsidic augite and leads ultimately to the formation of nepheline-pyroxene rocks. On the other hand Kukharenko and Dontsova (1964) believe that the melteigite–ijolite rocks are magmatic but they then envisage a series of reactions between the pyroxenite and the alkaline magma or its derivatives that are essentially similar to Borodin's scheme.

In either case replacement of diopsidic augite by aegirine releases Ca and Mg which becomes concentrated in the solutions and eventually forms calcite or dolomite. These solutions are considered to be supercritical (450–250° C) with a high partial pressure of CO_2 during calcite crystallization but become subcritical and enriched in Mg and Fe with falling temperature causing replacement of calcitic carbonatite by dolomite, ankerite and siderite. Three stages of the metasomatic processes are recognized as follows:

1.   Na – Ca metasomatism which results in nephelinization and formation of melilite and aegirine.
2.   K – Ca metasomatism which results in the formation of phlogopite and melanite.
3.   Breakdown of previously formed minerals (e.g. melilite to cebollite and juanite, and phlogopite to tremolite and actinolite). Calcite appears as an independent mineral at this stage.

There are then four stages in the evolution of the actual carbonatite:

1.   Early calcite carbonatite.
2.   Late calcite carbonatite.
3.   Calcite-dolomite carbonatite.
4.   Ankertite and ankerite-siderite carbonatite.

Each of these stages can be further subdivided into types as follows:

Stage 1

(*a*) Calcitic carbonatites with augite-diopside and ferriferous phlogopite.
(*b*) Calcitic carbonatites with ferriferous phlogopite.
(*c*) Calcitic carbonatites with no dark minerals except magnetite.

The first two are always metasomatic; the third may be fissure-filling. The metasomatic varieties are characterized by a distribution of the minerals in streaks and clots to produce great inhomogeneity.

Stage 2

(*a*) Calcitic carbonatites with diopside, phlogopite, apatite and magnetite.
(*b*) Calcitic carbonatites with forsterite, phlogopite, apatite and magnetite.
(*c*) Calcitic carbonatites with phlogopite, apatite and magnetite.
(*d*) Calcitic carbonatites with no dark silicates.

The first three are always metasomatic and the fourth may be fissure-filling.

Stage 3

(*a*) Metasomatic development of calcitic and dolomitic carbonatite from earlier carbonatites and from silicate rocks.

(*b*) Fissure fillings.

Stage 4

(*a*) Metasomatic development of ankeritic and ankeritic–sideritic carbonatites from earlier carbonatites and from silicate rocks.

(*b*) Fissure fillings.

The processes might be summed up in this quotation from Kukharenko and Dontsova (1964): '... there is no difficulty in arriving at the conclusion that the rocks themselves in the masses are the main source of the calcium in the carbonatites and that the bulk of the element is liberated and mobilized by the solutions and deposited as carbonates during the metasomatic reconstitution of the pyroxenites and pyroxene-nepheline alkaline rocks'.

Very little discussion of carbonatite lavas appears but it is generally admitted that late carbonatites in a sequence may be related to extrusive alkaline magma.

These same authors explain the concentration of rare elements so characteristic of most carbonatite complexes as derived from the minerals of the original pyroxenite by the series of metasomatic transformations. Others say that they were introduced by the juvenile CO_2–rich solutions.

There appears, then, to be a school of thought which, although it has some views in common with non-Russian geologists, is still for the most part uniquely Russian. Its main feature is the very extensive appeal to metasomatism beginning with a pyroxenite intrusion. Some earlier writers (e.g. Belyankin and Vlodavetz, 1932), however, favoured a magmatic origin of carbonatites and Egorov (1960) does today.

A selection of Russian writings on carbonatite petrogenesis is given below and in full in the references at the end of the book.

Belyankin and Vlodavetz, 1932

Borodin, 1957, 1958a, b, 1960, 1961, 1962

Butakova, 1956, 1959

Butakova and Egorov, 1962

Dmitriev, 1959

Egorov, 1957, 1960a, b, 1964

Egorov, Goltburt and Shikhoria, 1959

Egorov and Surina, 1958, 1961

Elyanov, 1961

Epshtein, 1959

Epshtein, Anikeeva and Mikhailova, 1961

Glagolev, 1962

Ivanov and Safronov, 1959

Ivensen, 1941

Kirilov and Rylov, 1963

Konev, 1958, 1960a, 1962

Kononova, 1957, 1961

Korzhinsky, 1951, 1952, 1955, 1956, 1957a, b, 1960

Koshitz, 1934

Kukharenko and Dontsova, 1962, 1964

Kuznetsov and Pinus, 1949

Lavrenev, 1960

Lavrenev and Epshtein, 1962a, b

Lavrenev and Pozharitskaya, 1960

Motycho, 1957

Pazyuk, 1954

Pozharitskaya, 1960, 1962

Pozharitskaya and Epshtein, 1962
Samoilova, 1962
Serba, 1959, 1963
Sergeev, 1959, 1962
Sheinman, 1947, 1955
Vainshtein, Pozharitskaya and
  Turanskaya, 1961

Volotovskaya and Fizhenko, 1960
Volotovskaya, 1958
Volotovskaya and Kukharenko, 1959
Zdorik and Runov, 1961
Zhabin, 1959
Zlatkind, 1945, 1948
Zlatkind and Shailov, 1946

Part IV

Economic Aspects

Economic Mineralogy of African Carbonatites

INTRODUCTION

The idea that carbonatite complexes have characteristic geochemical features which may sometimes be so accentuated as to include valuable mineral deposits was first postulated in relation to Africa about 1948. It arose from the independent discoveries of large apatite deposits associated with carbonatites in Uganda (Davies, 1947) and Rhodesia (Mennell, 1946), which, coupled with the knowledge that niobium minerals occurred in all the classic carbonatites of Europe (Alnö, Fen and Kaiserstuhl), inspired the belief that among the widely scattered carbonatites of Africa there must surely be interesting and valuable minerals awaiting recognition. An opportunity of testing this idea presented itself in Uganda during the examination of the Tororo and Sukulu carbonatites in connection with the development of the first cement industry in East Africa, and was quickly justified by the discovery in 1950 of the large residual deposits of apatite, magnetite and pyrochlore mantling the Sukulu Complex. In the following year the Malawi carbonatites were revisited and found to contain not only niobium (pyrochlore) deposits, but at Kangankunde Hill a rare earth (monazite) deposit which was clearly analogous to the newly discovered bastnaesite carbonatite of Mountain Pass, California. Stimulated by these discoveries, and by high prices offered for niobium minerals, a search for carbonatites spread to neighbouring countries, and between 1952 and 1957 no less than twenty new carbonatite complexes were discovered between the Zambesi and the Equator. The investigation of African carbonatites by both governmental geologists and mining companies has contributed enormously to the general understanding of this group of rocks, and so it is fitting that a chapter of this book should be devoted to the minerals which prompted this work, or were discovered as it progressed.

Disregarding the nine most abundant rock forming elements, carbonatite complexes are commonly enriched in carbon, fluorine, phosphorus, manganese, strontium, niobium, barium, and the rare earths, especially the lighter lanthanons. In certain cases there are also enrichments of vanadium, copper, zinc, molybdenum, lead, thorium and uranium. Some of these enrichments have no economic significance at present, and in Africa to date the carbonatite mineral deposits established in commercial production are few in number. They comprise

TABLE I

Principal mineral deposits of African carbonatite complexes

Complex	Deposits	Synopsis of resources
Lueshe, Kivu Province, Republic of the Congo	Niobium	30 million tons ferruginous residual ore @ 1.34% Nb_2O_5; additional weathered micaceous contact rocks @ 0.86% Nb_2O_5, and pyrochlore-sövite ore @ 0.55% Nb_2O_5.
	Phosphate	Apatite is a potential by-product from residual ores.
Bukusu, Eastern Uganda	Phosphate	Residual and secondary apatite deposits contain moderate reserves of ferruginous secondary phosphate rock @ *c.* 25% P_2O_5, and large reserves of apatite-bearing soils @ *c.* 11% P_2O_5.
	Iron and titanium	Moderate reserves of rubble magnetite, both low-titania (*c.* 1% TiO_2) and high-titania (14–22% TiO_2).
Tororo and Sukulu, Eastern Uganda	Vermiculite	Easily won from weathered pyroxenite areas.
	Cement and lime	Tororo sövite is basis of Uganda cement and lime industry. Annual capacity 160,000 tons portland cement.
	Phosphate	Sukulu residual apatite-rich soils; 200 million tons @ 13% P_2O_5, *c.* 25% magnetite, and 0.25% Nb_2O_5 as pyrochlore. Superphosphate plant treats 14,000 tons apatite concentrates annually.
	Niobium	Minor by-product recovery of 75 tons pyrochlore concentrate (50% Nb_2O_5) is anticipated.
	Iron	Magnetite concentrates (*c.* 1% TiO_2) stocked for future use.
Mrima Hill, Coast Province, Kenya	Niobium	Ferruginous residual pyrochlore ores; 49 million tons @ 0.7% Nb_2O_5, including $4\frac{1}{2}$ million tons @ 1.25% Nb_2O_5.
	Rare earths	Above include 6 million tons @ *c.* 5% Ln_2O_3 (as earthy secondary phosphates), and small/medium reserves of barite–rich niobium-rare earth ores @ >1% Nb_2O_5 and >10% Ln_2O_3.
	Iron and manganese	Potential by-products, as niobium ores are largely low-grade manganiferous goethites, with intercalations of ferruginous manganese ore.
	Barytes	Potential by-product from rare earth ores.
Oldoinyo Dili, Northern Tanganyika	Niobium	Pyrochlore–sövites @ 0.35% Nb_2O_5, mainly low grade, limited reserves.
Wigu Hill, Eastern Tanganyika	Rare earths	Substantial reserves of bastnaesite-monazite-bearing carbonatite veins @ > 10% Ln_2O_3.
Panda Hill (Mbeya) South-West Tanganyika	Niobium	125 million tons pyrochlore-bearing sövite @ 0.3% Nb_2O_5, and 3,800,000 tons biotitic contact rocks @ 0.79% Nb_2O_5.
	Phosphate	Apatite is a potential by-product.
Ilomba Hill— Nachendezwaya, Malawi— Tanganyika border	Uranium and niobium	Small lenses of high-grade uranium pyrochlore ore in foyaite complex (Ilomba, Malawi).

Complex	Deposits	Synopsis of resources
Nkombwa Hill, North-Eastern Zambia	Niobium	Pyrochlore in ankeritic carbonatite, rather low grade; details not available.
	Rare earths	Limited areas of monazite-rich ore.
Kaluwe (Rufunsa Valley) Central Province, Zambia	Niobium	Sövite breccia sill constitutes large potential reserve of low-grade pyrochlore ore.
	Phosphate	Limited reserves of apatite-rich soils @ *c.* 10% P_2O_5.
Kangankunde Hill, Southern Malawi	Rare earths	Large reserves of monazite in strontianite-rich carbonatite @ 5% Ln_2O_3 and 10–20% strontianite. Also 100,000 tons monazite in soils.
	Strontianite	Potential by-product from monazite ores, and limited reserves — 25–75% strontianite.
Chilwa Island, Southern Malawi	Niobium	One ore body contains 650,000 tons of pyrochlore-rich sövite @ *c.* 1% Nb_2O_5 to 1000 ft depth; additional lower grade sövite ores occur, and limited reserves of residual ores.
Tundulu, Southern Malawi	Phosphate	Apatite-rich rocks of Nathace Hill contain, per 100 ft depth, >800,000 tons @ >20% P_2O_5, plus 1 million tons @ 10% P_2O_5.
	Niobium	Pyrochlore is a potential by-product.
Dorowa, Southern Rhodesia	Phosphate	37 million tons of apatite-bearing fenites, @ >8% P_2O_5, and weathered (carbonate-free) rocks @ 6–8% P_2O_5. Output 90,000 tons apatite annually from 1965.
Glenover, Western Transvaal, Republic of South Africa	Phosphate	9,750,000 tons of secondary apatite rock @ 20–32% P_2O_5. Annual output *c.* 13,000 tons.
	Niobium	Potential by-product from marginal zone @ 0.68% Nb_2O_5.
Palabora, Eastern Transvaal, Republic of South Africa	Copper	315 million tons of sulphide copper ore @ 0.69% Cu available opencast. Production of 80,000 s. tons Cu started in 1966, decreasing later to average 70,000 s. tons annually.
	Iron	By-product output 1,800,000 tons of low-titania magnetite anticipated annually from copper mine; titaniferous magnetite also recoverable.
	Phosphate	Large apatite reserves in phoscorite @ *c.* 10%, P_2O_5, and in pyroxenite @ 6–8%, P_2O_5. Current production 500,000 tons apatite concentrates annually, and copper mining will provide additional quantities.
	Thorium and Uranium	By-product uranothorianite anticipated from copper ores.
	Zirconium	2,000 tons by-product baddeleyite (95% ZrO_2) annually from phoscorite from 1966.
	Vermiculite	Large reserves in separate areas of vermiculite-rich pyroxenite. Output 100,000 tons annually.
Okorusu, South West Africa	Fluorite	About 7 to 10 million tons @ >35% CaF_2.

NOTE: The estimates of reserves given in this table are from various sources and are often not strictly comparable for different deposits. In several cases economic processes for the treatment of these ores have not yet been developed. Data for many carbonatite complexes, especially in Angola, Mozambique and South West Africa, are too fragmentary for inclusion.

a sövite deposit worked for lime and cement, four apatite deposits, and the recently opened Palabora[1] copper deposit in South Africa which has caused a sixfold increase in the value of the output from African carbonatite deposits. By-products from these operations include iron ore and baddeleyite, and vermiculite is mined from adjacent pyroxenite. On the other hand plans to exploit the principal niobium, rare earth and strontium discoveries are still unfulfilled. Nevertheless, the list of the more important carbonatite mineral discoveries in Africa south of the equator, shown in Table I, will indicate that the economic potentialities of this class of deposit are considerable.

The salient features of the more important mineral assemblages will be summarized in the following pages, based largely on the occurrences of which the author has personal knowledge arising from investigations undertaken since 1949 by the Mineral Resources Division of Overseas (formerly Colonial) Geological Surveys. The writer was privileged to co-ordinate work in the London laboratories with field and laboratory investigations undertaken by the Geological Survey Departments of Uganda, Kenya, Tanganyika, Zambia and Malawi, and wishes to acknowledge here the collective effort of all who participated in this work. Information from the literature on other important African occurrences is included where appropriate, but the Moroccan carbonatites, which Agard (1960) describes as having similar mineralization, are excluded as being in too distant and different a setting.

EXPLORATORY MINERALOGICAL TECHNIQUES

The valuable minerals in carbonatite complexes have frequently been overlooked or misidentified by prospectors, geologists and petrologists alike. Residual deposits mantling the carbonatites and the supergene alteration products have also proved as important in economic investigations as the primary mineralization of the complex, especially in tropical Africa. For these reasons, and so as to establish as quickly and completely as possible the suite of elements and minerals present in and around a complex, a combined study of both rocks and surface soils along lines radiating from the centre of the area is recommended. The soils, especially the fine-grained red earths, provide excellent well mixed composite samples for both chemical and mineralogical examination, representative of both the outcropping rocks and those which may be largely concealed. Normally they will be enriched, relative to the *average* grade of the parent rocks, in phosphorus, niobium and rare earths, and apart from the carbonates, sulphides and some of the less resistant silicates, virtually all the accessory minerals of the rock suite will be present. Mineralogical study of the soils requires the elimination of the finely divided goethite which coats all other constituents. A simple, but drastic, treatment is to digest the soil (divided into coarse and fine fractions at about 10 mesh) in hot hydrochloric acid, followed by washing, and if gelatinized silicates are in evidence, by leaching in hot caustic soda. This destroys apatite, magnetite and perhaps other significant constituents, but leaves a

[1] This is the accepted spelling by geological and mining usage, although the township is now styled Phalaborwa.

relatively small and clean fraction including the niobium, titanium and zir-conium minerals, and monazite, if these are present. To reveal the complete mineral suite, non-destructive cleaning in water is essential. Formerly this was achieved by rapid attrition scrubbing as thick pulps, but recently ultrasonic cleaning has proved much more effective. By treating the soil in water in an ultrasonic cleaning tank or with an ultrasonic probe (for quicker results), the fine goethite and any clay is dispersed and can be poured off or removed by a small hydrocyclone, the process being repeated until a clean residue is obtained. Ultrasonic cleaning at high frequency (85kc/s) is remarkably kind to soft and friable minerals, such as altered pyrochlore, which emerge undamaged, whereas acid treatment or scrubbing would reduce them to slime or skeletons. Identifica-tion and quantitative estimation of the cleaned soil minerals is facilitated by normal heavy liquid and magnetic separation techniques. The predominant constituents of most carbonatite soils are goethite, magnetite, martite, apatite and barite, and, since these are all heavy, panning is quite ineffective in con-centrating the more interesting minor constituents such as pyrochlore, monazite or baddeleyite. Closely sized sand fractions, however, may be separated with the Haultain superpanner, especially if magnetite is removed by hand magnet beforehand. The chemical and mineralogical examination of the soils should indicate fairly clearly what elements and minerals of possible economic interest occur in the complex, and will often suggest which areas merit first attention.

In examining rock specimens normal thin section techniques should be supplemented by inspection of acid insoluble residues to acquire maximum information about the accessory minerals. An alternative means of concentrat-ing these is to calcine small lumps of the carbonatites at about 950°C, slake in an excess of water, and, after scrubbing, to eliminate the finely divided calcium and magnesium hydroxides by hydrocyclone. Most accessories, including apatite and strontianite, are unaltered by this treatment.

Here it may be appropriate to note briefly some of the characteristics of the commoner accessory minerals. Apatite from sövites is often in ovoid grains, sometimes prismatic, and occasionally in basal plates showing sector twinning. Pyrochlore is always octahedral, but may be regular or flattened, with or without small cube faces, of any hue from colourless to black, and from perfectly trans-parent to semi-opaque or patinated. The secondary hydrated pyrochlores (see p. 398) are usually pale in colour, opacified, and show a microgranular texture. Pale octahedral perovskite from alnöitic rocks may be hard to distinguish optic-ally from some types of pyrochlore. Columbite pseudomorphous after pyro-chlore has a porous coke-like appearance, and may be confused with hematite (martite) pseudomorphous after magnetite. The zircons almost invariably have little or no prism zone and appear as bipyramids, hardly distinguishable from octahedra. Baddeleyite is rather rare (as yet known in only eight African occur-rences) and is usually from apatite-rich rocks, and like perovskite indicates an undersaturated association. Although in soils it is usually accompanied by zircon, one may sometimes contrast a baddeleyite-perovskite assemblage with one of zircon and sphene. Rutile, brookite and anatase are very variable, and although niobium-rich varieties are usually dark, the converse does not always hold. Blue octahedral anatase has been noted in several localities. Monazite from carbonatites is often lime or epidote green, and of exceptionally low radio-activity. Accessory pyrite almost invariably forms striated cubes, pseudomor-phed in soils by a mixture of goethite and hematite, and pyritohedra are seldom seen. Abundant sodic amphiboles or pyroxenes often reflect the close proximity of fenites.

Many carbonatite complexes, and the residual mantles around them, are radioactive, and surface or airborne radiometric surveys may reveal very signifi-cant features. On the other hand the radioactive elements are seldom of economic significance, and although they may reside largely in pyrochlore or monazite, they may also accumulate in secondary goethite, and their relative concentration and distribution patterns may differ widely from those of niobium or rare earths, so that as guides to the latter they are sometimes very misleading.

Geochemical prospecting techniques applicable to niobium-bearing carbon-atites have been discussed by Van Wambeke (1960), especially in relation to x-ray fluorescence techniques and the Congo occurrences, and by Watts, *et al.* (1963), in relation to the dispersion of niobium and zinc in Zambian carbonatite soils and stream sediments.

PHOSPHORUS

Carbonatite complexes are the principal sources of phosphates in southern and eastern Africa and are of growing importance in the agricultural economy of the region, which is rather deficient in sedimentary phosphates. Deposits of im-portance are of three types: apatite concentrations in pyroxenitic or ijolitic zones of carbonatite-cored complexes, apatite-rich carbonatites, and secondary residual deposits derived from either of these types. In all cases, apatite, primary or secondary, is the only important phosphate. The rare earth and aluminous phosphates (see p. 402) and isokite ($CaMgPO_4F$), a late replacement mineral at Nkombwa Hill, are insignificant in relation to industrial phosphate requirements. As separation of apatite from carbonates by flotation is rather difficult, the apatite-rich carbonatites have hitherto been less attractive econom-ically than carbonate-free residual deposits or primary apatite-magnetite-silicate assemblages.

The Palabora and Dorowa deposits are good examples of the pyroxenitic type. At Palabora, in the eastern Transvaal, the Loolekop carbonatite is surrounded by an earlier zone of apatite-rich rock, known as 'phoscorite', some 400 ft in width, which grades outwards into the much larger pyroxenite mass. The phoscorite is a heterogeneous, often brecciated, assemblage of apatite, titano-magnetite and serpentinized olivine, with subordinate vermiculite and calcite. Reserves are considerable and altogether 10 million tons, averaging 25% apatite, have been quarried since 1956 by the Phosphate Development Corporation and processed to yield flotation concentrates containing more than 36% P_2O_5. Present by-products are copper concentrates, baddeleyite and magnetite. Much larger reserves of apatite occur disseminated through vermiculite-rich pyrox-enite, which carries from 15–20% apatite and in one proved area alone reserves of this ore are estimated at 39 million short tons, averaging 6% P_2O_5, per 10 ft of depth. Exploitation of this pyroxenite ore is expected to commence in 1967. However, with the development of the Palabora copper mine, which will work much phoscorite as well as carbonatite (see p. 394), an advantageous integration of copper and apatite concentration may occur, and the copper smelter will also provide the sulphuric acid required for superphosphate manufacture.

In the Dorowa Complex, Rhodesia (Johnson, 1961; this vol., p. 205) magnetite-apatite rubble shed from narrow veins first attracted attention, but the main apatite enrichments have been found in pipe-like bodies containing apatite, vermiculite and calcite in altered fenite near the north and south margins of the fenite complex. The southern 'pipe' surrounds an ijolitic core and is believed to average more than 20% apatite, reserves to a depth of 400 ft totalling 30 million tons. One of the northern 'pipes', which is weathered and decalcified to a depth of 200 ft, averages 15–20% apatite. Industrial production of apatite started at Dorowa in 1965.

Apatite, although almost ubiquitous in carbonatite complexes, is generally a mere accessory which assumes economic significance only where secondary concentrations are found. In the Tundulu Complex, Malawi (Garson, 1962; this vol., p. 36) however, there are good examples of apatite-rich carbonatites of potential importance. Here, in the second ring structure which forms Nathace Hill, successive ring dikes of apatite rock, apatite sövite, and bastnaesite-bearing ankeritic sövite were emplaced in the plug of feldspathic breccia and agglomerate. The ring dikes, steeply inclined, lenticular, and from about 40–120 ft in thickness, may be of apatite rock with from 33–90% apatite, apatite sövite with 10–33% apatite, or bastnaesite-bearing rocks with up to 25% apatite. Streaky flow structures are characteristic, and the apatite is finely-granular, magnetite is absent or very subordinate, but siderite, now oxidized to goethite, was originally abundant, and pyrochlore and anatase are persistent accessories. In the bastnaesite-bearing types strontianite and barite also appear, but Garson indicates that these are hybrid rocks formed by admixture of younger rare earth carbonatites with earlier apatite rocks. There has been some late silicification, leaching, and supergene recrystallization of apatite as radial-fibrous staffelite, but the deposits are essentially primary. Reserves to a depth of 100 ft exceed 800,000 tons of apatite rock averaging more than 50% apatite, plus more than 1 million tons of carbonatite averaging 25% apatite.

Secondary apatite rock forms the core of a small hill, Glenover Kopje, in the centre of a large carbonatite plug near Matlabas River in the Waterberg district of the western Transvaal. The carbonatite, intrusive into quartzites, carries about 10% apatite, but in the top of the residual kopje is a mass of fragmented and re-cemented ferruginous apatite rock about 200 by 300 yd in diameter. The ore-body is apparently underlain by carbonatite about 400 to 500 ft below the surface, and is zoned, the upper and central portions comprising 3 million short tons averaging 32.8% P_2O_5 and 9.3% Fe_2O_3, surrounded and underlain by more ferruginous zones totalling 6,750,000 short tons averaging 21.8% P_2O_5 and 26.4% Fe_2O_3. Secondary apatite and finely divided goethite and hematite are the major constituents, with minor martite and anatase after titaniferous magnetite

and locally pyrochlore. Apatite enrichment here appears to be essentially supergene, caused by leaching of carbonates, accompanying the formation of collapse
breccias, and a downward migration of iron. Since 1957 some 65,000 tons of
apatite rock has been extracted from this deposit.

The greatest accumulations of secondary and residual apatite occur around
the Sukulu and Bukusu Complexes of south eastern Uganda (Davies, 1947, and
1956). Initially interest centred in secondary phosphate rock found intercalated
among ferruginous phosphatic soils, with variable proportions of residual magnetite and vermiculite, in the Busumbu area of the Bukusu Complex. This
material derives from an underlying belt of apatite and magnetite-rich rocks and
biotite pyroxenites which fringes an arcuate zone of carbonatites. The rock,
which is hard but cavernous, consists of francolite (carbonate fluor-apatite) in
a variety of forms, minutely platy, radial-fibrous (staffelite) or colloform (collo-
phane), but includes residual grains of primary apatite and admixed goethite
and magnetite. Although unsuitable for superphosphate manufacture, owing to
its iron content, the rock, averaging 25–30% P_2O_5, was used on a small scale for
many years for the manufacture of fused soda phosphate fertilizer, total usage
being 57,000 tons.

More extensive, however, and yielding apatite concentrates of exceptional
purity, are the unconsolidated residual soils which fill the dry valleys on the
Sukulu carbonatite. The soil is fairly uniform in composition and contains
about 30% of apatite and 25–30% of magnetite in granular form, 30% of
finely divided goethite, about 7% of quartz and minor amounts of ilmenite,
zircon, pyrochlore and baddeleyite. The apatite grains are mainly from 0.4–
0.05 mm in diameter and have the characteristic ovoid shape seen in the parent
sövites, whereas the magnetite is distinctly coarser and the goethite and quartz
are appreciably finer. Secondary apatite and mica appear only in the deeper
parts of the deposit, which varies from 50 ft to a maximum of 220 ft in thickness.
Calculated reserves total 202 million long tons of soil, including 130 million tons
of measured soil which averages 13% P_2O_5; additional reserves occur outside the
perimeter of the hills. The development of the process for recovering apatite
from this soil has been described (Fleming and Robinson, 1960), and industrial
production of apatite and superphosphate commenced in 1963. The separated
magnetite is stocked for future use, and a small by-product recovery of pyrochlore
is planned.

Smaller occurrences of apatite-rich soils occur on many other carbonatite
complexes, but the Sukulu deposits are outstanding in tonnage and grade and
appear to indicate optimum conditions of source rock area (7 sq. miles) and
composition (very low silicate content), and of soil accumulation and degree of
weathering. More intense weathering, due to both climate and the presence of
more reactive minerals (e.g. abundant pyrite) may explain the scarcity of apatite
in the thick residual deposits at Mrima (see p. 397), where the only residual
phosphates are the highly insoluble secondary gorceixite and monazite. On the
large Kaluwe carbonatite sill in the Rufunsa Valley, Zambia (Bailey, 1960; this
vol., p. 130), with a surface area of 4.8 sq. miles, soils of the central zone carry
more than 24% apatite, but unfortunately appear to be rather thin.

Chemical analyses of some apatites and apatite rocks from carbonatite complexes are shown in Table II. They emphasize the prevalence of fluor-apatite, and, except in the case of the secondary Busumbu francolite, the lack of carbonate-apatites. Strontium and cerium earths are characteristic minor constituents.

TABLE II

Analyses of apatites and apatite rocks and concentrates from carbonatite complexes

	1	2	3	4	5	6	7	8
CaO	52.4	52.78	36.12	55.35	54.60	55.0	54.2	51.04
SrO	—	—	0.67	—	(0.41)[a]	(c.0.8)[a]	0.62	4.72
Ln_2O_3	—	—	1.84	—	(0.32)	—	0.84	0.48
MgO	1.6	tr.	0.36	0.14	—	—	—	0.10
P_2O_5	36.3	38.94	24.58	39.55	41.85	41.3	41.8	40.20
F	3.2	3.70	2.44	3.79	2.13	4.1	1.7	3.40
Cl	—	—	—	—	—	0.05	0.1	0.05
CO_2	—	0.87	3.60	1.80	0.10	0.2	0.2	n.d.
H_2O+	—	0.10	1.30	0.53	0.20	0.12	0.1	0.59
H_2O-	—	0.04	0.90	0.30	—	—	—	—
SiO_2	0.88	3.40	14.88	—	—	0.9	—	—
Al_2O_3	0.42	0.59	2.56	n.d.	0.19	—	—	—
Fe_2O_3	0.76	0.28	8.24	0.11	0.28	—	—	0.45
MnO	0.03	0.04	1.46	—	—	—	0.04	—
Na_2O	—	0.36	0.17	—	—	—	0.26	—
K_2O	—	0.09	0.66	—	—	—	0.01	—
Insol.	—	—	—	0.05	0.15	—	—	0.10
Total[b]	99.41	99.80	99.70	100.52	100.35	99.93	99.0	99.96

[a] From additional analyses, excluded from total.
[b] Corrected for F and Cl. n.d. = not detected.

1. Industrial apatite concentrate (87% apatite), Palabora, Transvaal. Phosphate Development Corporation, 1964. Total includes 0.13 TiO_2, 0.08 Cu, 0.06 ZrO_2.
2. Apatite rock (93% apatite, 3% feldspar, 1.8% calcite), Nathace Hill, Tundulu, Malawi. Mrs. M. H. Kerr, anal. Total includes 0.09 FeO, and 0.08 TiO_2. After Garson (1962), p. 97.
3. Apatite rock (60% apatite with secondary quartz and goethite, feldspar, bastnaesite, pyrochore, etc.), Nathace Hill, Tundulu, Malawi. R. Pickup, anal. Total includes 0.42 BaO, 0.29 Nb_2O_5, and 0.24 TiO_2. After Garson (1962), p. 98.
4. Francolite from secondary phosphate rock, Busumbu, Uganda. L. C. Chadwick, anal. After Davies (1947), p. 143.
5. Apatite flotation concentrate from residual soil, Sukulu, Uganda. After Fleming and Robinson (1960), p. 971.
6. Apatite from limonitic weathered zone, Lueshe carbonatite, Kivu, Congo. After Brasseur, *et al.* (1961), p. 76.
7. Apatite from Panda Hill carbonatite, Tanganyika. After van der Veen (1963), p. 81.
8. Strontian apatite from residual soil on Nkombwa Hill carbonatite, Zambia. R. Pickup, anal.

Basal plates of apatite with sector twinning are seen in several carbonatites, but it should not be assumed that these are carbonate-apatites, as the Nkombwa apatite (analysis 8), in which this feature is very pronounced, contains very little CO_2.

COPPER

Sulphides of iron, zinc, lead and copper have been noted in several African carbonatites, but most of the occurrences are so sporadic or low-grade as to merit little interest. The Loolekop carbonatite in the centre of the Palabora Complex in the Transvaal, however, is a striking exception, and the decision, taken in 1963, to make it one of the major copper mines of Africa, yielding an average of about 70,000 short tons of metal annually, must have surprised many geologists familiar only with other carbonatites. At that time it appeared that no other carbonatite complex revealed any comparable enrichment in copper, however feeble, and indeed the rather scanty geochemical data suggested that usually carbonatites contain less copper than most igneous rocks. A few determinations of the copper contents of soils from 15 carbonatite complexes, situated between the Chilwa and Rufunsa groups in the south, and Sukulu in the north, showed amounts not exceeding 60 ppm, and mostly between 5 and 30 ppm, whereas the zinc contents ranged from 150 to more than 2000 ppm. In places other than Loolekop, where minor late stage sulphide mineralization is evident, as in the Tororo quarry, Uganda, pyrite is the principal sulphide with sphalerite next in abundance and galena not uncommon, but chalcopyrite is a very minor constituent. Sphalerite, on the other hand, is rather persistent in some carbonatites, such as Kangankunde Hill and Wigu Hill, although much below economic concentrations.

The following brief account of the Palabora copper deposit is based on press reports, which supplement the short papers by Russell, *et al.* (1954) and Forster (1958), and on information kindly provided by the Palabora Mining Company. Lombaard, *et al.* (1964) and Hanekom, *et al.* (1965) give fuller descriptions. Although Africans worked copper and iron at Palabora perhaps two centuries ago, the potentialities of the deposit emerged only in 1956 on completion of a government drilling programme for radioactive minerals (uranothorianite). This disclosed large reserves of magnetite-rich carbonatite containing only uneconomic amounts of uranothorianite, but with very persistent copper sulphides. Subsequently the Palabora Mining Company has found the ore to extend to a depth exceeding 3000 ft, and has proved reserves of 315 million tons of ore averaging 0.69% copper available for opencast mining to a depth of 1200 ft. The copper content, although low by African standards, is comparable with that of American 'porphyry copper' mines, and exceptionally little waste rock will have to be moved. Gold and silver will be minor by-products, and iron ore production may be important, as about 1.8 million tons of low-titania magnetite will be recovered annually. The mine and smelter came into production in 1966.

The copper ore-body comprises the central vertical mass of transgressive carbonatite, some 100 by 600 yd in cross section, which averages about 1% copper, and a surrounding low-grade (about 0.5% copper) zone of earlier banded carbonatite and interlayered phoscorite (see p. 390), including many bands very poor in copper. Calcite is the predominant carbonate and magnetite is very abundant (about 25%), that in the carbonatite core containing less than 0.5% titania, whereas in the phoscorite the magnetite carries exsolved ilmenite and may contain up to 8% titania. Ores from the inner and outer zones are milled in separate circuits, thereby securing a valuable low-titania magnetite from the carbonatite, and segregating the titaniferous magnetite from the outer zone. Baddeleyite and uranothorianite occur as early formed minor accessories.

Two stages of sulphide mineralization are apparent, both clearly later than the crystallization of the magnetite and minor oxide minerals. The earlier one, which pre-dated the emplacement of the transgressive carbonatite, is characterized by the development of bornite and a fair amount of chalcocite in the banded carbonatite and phoscorite. In a later and more important stage, associated with the transgressive carbonatite both in the central core and in narrow veinlets throughout the phoscorite and banded carbonatite, chalcopyrite predominates and locally cubanite is common. Other sulphides present include fairly widespread valleriite and pyrrhotite, and minor amounts of covellite (secondary), pentlandite, millerite, bravoite, linnaeite, violarite, sphalerite, tetrahedrite, pyrite and marcasite. The concentrations of minor metallic constituents in the ores and concentrates have not yet been disclosed. Malachite characterizes the zone of oxidation, which varies in depth from 10 ft on the crest of Loolekop to a maximum of 200 ft beneath the lower ground. There has been no secondary enrichment of copper.

These developments at Palabora gave new zest to carbonatite investigations. Already there is evidence of minor copper enrichments in other complexes, similarly associated with pyroxenites and magnetite ores, both at Iron Hill (Powderhorn) Colorado (Temple and Grogan, 1965) and at Bukusu, Uganda (Uganda Geol. Surv., *in litt.*). Although neither attains ore grade, the inference is that the copper mineralization is an intrinsic phase of the carbonatite activity, rather than that carbonatites are merely hosts to extraneous mineralization.

NIOBIUM

Until 1950 it was commonly believed that niobium was essentially an element of certain granites, alkali syenites and their pegmatites, and world reserves were deemed quite inadequate in relation to its potential usefulness. Within five years the discoveries of large pyrochlore deposits in carbonatites, first in Africa and later in America, reversed that position, and since 1960 exploitation of these deposits has begun in Canada and Brazil, but in Africa it still awaits increased demand and improved extraction techniques.

Pyrochlore has been found in most of the African carbonatites in which it has been specifically sought, but often only in minor quantity and it clearly belongs to restricted phases of carbonatite formation. It appears to be absent or very subordinate in such complexes as Palabora, Shawa and Dorowa where carbonatite is subordinate to syenite, pyroxenite and dunite, and is at a minimum in the late-stage rare earth-strontium-barium carbonatites (unless the latter are superimposed on earlier pyrochlore-bearing phases), and in the modern sodic carbonatite lava of Oldoinyo Lengai. The major occurrences are in the eroded and relatively large carbonatite plugs, or intrusions such as the large Kaluwe carbonatite breccia sill, in which intrusive silicate rocks are subordinate or absent. Only in a few occurrences has niobium transgressed significantly from the carbonatite into adjacent fenites, as in the biotitic roof-pendants at Panda Hill and the contact zones at Lueshe. At the few localities, e.g. Lueshe, where pyrochlore is found in both syenites and carbonatites, it is much more abundant in the latter. Trace amounts of pyrochlore are not uncommon in nepheline syenites and foyaites unaccompanied by carbonatites, although the latter qualification may sometimes be uncertain. In the foyaite-pyroxenite intrusion of Ilomba Hill, Malawi, small but high-grade lenses of pyrochlore-aegirine-sphene rock occur and there is no evidence whatever of carbonatite, but as the Nach-endezwaya carbonatite (with traces of pyrochlore), across the Tanganyika border less than two miles away, is clearly part of the same complex, a genetic link with carbonatite exists. At Chilwa Island the pyrochlore is confined to the sövite core of the complex, but it also occurs in a small aegirine-riebeckite syenite intrusion forming part of the Mpyupyu Hill perthosite and quartz-syenite complex of the same age only 8 miles distant (Garson, 1960). It remains true, however, that no occurrences in Africa clearly bridge the gap between the pyrochlore-rich carbonatite plugs and the columbite-bearing alkali granite ring complexes of Nigeria, in which in the extreme cases the niobium content reaches its maximum in central bodies of pyrochlore-albite-riebeckite granite (Jacobson, et al., 1958).

Many of the 25 niobium-bearing carbonatites scattered between Damaraland in South West Africa, the Eastern Transvaal and Northern Uganda are in-adequately described, and the present discussion will be based on the better known occurrences. At Chilwa Island, apart from low-grade disseminations in sövite and rather limited residual soil deposits, the major concentrations of pyrochlore are found in steeply-inclined dike-like zones of fine-grained ankeritic carbonatite containing apatite, sodic tremolite, altered acmite, phlogopite and up to 3 per cent of euhedral pyrochlore, sometimes of two generations (Garson and Campbell Smith, 1958). The hanging wall of the main ore body is of acmite sövite, and the foot wall is generally rich in pyrite. The ore zones have had a complex history, abundant schlieren rich in phlogopite representing meta-somatized relics of fenite screens which were invaded by the ankeritic pyrochlore-rich carbonatite and then brecciated and carried upwards during renewed intrusion of the plug. Details have recently been published (Garson, 1965 b) of the one ore-body explored up to 1955, when work stopped as soon as prices fell. They indicate a probable reserve on the Northern Plateau of 650,000 tons of ore averaging 1% pyrochlore to a depth of 1000 ft. Here the zone is mainly 15–25 ft wide, and extensions further south are wider but of lower grade. Although this ore-body is relatively small, it should be borne in mind that exploration was limited and incomplete and disregarded fine-grained (−200 mesh) pyrochlore. In the Tundulu Complex the principal potential reserves of pyrochlore are in the apatite rock and apatite-sövite ring dikes of Nathace Hill (see p. 391); the grade is low (about 0.25% Nb_2O_5) but if the deposits are worked for apatite using flotation processes by-product recovery of pyrochlore might be feasible.

In the Panda Hill (Mbeya) carbonatite visible pyrochlore is widespread and extensive drilling and sampling has proved 125 million tons of ore averaging 0.3% Nb_2O_5. The ore is largely apatite-bearing sövite and dolomitic sövite, with numerous accessories (van der Veen, 1963), but among the small richer ore zones is an area of biotitic contact rock rich in pyrochlore (including pandaite) of which 3.8 million tons were proved averaging 0.79% Nb_2O_5. The pyrochlore crystals are prone to carry inclusions of apatite, rutile, ilmenite, etc., and may be replaced by calcite, fluorite, barite or quartz, or altered to fersmite, columbite or secondary hydrated pyrochlores (see p. 398). A large pilot mill operated at Panda Hill from 1957 to 1960 and several hundred tons of concentrates containing 10 to 25% Nb_2O_5 were shipped to Europe for further test work, but operations have since been suspended.

The apatite-rich residual soils at Sukulu (see p. 392) carry approximately 0.2–0.25% Nb_2O_5, and pyrochlore can be recovered by flotation from the apatite flotation tailings, but plans to recover 75 tons of 50% Nb_2O_5 concentrate per annum have not been implemented. The total reserve is very large (400,000 tons Nb_2O_5), but as the pyrochlore is very fine-grained (mainly 5–40 microns), cost factors may permit only rather low recoveries.

Much higher grade but less tractable residual deposits mantle the Mrima carbonatite near the coast of Kenya (Coetzee and Edwards, 1959). Here an internal drainage system has produced basins of residuum extending in one case to a depth exceeding 600 ft. Proved reserves exceed 55 million short tons averaging 0.7% Nb_2O_5, but wide variations in grade occur, surface soils often being rather low grade. Rich areas contain more than 1% Nb_2O_5, and one recently investigated in detail has proved reserves of 5 million tons averaging 1.25% Nb_2O_5 which could be worked with little or no waste removal. The principal type of rich ore consists of powdery goethite (40–70%) and hydrated manganese oxides (about 10%), with minor barite, clay and gorceixite, and the niobium occurs as pandaite, hydrated barium pyrochlore (Harris, 1965). In more restricted areas of secondary rare earth ores (see p. 404), in which barite is the main gangue, a little barium pyrochlore is detectable but the bulk of the niobium appears to be in fine-grained earthy decomposition products which have defied identification. Limited exploration of the underlying carbonatite suggests that zones of amphibole sövite with accessory pyrite and 0.1–0.3% of common pyrochlore are the parent rocks of the richer residual ores. The buried karstic surface of the carbonatite plug is pinnacled and potholed, and slumping of the residuum and its localized induration with secondary barite and manganese ores contribute to the complexity of the deposit. Ore-dressing studies have as yet failed to indicate methods of treating these ores.

At Lueshe in Kivu Province, Republic of the Congo, niobium mineralization combines features found at Panda Hill and at Mrima. There are considerable reserves of pyrochlore aegirine sövite carrying about 0.5% Nb_2O_5, biotitic contact rocks with pyrochlore, and locally lueshite (see p. 399), and deeply weathered ferruginous rocks which constitute the richest ore, reserves being reported as 30 million tons averaging 1.34% Nb_2O_5.

Pyrochlore is the primary and most important niobium mineral in all carbonatite deposits, but this mineral includes several varieties, and other niobium minerals are frequently present. Table III lists the niobium-bearing minerals known in African carbonatites, and, since some of these are relatively new, simplified formulae have been included and principal occurrences are cited.

From the standpoint of niobium recovery it is clearly desirable that the pyrochlore should be uniform in physical properties and account for the bulk of the

o

niobium in the deposit, with a minimum dispersed in the associated titanium minerals. In general, the more promising niobium carbonatites are relatively poor in titanium, and although the niobium content of the rutile, anatase, sphene and ilmenite may often reach 1%, and occasionally 2%, this seldom accounts for a significant proportion of the niobium present. Niobian rutiles with 10–15% Nb_2O_5 occur at Chilwa Island and Mrima, but are a minor problem, and niobian perovskites of the dysanalyte type appear to be less important than

TABLE III

Niobium minerals found in African carbonatites

Mineral	Formula (simplified)	Occurrences
Common pyrochlore	$CaNaNb_2O_6F$	Common primary Nb mineral in all Nb-bearing carbonatites, and in many residual deposits.
Uranian pyrochlore[a]	$(Ca,Na,U)_{2-x}(Nb,Ti)_2(O,OH,F)_{7-y}$	Minor occurrence at Nkombwa; in associated syenites at Ilomba, Mpyupyu, *etc.*
Hydrated barium pyrochlore (pandaite)	$(Ba,Sr)_{<1} Nb_2O_{6-x}(H_2O)_{<1}$	In weathered silicified carbonatites and biotite contact rocks at Panda Hill; as supergene alteration product in residual deposits at Panda Hill, Mrima, Chasweta and Nachomba.
Hydrated strontium pyrochlore	$(Sr,Ba,K)_{<1} Nb_2O_{6-x}(H_2O)_{<1}$	In weathered rocks at Panda Hill, Lueshe and Nkombwa.
Fersmite	$CaNb_2(O,OH)_6$	Replacing pyrochlore, Panda Hill and Lueshe.
Columbite	$FeNb_2O_6$	Pseudomorphs pyrochlore at Chilwa Island, Panda Hill, Ngualla, Lueshe and Ondurakorume.
Lueshite	$NaNbO_3$	In biotite contact rock at Lueshe.
Aeschynite	$(Ce,La,Nd)NbTiO_6$	In residual soils at Ngualla.
Niobian rutile	$(Ti,Nb,Fe)O_2$	In residual deposits at Chilwa Island, Muambe and Mrima.

[a] The ideal formula of pyrochlore, $A_2B_2X_7$ allows multiple substitutions among both the larger A (Na,Ca,Ba, U, *etc.*) cations and the smaller B (Nb,Ta,Ti, *etc.*) cations, but in addition, large deficits in the A positions are common, and these defect varieties often contain much water.

at Oka and Kaiserstuhl. Niobium-rich silicates, such as the niocalite of Oka, have not yet been encountered in African carbonatites.

Of the primary varieties of pyrochlore found in carbonatites, common (sodium-calcium) pyrochlore is always the most abundant and usually carries only very minor amounts of titanium, rare earths, thorium and uranium, although these may vary appreciably even within a single complex. Highly uraniferous pyrochlores appear to be more characteristic of silicate rocks, and the one significant occurrence linked with an African carbonatite is that of the pyrochlore-aegirine-sphene lenses in the Ilomba foyaite complex, which is a uranian-titanian pyrochlore transitional towards betafite (analysis 6, Table IV). The secondary alteration of pyrochlores to hydrated barium–strontium varieties was first demonstrated at Panda Hill (Jäger, *et al.*, 1959), and has since been found to be of great importance at several major deposits in the tropics, especially at Araxa (Brazil), Lueshe and Mrima. Details of several of these secondary pyrochlores have been described by van der Veen (1963), characteristic features being replacement of the normal (Na, Ca) 'A' cations by a smaller number of much larger ions, especially barium, strontium and sometimes potassium, and hydration, resulting in a greatly expanded unit cell, a microgranular texture and low specific gravity. These alterations are most probably largely supergene, but in part, or locally, may also perhaps be low temperature hydrothermal, for in such an environment late hydrothermal solutions and descending tropical groundwaters may have much in common. Slightly metamict pyrochlores are presumably more prone to this type of alteration than well-crystallized types, but intensity of weathering or metasomatism is probably more important, and may account for the contrast between the fresh common pyrochlore in the apatite-rich Sukulu soil, and the almost complete conversion to pandaite in the apatite-free residuum at Mrima. The Lueshe residual ores contain an interesting strontium-potassium pyrochlore, again pseudomorphous after common pyrochlore. From the standpoint of pyrochlore recovery, the softness and granular texture of the secondary pyrochlores appear disadvantageous, but at Araxa (Brazil) recovery by flotation has been successful.

Replacement of pyrochlore by columbite has occurred locally at Chilwa Island, Panda Hill, Ngualla (James and McKie, 1958), and Lueshe, and results in finely granular and porous epimorphs or pseudomorphs, primary columbite being as yet quite unknown among African carbonatites. In x-ray photographs of these pseudomorphs (and similar ones from Fen, Norway) the 7.1 Å reflections are very faint, but if the mineral is heated the pattern conforms to that of normal columbite. Van der Veen (1960, 1963) has also found fersmite developed within Panda Hill pyrochlore, often with remarkable Widmanstätten textures, and sometimes showing later replacement by columbite. These replacements appear to be linked with the cooling history of the pyrochlore and late autometasomatic reactions. While this chapter was in the press Van Wambeke (1965) described in full detail similar late-stage replacements at Lueshe, but indicated also the sequence pyrochlore-columbite-fersmite, and an increase of tantalum and rare earths in the later phases.

Chemical analyses of a selection of pyrochlores are shown in Table IV, which also includes an analysis of lueshite, the end member of the niobian perovskite series, from a biotitic contact rock at Lueshe, but since discovered in similar rocks at Gem Park, Colorado, and at Kovdor, Kola Peninsula. Comment on the analyses will be restricted to niobium/tantalum ratios. A striking feature of carbonatites is the high Nb/Ta ratio which commonly ranges from 50 to more than 1000, in contrast to an average of 5 for granitic rocks, and about 16 for ultrabasic and basic rocks, and syenites. Owing to analytical difficulties some of the earlier ratios reported were rather doubtful, but the more precise analyses, and recent tantalum determinations by neutron activation, (Bakes, *et al.*, 1964), have established very high ratios in several carbonatite pyrochlores. Concentrates from the principal Chilwa Island ore body contain more than 60% Nb_2O_5 and barely 0.01% Ta_2O_5, and thus the Nb/Ta ratio exceeds 5000, and the

TABLE IV

Chemical analyses of pyrochlores and lueshite

	Common pyrochlores				Uranian pyrochlores		Barium pyrochlores		Lueshite
	1	2	3	4	5	6	7	8	9
Na_2O	6.45	5.63	7.24	7.80	1.1	2.99	0.28	0.2	17.7
K_2O	0.03	—	0.07	0.12	0.5	0.54	0.15	0.2	2.0
CaO	17.50	14.89	14.82	14.91	8.0	7.90	0.86	1.3	0.74
SrO	1.56	0.69	—	2.02	3.8	0.34	6.60	tr.	n.d.
BaO	—	0.12	—	—	1.4	n.d.	12.88	14.9	—
Ln_2O_3	—	0.31	2.00	tr.	2.7	1.57	2.06	2.1	n.d.
ThO_2	0.28	2.02	0.37	0.50	1.5	0.65	0.62	0.9	0.7[b]
ZrO_2	0.43	1.27	1.91	—	1.1	—	—	—	—
U_3O_8	0.35	—	—	—	2.8	12.83	—	—	n.d.
PbO	—	0.03	—	—	—	tr.	—	0.2	—
MgO	—	—	0.49	0.05	—	tr.	—	0.5	—
Fe_2O_3[a]	0.16	0.40	0.48	1.25	1.2	1.84	0.44	1.1	1.1
Al_2O_3	—	—	0.20	n.d.	—	tr.	—	0.2	—
SiO_2	—	—	—	—	3.4	0.77	—	1.2	—
TiO_2	3.42	6.36	0.56	4.25	1.4	10.10	3.87	4.5	2.3
Nb_2O_5	69.37	67.17	68.72	67.49	51.9	53.60	69.06	63.9	73.7
Ta_2O_5	0.10	0.25	0.20	0.04	7.5	0.35	0.23	0.5	1.1
F	3.87	2.01	3.87	tr.	3.7	1.52	tr.	—	c.0.6
H_2O+	0.58	0.74	0.50	1.36	9.2	5.61	4.11	8.0	0.88
H_2O-	—	—	0.14	—	—	—	—	—	—
Total[c]	102.5	101.2	99.94	99.79	99.6	99.98	101.16	99.7	100.57

1. Black pyrochlore, Lueshe, Kivu, Congo. Corrected for 7% impurities. Billiton, anal.[d] Total includes 0.04 Sb_2O_3, and 0.01 SnO_2. After van der Veen (1963), p. 77.

2. Brown pyrochlore, Museum Zone, Panda Hill, Tanganyika. Corrected for 6% impurities. Billiton, anal. Total includes 0.075 Sb_2O_3, 0.01 Bi_2O_3, 0.06 SnO_2 and 0.06 WO_3. After van der Veen (1963), p. 75.

3. Brown pyrochlore, Sukulu Hills, Uganda. W. H. Bennett, anal. After Davies (1956), p. 36.

4. Light brown pyrochlore, Lokupoi, Napak, Uganda. P. G. Jeffery, anal.

5. Uranian pyrochlore, Nkombwa Hill, Zambia. R. Pickup, anal.

6. Uranian pyrochlore, from aegirine-sphene-pyrochlore rock, Ilomba Hill, Malawi. Corrected for 3.6% impurities. R. Pickup, anal.

7. Strontian pandaite, from weathered biotite rock, Panda Hill, Tanganyika. Corrected for 3% impurities. Billiton, anal. After Jäger, *et al.* (1959), p. 20.

8. Pandaite, from residual goethite-rich niobium ore, Mrima Hill, Kenya. Corrected for 10% impurities. R. Pickup, anal.

9. Lueshite, from phlogopite rock, Lueshe, Kivu, Congo. R. Pickup, anal.

[a] Total iron equivalent.

[b] Radiometric determination.

[c] Corrected for O = F.

[d] Analytical laboratories of N. V. Hollandse Metalurgische Industrie Billiton, Arnhem, Netherlands.

atomic ratio exceeds 10,000. Ratios exceeding 1000 also occur in some samples from Lueshe, Mrima, Lokupoi (Napak) and Nkombwa Hill, both in common pyrochlores and in secondary barium and strontium pyrochlores. Equally common however are ratios between 500 and 50, and in the uranian pyrochlore from Nkombwa Hill, which is of rather restricted occurrence, the ratio is only 5.9 (analysis 5).

MOLYBDENUM

This element, one of the most elusive of those associated with carbonatites, has not yet been found in workable concentrations, but deserves notice as the possibility of future discoveries of economic interest should not be excluded. It was first detected at Kangankunde Hill, only in trace amounts, but this prompted an examination of a few samples from each of fifteen other African carbonatites. All proved to contain molybdenum, the majority from 10–100 ppm, the amounts in rocks frequently equalling that in associated soils, in conformity with the known mobility of this element in the zone of weathering. The residual soils and ores of Mrima Hill, Kenya, however, showed much higher values, and further investigation of this deposit indicated that the near-surface soils (to a depth of about 20 ft) averaged about 0.04% MoO_3, some of the richer niobium ores contained about 0.1%, and the residual manganese ores carried 0.1–0.2% MoO_3. Much, but not all, of this molybdenum is adsorbed in secondary manganese oxides, and small specimens of botryoidal psilomelane from niobium and rare earth rich residual ores contain as much as 1.2% MoO_3 (together with 0.4% V_2O_5 and 0.4% P_2O_5, but without any analogous enrichment in As, W, Cu, Ni or Co). This selective adsorption of molybdenum in secondary manganese ores has subsequently been found to a lesser degree over several other carbonatites, in some cases giving the first evidence of the element in the complex, but it has not yet led to the discovery of promising enrichments in the underlying rocks. The limited investigations have indicated only very variable molybdenum contents in fresh rock specimens, with rare maxima around 0.1% MoO_3, (e.g. at Chilwa Island, Malawi, and at Wigu Hill and Songwe Scarp, Tanganyika (Brown, 1964)). No pattern of mineralogical associations is apparent, and no primary molybdenum mineral has yet been identified. There is limited evidence that molybdenum is more abundant in the late-stage ankeritic carbonatites than in the niobium-rich sövites, and also that molybdenum appears sporadically in the feldspathic aureoles around carbonatites, but the data available are too fragmentary for further generalizations.

BARIUM AND STRONTIUM

Although barite is known to occur in many of the African carbonatites, there has been little systematic search for workable deposits, largely because of the relatively low price of the mineral and the lack of local demand for it. The fact (perhaps fortuitous) that the world's largest barite mine at Chamberlain Creek, Arkansas, lies adjacent to the Magnet Cove syenite-carbonatite complex (Scull, 1958), has prompted speculation as to the existence of comparable deposits in Africa, but nothing more. The most extensive barite occurrence yet recognized among the African carbonatites is at Mrima Hill, Kenya, where the mineral forms irregular veins and bands in the residuum, and, in finely granular form, is the principal gangue mineral in the earthy monazite-niobium ores. As satisfactory methods of concentrating the latter have still to be devised, however, the proportion and quality of by-product barite remains unknown. The gorceixite, psilomelane and hydrated pyrochlore of this deposit also all contain barium. Small lenticular ore-bodies of crystalline barite at Nathace Hill, Malawi, have been described by Garson (1962, p. 221; this vol., p. 48), but these, and comparable occurrences elsewhere, appear unlikely to be of more than local interest.

Whereas barium occurs predominantly as the sulphate in most carbonatites, the strontium sulphate, celestite, has been recognized only in minor amounts, and strontianite is much more important. Owing to its solubility it is not found in the residual soils and it is rather difficult to recognize in the carbonatites unless found in veins. It appears to be characteristic of the rare earth carbonatites, being very abundant in the monazite-rich rocks of Kangankunde Hill, and a significant constituent of the monazite and bastnaesite-bearing rocks at Nathace, Nkombwa and Wigu.

At Kangankunde Hill small irregular veins of strontianite were recorded as early as 1907, but these are of minor importance and the abundance of strontianite in the medium-grained rare earth carbonatite only emerged during detailed investigations of the monazite ores. The strontianite content of the latter varies widely and rather erratically from less than 2% to more than 50%, and in the two areas which have been drilled the monazite ore-bodies average about 10 and 20% respectively. In one trench the strontianite content averaged 29% over 90 ft, including a 40 ft section averaging 38%. Such rich sections, however, include shallow supergene replacements of oxidized ankerite which are chocolate brown in colour and contain 50–75% strontianite. The tonnage available is clearly large in relation to the present world consumption of strontium compounds, which is derived solely from celestite, and Kangankunde must rank as one of the very few major strontianite deposits of the world. Analyses show that the mineral is exceptionally pure, containing less calcium carbonate in solid solution than usual, the $SrCO_3$ content varying from 95% to more than 98%, and barium is absent. Despite many impurities the Kangankunde ores yield pure strontium hydroxide by calcination and aqueous leaching processes (British Patent applications nos. 18578/63 and 29755/64), and it is probable that strontium compounds will become important co-products of monazite when mining is established. The predominance of strontianite in the African rare earth carbonatites contrasts sharply with circumstances at Mountain Pass, California, where barite is a major constituent.

RARE EARTHS

Carbonatites as a class are enriched in rare earths as compared with all major rock types, and several of the African complexes include rocks containing from 1–20% of rare earth oxides. These rocks are predominantly dolomitic or ankeritic and are usually characterized by significant enrichments of strontium, barium and manganese, and in some cases zinc and molybdenum. The rare earth minerals comprise the phosphates monazite, florencite and goyazite, which are seen to have developed in both hypogene and supergene phases, and gorceixite which is probably essentially supergene, and the fluocarbonates bastnaesite, parisite and synchisite. Pyrochlore, which carries only minor amounts of rare earths, is subordinate or absent from these rocks, and when present probably belongs to a separate (earlier) phase of carbonatite activity. This mineralization is fully described as Kangankunde Hill (Garson, 1965a,b; this vol., p. 63), and Tundulu (Garson, 1962; this vol., p. 90), and is also found at Wigu Hill, Tanganyika (McKie, 1962), and Nkombwa Hill, Zambia, and is represented among the residual ores of Mrima Hill, Kenya. Although all have features in common, each has its distinctive characteristics.

At Kangankunde Hill the central core of the complex is occupied by numerous dikes and veins of ankeritic carbonatites heavily mineralized with strontianite, monazite, barite and quartz and with minor amounts of strontian florencite, pyrite and sphalerite. Bastnaesite appears locally as fine flaky crystals in a brown ankeritic rock, which is more abundant in adjacent subsidiary knolls. The monazite forms minute (0.02–2 mm) green and colourless crystals which were mistaken for epidote in 1907, a misnomer which persisted until the writer re-examined specimens in 1951. Analysis shows it to be a very simple monazite, almost free from thorium and yttrium, but with an interesting substitution of strontium (1.4% SrO) in place of lanthanons. Its feeble radioactivity is as low as that of the thorium-free monazite from Llallagua, Bolivia, which contains uranium and is yttrium-rich. The monazite ore zones are medium to coarse-grained carbonatites with disseminated monazite and strontianite, cut by lenses and irregular drusy veins in which aggregates of coarse radiating hexagonal crystals are now pseudomorphed by a mixture of strontianite, monazite, barite and quartz. Grade is extremely variable, but over widths of from 25–100 ft may average from 5 to 10% monazite, 10–30% strontianite and 2 to 5% barite. The assemblage must be presumed to originate from a residual accumulation of large ions (Sr,Ln,Ba) in solutions which finally crystallized and replaced earlier minerals in the last stages of the cooling and solidification of the carbonatite plug. Trenching and a limited drilling programme has indicated individual ore-bodies, steeply dipping and averaging more than 5% monazite, containing from 4000 to more than 14,000 tons of monazite per 100 ft vertical depth, and the total reserves probably amount to several hundred thousand tons of monazite accompanied by about twice that amount of strontianite. Methods of extracting the monazite and strontium have been tested with promising results, and industrial development is now anticipated (Holt, 1965).

In the Nkombwa Hill carbonatite, Zambia, green monazite (called epidote in the 1930's) is developed locally, again in highly magnesian rocks (ankerite with some breunnerite (ferroan magnesite)) and largely as late replacements. It may be euhedral, but more commonly forms minute spherulites strung along cleavage planes of ankerite. These spherulites are almost unique in showing concentric extinction bands as well as an extinction cross between crossed polars (Deans and McConnell, 1955, plate 18, Fig. 2). This monazite is most abundant in pseudomorphs of radiating hexagonal crystals up to 2 inches in length, identical with those of Kangankunde, but here isokite accompanies the monazite and strontianite. A little bastnaesite is also found, in part replaced by monazite. At Wigu Hill, Tanganyika (Harris, 1961; McKie, 1962), in a complex of dolomitic carbonatite dikes there are rare earth rich zones up to 4 ft in width, and often exceeding 500 ft in length. Some of these contain 16–20% of rare earth oxides, the mineral assemblage comprising bastnaesite, monazite and cerian goyazite (which hardly differs from the strontian florencite of Kangankunde; see McKie, 1962), with dolomite, calcite, barite, celestite, quartz and minor pyrite and sphalerite. The rare earth minerals are essentially replacive, often pseudo-morphous after the elusive unknown hexagonal mineral, and McKie (1962) suggests that they crystallized at temperatures well below 500°C and at low pressures.

At these three localities the rare earth mineralization appears to be largely a hydrothermal (?) end phase of carbonatite activity, but one which was confined to the carbonatite rocks, and there is no clear evidence of transport of rare earths through the surrounding fenites into the country rocks. The latter process, however, has possibly been responsible for the bastnaesite-barite veins developed in schists and quartzites at Karonge in Burundi, for the geochemical assemblage is indistinguishable from that of the rare earth carbonatites (even down to traces of molybdenum), and Thoreau, *et al.* (1958) have cited the importance of carbon-atite activity in this region.

The synchisite and bastnaesite-bearing carbonatites of the Chilwa Island and Tundulu Complexes provide examples of a lower grade of rare earth mineraliza-tion, best developed at the Nathace Hill centre, Tundulu (Garson, 1962). Here, 2–5% of finely disseminated flaky bastnaesite occurs in arcuate dikes of both apatite-rich sövites and ankeritic carbonatites, but although the reserves are very large there seems little prospect of exploiting such occurrences. Despite similarities with the Mountain Pass bastnaesite-barite carbonatite of California, none of the African occurrences yet described is identical with it.

The primary monazite and florencite of carbonatites survives unaltered in the overlying residual soils, and at Kangankunde Hill, for example, although the soil is relatively thin, sampling shows that it contains at least 100,000 tons of monazite. In tropical weathering, however, bastnaesite and other fluorocarbon-ates are decomposed, and their rare earths, together with trace amounts liberated from apatite and perhaps from ankeritic carbonates, are reprecipitated in the residuum as earthy secondary monazite, and in some cases, probably as gor-ceixite-type minerals. This earthy monazite, identified with certainty only by its x-ray pattern, often accounts for the presence of up to 1 or 2% of rare earths in soils overlying carbonatites which appear to be devoid of discrete rare earth minerals, and it is also found in some oxidized (limonitic) ankeritic carbonatites. A comparable development of secondary earthy monazite has been described from the Magnet Cove carbonatite, Arkansas (Rose, *et al.*, 1958). In the deeply weathered Mrima carbonatite near the seacoast of Kenya, however, where the decalcified residuum has accumulated on the karst surface of the carbonatite to great depths (see p. 397), secondary rare earth deposits are developed on an im-pressive scale. Much of the widespread ferruginous residuum contains only up to 4% rare earths, but in one prospecting shaft the rare earth oxide content from surface to bedrock at 87 ft averaged 14%, and from 12–67 ft averaged 17.7%. The material is a powdery buff or yellow 'earth', with occasional hard masses cemented by barite or manganese oxides, consisting of finely-divided barite, earthy cryptocrystalline monazite, buff or white chalky gorceixite, goethite and psilomelane, as well as altered finely-divided niobium and titanium minerals. Although the minerals are difficult to resolve and separate, it is believed that earthy monazite accounts for most of the rare earths present, for the gorceixite, which is a strontian variety, appears to contain only traces to a few per cent of rare earths. At Mrima the carbonatites are seldom exposed and have not been studied in

TABLE V

Carbonatite rare earth ores compared with monazite sands

	Carbonatite ores			Monazite sands		
	1	2	3	4	5	6
	Percentage in mineral or ore					
Ln_2O_3	69.78	13.5	72	64	58.92	59.44
ThO_2	0.08	0.12	<0.1	6	6.80	7.33
	Percentage composition of rare earths					
La_2O_3	36	33	33	24	27	20
CeO_2	50	45	49	47	45	47
Pr_6O_{11}	3.2	3.9	4.5	4.5	4.4	4.5
Nd_2O_3	10.1	13.5	13.5	18.5	18.7	20
Sm_2O_3	0.6	1.6	0.6	3.0	2.2	3.4
Eu_2O_3	0.06*	0.6	0.1	0.05	0.03	—
Gd_2O_3	0.01	—		1.0	0.5	1.6
Tb_4O_7	—	—		0.1	—	—
Dy_2O_3	0.01	0.3		0.35	0.3	—
Ho_2O_3	≯0.01	—	<0.3	0.03	tr.	—
Er_2O_3	0.01	0.4		0.07	—	—
Tm_2O_3	—	—		0.005	—	—
Yb_2O_3	≯0.01	0.1		0.02	—	—
Y_2O_3	0.03	1.0	0.1	1.4	1.0	3.0

1. Monazite, Kangankunde Hill, Malawi: Johnson Matthey Research Laboratories, and National Chemical Laboratory, 1964, anal.* (Correction: later analyses show 0.12 per cent Eu_2O_2 as more typical of Kangankunde Monazite.)

2. Residual ore, Mrima Hill, Kenya. Johnson Matthey Research Laboratories, 1964, anal.

3. Bastnaesite, Mountain Pass, California. Mean composition, courtesy Molybdenum Corporation of America, 1964.

4. Monazite sand, Espirito Santo, Brazil. After P. Krumholz, 1957.

5. Monazite sand, Capel, Western Australia. From Western Titanium N.L., 1961.

6. Monazite sand, Kinta, Perak, Malaya. Sample 4 of Flinter, *et al.* (1963).

detail, so that little is yet known of the primary source of the rare earths. The reserves of this residuum rich in rare earths may be relatively limited, but they are quite large in relation to current consumption of these elements.

The relative proportions of individual rare earths, and of yttrium and thorium, in the Kangankunde and Mrima deposits are shown in Table V, together with comparable data for typical ores now in use. From an industrial standpoint the rare earth ores now available in abundance are of two kinds, the carbonatite type, exceptionally rich in lanthanum and free from thorium and yttrium, and the monazite sand type, won from beach sands of metamorphic or granitic derivation or from tinfield alluvials, rich in thorium and with rather more neodymium, samarium and gadolinium. In both types cerium is the principal rare earth, but it is more abundant in the carbonatite ores. The similarity of the rare earth assemblages of the Kangankunde monazite and the Mountain Pass bastnaesite is very striking, despite the differing mineralogy. In the Mrima ore, a weathered residual accumulation, there is a slightly higher content of heavier earths and yttrium, presumably because earths derived from apatite, sphene and pyrochlore are present, and europium, one of the scarcest of the rare earths, is abundant. It should be noted that rare earth assemblages in the enrichments which constitute ores may differ somewhat from the trace element assemblages found in the more normal carbonatites, in which, for example, yttrium may sometimes be moderately abundant and the europium content may exceed 1% of the total rare earths. This is seen in recent neutron activation analyses by Schofield and Haskin (1964).

THORIUM AND URANIUM

Many carbonatite occurrences are distinctly radioactive, and radiometric surveys may often outline the boundaries of a complex remarkably well, so naturally in the early 1950's consideration was given to their potentialities as sources of uranium and thorium. Results were never encouraging, however, and the investigations were mostly short-lived. The radioactivity of the soils was found to be greatly enhanced by selective concentration of daughter elements, causing radiometric assays which were usually several times greater than chemical analyses, and the latter usually showed a great preponderance of thorium over uranium. Thorium-bearing pyrochlore proved to be the common primary source of the radioactivity, and even liberal estimates of by-product recoveries of thorium and uranium, from pyrochlore and apatite production on a grandiose scale, were unimpressive. Other radioactive minerals were found, notably uranothorianite at Palabora, but never uraninite or pitchblende. In the writer's opinion the overall abundance of thorium and uranium in carbonatites is probably not very high, but reliable data are lacking, as analyses are heavily biased towards abnormally radioactive carbonatites.

The Palabora ore bodies are unique among African carbonatites in containing uranothorianite. It occurs as small cubic crystals and in veinlets, and is most abundant in the younger transgressive carbonatite, where it has replaced calcite and may enclose apatite, but preceded the sulphide and copper mineralization. Russell, *et al.* (1954), published analyses of two concentrates both containing about 77% combined $ThO_2 + U_3O_8$, but the ratio of thoria to urania is 2.0 in the composite sample from depth, and 3.6 in the surface sample. Government exploration in 1953–1956 revealed erratic low-grade radioactivity and an overall grade of about 0.16 lb/ton equiv. U_3O_8, with a mean ThO_2 U_3O_8 ratio of 2.81 (Hanekom, *et al.*, 1965). These values correspond to about 0.004% U and 0.012% Th, but in the copper-rich core of the orebody grade averages about 0.006% U and 0.033% Th. This data, and preliminary tests, suggest that only small tonnages of by-product uranothorianite may be anticipated.

Pyrochlore is the principal radioactive mineral in most carbonatites, usually with thorium predominating over uranium, but wide variations may occur within a single complex, and even between different generations of pyrochlore in the same hand specimen. The variations commonly extend from about 0.1–3% ThO_2, and from about 0.01–0.5% U_3O_8. Typical thoria contents of experimental pyrochlore concentrates have been 2.7% ThO_2 at Sukulu, 0.8% ThO_2 at Panda Hill, and 1.3% ThO_2 at Chilwa Island (oreshoot). The secondary barium pyrochlores, as far as is known, tend to be less radioactive than the primary common pyrochlores. At Nkombwa Hill the general level of radio-activity is extremely low, and in most samples the pyrochlore is only feebly radioactive (about 0.1% equiv. ThO_2 or less), but some samples from near the margin of the plug contain, in addition to the prevalent colourless pyrochlore, a brown radioactive pyrochlore which carries 2.0–2.8% U_3O_8 and 0.5–1.6% ThO_2. An analysis of this pyrochlore, which is also richer in tantalum than is usual in carbonatites, appears in Table IV (p. 400). There is some evidence that the pyrochlores in the syenitic rocks associated genetically or geographically with carbonatites are more uraniferous than those found in the latter. Thus at Mpyupyu Hill, near Chilwa Island (see p. 396), the pyrochlore in the alkali syenite contains 1.0% U_3O_8, whereas that in the Chilwa sövites has only 0.01% U_3O_8, and in northern Malawi in the Ilomba Hill complex the sodalite syenite carries traces of betafite (i.e. Ti-pyrochlore with more than 15% U_3O_8), and in thin lenses of high grade aegirine-sphene-pyrochlore rock in the foyaite the pyrochlore carries 12.8% U_3O_8 and only 0.65% ThO_2, whereas the rare pyrochlore in the related Nachendezwaya sövite nearby is only weakly radio-active.

The rare earth carbonatites are much less radioactive than the pyrochlore-bearing types, and the negligible radioactivity of monazite-rich ore bodies is very striking, the reason being that the monazite usually contains only 0.1–0.2% ThO_2 as compared with 5–10% ThO_2 common in monazites derived from granites or migmatites. Only in very minor related occurrences, such as the radioactive feldspathic dike, 1.5 miles from Kangankunde Hill, is moderately radioactive monazite found (about 2.3% ThO_2) together with bastnaesite and parisite (Garson, 1965a), in a manner which suggests that the radioactivity may be inversely proportional to the gross reserves of rare earths, i.e. the abundance of rare earth minerals may disperse rather than concentrate the available thorium.

Secondary enrichments of thorium are found in a few residual deposits on carbonatites. At Mrima Hill, for example, the niobium rare earth ores contain from about 0.1–0.2% ThO_2, and smaller occurrences associated with secondary goethite are recorded at Chilwa Island (Garson and Campbell Smith, 1958, pp. 86–89), and at Nachomba (Bailey, 1960, pp. 71–72). The Chilwa occurrences are traceable as radioactive dikes containing quartz, barite and/or fluorite, which Garson regards as probably of late hydrothermal origin, but no primary radioactive mineral has been detected. Strongly radioactive specimens carry 2.1% ThO_2 and an equal amount of rare earth oxides, apparently associated with (adsorbed in ?) goethite, and the material from Nachomba is rather similar, but both occurrences are small.

OTHER ELEMENTS

In this section brief mention will be made of some of the other elements which might constitute useful by-products in working some of the deposits already discussed, either initially, or when a more diversified economy has developed. These are mostly elements such as iron, manganese, titanium and zirconium which are readily available from other types of mineral deposit, and likely to be utilized only if special incentives arise. The carbonates themselves also deserve comment, as well as some of the fugitive constituents from carbonatites which can be found and worked in certain lakes and salt pans.

Magnetite is the only primary iron mineral to be considered, and it may assume importance as a by-product at both Palabora and Sukulu. At Palabora output of by-product magnetite concentrates from the copper mine may amount to 2.5–3 million tons annually. About two-thirds of this is low-titania magnetite from the carbonatite core, acceptable for iron smelting, and one-third is titaniferous magnetite from the periphery of the ore body, requiring separate marketing arrangements. The Sukulu magnetite from the apatite soil deposits contains less than 1% TiO_2, but as the concentrates cannot be freed completely of apatite they will be classed as phosphoric ores. Both these magnetites contain a little vanadium, but only about 0.1%, a very minor amount compared with the 0.8% in the titanomagnetites in the Bushveld Igneous Complex which are worked as vanadium ores. The rubble magnetite deposits which cap several ridges in the ijolitic zone of the Bukusu Complex, Uganda (Davies, 1956, pp. 72–76; Broughton, *et al.*, 1950), show a remarkable range in composition from limited deposits of fairly pure magnetite ore with not more than 1% TiO_2, through a widespread development of titaniferous magnetites with $6-14\%$ TiO_2, to the perovskite-bearing titanomagnetites of Surumbusa Hill which contain more than 20% TiO_2. Perhaps the latter type may ultimately find a use in the titanium industry.

Much of the residual niobium ore at Mrima Hill, Kenya (see p. 397), consists predominantly of goethite and manganese oxides, and contains about 30% iron and more than 5% manganese. Despite their high niobium content no economic concentration process has yet been devised and it is thought possible that it may be necessary to develop a pyrometallurgical process to solve this problem. Such a process might well yield modest tonnages of by-product iron, and possibly manganese, which would be important both in helping to meet the cost of the process and in establishing a new industry in this region.

The ankeritic carbonatites usually contain manganese, and by weathering give rise to residual manganiferous iron ores or, occasionally, to ferruginous manganese ores. These tend to be impure, however, and in a continent well endowed with ores of these metals they have little economic interest. In general, the processes of separation of iron from manganese which might give rise to high grade ores have not proceeded far enough. At Chilwa Island and Kangankunde Hill the ratio of iron to manganese in the residual ore is about 3 or 4 to 1, and even at Mrima where downward migration of iron has enhanced the surface enrichment of manganese, it is only slightly less than one, an analysis of typical boulder ore showing 23% manganese and 19% iron.

Zirconium is not very abundant in carbonatites, and enrichments such as occur in lujavrites and other zirconium-rich nepheline syenites are quite unknown. Even as a by-product, the zircon associated with pyrochlore in carbonatite deposits could hardly compete with beach-sand zircon which is so pure, cheap and abundant. In contrast to the by-product zircon from the columbite granites of Nigeria which sells at a premium on account of its high hafnia content ($5-6\%$ HfO_2), carbonatite zircons appear to be exceptionally poor in hafnium (e.g. zircon from the Panda Hill (Museum Zone) pyrochlore deposit contains only 0.5% HfO_2). However, unless zircon with much less hafnia can be found, perhaps less than 0.1% HfO_2, which might be usable for nuclear reactors without separation of hafnium, this tendency has little practical significance. Baddeleyite would appear to have rather greater industrial possibilities, and the apatite-rich zones of the Palabora copper-apatite deposit have recently begun to yield useful tonnages, as a by-product from phoscorite, and output soon may rise to 2000 tons of baddeleyite annually, and increase further when the copper mine is in full production. If required, mixed zircon-baddeleyite concentrates are recoverable with pyrochlore from the apatite flotation plant at Sukulu, and if a keener interest in baddeleyite arose it is probable that it could be obtained in greater amount from residual deposits on the nearby Bukusu Complex.

In the field of non-metallic industrial minerals the potentialities of African carbonatites are rather hard to assess, much depending on location and the level of industrialization. Where limestones are not available, as in large tracts of East Africa, the purer sövites may be valuable sources of lime, and in Uganda they form the basis of the cement industry, despite problems caused by their high phosphorus content (Davies, 1954). As yet no use has been made of the dolomite rocks, some of which are fairly pure, or of the rarer occurrences of magnesitic carbonatites which have been found, for example, at Lueshe and at Nkombwa Hill. Most of the abundant fluorine involved in carbonatite intrusions is dispersed uneconomically, held in apatite or phlogopite, or carried into the drainage in saline solutions. Nevertheless late-stage hydrothermal quartz-fluorite deposits of potential interest are fairly common. Notable among these are the Okorusu deposits in South West Africa (Van Zijl, 1962), with reserves of 7 to 10 million tons carrying more than 35% calcium fluoride. Important volatile and water soluble constituents of the carbonatite suite are not to be found in the eroded carbonatite plugs, but rather in the salt lakes, springs and playas of the rift valleys. It is difficult to estimate what proportion of the vast reserves of salt and soda in some of these lakes derives from the weathering of alkaline (silicate) lavas and tuffs, and how much comes from carbonatite magma and hydrothermal solutions, but the predominance of sodium carbonate in the anhydrous carbonatite lavas and tuffs recently erupted from Oldoinyo Lengai (Dawson, 1962b and DuBois, *et al.*, 1963) near Lake Natron is suggestive of an important contribution from carbonatites. The economic deposits in this case are, of course, lacustrine brines and evaporites, both Lakes Natron and Magadi containing enormous reserves of sodium carbonate, chloride and fluoride. At Lake Magadi some 130,000 tons of anhydrous sodium carbonate, and about 16,000 tons of salt are produced annually, and sodium fluoride has been produced when required. A similar carbonatitic derivation may also be assigned to the small soda and salt industry which existed for many years at the Pretoria Saltpan in the Transvaal, for there seems little reason to doubt that the Saltpan is a carbonatite vent.

Potassium originating in carbonatite intrusions has in many cases become fixed in the surrounding potash feldspar rocks, breccias and trachytic intrusives, which frequently contain 13–15% K_2O. If ever the fertilizer industry develops an economic process for utilizing this material, deposits around several complexes (e.g. Palabora, the Chilwa Alkaline Province, the Panda Hill region and Eastern Uganda) may acquire economic significance.

CONCLUSIONS

There is still a great deal to be learned about the minerals of African carbonatites, and before an adequate systematic classification and discussion of carbonatite mineral deposits can be made, more information from other continents is desirable. Here, comment will be restricted to what appear to be some of the more significant features of the primary phases of mineralization found in Africa.

The distinction which Pecora (1956) made between the apatite-magnetite carbonatites and the rare earth carbonatites is broadly sustained by later work, and is a useful starting point for summarizing the African evidence. The apatite-magnetite mineralization appears to be a relatively early phase of carbonatite activity, associated with the intrusion of relatively large bodies of sövite, and the principal pyrochlore occurrences are usually associated with this phase, but in some cases niobium may be virtually absent. Rare earth-rich carbonatites, on the other hand, appear to be very late-stage enrichments of rare earths with strontium and/or barium in ankeritic rocks, probably in part hydrothermal, without significant amounts of magnetite or niobium, and usually form multiple vein and dike complexes. Many carbonatite complexes, however, reveal at least two or three stages of intrusion and alternations of metasomatic activity, so that it is not unusual to find several phases of hypogene mineralization in one complex. To cite African examples, the apatite-magnetite stage is well developed at Palabora, Dorowa, Chilwa Island, Panda Hill, Sukulu and Bukusu, and in all but the first two, pyrochlore is also present in some quantity. At Chilwa Island rare earth enrichment is evident in the later central core of ankeritic sövites, while at Palabora there is the unique super-position of late copper sulphide mineralization, also in the core. At Tundulu, however, the Nathace Hill ring dikes of apatite rock and apatite sövite with little magnetite, suggest a rather different phase of phosphate mineralization. Kangankunde Hill and Wigu Hill are typical late-stage rare earth carbonatites, and in the Karonge (Burundi) bastnaesite veins we may see migrant offshoots of such mineralization. At Nkombwa Hill rare earth mineralization appears to be superposed on apatite-pyrochlore mineralization, and one may suppose that the same has occurred at Mrima, although it is presumptuous to speculate on primary mineralization when only supergene products can be studied.

The common pattern of carbonatite mineralization, despite its variety in detail, leaves no doubt that it is a characteristic and intrinsic part of carbonatite activity, and prompts comparison and contrast with types of mineralization linked with other suites of igneous rocks. Niobium, rare earths and fluorine were formerly commonly accepted as typical of alkali granite mineralization, especially of the pneumatolytic and pegmatitic phases, but in that paragenesis they are commonly accompanied by many elements such as lithium, beryllium, boron, yttrium, tin, tantalum and tungsten which are rare, or virtually absent, in the carbonatites. In the latter there is a very noticeable enrichment of the lighter elements of such coherent pairs as niobium and tantalum, zirconium and hafnium, and the lighter lanthanons (Ce–Eu) rather than the heavier (Gd–Lu), as compared with the granitic suite. It may be that traces of the more granitophile elements will in time be reported from carbonatites, but the quantitative difference between the two suites appears to be very real and important. This restricted geochemical assemblage has an interesting consequence for the mineralogist, and perhaps for the economic geologist, in that carbonatites can provide much simpler and purer 'end members' of many minerals usually found elsewhere only as intermediate members of complex isomorphous series, e.g. niobates almost free from tantalum and low in titanium, monazites and aeschynites low in thorium and yttrium, and even strontianites with much less calcium than in other environments. Although some general geochemical similarities exist between the carbonatites and the feldspathoidal rocks, especially the nepheline-syenite pegmatites, the latter carry much more titanium and zirconium, and probably more beryllium, thorium and uranium than the carbonatites, but certainly less niobium, strontium and the lighter lanthanons. The relationship between the carbonatites and the kimberlites deserves a fuller discussion than can be given here, especially in view of the carbonatite-alnöite association, but interesting geochemical similarities may be noted, particularly the persistence of niobium and rare earths in the diamondiferous kimberlites, demonstrated from both Siberian and Basutoland pipes (Litinskii, 1961, and Dawson, 1962a). On the other hand, the scarcity of chromium in carbonatites is noticeable, and, of course, the absence of eclogitic inclusions and 'kimberlite indicator minerals' (pyrope and magnesian ilmenite) leaves a significant gap between the carbonatites and the diamondiferous kimberlites.

To the writer, it appears that the ultimate source of the characteristic minor elements of the carbonatites lies in the depths where the carbonatites originate, that is to say, they are intrinsic elements concentrated with the carbonates, and not scavengings picked up during ascent through the upper part of the crust. Isotopic studies may throw more light on this. The variety of carbonatite mineral deposits, however, clearly involves further remarkable differentiation and concentration processes operating in the magma chamber at the root of the carbonatite volcano, as energy builds up for successive higher ascents, and as alkalis stream out to metasomatize the wall rocks.

412 *Economic Mineralogy of African Carbonatites*

REFERENCES

Agard, J., 1960, Les carbonatites et les roches à silicates et carbonates associés du massif de roches alcalines du Tamazert (Haut Atlas de Midelt, Maroc) et les problèmes de leur genèse: *Internat. Geol. Congr. 21st sess.*, Pt. **13**, pp. 293–303.

Bailey, D. K., 1960, Carbonatites of the Rufunsa Valley, Feira district: *Northern Rhodesia Geol. Surv. Bull.* **5**.

Bakes, J. M., Jeffery, P. G. and Sandor, J., 1964, Pyrochlore minerals as a potential source of reactor-grade niobium: *Nature*, v. **204**, pp. 867–868.

Brasseur, H., Herman, P. and Hubaux, A., 1961, Apatites de l'est du Congo et du Ruanda: *Ann. Soc. Géol. Belgique, Bull.* 2, v. **85**, pp. 61–85.

Broughton, H. J., Chadwick, L. C. and Deans, T., 1950, Iron and titanium ores from the Bukusu Hill alkaline ccmplex, Uganda: *Colon. Geol. Mineral Resources*, v. **1**, No. 3, pp. 262–266.

Brown, P. E., 1964, The Songwe scarp carbonatite and associated feldspathization in the Mbeya Range, Tanganyika: *Geol. Soc. London Quart. Jour.*, v. **120**, pp. 223–240.

Coetzee, G. L. and Edwards, C. B., 1959, The Mrima Hill carbonatite, Coast Province, Kenya: *Geol. Soc. S. Africa Trans.*, v. **62**, pp. 373–397.

Davies, K. A., 1947, The phosphate deposits of the Eastern Province Uganda: *Econ. Geology*, v. **42**, pp. 137–146.

Davies, K. A., 1954, Cement Manufacture in Uganda: *Colon. Geol. Mineral Resources*, v. **4**, No. 4, pp. 366–372.

Davies, K. A., 1956, The geology of part of South-East Uganda with special reference to the alkaline complexes: *Uganda Geol. Surv. Mem.* **8**.

Dawson, J. B., 1962a, Basutoland kimberlites. *Geol. Soc. America Bull.*, v. **73**, pp. 545–560.

Dawson, J. B., 1962b, The geology of Oldoinyo Lengai: *Bull. Volcanol.*, v. **24**, pp. 349–387.

Deans, T. and McConnell, J. D. C., 1955, Isokite, CaMgPO$_4$F, a new mineral from Northern Rhodesia: *Mineralog. Mag.*, v. **30**, pp. 681–690.

DuBois, C. G. B., Furst, J., Guest, N. J. and Jennings, D. J., 1963, Fresh natro carbonatite lava from Oldoinyo Lengai: *Nature*, v. **197**, pp. 445–446.

Fleming, M. G. and Robinson, A. J., 1960, Development of a process for the concentration of Sukulu apatite: *Proc. Int. Min. Process. Congr.* 1960 (Instn. Min. Met. Lond.), pp. 953–972.

Flinter, B. H., Butler, J. R. and Harral, G. M., 1963, A study of alluvial monazite from Malaya: *Am. Mineralogist*, v. **48**, pp. 1210–1226.

Forster, I. F., 1958, Paragenetical ore mineralogy of the Loolekop-Phalaborwa carbonatite complex, eastern Transvaal: *Geol. Soc. S. Africa Trans.*, v. **61**, pp. 359–365.

Garson, M. S., 1960, The geology of the Lake Chilwa area: *Nyasaland Geol. Surv. Bull.* **12**.

Garson, M. S., 1962, The Tundulu carbonatite ring-complex in southern Nyasaland: *Nyasaland Geol. Surv. Mem.* **2**.

Garson, M. S., 1965a, Carbonatite and agglomerate vents in the western Shire Valley: *Malawi Geol. Surv. Mem.* **3**.

Garson, M. S., 1965b, Carbonatites in southern Malawi: *Malawi Geol. Surv. Bull.* **15**.

Garson, M. S. and Campbell Smith, W., 1958, Chilwa Island: *Nyasaland Geol. Surv. Mem.* **1**.

Hanekom, H. J., van Staden, C. M. v. H., Smit, P. J. and Pike, D. R., 1965, The geology of the Palabora Igneous Complex: *S. Africa Geol. Surv.*, Mem. **54**.

Harris, J. F., 1961, Summary of the geology of Tanganyika, Pt. IV: Economic geology: *Tanganyika Geol. Surv. Mem.* **1**.

Harris, P. M., 1965, Pandaite from the Mrima Hill niobium deposit (Kenya): *Mineralog. Mag.*, v. **35**, pp. 277–290.

Holt, D. N., 1965, The Kangankunde Hill rare earth prospect: *Malawi Geol. Surv., Bull.* **20**.

Jacobson, R. R. E., MacLeod, W. N. and Black, R., 1958, Ring-complexes in the younger granite province of Northern Nigeria: *Geol. Soc. London, Mem.* **1**.

Jäger, E., Niggli, E. and van der Veen, A. H., 1959, A hydrated barium-strontium pyrochlore in a biotite rock from Panda Hill, Tanganyika: *Mineralog. Mag.*, v. **32**, pp. 10–25.

James, T. C. and McKie, D., 1958, The alteration of pyrochlore to columbite in carbonatites in Tanganyika: *Mineralog. Mag.*, v. **31**, pp. 889–900.

Johnson, R. L., 1961, The geology of the Dorowa and Shawa carbonatite complexes, Southern Rhodesia: *Geol. Soc. S. Africa Trans.*, v. **64**, pp. 101–145.

Litinskii, V. A., 1961, On the content of Ni, Cr, Ti, Nb and some other elements in kimberlites and the possibility of geochemical prospecting for kimberlite: *Geochemistry* (Transl. from Geokhimiya, U.S.S.R.), No. **9**, pp. 813–822.

Lombaard, A. F., Ward-Able, N. M. and Bruce, R. W. (1964), The exploration and main geological features of the copper deposit in carbonatite at Loolekop, Palabora Complex: in *The Geology of Some Ore Deposits in Southern Africa*. Ed. S. H. Haughton, v. **2**, pp. 315–337. Pubd. by Geol. Soc., S. Africa, Johannesburg.

McKie, D., 1962, Goyazite and florencite from two African carbonatites: *Mineralog. Mag.*, v. **33**, pp. 281–297.

Mennell, F. P., 1946, Ring structures with carbonatite cores in Southern Rhodesia: *Geol. Mag.*, v. **83**, pp. 137–140.

Pecora, W. T., 1956, Carbonatites: a review: *Geol. Soc. America Bull.*, v. **67**, pp. 1537–1556.

Rose, H. J., Blade, L. V. and Ross, M., 1958, Earthy monazite at Magnet Cove, Arkansas: *Am. Mineralogist*, v. **43**, pp. 995–997.

Russell, H. D., Hiemstra, S. A. and Groeneveld, D., 1954, The mineralogy and petrology of the carbonatite at Loolekop, Eastern Transvaal: *Geol. Soc. S. Africa Trans.*, v. **57**, pp. 197–208.

Schofield, A. and Haskin, L., 1964, Rare-earth distribution patterns in eight terrestrial materials: *Geochim. et cosmochim. Acta*, v. **28**, pp. 437–446.

Scull, B. J., 1958, Origin and occurrence of barite in Arkansas: *Arkansas Geol. & Conserv. Commn., Inform. Circ. No.* **18**.

Temple, A. K. and Grogan, R. M., 1965, Carbonatite and related alkalic rocks at Powderhorn, Colorado: *Econ. Geol.*, v. **60**, pp. 672–692.

Thoreau, J., Aderca, B. and Van Wambeke, L., 1958, Le gisement de terres rares de la Karonge (Urundi): *Bull. Acad. Roy. Sci. Colon.*, v. **4**, (n.s.), pp. 684–715.

van der Veen, A. H., 1960, The alteration of pyrochlore to fersmite in the Mbeya carbonatite: *Geol. en Mijnbouw.*, v. **39** (n.s. v. **22**), pp. 512–515.

van der Veen, A. II., 1963, A study of pyrochlore: *Verh. Kon. Ned. Geol.-Mijnb. Genoot., Geol. Ser. No.* **22**.

Van Wambeke, L., 1960, Geochemical prospecting and appraisal of niobium-bearing carbonatites by x-ray methods: *Econ. Geol.*, v. **55**, pp. 732–758.

Van Wambeke, L., 1965, A study of some niobium-bearing minerals of the Lueshe carbonatite deposit. *EURATOM Rep.* EUR. **2110.e**, (Brussels).

Van Zijl, P. J., 1962, The geology, structure and petrology of the alkaline intrusions of Kalkfeld and Okorusu and the invaded Damara rocks: *Ann. Univ. Stellenbosch*, v. **37**, ser. A, No. 4, pp. 237–346.

Watts, J. T., Tooms, J. S. and Webb, J. S., 1963, Geochemical dispersion of niobium from pyrochlore-bearing carbonatites in Northern Rhodesia: *Trans. Inst. Min. Met.*, v. **72**, pp. 729–747.

Part V

Summaries and Bibliographies

of Carbonatite Complexes

J. GITTINS

Summaries and Bibliographies
of Carbonatite Complexes

In the bibliography of each complex, references to mining company reports and unpublished reports of government geological surveys have been omitted where these are not generally available.

AFRICA
Angola

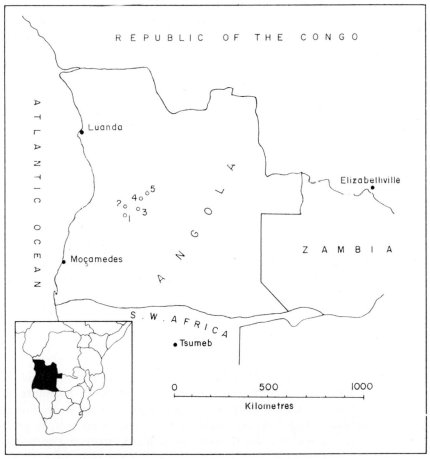

Fig. 1. Carbonatites in Angola (after De Sousa Machado, 1958).
417

1. Longonjo   4. Bailundo
2. Coola   5. Capuia
3. Chianga

Longonjo (1)

This is a ring complex with a diameter of 7–8 km centred 4 km SW of Longonjo. A second inner ring has a diameter of 2 km. The central part is underlain by carbonatite that is in places rich in hematite. The outer ring appears to be formed of a weathered basic rock that encloses a screen of quartzite on its inside but is surrounded by granite. Apatite, barite and magnetite are abundant in parts of the carbonatite and rare earth-columbium-tantalum minerals are also present.

de Sousa Machado, 1958.

Coola (2)

The complex consists of two small ring structures at the foot of Mount Moco. The northern one is 2.2 km in diameter and separated by 1 km from the southern one of 1.5 km diameter. The north ring is bordered on its west side by a breccia dike 50–100 m wide. The breccia is composed of rounded and angular fragments of trachyt-andesite in a reddish-violet, fine-grained matrix of similar composition. Porphyritic biotite granite forms the centre of the ring and the complex is surrounded by gneisses. The south ring structure has an outer ring of hematite-bearing, brownish laminated carbonatite dipping vertically to 75° inwards. The centre of the ring is fine-grained tuff and yellowish brown carbonatite. Rare earth and thorium minerals are present.

de Sousa Machado, 1958.

Chianga (3)

This is a very poorly exposed complex with little relief. Porphyritic nepheline syenite has been observed on the rim as well as basaltic to phonolitic rocks, tuffs and breccias. The interior of the complex is poorly exposed but small outcrops of dark brown, altered rocks are probably weathered carbonatite. They contain rare earths and thorium.

de Sousa Machado, 1958.

Bailundo (4)

Bailundo is a ring structure with a diameter of 8 km and an inner carbonatite mass of 1–2 km diameter. The central carbonatite is probably dolomitic and is roughly enclosed by a steeply dipping breccia dike 3–4 m wide containing abundant fragments of the dolomitic carbonatite. The outer part is probably an altered syenite. Rare earth and thorium minerals occur in the carbonatite.

de Sousa Machado, 1958.

Capuia (5)

The Capuia Complex has a carbonatite core 4 km in diameter which is magnetite-rich at the centre and strongly silicified in its western part. Foliation is steep-dipping. The carbonatite is surrounded by breccia-like tuff which grades over into red sandstone breccia. The entire complex was emplaced into biotite granite, mica schists and amphibolites. Rare earth and niobium minerals are present.

de Sousa Machado, 1958.

Ethiopia (Abyssinia)

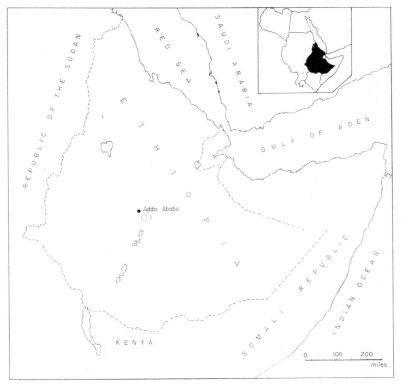

Fig. 2.   Carbonatite in Ethiopia (Abyssinia).

Bishoftu (1)

It is possible that the Bishoftu explosion craters are related to carbonatite volcanism.

Mohr, 1961.

Kenya

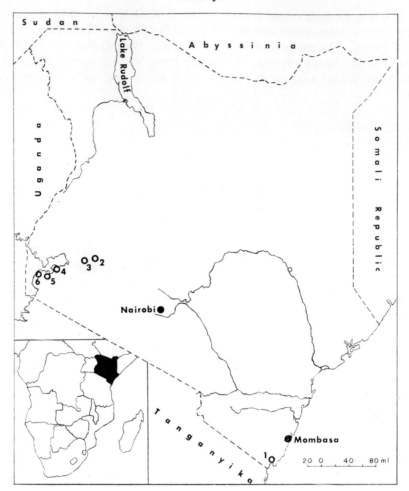

Fig. 3.   Carbonatites in Kenya.

1. Mrima Hill	4. Homa
2. Tinderet	5. North Ruri, South Ruri, Tuige,
3. Buru	and Sokolo
	6. Rangwa

Mrima Hill (1) (Fig. 4)

The Mrima Hill carbonatite can be considered part of the Jombo alkaline complex. Jombo Hill is an alkaline intrusion about 2 miles in diameter made up of an outer zone of fine-grained foyaite and alkali pyroxenite, with a core of coarse-grained nepheline syenite and several variants. Two agglomerate vents, Nguluku and Kiruku, occur 2.5 and 5 miles respectively from the Jombo intrusion and are made up of explosion breccia (chiefly sedimentary fragments) set in a carbonate matrix that has subsequently been extensively silicified. Mrima

Hill, about 3 miles from the Jombo intrusion, is a carbonatite plug with
agglomerate. Exposure is very poor, the hill being covered with dense rain forest
and grassy patches overlying a deep lateritic soil. Exploratory shafts and drilling
have penetrated sövite, dolomitic carbonatite, biotitic carbonatite and agglomeratic carbonatite. The whole plug is surrounded by a zone of fenitized Karroo

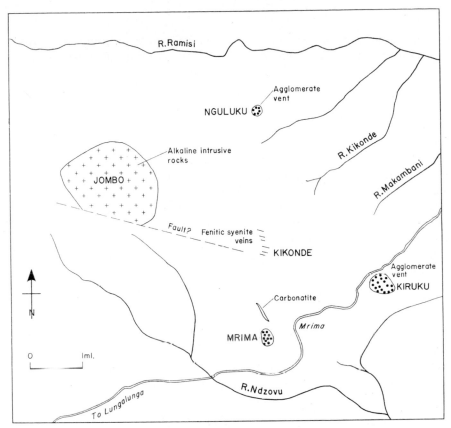

Fig. 4.   Mrima (after Baker, 1953).

siltstone. A dike of carbonatite occurs just north of Mrima Hill. Dikes of
nephelinite, lamprophyre, vogesite and camptonite cut the country rocks for a
radius of 15 miles around the Jombo intrusion. A number of fenitic veins on
Kikonde Ridge some 2 miles from Jombo are taken to indicate the presence of
a carbonatite body under the ridge.

Baker, 1953.   Tyrrell and Nielson, 1938.
Coetzee and Edwards, 1959.

Tinderet (2)

   This is a volcano composed of nephelinitic-agglomerate, nephelinite, phonolite and basanite, and is probably part of an alkaline-carbonatite complex. Grey

carbonatite with apatite and pyrochlore occurs on Legetet Hill on the SW flank of Tinderet.

Binge, 1962.

Pulfrey, 1953.

LeBas and Dixon, 1965.

Shackleton, 1951.

McCall, 1959.

Buru (3)

This is a small vent of iron-stained breccia 200 yd across containing monazite and pyrochlore and may be part of a carbonatite complex although no carbonatite has been observed. There are also fenites.

Binge, 1962.   McCall, 1959.

Homa (4) (Fig. 5)

The Homa complex consists of a number of hills whose lower slopes are covered by Pleistocene and recent deposits. The volcano pierces highly folded rhyolite, andesite and basalt lavas; near the complex these are brecciated, zeo-litized, hematite-stained, impregnated by calcite and fenitized. Lavas exposed are phonolite, nephelinite and phonolitic nephelinite; intrusive rocks are ijolite, urtite, melteigite and nepheline syenite. The ijolites and urtites outcrop at the base of the hills but the rest occur as xenoliths. The volcanic history is complex with more than one intrusive centre. The main carbonatite mass is a series of sövite breccia cone sheets and is exposed 2000 ft. above Lake Victoria. The breccia is coloured orange by limonite staining and is thought to be underlain by a sövite core. It is cut by incomplete carbonatite ring dikes, both calcitic and dolomitic, and the ijolite is cut by a northerly dipping plug of biotite sövite. Apatite and magnetite frequently impart flow banding to the rocks. Pyroxene and biotite are also common. The main sövite breccia is surrounded by un-sorted agglomerate which represents the original fragmentary material ejected from the Homa vent. Fine-grained dolomitic carbonatite dikes less than one foot wide were intruded into minor faults.

Clarke and Flegg, 1966.

Pulfrey, 1944, 1950.

McCall, 1959.

Saggerson, 1952.

North Ruri, South Ruri, Tuige and Sokolo (5) (Fig. 6)

Four carbonatite ring complexes occur close together on the west side of Homa Bay. The relation of the associated alkaline bodies, the oldest rocks, is obscure; there is a possibility that the four explosion vents pierce a single, larger alkaline ring complex, but there is no obvious connection.

North Ruri and South Ruri. These are two distinct ring complexes; North Ruri has a diameter of 1.25 miles and its margin touches South Ruri with a diameter of 1.5 miles. The initial intrusions of ijolite and nepheline syenite appear to have been pierced by two large explosion vents now filled with breccia and tuff. Rather than simple pipe-fillings these appear to be multiple cone sheets separated by screens of the alkaline rocks and Precambrian basalts. Most dip steeply inwards but some dip outwards. Carbonatites form nearly perfect ring-

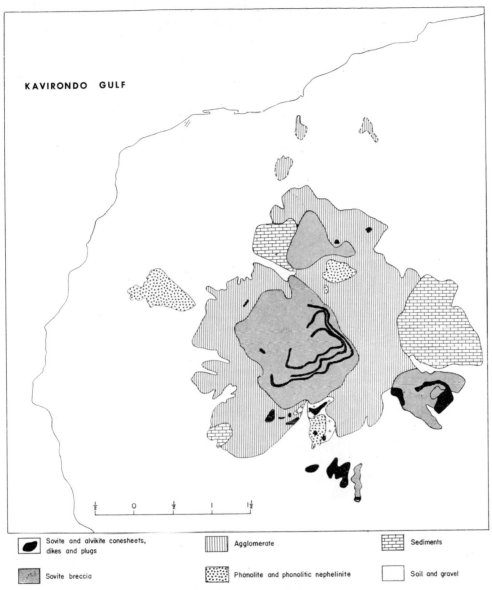

KAVIRONDO GULF

Sovite and alvikite conesheets, dikes and plugs	Agglomerate	Sediments
Sovite breccia	Phonolite and phonolitic nephelinite	Soil and gravel

Fig. 5.   Homa (after Saggerson, 1952).

shaped intrusions. These are great, composite ring dikes separated by screens of pyroclastics; the latter have been extensively carbonated to give the impression of very large ring dikes. At South Ruri there are two separate rings and a central core, while at North Ruri the ring dikes are closer in form to a figure of eight than a simple ring. They are principally pyroxene sövites and magnetite-rich sövites with phlogopite and apatite as accessories. Magnetite is often oxidized to limonite or hematite. Sideritic carbonatite with accessory fluorite cuts most other rocks at North Ruri. Alignment of these minerals has produced a banding that is generally vertical but also steep inwards and outwards. There is a great variation in grain size from aphanite to coarse (5 mm). Some of the magnetite occuring at North Ruri is radioactive, probably due to the presence of thorium, and pyrochlore also occurs. The outer margins of the com-

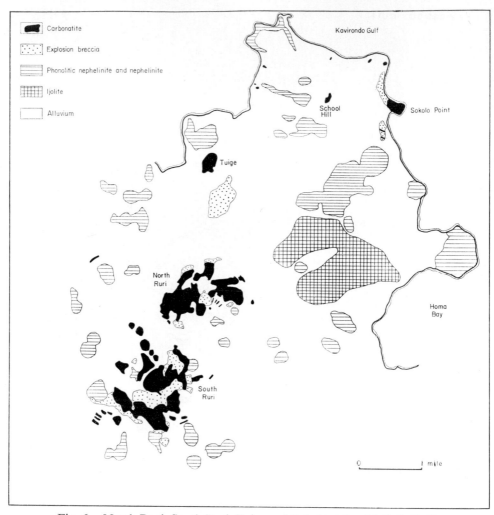

Fig. 6.   North Ruri, South Ruri, Tuige and Sokolo (after McCall, 1958).

plex are poorly exposed but there appears to be a zone of fenite derived from Precambrian basalt and rhyolite. Plugs of nephelinite were later emplaced in the complex and in the surrounding country rocks for a radius of one or two miles. Finally came the intrusion of minor dikes of explosion breccia, and dikes and cone sheets of fine-grained red and grey carbonatite.

Collins, 1966.   Pulfrey, 1954.
Dixon, 1966.   Shackleton, 1951.
McCall, 1958, 1959, 1963.

Tuige. The outer part of the vent is marked by the hill Luwala 0.5 mile south of Tuige Hill, and made up of red to dark brown breccia. Tuige itself is a gentle hill about 200 ft high made up of a roughly oval central plug of carbonatite 0.25 mile in maximum diameter cutting the explosion breccia. Flow structure that is near vertical but with steep inward and outward variations can be traced completely round the hill. Magnetite and pyrochlore are present. On the north side the vent is obscured by later plateau lavas.

McCall, 1958, 1959, 1963.

Sokolo. Sokolo is an eroded vent of feldspar agglomerate cut by dikes of white biotite carbonatite with some phonolite xenoliths. These are cut by brown carbonatite dikes containing iron oxides, fluorite and rare synchysite. Phonolite lavas overlie and largely hide the carbonatites. Exposures are on Sokolo Point, School Hill and on the coast within a mile radius of School Hill.

Le Bas, 1966.   McCall, 1958, 1959, 1963.

Rangwa (6) (Fig. 7)

The Rangwa complex has a roughly circular outcrop with a maximum diameter of 7.5 miles, and lies in the eroded core of the Kisingiri volcano which covered an area of about 2500 sq miles. Rangwa Hill rises about 2000 ft above Lake Victoria and still displays much of its original volcanic form. The complex is of ring form, lying within a central inlier of Precambrian granite and metamorphic rock, and it can be demonstrated that the Precambrian surface has been updomed 2000 ft above the level of the surrounding peneplain. Ijolite is now preserved as a partial outer ring with steep outward-dipping banding, and is interpreted as a cone sheet later than the carbonatite. A partial inner ring of uncompahgrite showing compositional banding dipping inwards at an average of 30° is interpreted as a cone sheet later than the ijolite. The ijolite effected large-scale fenitization converting the wall-rock to aegirine- and arfvedsonite-rich rocks, and its intrusion was accompanied by peripheral dike-swarms of microfoyaite and microijolite. Alkaline syenites are restricted to the margin of the ijolite zone and are regarded as hybrids. There is a central vent, 3·5 miles in diameter, which is filled with tuff and agglomerate. These are extensively replaced by calcite, only relicts of pyroclastic fragments remaining in places. The degree of calcite replacement increases towards the centre of the vent. The main pyroclastic vent is intruded by foliated magnetite-calcite carbonatite with apatite, phlogopite and pyrochlore, while cone sheets a few feet thick, and vertical radial dikes of carbonatite are found in the outer parts of the complex. At some stage the whole of Rangwa has subsided along ring faults by up to 600 ft. round the edges and at least 1000 ft. in the middle. Late alnöite dikes cut the complex. Erosion has reached the stage where both plutonic and extrusive phases of the volcano are exposed.

McCall, 1958, 1959, 1963.   Whitworth, 1953, 1961.
Shackleton, 1951.

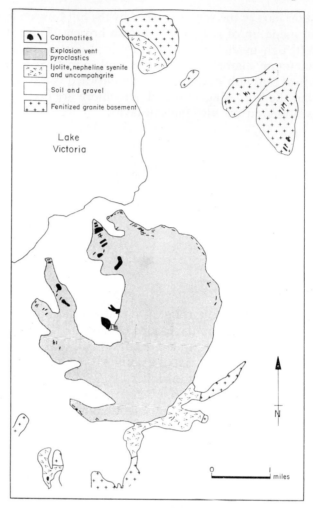

Fig. 7.   Rangwa (after McCall, 1958).

Malawi (formerly Nyasaland)

All the summaries of Malawi complexes were prepared by or condensed from manuscripts written by Dr. M. S. Garson.

1. Lake Malombe vents
2. Chaumbwi vent
3. Kangankunde
4. Palula
5. Mtsimukwe
6. Nailuwa
7. Kalambo Stream
8. Kapiri vent
9. Nsengwa vent

10. Kadongosi vent
11. Mongolowe agglomerate vent
12. Chilwa Island
13. Tundulu
14. Nkalonje-Matopon
15. Songwe vent
16. Bangala
17. Namangali vent

Lake Malombe vents (1)

Agglomeratic vents, situated adjacent to rift fractures west of Lake Malombe, are emplaced in Basement Complex gneisses. The two northern crater-like vents, Nsala and Kongwe, which are both over half a mile in diameter, comprise

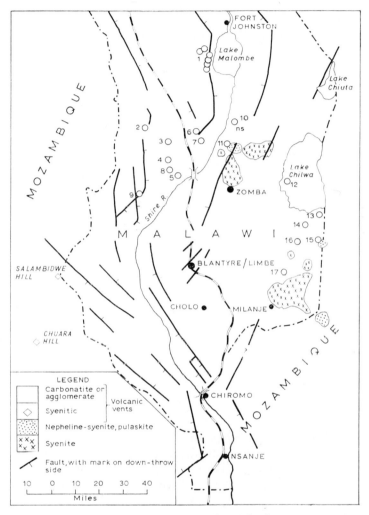

Fig. 8.   Carbonatites in Malawi.

mainly feldspathic-agglomerate, sometimes partly carbonatized, fenite and associated nephelinite and alkalic rocks. The centre of the Nsala vent comprises a circular plug of microfoyaite with small plugs of phonolite and carbonatized phonolite (?). Nephelinite and alkalic rocks are disposed in arcuate and radial fashion towards each vent. A thin sheet of feldspar-carbonatite is inclined towards the Nsala vent.

The smaller vents to the south (Liperembe, Kawanula, Aligomba, Achirundu) consist mainly of nephelinitic-agglomerate which is altered in part to feldspathic-agglomerate, locally rich in carbonates.

Garson, 1965a, c.

Chaumbwi vent (2)

The vent agglomerate at Chaumbwi, 10 miles NW of Kangankunde Hill, in-fills a small fissure about 6 ft wide along the line of a N–S fault adjacent to the main rift valley fault in the area. The agglomerate consists of close-packed, rounded and sub-rounded fragments of fenitized gneiss in a matrix which is partly vogesitic and partly feldspathic with abundant comminuted material. In some parts of the vent the matrix is considerably carbonatized.

Bloomfield and Garson, 1965.   Garson, 1956b, c.

Kangankunde (3) (p. 59, Fig. 7)

The Kangankunde complex differs from the other Malawi occurrences in having ankeritic carbonatite rich in strontianite rather than sövite and in the vir-tual absence of silicate intrusives apart from a few minor dikes and plugs. From the outside inwards it consists of zones of fenitized gneisses, feldspathized fenite, feldspathic breccia, carbonatized feldspathic rock and carbonatite. Fenitization extends half a mile from the complex and probably began along cracks during an initial updoming of the country rocks. Carbonatite dikes in the central part of the complex roughly parallel the margins of the elliptical zone of carbonatized feldspathic rock and a plug of carbonatite. Dikes on the Southern Knoll are arcuate to a separate satellitic centre and on the Northern Knoll are tangential to the main vent. Most dip outwards at as much as 60° and are streaked with mineral segregations. There are four main types of carbonatite: early fine-grained sideritic carbonatite with xenoliths of feldspathic rocks; coarser-grained carbonatite rich in rare earth minerals and with siderite replaced by ankerite; leucocratic ankeritic carbonatite rich in rare earth minerals; carbonatite con-taining iron and manganese oxides and pink apatite-rock segregations. Many of these contain a great deal of strontianite. Late silicification has produced irregular bodies and arcuate dike-like bodies of siliceous rock containing numerous rare earth minerals and carbonate. The only intrusive silicate rocks are a few sölvsbergite dikes and possibly biotite alnöite.

Bloomfield and Garson, 1965.   Holt, 1965.
Garson, 1958, 1965b, c.   Snelling, 1965.

Minor carbonatite intrusions in the Shire Valley (4–7)

There are four minor occurrences of carbonatite and agglomerate in the western Shire Valley. These are as follows:
Palula. Thin veins of dark brown carbonatite cutting dolomitic marble about 2.5 miles NW of Kapiri Hill; the carbonatite is similar to that at the Nsengwa

vent and consists of goethite with shells of ankerite, much fluorite and traces of apatite and brookite.

Mtsimukwe. Carbonatite-agglomerate, 4 miles ESE of Kapiri Hill, consisting of chips of feldspar and fenitized rocks in a matrix of siderite, clear carbonate and apatite.

Nailuwa. Carbonatite-agglomerate forming a small outcrop a few feet across in marble, 11 miles ENE of Kangankunde Hill. The matrix of the agglomerate consists of siderite, zoned calcite, tiny rhombs of ankerite, quartz and traces of apatite.

Kalambo Stream. A 2.5 in. vein of dark brown carbonatite with ochraceous and manganiferous patches cutting Basement Complex rocks, 15 miles E of Kangankunde Hill; this consists of goethite, manganese oxides, clear interstitial calcite and ankerite, and accessory apatite and monazite.

Bloomfield and Garson, 1965.   Garson, 1965*b, c.*

Kapiri vent (8)

Vent-rocks intruding Kapiri Hill, a low ridge of dolomitic marble of the Basement Complex, comprise two large dikes of closely associated carbonatite, nephelinite and related agglomerate, and several similar minor dikes, all trending N–S parallel to an adjacent rift valley fracture. The nephelinites, which are heavily carbonatized, in places contain olivine and melilite. The agglomerates are crowded with rounded fragments of fenite in a sparse carbonatitic matrix. The carbonatites consist of calcite and siderite with subordinate ankerite, and small amounts of apatite, barite, pyrite, anatase, fluorite, florencite, monazite and synchysite (?).

Bloomfield and Garson, 1965.   Garson, 1958, 1965*c.*

Nsengwa vent (9)

The core of Nsengwa Hill is partly formed of a plug of microsyenite which has been intruded and altered by an arcuate dike-like body of agglomerate with a series of other minor intrusions of agglomerate, carbonatite-agglomerate and quartz-rich carbonatite, seldom exceeding more than a few feet in width. This series was intruded into Basement Complex gneisses and dolomitic marbles in a crescent-shaped area, with maximum dimensions of 6000 ft and 2000 ft. Associated igneous intrusions include dikes of monchiquite and sölvsbergite. Minerals identified in the quartz-carbonatites and carbonate-rich matrix of the agglomerates include ankerite, siderite replaced by calcite, fluorite, brookite, anatase, rutile, pyrite, chalcopyrite, magnetite and traces of barite, zircon, pyrochlore and monazite.

Bloomfield and Garson, 1965.   Garson, 1959*b*, 1965*b, c.*
Dixey, Smith and Bisset, 1937 (1955).

Kadongosi vent (10)

Kadongosi Hill, which lies about 2 miles NE of the Junguni foyaitic ring structure, consists of fenitized gneisses intruded by an agglomeratic body about

P

6 ft wide. The agglomerate comprises fragments of gneiss, leucotrachyte and fenite in a matrix of finely comminuted quartz, feldspar, clinopyroxene and biotite; this matrix is extensively replaced by calcite in parts of the vent. Some of the fenitic rocks contain assemblages of albite, aegirine and eudialyte (up to 12 per cent).

Garson, 1965c.

Mongolowe agglomerate vent (11)

This roughly circular vent, about 1000 ft across, on the north-west edge of the Mongolowe alkalic ring structure is infilled by agglomeratic rocks. These comprise angular xenoliths of various sorts and xenocrysts of feldspar in a fine-grained, partly carbonatized matrix of feldspar, aegirine, epidote and magnetite. The foyaites and pulaskites adjacent to the vent have been metasomatically altered.

Vail and Mallick, 1965.   Garson, 1965c.

Chilwa Island (12) (p. 51, Fig. 6)

Chilwa Island is a prominent volcanic structure in Lake Chilwa about 1 mile from the southwest shore. Four igneous centres are recognizable on a vertical axis extending from a depth of more than 8000 ft to above the present lake level. Each focus is about 0.5 mile above the previous one in the breccia zone associated with it. The country rocks are Basement gneisses, granites and syenites and have been extensively fenitized. The central carbonatite is separated from the fenites by a zone of breccia consisting entirely of fenitized country rock fragments and becoming increasingly feldspathized towards the carbonatite. There are three principal types of carbonatite: sövite, ankeritic sövite and sideritic carbonatite. The outer ring of sövite is composed of a number of steeply inclined ring dikes with many screens of feldspathic breccia remaining between them. Some sövites contain essential acgirine and apatite, some biotite, and all contain accessory apatite and magnetite. The sövite contains dike-like bodies and streaked out segregations of pyrochlore, apatite, amphibole and siderite. Within the sövite ring is an inner ring of ankeritic sövite. Thin dikes and sheets from this intrusion also cut the earlier sövite. The central core of the complex is a manganiferous sideritic carbonatite. A number of plugs and arcuate dikes of nepheline syenite and ijolite cut both the outer sövite ring and the brecciated and fenitized zones. In addition there are cone sheets and radial dikes of many related alkalic rocks such as alnöite, nephelinite, phonolite, etc. The last stage of intrusive activity is represented by veins of fluorite-quartz and of barite. The size of the complex is about 2 miles by 1.5 miles.

Dixey, 1930.   Garson and Smith, 1958.
Dixey, Smith and Bisset, 1937 (1955).   Smith, 1953.
Garson, 1953a, 1956, 1960, 1965c.

Tundulu (*13*) (p. 37, Fig. 3)

Three intrusive centres are recognizable each with a set of ring structures and a wide variety of rock types. The country rocks are Basement gneisses, granites and syenites cut by Jurassic dolerites and are variably fenitized in a nearly circular zone extending up to 7500 ft from the margin of the early vent. The surrounding rocks have also been updomed by about 1500 ft.

The ultimate fenitization product is an aegirine syenite. Cutting the fenites are several arcuate zones of feldspathic breccia and agglomerate belonging to the first centre. On the inward side of these zones is an arcuate remnant of carbonatized breccia (carbonatite-agglomerate) cut by numerous thin ring dikes of sideritic sövite and thick dikes of calcite-rich sövite. These dip outwards at 60–75°.

The second centre is made up largely of reddish agglomerate enclosing screens of feldspathic breccia from the first centre, and cut by ring dikes of apatite sövite, apatite rock and bastnaesite carbonatite (apatite-rich and apatite-poor) containing a lot of siderite. All these rocks are surrounded by a ring dike up to 1800 ft wide of foyaite and ijolite. The outer margin of this dike is in contact with fenites and these have been nephelinized in a narrow border against the foyaite–ijolite. On the eastern side a hybrid zone of feldspathoidal carbonate-silicate rocks with an outer zone of biotite-magnetite rock has been developed from the carbonatized breccia (carbonatite-agglomerate) of centre 1. Radial and arcuate dikes of phonolite and leucite-, and analcite-rich rocks extend up to 5.5 miles from the complex and are associated with centre 2.

Prior to the formation of the third ring structure tear-faulting occurred along roughly N–S directions with subsidiary NW–SE and NE–SW faults. The third centre is vertically below the second centre and gave rise to sheets and small plugs of melanephelinite and olivine melanephelinite typically crowded with xenoliths of previously formed rocks, and thin sheets and dikes of beforsite.

Dixey, Smith and Bisset, 1937 (1955).   Smith, 1953.
Garson, 1955*b*, 1959*a*, 1961*b*, 1962,
    1965*c*.

Nkalonje-Matopon Ring Complex (*14*)

Six miles southwest of the Tundulu Complex, the isolated hills of the Nkalonje area comprise relict portions of a ring complex of the Chilwa Alkaline Province with indications of two separate igneous centres at Nkalonje Hill. Rocks of the first ring structure comprise arcuate stretches of feldspathic and contact breccia associated with a vent of feldspathic breccia and agglomerate, about half a mile in diameter, at Nkalonje Hill. Leucotrachtic inclusions in these rocks are considered to be mobilized feldspathic rocks derived from fenites. Rocks of the second ring structure include plugs of nepheline syenite and dikes and sheets of microfoyaite, phonolite, carbonatite, lamprophyre and melanephelinite. The carbonatites comprise siderite sövites on Matopon Hill, and sideritic carbonatites and sövites on Nkalonje Hill with pyrochlore (up to 1 per cent), fluorite, apatite, rare earth fluo-carbonate minerals and florencite.

Dixey, Smith and Bisset, 1937 (1955).   Garson, 1953*b*, 1955*b*, 1963, 1965*c*.

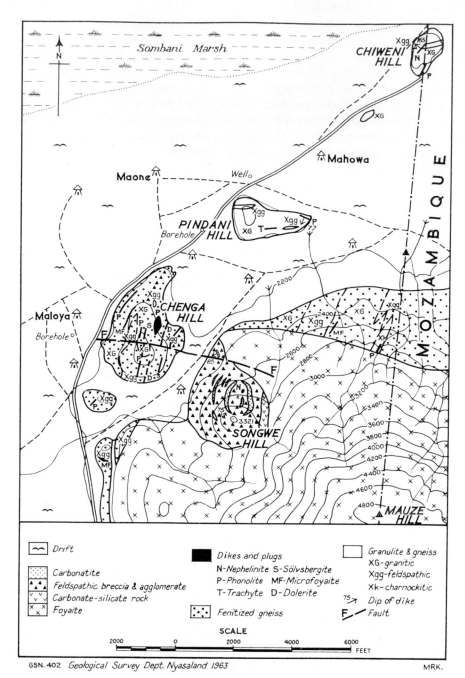

GSN. 402 *Geological Survey Dept. Nyasaland 1963*   MRK.

Fig. 9. Songwe.

Songwe vent[1] (*15*) (Fig. 9)

The Songwe vent takes the form of a steep-sided conical hill, lying between the NW foot of the Mauze foyaites and the broken rim of Basement Complex rocks enclosing the foyaites. The vent-rocks comprise feldspathic breccia, arcuate craggy outcrops of dark carbonatite, and mixed feldspathoidal carbonate-silicate rocks near the foyaite margin. The carbonatites comprise siderite-sövites with variable amounts of manganese and iron oxides. Accessory minerals are pyrochlore, apatite, barite and synchysite. The western part of the vent, at Changa Hill, which is isolated from Songwe Hill by faulting and subsequent erosion, is composed of coarse breccia with large fragments of fenitized gneisses and schists. Associated intrusives include shallow-dipping trachytes, phonolites and eudialyte microfoyaites.

Dixey, Smith and Bisset, 1937 (1955).   Garson, 1955*b*, 1965*c*.

Bangala carbonatite dike (*16*)

On the northwest slopes of Bangala Hill, 12 miles SW of Tundulu, a thin dike of sövite, with large euhedral crystals of barite and much orthoclase, is associated with small plugs of phonolite, and dikes of phonolite and sölvsbergite of the later alkaline dike-swarm.

Garson, 1959*b*, 1965*c*.

Namangali vent (*17*) (Fig. 10)

The principal feature of Namangali Hill is an elliptical vent, half a mile long by 600 yd wide, infilled by feldspathic breccia and agglomerate. Agglomeratic fragments include leucotrachyte-porphyry, dolerite and feldspathized fenite. Porphyritic trachyte also occurs as dikes and plugs which have been involved in the formation of the vent rocks. The vent and surrounding fenitized slopes of Namangali have been invaded by an igneous breccia with a phonolitic matrix. Later alkaline dikes and plugs show a range in composition from phonolitic trachyte through leucophonolite and phonolite to microfoyaite porphyry. These are replaced in part by sodalite, apparently associated with the late intrusion of small amounts of acmite sövite. Slight mineralization occurs as local impregnations of pyrite and chalcopyrite.

Garson, 1961*a*, 1965*c*.

Ring structures with possible deep-seated carbonatite

In addition to the fenitized rocks at the Junguni and Mongolowe ring structures mentioned above, fenites and related rocks occur at the adjacent comagmatic structures of Chikala (Garson, 1960), Chaone (Vail and Monkman, 1961) and Chinduzi (Bloomfield, 1965). It is possible that the presence of these fenites is due to occurrences of carbonatite below the present erosion

---

[1] The name Songwe Vent is used to distinguish this occurrence from Songwe Scarp in Tanganyika.

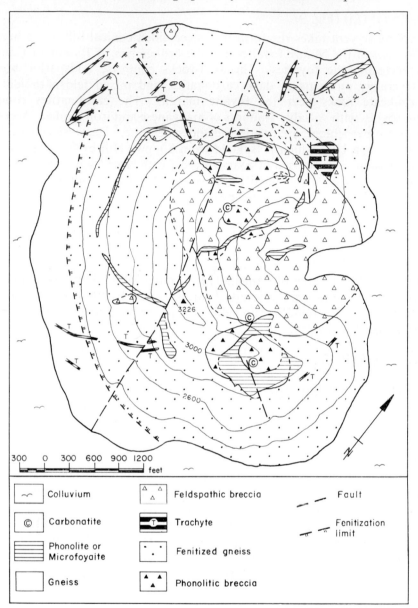

Colluvium

Carbonatite

Phonolite or
Microfoyaite

Gneiss

Feldspathic breccia

Trachyte

Fenitized gneiss

Phonolitic breccia

Fault

Fenitization
limit

Fig. 10.   Namangali (after *Malawi Geol. Surv.* GSN 403, 1963).

levels. Similar postulations may be made regarding the Chambe perthositic ring structure, with associated fenitized rocks, at the western edge of the Mlanje massif (Stringer *et al.*, 1956), and the Salambidwe syenitic ring structure in the south western part of Malawi, which has associated nephelinized rocks and which exhibits an alkali-increasing trend of ring intrusions and agglomerates.

Garson, 1965c.

Mali

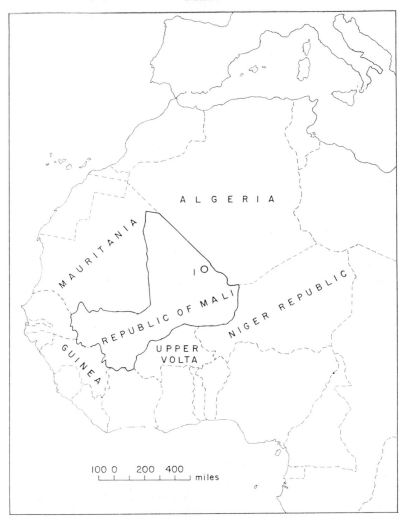

Fig. 11.   Carbonatite in Mali.

Adrar Tadhak (1)

A carbonatite mass 500 m across is reported in a nepheline syenite ring complex at Adrar Tadhak in the Adrar des Iforas region but remains unconfirmed.

Barrere, 1961.

Morocco

Tamazert (1)

The alkaline complex of Tamazert comprises nepheline syenites, jacupirangite, carbonatite, carbonatite breccia and a suite of trachyte, alnöite and tinguaite dikes, and has intruded the Liassic limestones of the High Atlas

Mountains. Carbonatites forms dikes and irregular bodies of varied character both coarse- and fine-grained. Minerals present are calcite (some dolomitic), celesite, strontianite, witherite, barite, fluorite, apatite, vermiculite, sulphides,

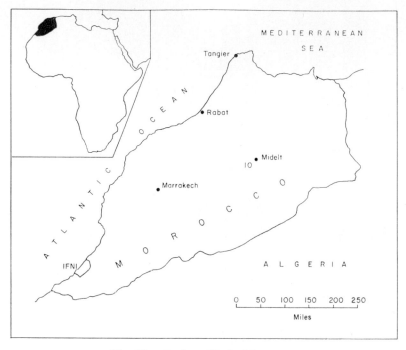

Fig. 12.   Carbonatite in Morocco.

pyrochlore and possibly monazite. Some carbonatite is very rich in strontium (up to 3 per cent) and some parts are manganiferous. The structural setting is uncommon but does resemble Ice River, Canada (p. 525).

Agard, 1956*a*, *b*, 1960.   Jérémine and Dubar, 1947.
Agard and Menyr, 1958.   Tilloy and Tournoud, 1946.
Jérémine, 1949, 1950.

Mozambique

1. Muambe Hill and satellite vents
2. Chuara
3. Chandava
4. Xiluvo and satellite vents (including Nharuchonga
5. Cura
6. Cone Negose

Muambe Hill and satellite vents (1) (Fig. 14)

The Muambe carbonatite complex still retains much of its original volcanic form. It is a fairly symmetrical, circular hill about 4 miles in diameter rising about 1300 ft above the surrounding plain. Its central vent forms a basin-shaped, steep-sided crater about 600 ft deep. The complex cuts Karroo sediments which, around the vent, are fractured and jointed. Iron staining and feldspathic

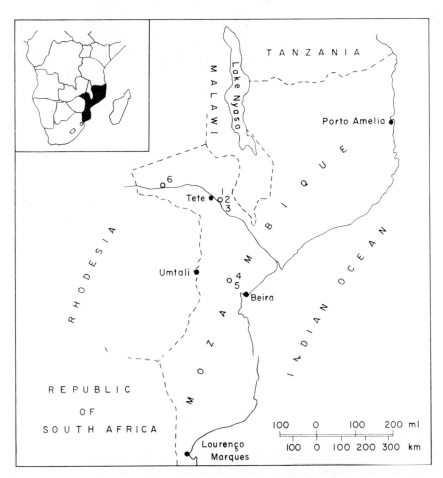

Fig. 13.   Carbonatites in Mozambique.

material have been introduced into these fractures. There is a central core of carbonate rock, agglomerate and breccia, surrounded by feldspathic breccia. All are cut by dikes of olivine nephelinite and phonolite. The carbonate rock forms craggy, deeply dissected hills rising about 200 ft above the floor of the vent. It is usually pale grey but is also dark grey, purplish, and chocolate coloured depending on how much siderite or rhodochrosite is present. Some feldspathic breccia is impregnated by fluorite.

Dias, 1961.   Pinto Coelho, 1961.
Dixey, Smith and Bisset, 1937 (1955).

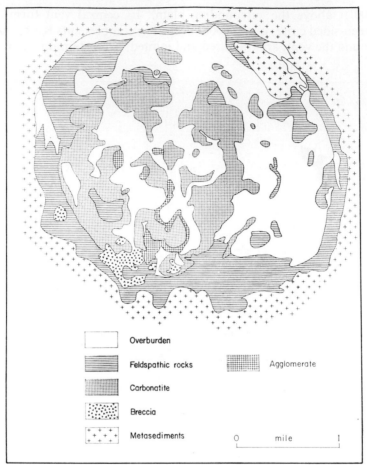

Overburden

Feldspathic rocks   Agglomerate

Carbonatite

Breccia

Metasediments   0   mile   1

Fig. 14.   Muambe (after Dias, 1961).

Chuara (2)

Chuara is not a clear carbonatite but it has certain carbonatite affinities. It is a ridge about 2 miles long, striking NW–SE that rises about 1000 ft above the surrounding plain of Karroo sediments and gneisses. It is a sill of aegirine microfoyaite, 500–600 ft thick resting on baked Karroo shale and dipping gently to the southwest. Dikes of sölvsbergite and phonolite, that may be feeders of the sill, cut the country rocks. The sill is associated with feldspathic and calcareous intrusive breccia. Much of this is feldspathic breccia veined by calcite and siderite, and stained with iron oxide.

Dixey, Smith and Bisset, 1937 (1955).

Chandava (3)

No adequate description is available. The complex contains syenite, trachyte and carbonatitic-agglomerate cut by a carbonatite dike and diabase dikes.

Dias, 1961.

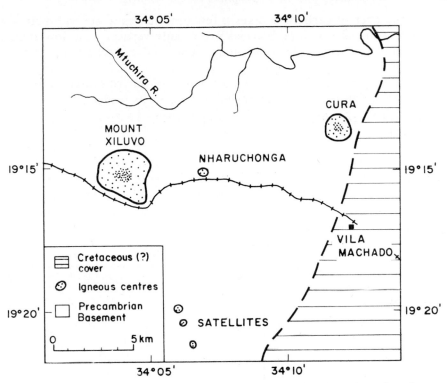

Fig. 15.   Xiluvo and Xiluvo satellite vents (including Nharuchonga) and
Cura.

Xiluvo and satellite vents (including Nharuchonga) (4) and Cura (5) (Fig. 15)

Mount Xiluvo (Siluvo) lies alongside the Beira–Umtali railway 15 km west of the village of Vila Machado. It consists of a circular ring of hills about 5 km in diameter which rise approximately 150 m above the flat plains of central Mozambique. Five smaller vents occur near by comprising Nharuchonga and Cura in the east and a southern group of three unnamed satellite vents. They all penetrate granitic gneisses of the Basement Complex which are unconformably overlain by Cretaceous (?) and Tertiary sediments in the east.

No petrographic descriptions have been published for these complexes, although they are briefly mentioned by Teale (1924), Vail (1962), and Rebollo and Ferro (1962).

The complexes are made up of three principal rock types:

1.   A central plug of carbonatite, present at Xiluvo, Nharuchonga and Cura, is generally a light-coloured, fine-grained, calcitic rock containing pyrochlore.

2.   An outer ring of volcanic breccia forms the main arcuate structure of Xiluvo and Cura. A highly calcareous, fine-grained groundmass encloses angular fragments of variable size which consist of Basement gneiss, volcanic rocks and some carbonatite fragments. Calcite and fluorite-lined cavities are common in the breccias.

A number of carbonate dikes a few centimetres to several metres wide that cut the surrounding breccias are usually vertical with flow structures parallel to their walls, and may represent a second generation of carbonatite.

3. Associated with the vents are basic, porphyritic dikes and trachyte masses, which may be an extrusive phase and its feeders.

Rebollo and Ferro, 1962.   Vail, 1962.
Teale, 1924.

Cone Negose (6)

Several carbonatite bodies including Cone Negose occur as prominent volcanic vents and dikes cutting Karroo sediments and the Basement Complex. There are also carbonatite breccias. Information was supplied by the Mozambique Geological Survey.

Republic of the Congo

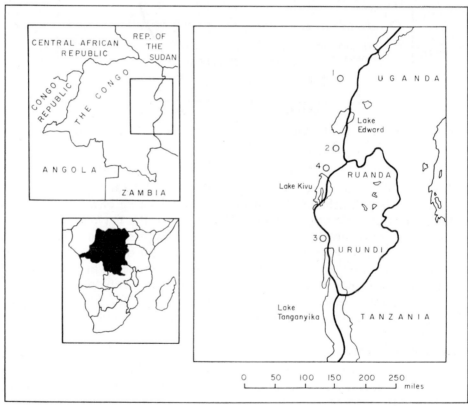

Fig. 16.   Carbonatites in the Republic of the Congo.

	PROBABLE CARBONATITE
1. Bingu (Bingo)	4. Nyiragongo
2. Lueshe	POSSIBLE CARBONATITE
3. Kawezi	5. Mwana Kusu (not shown on 16)

Bingu is mentioned by Verhaeghe (1963) and de Kun (1961) as a carbonatite with an enormous phosphate reserve. Kawezi is listed by de Kun (1961) without description. Mwana Kusu (on the Congo River southeast of Kasongo) is described briefly by Verhaeghe (1963) (quoting Meyer) as possibly a carbonatite and possibly sedimentary dolomite. de Kun (1961), Verhaeghe (1963) and Meyer (1957) also describe Kibuye (Kibuy) in Rwanda (Ruanda) as a plug of tremolite-bearing dolomitic carbonate 400m across without rare earths or feldspathoidal rocks but possibly with an albitized aureole. Meyer suggests that it is remobilized sedimentary dolomite and it is therefore not listed here as a true carbonatite.

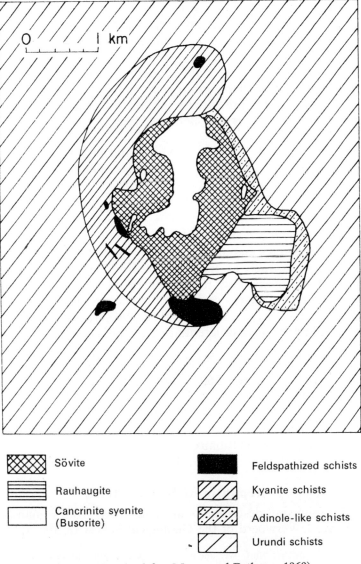

Fig. 17. Lueshe (after Meyer and Bethune, 1960).

Lueshe (2) (Fig. 17)

The Lueshe carbonatite complex intrudes metasedimentary schists that include fine-grained biotite quartzite and garnetiferous biotite schists, the metasomatic zone around the complex includes albitized rocks resembling adinoles, and albitized rocks containing aegirine and sodic amphibole together with a half a mile wide zone on the western side in which the metasediments have been transformed into kyanite schists. The complex is an elliptical plug (1.9 miles × 1.2 miles) with a central core of cancrinite syenite (in which the cancrinite is primary) surrounded by a nearly continuous ring of aegirine sövite containing small syenitic areas. Adjacent to this is a plug of dolomitic carbonatite. The sövite is coarse-grained (up to 1 cm) with aegirine, apatite, alkali feldspar, pyrrhotite and pyrochlore. Biotite and vermiculite are of frequent occurrence along the contacts. Banding is common and curves around xenoliths of altered country rocks and cancrinite syenite. The dolomitic carbonatite is distinctly finer-grained with apatite as the main accessory mineral. The absence of explosion breccias, the very coarse-grain size, and the development of kyanite suggest slow cooling at high pressure (depth of 10–15 miles?) and no communication with the surface (Meyer and Bethune, 1960).

Bethune, 1952, 1956, 1957.   Meyer and Bethune, 1958, 1960.
Bethune and Meyer, 1956, 1957.   Wambeke, 1965, in press *a*.
Meyer, 1958.

Nyiragongo (4)

Nyiragongo is an active volcano with a cone composed of melilitite tuffs and lavas overlain by leucitites and at the top of the mountain by nephelinites, with intermediate members such as leucite nephelinites and nepheline leucitites. Kalsilite-bearing rocks are also found together with rocks resembling the katungites of Uganda. Calcite occurs both in the groundmass and in vesicles of these rocks and it is felt (Sahama, 1962, Meyer, 1958*a*) that the Nyiragongo magma is in process of differentiation towards carbonatite at the present day.

Chaigneau, Tazieff and Fabre, 1960.   Meyer, 1958*a*.
Denaeyer, 1960, 1965.   Sahama, 1953, 1957, 1960, 1961,
Denaeyer and Tazieff, 1957.   1962.
Denaeyer and Wallendael, 1961.   Sahama and Meyer, 1958.
Herman, Vanderstappen and Hubaux,
   1960.

Republic of South Africa

Most of the following descriptions are condensed from a manuscript[1] prepared by Dr. W. J. Verwoerd of the Geological Survey of South Africa.

---

[1] Published under South African Government Printer's Copyright Authority No. 3084 of November 2nd, 1962.

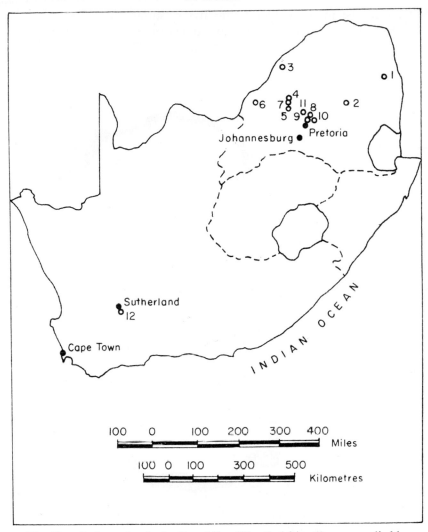

Fig. 18. Carbonatites in the Republic of South Africa (figure supplied by
W. J. Verwoerd, *Geol. Surv. Rep. South Africa*).

1. Palabora (Loolekop)
2. Spitskop
3. Glenover
4. Nooitgedacht
5. Tweerivier
6. Goudini
7. Kruidfontein
8. Roodeplaat
9. Derdepoort
10. Premier Mine
11. Pretoria Salt Pan (Soutpan)
12. Salpeterkop

General references to South African carbonatites: Verwoerd *a, b, c,* 1963.

Palabora (Loolekop) (1)

The Loolekop carbonatite is the central and youngest part of the Palabora alkaline complex which was emplaced in Archean granite and gneiss. It comprises,

in addition to the main composite intrusion, numerous dikes and separate plugs of syenite and carbonate-bearing injection breccia extending along a roughly E–W zone 45 miles long by 12 miles wide. The main plug covers about

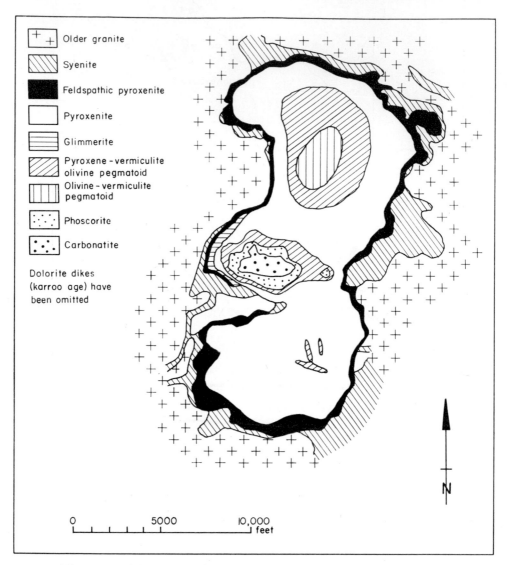

Older granite	
Syenite	
Feldspathic pyroxenite	
Pyroxenite	
Glimmerite	
Pyroxene - vermiculite olivine pegmatoid	
Olivine - vermiculite pegmatoid	
Phoscorite	
Carbonatite	

Dolorite dikes (karroo age) have been omitted

0   5000   10,000 feet

N

Fig. 19.   Palabora (Loolekop) (after Lombard, Ward-Able and Bruce, 1964).

8 sq miles and appears to represent three overlapping intrusive centres along a N–S line. There is a well-defined zonal arrangement of rock types around these centres. The most widespread is diopside pyroxenite which grades into a narrow marginal rim rich in microcline. This is in sharp contact with fenitized country rock and is cut by syenite. On the western slopes of Loolekop a crescent-shaped

mass of hydrobiotite glimmerite intervenes between the pyroxenite and the feldspathic pyroxenite. Within the pyroxenite are three pegmatitic bodies consisting of phlogopite, vermiculite, diopside, apatite and serpentinized olivine. The central pegmatitic body forms a broad belt around the Loolekop carbonatite and is essentially a magnetite-olivine-apatite rock (phoscorite); its composition is 35% magnetite, 25% apatite, 18% carbonates and 22% serpentine, vermiculite, hydrobiotite, diopside, baddeleyite and copper minerals. The carbonatite is essentially a magnetite-rich sövite with 3–8% MgO present as exsolution lamellae of dolomite in the calcite. The most unusual feature is the amount of sulphide minerals; these include pyrrhotite, pentlandite, cubanite, chalcopyrite, bornite, chalcocite, valleriite, bravoite, millerite, linnaeite, galena, pyrite, sphalerite and covellite. The cabonatite covers an area about 750 by 400 yd, is elongated at right angles to the main axis of the complex and is a vertical pipe with cylindrical structure that persists to a depth of at least 3500 ft. Near-vertical carbonatite dikes radiate from the central body and cut all the surrounding rocks to a distance of almost a mile. There are two types of carbonatite—an older banded and a younger transgressive. There is no clear boundary between the banded carbonatite and the enclosing phoscorite. The banding is due principally to magnetite and is parallel to the banding in the phoscorite, also caused by magnetite. The rock is relatively coarse-grained with about 20% magnetite. The transgressive carbonatite is a well-defined elongate body together with a multitude of narrow dikes and veins as offshoots from the main body. It intrudes and offsets both the banded carbonatite and the phoscorite, the rock being finer grained with a higher magnetite content (25–30%) than the banded type and the magnetite and silicates are concentrated in ragged lenses rather than bands. The titanium content of the magnetite increases outwards from the centre of the body towards the surrounding older carbonatite and phoscorite. The copper minerals occur principally in the younger transgressive carbonatite and as discontinuous veinlets generally less than one inch wide and often with marked parallelism. They are believed to have been introduced along fractures.

Bouwer, 1957.
Du Toit, 1931.
Forster, 1958.
Gevers, 1949.
Hall, 1912.

Lombaard, Ward-Able and Bruce, 1964.
Russell, Hiemstra and Groeneveld, 1954.
Shand, 1931.
Verwoerd, *a*

Spitskop (2) (Fig. 20)

The Spitskop Complex was emplaced in red Bushveld granite and is surrounded by a multiple zone of fenitization. An aureole of red cellular fenite was formed first and then partly consumed by recrystallization to form white soda amphibole fenite which forms a continuous zone around the complex. On the inner boundary of this zone the amphibole gives way to aegirine-augite concomitant with the total disappearance of quartz.

The principal rock type is ijolite comprising several textural varieties. Fine-

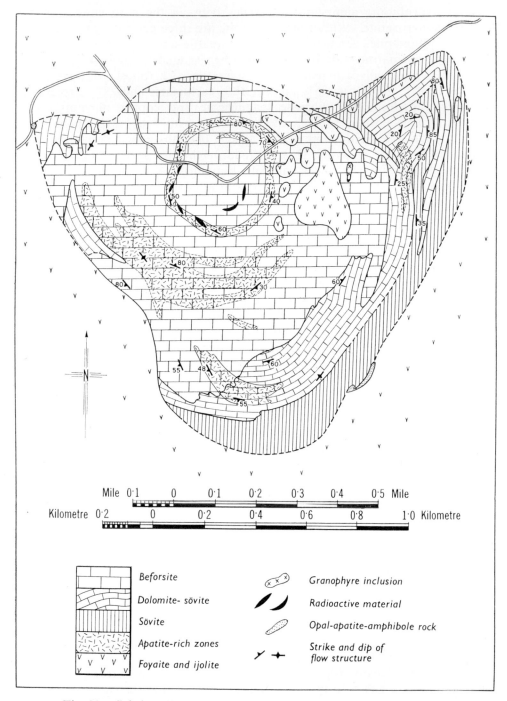

Mile 0·1 0 0·1 0·2 0·3 0·4 0·5 Mile

Kilometre 0·2 0 0·2 0·4 0·6 0·8 1·0 Kilometre

Beforsite

Dolomite- sövite

Sövite

Apatite-rich zones

Foyaite and ijolite

Granophyre inclusion

Radioactive material

Opal-apatite-amphibole rock

Strike and dip of flow structure

Fig. 20. Spitskop (figure supplied by W. J. Verwoerd, *Geol. Surv. Rep. South Africa*).

grained, black ijolite is considered to represent nephelinized biotite pyroxenite, in part at least; it was intruded by coarse-grained red ijolite which may be truly magmatic. Biotite pyroxenite, older than the ijolite but intrusive into the theralite forms a poorly exposed body in the western half of the ijolite mass.

All these rocks were intruded by two huge ring dikes of foyaite—an incomplete outer one and a roughly elliptical inner one. In detail both ring dikes are multiple and enclose big blocks of ijolite. In addition, cone sheets and radial dikes of foyaite, tinguaite and syenite were intruded on a large scale and two small plugs of soda basalt pierced the alkaline rocks at a late stage.

Finally an eccentrically situated carbonatite body a mile across was emplaced. No contacts are exposed but its intrusive nature is demonstrated by offshoots in the surrounding rocks and the presence of huge rounded inclusions of alkaline rocks in the carbonatite. Flow banding curves around these inclusions. An inclusion of unaltered granophyre 75 yd long shows that the carbonatite magma was not itself accompanied by fenitizing fluids. Brown-weathering beforsite forms the bulk of the intrusion. It is usually massive with its accessory minerals erratically distributed. Ankerite is the main constituent, sometimes with magnesio-dolomite cores and late-stage calcite. Accessory minerals are apatite, soda hornblende (both generally in streaks), magnetite, pyrite, sphalerite, aegirine, albite, phlogopite, ancylite and monazite.

White, coarse-grained sövite occurs as irregular, isolated patches along the margins of the carbonatite that are thought to be remnants of a former, more continuous zone.

Grey dolomite-bearing sövite is intermediate in position as well as composition between the white sövite and the beforsite. Calcite in this rock appears to have been replaced by magnesio-dolomite.

Apatite-rich zones occur in three concentric positions mostly in beforsite. The innermost zone is a complete ring about 40 yd wide and 440 yd in diameter. The rock is ordinary beforsite with near-vertical schlieren of micro-crystalline apatite giving it a streaky, banded appearance. The other zones are not so clearly defined and much more irregularly shaped. The zones are slightly radioactive. There is well developed steeply dipping flow banding in the apatite beforsite and the dolomite-bearing sövite. The carbonatite plug appears to be pipe-like and was probably emplaced in several stages marked by progressive enrichment in magnesium and iron.

Strauss and Truter, 1951*a*.   Verwoerd, *a, d.*

Magnet heights. The occurrence is 14 miles NNE of Spitskop and may be a related satellite. Five explosion vents filled with tuff and agglomerate penetrate gabbroic country rocks along a single axis. There is a range in fragment size from microscopic to about 9 in, the rock types being principally assorted Basement rocks in angular to rounded blocks. The tuffs are carbonate rich. A carbonatite dike about 12 in wide and 1100 yd long cuts all five diatremes; it is a very fine-grained massive calcite rock with bands of more coarsely crystalline calcite. The dike is paralleled by a dike of analcite picrite and there is a small plug of albitite. A similar carbonatite dike up to 3 ft wide and at least 650 yd long occurs 2 miles to the west and is also associated with minor agglomerates.

Strauss and Truter, 1951*b*.

Glenover (3)

This is a poorly exposed occurrence discovered during regional mapping in 1953. It has nevertheless become the second South African carbonatite to be exploited as a mineral deposit. The complex has an oval outline with a longer diameter of 3 miles and appears to consist predominantly of coarse-grained, non-ferruginous beforsite with an outer zone of sövite. Lenticular strips of sövite are also enclosed in beforsite. From drill hole information it is concluded that about one third of the complex in the north may be underlain by phlogopite-serpentine-diopside-apatite-magnetite rock averaging 5 per cent P_2O_5.

Almost in the centre of the carbonatite is a peculiar breccia body constituting high-grade phosphate ore. The fragments of the breccia show traces of bedding but have been almost completely replaced by apatite contaminated with red ferruginous dust. Drusy apatite veinlets cement the breccia. Drilling has shown that the body is irregularly bowl-shaped and bottoms on carbonatite at a depth of about 500 ft. The most likely explanation seems to be that it was formed by the collapse and subsequent mineralization of a bedded cave deposit.

The carbonatite contains disseminated apatite, magnetite, phlogopite and a number of accessory minerals including pyrochlore. Columbite and other alteration products of pyrochlore have accumulated by gravity in a highly ferruginous marginal zone of the breccia body which gives rise to a radiometric anomaly. Fluorite-barite veins are found in beforsite at several localities while numerous quartz stringers fill fractures in the carbonatite. The fluorite veins and quartz stringers contain abundant synchysite. Late-stage silicification has also affected part of the breccia body. A mineralogical curiosity associated with the drusy apatite veinlets is the presence of monazite pseudomorphs after an unknown hexagonal mineral.

Although there is hardly any outcrop, loose blocks of country rock clearly indicate that the sediments (mainly feldspathic sandstone) of the surrounding Loskop System have been fenitized. As at Spitskop, two types are recognized, —a red fenite around the complex, and white aegirine-augite–microperthite fenite occurring as large inclusions within carbonatite.

Verwoerd, *a*.

Nooitgedacht (4)

The Nooitgedacht carbonatite was emplaced in an area of intensely folded Precambrian strata of the Transvaal System and comes in contact with dolomite, carbonaceous shale and quartzite, but exposures are poor.

The complex has an oval outline with arcuate offshoots (ring dikes?). Its longer diameter is about two miles. Silicate rocks are more or less restricted to small external plugs of foyaite and inconspicuous microijolite outcrops within the carbonatite. Fenitized quartzite containing minute scattered crystals of green pyroxene, bluish green amphibole and perthite occurs mainly as xenoliths in the carbonatite. Heterogeneous fenite, ranging from dark green aegirine rock to a migmatite in which feldspar and aegirine predominate in alternating streaks, appears to occupy a sill-like position adjacent to the complex. The rest of the complex consists of carbonatite, three varieties of which have been distinguished:

(*a*) Sövite is the most extensive component. It has a well-developed concentric flow structure, generally with a vertical or steep inward dip. This is best shown by the concentration of apatite and magnetite in layers. Pyrochlore occurs in some sövite bands and offshoots while cerium and lanthanum are present in spectrographic traces.

(*b*) Quartz-ankerite sövite forms a little ring complex near the centre of the carbonatite. The rough-weathering arcuate outcrops cut at right-angles through the flow structure of the sövite at this locality. Isolated patches of the same rock type are also found farther afield. Microscopic observations reveal that the groundmass of calcite has undergone partial replacement by ankerite while quartz may constitute up to 50 per cent of the rock.

(*c*) Beforsite occurs as conformable and transgressive dike-like bodies. It is a moderately iron-rich variety consisting essentially of arankerite with serrated remnants of magnesio-dolomite. Apart from apatite and quartz the beforsite also contains disseminated monazite.

Verwoerd, *a*.

Tweerivier (5)

On previous geological maps the Tweerivier carbonatite complex was shown as a metamorphosed xenolith of Transvaal dolomite in Bushveld granite. Fockema (1935) recognized a system of beforsite dikes in the northern part of the limestone mass and at the neighbouring hill Bulhoekkop. It is now believed that all the carbonate rocks are probably of carbonatitic origin, although proof is lacking in the case of the older tremolite bearing dolomites of Tweerivier North.

The complex is a pear-shaped body between 1 and 2 miles wide and 4 miles long. Two near-by volcanic vents, Spitskoppie (consisting of granitic vent breccia) and Bulhoekkop (consisting of red fenite, beforsite and volcanic breccia with gabbro fragments) are undoubtedly related to it. The broad, northern section of the pear-shaped mass is geologically different from the narrower, southern portion, but the junction between the two is obscured by alluvial deposits.

Tweerivier North is mainly dolomitic carbonatite. Impersistent sövitic bands are intercalated with the dolomite, but they are intimately mixed. This so-called 'older carbonatite' has a foliation and banding roughly conformable in strike to the nearest outer boundary. The concentric structure is further emphasized by huge tabular inclusions of foreign rock (metamorphosed banded ironstone, recrystallized quartzite and garnetiferous hornfels) and by two arcuate zones characterized by tremolite. One is an altered, greenish tremolite schist with sharp but highly irregular boundaries, apparently replacing the older carbonatite. The other zone consists of banded tremolite 'marble' grading into purer carbonatite on either side.

Into this heterogeneous assemblage two groups of ankeritic beforsite dikes were intruded. The outer group is best developed along the northern boundary of the complex where they follow the curvature of the contact but also transgress into the country rock. The dikes stand out as low, sub-parallel, bifurcating and coalescing ridges characterized by reddish schlieren of apatite. Rhombohedra of magnesio-dolomite partly replaced by ankerite tend to weather out as pits. The inner group of dikes is similar but devoid of apatite schlieren, contains a less ferruginous carbonate and carries abundant disseminated magnetite. They describe a semicircle fairly close to the structural centre of the carbonatite.

Tweerivier South is poorly exposed but exploratory drilling for limestone has helped to clarify the structure. In this area the only carbonate rock is sövite containing magnetite, apatite, phlogopite, pyrite, olivine and baddeleyite as accessory minerals. A radioactive silicified zone occurs in the central part. Scattered outcrops of gabbro and anorthositic gabbro are also present and in drill holes these were found to predominate over carbonatite. Sövite exposed in a pit next to the road cuts through gabbro in dike-like fashion. The gabbro is very similar to the gabbro in the Main Zone of the Bushveld complex and it is concluded that this southern body is essentially a sövite plug choked by xenoliths brought from below. From the distribution of outcrops it appears as if the nearly circular outline of the northern body is interrupted by the 'giant breccia' of sövite and gabbro. Tweerivier North is therefore considered to be the earlier intrusion.

The three main phases of carbonatite emplacement at Tweerivier (older carbonatite, beforsite dikes, sövite) all seem to have been accompanied by fenitization. Red fenite is well developed at Bulhoekkop where beforsite is the only carbonate rock present; a zone of fenitization some thousand feet wide surrounds the whole composite body of Tweerivier North, even where beforsite is absent, while at Tweerivier South a narrow (perhaps more extensive) strip of fenite is cut by sövite at the south eastern end of the body. Quartzite xenoliths in carbonatite have been fenitized by the introduction of fibrous blue-green amphibole and veinlets composed of plagioclase, aegirine, amphibole and calcite.

Fockema, 1953.   Verwoerd, *a.*

Goudini (6) (Fig. 21)

The Goudini volcano is essentially a basin-shaped accumulation of partly carbonatized lava and tuff surrounded by pyroclastic breccia, the whole being emplaced in norite. Its genetic relationship with carbonatites is indicated by fenitization of norite, the presence of monazite-bearing sövite dikes, a radiometric anomaly, and barium–titanium–fluorine metasomatism.

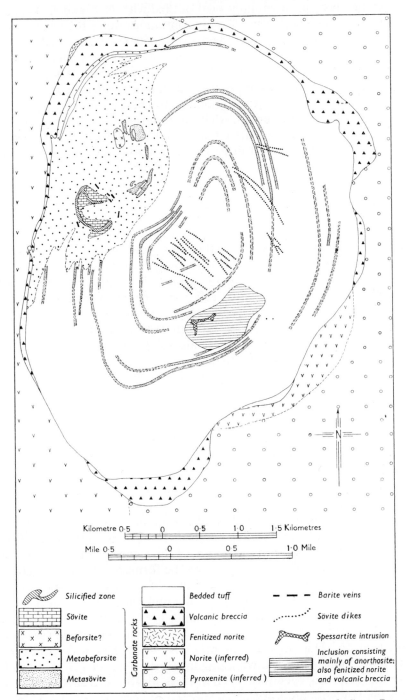

Kilometre 0·5   0   0·5   1·0   1·5 Kilometres

Mile 0·5   0   0·5   1·0 Mile

Silicified zone	Bedded tuff	Barite veins
Sövite	Volcanic breccia	Sövite dikes
Beforsite?	Fenitized norite	Spessartite intrusion
Metabeforsite	Norite (inferred)	Inclusion consisting mainly of anorthosite; also fenitized norite and volcanic breccia
Metasövite	Pyroxenite (inferred)	

Carbonate rocks

Fig. 21. Goudini (figure supplied by W. J. Verwoerd, *Geol. Surv. Rep. South Africa*).

The volcanic mass has a roughly oval outline with N–S and E–W diameters of 3.8 and 2.8 miles respectively. The discontinuous outer breccia ring consists predominantly of country rock fragments (bronzite norite, spotted anorthosite, chromitite, chilled diabase) but a few foreign fragments include quartzite, schorlomite granulite and perovskite-augite-magnetite rock. The major part of the composite body is occupied by well-bedded, inward-dipping tuffaceous shale with gritty intercalations. It is mostly of a dense, black, altered type resembling hornfels. A drill hole in the north, where outcrops are scarce, indicates that an appreciable thickness of carbonatized, amygdaloidal lava is also present in the basin. An area measuring two thirds of a mile across and consisting of brecciated anorthosite, fenitized norite and pyroclastic breccia cut by spessartite intrusions, is conformably enclosed by bedded tuff; it has been interpreted as an enormous inclusion or several closely spaced blocks derived from the crater rim.

By far the most interesting part is the north western quarter of the volcano, where tuffaceous beds, flow breccia, pillow lava and other volcanic rocks have been transformed to carbonate rock with the preservation of pseudomorphic structures. The result of this process is a fairly homogeneous ankerite-albite-aegirine rock with a granitoid texture referred to here as metacarbonatite. This term is used for all carbonate or carbonate-silicate rocks related to carbonatite but obviously formed by replacement of pre-existing rocks irrespective of their original composition. Metacarbonatites are subdivided according to composition into metasövites and metabeforsites.

The transition between tuffaceous beds and albite-aegirine-metabeforsite is not exposed but the centroclinal structure continues uninterruptedly through both components. Lenticular remnants of unchanged tuffaceous shale have been preserved in metabeforsite. The latter is often characterized by layers of angular fragments up to a few inches in diameter, which have been completely replaced, while pseudomorphs after idiomorphic pyroxene (?) crystals are encountered in thin sections. Rutile and anatase are disseminated throughout the metabeforsite. The rare sodium-titanium silicate ramsayite is a major constituent at a few localities.

Metasövite occurs as intercalated bands in the hornfelsic tuff east and southeast of the metabeforsite area. These bands often have gradational contacts and are closely conformable with the structure of the enclosing strata. The selective calcitization of the tuff must have preceded the formation of the metabeforsite. Where the latter interrupts the middle group of metasövite bands, lenticular inclusions of relatively smooth calcite-bearing rock fill the gap. These inclusions as well as the inner group of metasövite bands are concave in plan towards the metabeforsite, which possibly indicates pressure associated with the second stage of carbonatization. That this dominantly passive process was locally accompanied by movement is also shown along the western contact of the metabeforsite where the latter has been mobilized at three localities to such an extent that it intrudes the volcanic breccia ring.

A parallel swarm of sövite dikes up to three feet thick, seems to emanate from the metabeforsite area. They have been encountered only within the volcanic mass. Their accessory constituents are aegirine, monazite, biotite, fluorite and barite. An irregular, poorly exposed body of sövite also occurs within meta-beforsite in close association with a silicified zone, barite veins and a radiometric anomaly. The identity of these rocks as carbonatite is confirmed by their relatively high strontium content. Fluorite-dolomite veins are of limited extent.

Verwoerd, *a.*

Kruidfontein (7) (Fig. 22)

The Kruidfontein volcano is circular in outline with a diameter of about 3 miles and consists predominantly of denuded pyroclastic material. The central part is occupied by carbonatized tuffaceous deposits analogous to the metacarbonatites of Goudini. An outer and an inner zone can be distinguished.

The various rock types of the outer zone are all concentrically disposed, mostly in the form of overlapping arcs and probably dip inwards at a low angle. The earliest member is porphyritic basalt appearing as a single lava flow on the northern side. This was followed by a complete ring of pyroclastic breccia grading into lapilli tuff. Within the breccia ring there are several lenticular intercalations of trachyte, trachyandesite and andesite. Dolerite and gauteite dikes, corresponding in composition to the main lava flows are found within and around the volcano. Immediately to the north there are also a few small sill-like intrusions of highly altered gauteite. Following on the pyroclastic breccia in the south and east is a massive, rather homogeneous rock with a charac-teristic mottled appearance. This has been interpreted as ignimbrite although microscopic examination indicates that only traces of a vitroclastic texture re-main. The altered ignimbrite was succeeded by a second deposit of pyroclastic breccia, appearing as two opposite arcs, and consisting predominantly of more acid fragments than the older breccia. A peculiar deposit of conglomerate and quartzite, thought to represent a considerably disturbed intravolcanic sediment, is intercalated with the volcanic rocks at more than one level. Finally there was an outflow of rhyolite containing abundant fluorite and occasional flow layers.

The inner zone of the volcano consists of a central mountain block surrounded by a girdle of well-bedded sediments with a centroclinal dip. The main com-ponent of the central part is a massive, brown-weathering carbonate rock with exactly the same composition (ankerite, potash feldspar and chlorite) as the bedded rocks which can still be recognized as tuff. These rocks are designated as massive and bedded metabeforsite respectively. The zone of bedded meta-beforsite is interrupted at its base, especially in the north, by bedded metasövite. These two metacarbonatites fade into each other along a broad transition zone with much interfingering of more and less persistent layers. Microscopic ob-servation shows that ankerite is present in the metasövite as optically continuous rims around partly replaced calcite rhombohedra. It is therefore obvious that here, as at Goudini, carbonatization took place in two stages—calcitization, followed by ankeritization. Fluorite, barite, apatite and anatase occur as accessories in the carbonate rocks. The feldspar in the metabeforsite occurs as

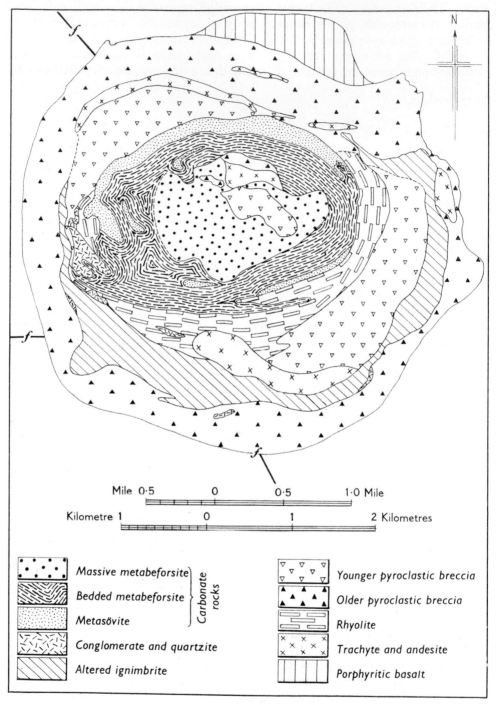

Mile 0·5   0   0·5   1·0 Mile

Kilometre 1   0   1   2 Kilometres

Massive metabeforsite	Younger pyroclastic breccia
Bedded metabeforsite	Older pyroclastic breccia
Metasövite	Rhyolite
Conglomerate and quartzite	Trachyte and andesite
Altered ignimbrite	Porphyritic basalt

Carbonate rocks

Fig. 22.   Kruidfontein (figure supplied by W. J. Verwoerd, *Geol. Surv.*
Rep. South Africa).

irregular, microcrystalline patches intimately intergrown with the carbonate and is probably untwinned orthoclase.

Intrusive bodies of carbonatite are not conspicuous but outcrops measuring a few yards across are found both in metacarbonatite and pyroclastic breccia. They are mostly of sövite with purple fluorite and subordinate quartz, barite and apatite.

The Kruidfontein volcano seems to be unique in that the full sequence from basic, through intermediate to acid silicate rocks is present, with an additional hydrothermal phase corresponding to carbonatite. It is not unreasonable to suppose that magmatic carbonatite and associated feldspathoid rocks may be present in depth. The volcano is obviously of the complex type. Large-scale foundering of the cone must have taken place to explain the huge blocks of rim rocks enveloped by carbonatized tuff near the centre of the volcano. The tuffaceous deposits of the inner zone are virtually undisturbed and must have reached their present position after active eruptions had ceased. There is little doubt that they conceal the site of the main vent. It is thought that the tuff was originally deposited along the rim and carried by water towards the caldera or crater lake. Subsequent hydrothermal activity (as suggested by the presence of potash feldspar, fluorite, apatite, barite and anatase in the metacarbonatites) led to the carbonization of the water-laid tuffaceous grit.

Verwoerd, *a.*

Roodeplaat (8)

The Roodeplaat volcano northeast of Pretoria was described by Lombaard (1930) as a 'centrocline'; its true character is recognized on the 1955 edition of the Geological Map of South Africa. The occurrence has not been examined in detail yet. Its structure and composition are closely comparable to those of the Goudini and Kruidfontein volcanoes while the carbonatite occurrence at Derdepoort appears to represent a satellitic vent. It is therefore considered to be a carbonatite-type volcano.

The volcano has an oval outline with a maximum diameter of 8 miles. Its outer zone consists of pyroclastic breccia, pebbly quartzite, trachyte, monchiquite, felsite and foyaite. The inner zone is poorly exposed but seems to consist mainly of inward-dipping, bedded tuffaceous shale with gritty layers. Two ring-shaped intrusions of diabase with a common northern limb cut through all these rock types and appear to be more or less concentric with the sediments and lavas.

Carbonatized tuff may be expected at this locality but has not been reported yet. There are abundant indications of infiltration and secondary alteration by carbonate-bearing solutions of trachytic rocks along the Pienaars River near the southern margin of the volcano. Fluorite is also much in evidence in the volcanic rocks of the outer zone; Lombaard (1930) describes a rather unusual deposit consisting mainly of fluorite and apatite.

Verwoerd, *a.*

Derdepoort (9)

This is a small breccia pipe with associated beforsite on the outskirts of Pretoria. It measures about 0.5 mile in diameter and has an irregular outline. The pipe interrupts one of a set of tear faults affecting the floor of the Bushveld Complex in this area. A series of smaller vents connects the Derdepoort pipe with the Roodeplaat volcano.

The material filling the pipe includes brecciated quartzite, volcanic breccia consisting essentially of felsite, biotite-rich breccia and carbonatite. Among the fragments are several deep-seated rock-types including two large blocks of red syenite and carbonatized alnöite. The carbonatite is best exposed along the northern margin of the pipe where it transgresses the country rock quartzite. Emplacement was mainly controlled by steep joints in the quartzite. Three varieties have been distinguished: an impure chlorite-bearing beforsite as the most widespread type is traversed in all directions by veins and dikes of smooth white beforsite. The main constituent of these two carbonatites is ankerite but quartz, feldspar and disseminated specularite plates are ubiquitous. The third variety is a red beforsite grading into the white beforsite. It consists of magnesio-dolomite contaminated with ferruginous dust. Finally, an apatite-bearing carbonatite dike in which ankerite is partly replaced by calcite intrudes biotite-rich breccia near the south-western end of the pipe.

Verwoerd, *a.*

Premier Mine (10)

Premier Mine is at present the principal producer of diamonds in South Africa. It is a kimberlite pipe cut by calcite-magnetite-serpentine dikes which have been interpreted as carbonatite in the sense of Brögger (Daly, 1925). Recent development work has shown that the dikes persist to depths of more than 1060 ft, but at this level some portions have the usual minerals and characteristics of kimberlite, and in particular of a late, carbonate-rich intrusive phase. Several successive generations of kimberlite have been distinguished in Premier Mine and these tend to show a progressive enrichment in lime. The dikes have a relatively high Ba/Sr ratio and a low Sr content which furthermore distinguish them from true carbonatite. It is therefore concluded that they were formed by replacement of pre-existing kimberlite dikes during either a hydrothermal or deuteric stage of waning volcanic activity.

Notwithstanding the above, arguments exist for relating the kimberlite of Premier Mine (with its appreciable calcium carbonate content) to carbonatite-type volcanism. In the past a late-Cretaceous age has been assumed in respect of all South African kimberlites, including Premier Mine. It has now been established beyond reasonable doubt, however, that the Premier Mine pipe is cut by a diabase sill genetically related to the Leeuwfontein alkaline complex. Since the kimberlite with its well-known sandstone inclusion is therefore post-Waterberg and pre-diabase in age, it fits exactly into the volcanic episode of Roodeplaat and Derdepoort already described, with the intrusions of the so-called 'Franspoort line' as the undersaturated, plutonic counterparts of the volcanic rocks.

Daly, 1925.   Verwoerd, *a.*

Pretoria Salt Pan (*Soutpan*) (*11*)

The volcano, 25 miles northwest of Pretoria, has been described in detail by Wagner (1922). It consists of a circular rim of ejected blocks and brecciated country rock, 0.6 mile in diameter, rising from 100 to 200 ft above the surrounding plain of Bushveld granite. The floor of the depression lies 194 ft below the average level of the plain and is occupied by mud impregnated with soda and salt. Drilling to a depth of 234 ft penetrated various layers of saline clay containing trona and gaylussite but no solid rock was struck. A preliminary gravimeter survey showed a negative anomaly over the depression. Dolomitic breccia was encountered at several points along the rim. This possible carbonatite is a fine-grained rock consisting of calcite, magnesio-dolomite and ankerite with specularite stringers and disseminated quartz-chlorite fragments, magnetite, pyrite, apatite and biotite. Wagner concluded that the volcano is a sunken caldera 'certainly of post-Cretaceous and probably of late-Quaternary age'. It is, in fact, the youngest volcanic phenomenon in South Africa. Its closest analogy is with the Tanganyika volcanoes Kerimasi and Oldoinyo Lengai.

Wagner, 1922*a, b.*   Du Toit, 1954.

Salpeterkop (*12*)

A number of breccia-filled volcanic vents, of which Salpeterkop is the largest, occurs near Sutherland in Cape Province. A possible relationship with carbonatite has long been suspected for these pipes since the breccia has been described as calcareous in places. Salpeterkop was recently examined by J. J. de Wet of Stellenbosch University, from whom the following notes were obtained.

The Salpeterkop neck measures approximately 5000 ft in diameter and is composed of lithic pyroclastic material mainly derived from comminuted Beaufort beds. The pipe was intruded near its western margin by sövite bodies carrying streaks of magnetite crystals and is cut by a younger agglomerate mass towards the east. In addition, numerous thin, dark brown beforsite dikes full of inclusions extend up to several miles from Salpeterkop, especially in a northerly direction. Some of the fragments in the dikes are apparently derived from the Cape System thousands of feet below. It seems probable that the dikes are offshoots from larger carbonatite bodies close to the surface. Other closely related intrusions in the area consist of a feldspathic rock and of olivine melilitite. Thin barite veins occur along joints and fractures in both country rock and pyroclasts. Apart from the fact that they post-date Karroo dolerites (Triassic) the age of the Sutherland vents is uncertain.

Verwoerd,

POSSIBLE CARBONATITES

Dr. W. J. Verwoerd of the Geological Survey of the Republic of South Africa lists the following possible but unsubstantiated carbonatites: Kobe volcano 18 miles ESE of Van Rhynsdorp in Cape Province, and three small vents at Grenaat Kop in the Prieska district, Cape Province.

Rhodesia (formerly Southern Rhodesia)

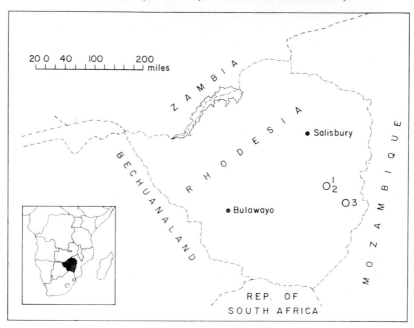

Fig. 23.   Carbonatites in Rhodesia.

1. Dorowa   3.   Chishanya
2. Shawa

Dorowa (1) (p. 206, Fig. 3)

Dorowa is a horseshoe-shaped hill a little under 2 miles in length. The complex consists essentially of syenitic fenites that become increasingly syenitic towards the centre and finally culminate in a central area of ijolite and foyaite thought to be mobilized fenite. Small carbonatite plugs and dikes cut the syenites and nepheline syenites together with dikes of magnetite-apatite-vermiculite-serpentine. The fenites can be divided into (*a*) fenitized granite gneiss and quartz syenitic fenite, (*b*) syenitic fenite, (*c*) pulaskitic fenite. The first signs of fenitization are seen about 3000 ft from the boundary of the syenitic fenite. Three kinds of carbonatite occur: (*a*) fine-grained calcitic, (*b*) coarse-grained calcitic, (*c*) fine-grained dolomitic. Magnetite, phlogopite and apatite occur as accessory minerals and some of the plugs and dikes have steeply dipping banding. Among the dolomitic carbonatite dikes are some that are porphyritic with subrounded phenocrysts (single crystals) of dolomite. In addition to carbonatite there are several dikes, veins and irregular masses of magnetite, magnetite-apatite, magnetite-serpentine, vermiculite-apatite and vermiculite.

Late silicification has resulted in local replacement of carbonate by microcrystalline quartz.

The country rocks are granitic gneisses enclosing small bodies of serpentinite, sandstone and iron formation and cut by diabase dikes and sills.

Dixey, 1946.   Mennell, 1946.
Johnson, 1961.   Swift, 1952, 1959.
Macgregor, 1947.   Tyndale-Biscoe, 1959.

Shawa (2) (p. 207, Fig. 4)

The Shawa complex has a diameter of about 3.5 miles and is essentially a plug of almost completely serpentinized dunite, partly enclosed by arcuate bodies of ijolite. These are encircled by an irregular zone of fenite that grades outwards into the granitic country rocks. Within the serpentinite-dunite plug there is a central ring dike of carbonatite. Where preserved the dunite consists of fresh green forsteritic olivine (Fa_{17}) with about 4 per cent magnetite but there are bands up to 2 cm wide that are rich in magnetite. It is assumed that the rock was intruded as dunite and later serpentinized.

All the carbonatite dikes are dolomitic. The main ring dike varies in width from 1000 ft to 100 ft. Its grain size is variable and the rock is strongly foliated in some places, less so in others. Green phlogopite and octahedra of magnetite are universal accessories with apatite common in some parts. Fragments of serpentinite are found in the carbonatite along the dike margins. In addition to and largely concentric with the main ring dike there are several smaller vertical dikes of massive, medium-grained dolomite cutting the serpentine. Several barite and vermiculite veins cut the serpentinite.

Dikes of nephelinite intrude the country rocks and there are two small plugs of ijolite 1 mile west and 4 miles south east of the complex.

Dixey, 1946.   Nicolayson, Burger and Johnson,
Johnson, 1961.   1962.
Macgregor, 1947.   Swift, 1952.
Mennell, 1946.   Tyndale-Biscoe, 1959.

Chishanya (3) (Fig. 24)

The complex consists of a small group of hills about 600 ft high. The country rock is Precambrian granite gneiss overlain by Umkondi sediments (early Paleozoic?), but the sediments have been eroded from the complex, their nearest outcrop being about 2 miles to the south east. The complex is somewhat elliptical, oriented NE–SW, and consists of syenite, nepheline syenite, ijolite and carbonatite. Ijolite forms a partial ring round a central core of carbonatite.

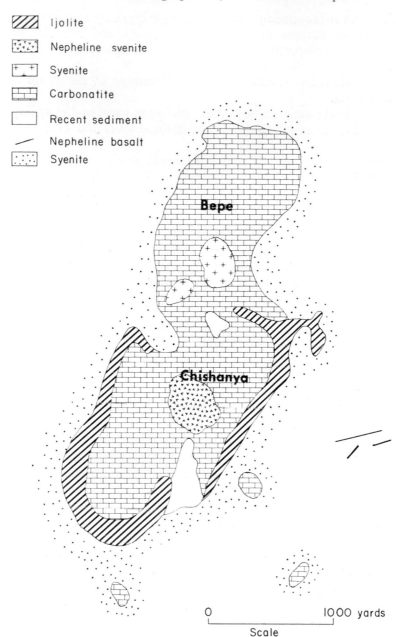

Fig. 24.   Chishanya (after Swift, 1952).

There are xenoliths or intrusions of syenite, nepheline syenite and ijolite within the carbonatite, and small plugs of carbonatite occur up to a mile from the complex. Fenitization of the granite gneiss extends to 2000 yd from the complex and it is thought to have gone to the extreme of producing syenite adjacent to the complex. The carbonatite is mostly massive calcite rock with a grain size of 0.125–0.25 in., cut by magnetite–apatite veins. The largest of these dip vertically but the smaller ones permeate the carbonate rock intimately. There are, however, variations. Thus the carbonatite on Bepe is very rich in magnetite while that on the hill south west of Chishanya has very little magnetite or apatite and is finer grained. On Chishanya large crystals of magnetite stand out on the weathered surface. Chalcedony represents local silicification of the carbonatite.

Time relations between carbonatite and ijolite are not known but dikes of nepheline basalt, phonolite and nephelinite cut the carbonatite and country rock, including the Umkondi sediments, to a distance of 5000 yd from the complex.

Swift, 1952.   Tyndale-Biscoe, 1959.

Somali Republic

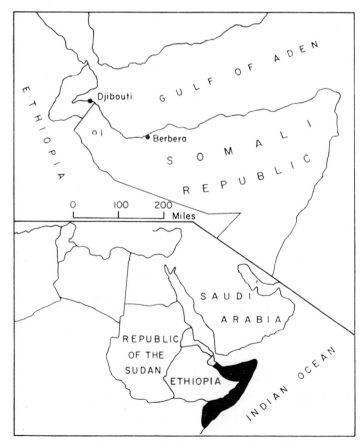

Fig. 25.   Carbonatite in the Somali Republic.

Q

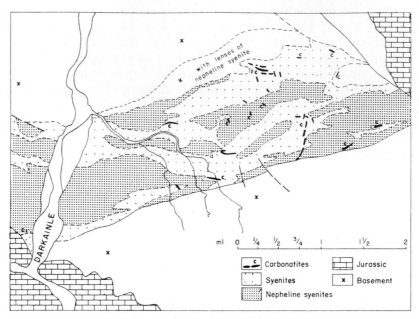

Fig. 26.   Darkainle (after Gellatly, 1963).

Darkainle (1) (Fig. 26)

This is a complex of alkaline rocks and carbonatite that outcrops as a narrow inclined sheet 21 miles in length and up to 1.75 miles wide. The principal rocks are foliated and folded syenites and nepheline syenites that are fairly leucocratic but do contain biotite, magnesioriebeckite and aegirine. Carbonatite is found within the nepheline gneisses in two forms: an early type consisting of concordant bands and lenses up to 300 yd in length, and a later discordant type consisting of thin veins. Dolomite appears to be more abundant than calcite and some carbonatite is very rich in limonite. Marble beds are present within the Basement rocks adjacent to the complex but in contrast to these the carbonatite is greatly enriched in Ba, La, Sr and Y. In addition there are small areas of carbonatitic intrusion breccia containing feldspathic fragments. The complex is overlain unconformably by Jurassic sediments.

Gellatly, 1962, 1963*a, b,* 1964.

South West Africa

1. Swartbooisdrif	5. Kalkfeld
2. Epembe	6. Osongombo
3. Okorusu	7. Brukkaros (Gross Brukkaros)
4. Ondurakorume	8. Chamais

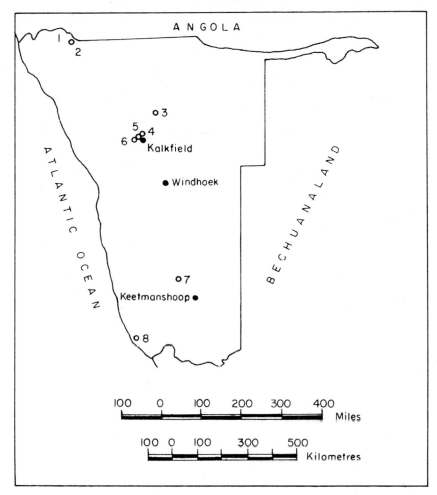

Fig. 27.   Carbonatites in South West Africa (figure supplied by W. J. Verwoerd, *Geol. Surv. Rep. South Africa*).

The following descriptions are condensed from a manuscript[1] prepared by P. J. van Zijl,[2] W. J. Verwoerd[3] and D. K. Toerien[4].

Swartbooisdrif (1)

The Swartbooisdrif complex of carbonatite and nepheline syenites of Precambrian age intrudes the anorthosite mass of the Kunene basic complex and the older granitic gneisses and amphibolites of the Epupa Formation. The intrusives seem to bear a structural relationship to the shape of the southern extremity of the basic complex.

[1] Published under South African Government Printer's Copyright Authority No. 3084 of November 2nd 1962, and No. 3081 of October 30th, 1962.
[2] Tsumeb Corporation Ltd., Tsumeb, South West Africa (Okorusu and Kalkfeld).
[3] Geological Survey, Pretoria, Rep. of South Africa. (Ondurakorume, Osongombo, Brukkaros, and Chamais.)
[4] Geological Survey, Windhoek, South West Africa (Swartbooisdrif and Epembe).

The Swartbooisdrif complex has been mapped to the Angolan border and nothing is known about a possible continuation to the north. South of the Kunene River it can be described as a more or less fan-shaped dike swarm approximately 30 km in length. An oblong (1·5 × 1 km) nepheline syenite plug occurs near its apex. Within this plug carbonatite outcrops in the form of a few thin scattered veins, and in a shapeless area covering approximately 2000 sq m. The dike swarm is composed of usually vertical or steep-dipping single-component and composite dikes of nepheline syenite (usually porphyritic), carbonatite, a lamprophyric rock type, and feldspar-rich carbonatites. These dikes are up to 50 m broad.

Nepheline syenite was the first intrusive. In the plug the rock is generally dark grey, varies from coarse- to fine-grained, and is rich in biotite, sodalite and cancrinite. Pre-syenite explosions occurred here. Next followed a coarse-grained pale brown to pinkish carbonatite preceded by violent explosions in the plug and in numerous places along the dikes. Brecciated nepheline syenite xenoliths of widely varying size appear in this rock. On the weathered surface the carbonatite is chocolate brown with visible magnetite, biotite and occasionally apatite crystals. Closely associated with the carbonatite was the introduction of much biotite into cracks in the brecciated rocks and the intrusion of dikes of a black porphyritic biotite-rich lamprophyric rock. Varying amounts of nepheline syenite were partly or wholly digested by this intrusive. The last to follow was another carbonatite carrying widely varying amounts of alkali feldspars dispersed more or less evenly through the rock and also concentrated in uneven bands. The colour of this rock varies from dark to pale grey, to pinkish and greenish grey. It penetrates the surrounding rocks to a much greater extent than its predecessors and has quite intensive reaction along its contacts.

A striking feature of these carbonatites is the presence in discontinuous areas of beautiful deep blue sodalite and yellow cancrinite of metasomatic origin. The sodalite has partly or wholly replaced the nepheline syenite xenoliths and feldspars and appears today as irregular patches of crystal aggregates up to 1 m in diameter. Cancrinite seems to preferentially replace the basic feldspars of the affected anorthosite. Together the cancrinite and sodalite turned patches of the impure carbonatite and altered wall rock into rocks beautifully banded in blue and yellow.

Verwoerd, *a*.

Epembe (2)

This occurrence is closely related to that at Swartbooisdrif 30–40 km to the northeast. It is represented by two hilly stretches of nepheline syenite, each approximately 14 × 2 km in extent that appear to be structurally connected with a WNW–ESE striking fault zone. The rock is coarse- to fine-grained as at Swartbooisdrif but paler in colour, contains probably less biotite, and is megascopically devoid of sodalite and cancrinite. The outcrop west of Epembe was extensively brecciated in the centre along strike by violent explosions which were followed by intrusive carbonatite now forming a ridge-like body roughly

6 km long and 400 m wide. The colour of this rock varies from bluish grey to pale pink on fresh and weathered surfaces. Brecciated xenoliths of nepheline syenite are abundant. The rock is apatite-rich and clusters of amphibole crystals and biotite are conspicuously concentrated in the eastern part of the intrusion.

Verwoerd, *a.*

Okorusu (3)

The Okorusu stock is an oval body with an inferred extent of 32 sq km. It has the typical ring structure, largely obscured by an extensive sand cover, of complex central volcanoes. The country rocks consist of Damara marbles, graywackes, feldspathic and calcareous quartzites and conglomerates that have undergone thermal metamorphism at the contact of the plug.

The two main intrusives are an older, medium-grained, partly foliated syenite constituting approximately 90 per cent of the complex and a core of younger, extremely coarse-grained leucocratic syenite, foyaite and urtite showing a continuous increase in nepheline content from the rim to the centre of this plug. Hortonolite monzonite forms several small bodies, probably inclusions, within the syenites. Minor intrusives consist of fine-grained, dark foyaite dikes and plugs and a large number of tinguaite, bostonite, melanephelinite and nephelinite dikes, filling radial and conical fractures within the complex and extending out into the adjoining sediments. A noteworthy characteristic of the intrusives as a whole is the gradational change from an almost pure diopside in the early syenite to aegirine-augite rich in acmite in the late foyaites.

The formation of the carbonatite is connected with extensive fenitization. This began with the impregnation of the country rock by aegirine-augite to form an almost pure alkali-pyroxene rock over large stretches. The order of susceptibility to replacement appears to be quartz followed by feldspar and biotite with calc-silicates and calcite, belonging to the Damara marbles, being the most resistant. Comparison between the pyroxene of the intrusives and the aegirine-augite of the metasomatic pyroxenite seems to indicate that the mass of the pyroxenite is of late-foyaite to post-foyaite age. The replacement took place in several waves, the gases or fluids becoming more sodium-iron rich with each successive invasion, resulting in a deeper green colour of the later pyroxenes. Concurrent explosive action gave rise to shatter breccia consisting of fragments of light green pyroxenite rimmed by later dark green pyroxene all cemented together by pure white calcite. Accessory minerals are coarse apatite, biotite, magnetite, pyrite, soda-amphibole, sphene, alkali feldspar and melanite. The calcite veins in the fractured pyroxenite locally merge into several small carbonatite bodies up to 400m in length composed of 90–95 per cent $CaCO_3$ and 5–10 per cent matter insoluble in hydrochloric acid—chiefly abundant coarse apatite and minor amounts of quartz, aegirine-augite, pyrite and magnetite.

Fracturing of the wall rock along the southern wall of the complex continued after the formation of the white carbonatite. Solutions entering along these fractures metasomatically replaced large portions of the pyroxenite, remaining sediments and syenite along the southern contact, forming a brown rock type consisting mainly of alkali-feldspar, iron oxides, quartz, calcite and fluorite. Continued fracturing affected even this metasomatic feldspar rock, the new fractures being filled with iron and manganese ore. Locally iron ore concentrations gave rise to three tabular bodies of titaniferous magnetite.

Fluorine-rich emanations apparently concluded the period of magmatic activity. Apart from the disseminated fluorite within the brown feldspar rock, vein deposits along prominent joints and replacement deposits within limestone formed numerous separate ore bodies with a total of between seven and ten million tons in excess of 35 per cent CaF_2.

Martin, Mathias and Simpson, 1960.   van Zijl, 1959, 1962.
Stahl, 1930.   Verwoerd, *a*.

Ondurakorume (4)

Ondurakorume is about 15 km N–NE of the Kalkfeld alkaline complex. The two carbonatites are similar in composition but Ondurakorume is structurally more complicated. Despite its smaller diameter (1.5 km), Ondurakorume attains greater topographic prominence than the Kalkfeld carbonatite rising abruptly to a height of 300 m above the surrounding peneplain. The presence of a mere foyaite arc instead of successive rings of alkaline rock suggests that it is less deeply eroded than the Kalkfeld Complex.

As at Kalkfeld the country rock consists of marble, quartzite and biotite schist of the Damara System, intimately associated with syntectonic Salem granite. These rocks have been fenitized up to about 300 m away from the carbonatite contact, probably in advance of the main intrusion.

Foyaite appears to have been the earliest intrusive forming an irregular body with an arcuate offshoot on the south east side of the carbonatite, and is separated from it by country rock. A single small outcrop in the north indicates the possible continuity of the zone in depth. Inclusions of country rock are found in foyaite. An isolated patch of reddish syenite, intruded into rocks of the Damara System, is surrounded by carbonatite and represents an inlier or a xenolith; its relationship to the foyaite is unknown.

The carbonatite was emplaced as a number of consecutive intrusives. Replacement seems to have played a relatively minor role. Explosive forces were operative during the early stages as testified by brecciated country rock and numerous carbonate-filled cracks and joints in the foyaite. Breccia bodies traversed by beforsite veins and containing fragments of fenite, granite, marble and greywacke are especially found in the north where some of them are enclosed by carbonatite. The greater part of Ondurakorume Hill is occupied by the following three types of carbonatite, arranged in their probable order of emplacement:

    (i) Micaceous sövite. This is a soft, heterogeneous rock in which the fine-grained mica is invariably altered to dark green chlorite or yellowish vermiculite. In places the rock is characterized by 'pisolitic' structure. Micaceous patches are sometimes intimately mixed with irregular bodies of pure carbonatite. As a whole the micaceous sövite forms a central, nearly circular plug with a concentric structure which was exploited and emphasized by later intrusions.

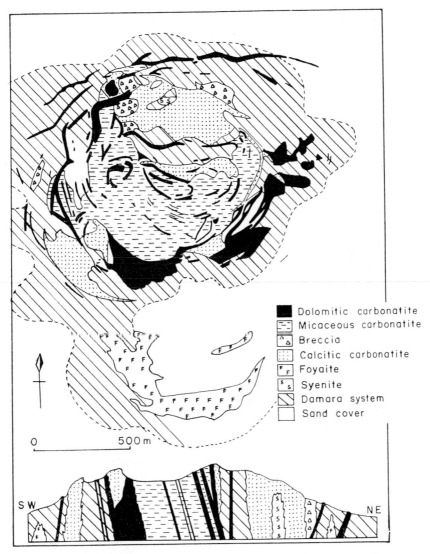

Fig. 28. Ondurakorume (after Martin, Mathias and Simpson, 1960).

(ii) Grey sövite occurs as five major bodies and several smaller ones, some in the shape of ring dikes. With one exception (a large arcuate mass enclosed by country rock in close proximity to the plug) these bodies adjoin the micaceous sövite plug and it seems clear that their position was determined by the outline of the latter. The rock is medium-grained (1–5 mm) and consists essentially of calcite showing incipient replacement by ankerite. Magnetite crystals are grouped in parallel flow layers, often giving the rock a streaky, banded appearance. Other accessories are apatite, pyrite, pyroxene and soda-hornblende.

(iii) Beforsite forms a complicated system of ring dikes locally swelling into larger bodies. They were mostly intruded into country rock along the outer margin of the complex, but seem to outline two adjacent centres within the micaceous sövite plug as well. They dip inwards and outwards at various angles and closely resemble those of the Tweerivier complex, Transvaal. They are often rich in apatite which occurs as schlieren and networks of opaque white microcrystalline streaks. Euhedral ankerite insets may impart a pseudoporphyritic texture to the rock. Blue soda-hornblende (arfvedsonite?) is a common constituent, especially in the largest beforsite mass where it is responsible for a primary banding in the form of lenticular concentrations. Sparsely disseminated pyrochlore and strontianite occur in association with the blue amphibole. Calcite and quartz are minor constituents.

A radiometric anomaly on Ondurakorume Hill was traced to the presence of several parallel veins of oxidized iron ore, analogous to that of the Kalkfeld carbonatite, emplaced in conformity with the primary structure of the micaceous sövite plug. Finally, the complex is traversed by a suite of parallel, N–S trending dikes of chilled, partly amygdaloidal dolerite.

Martin, Mathias and Simpson, 1960. Verwoerd, *a*.

Kalkfeld (5) (Fig. 29)

The Kalkfeld complex is oval and some 35 sq km in extent with the well-developed ring structure topographically emphasized. The four main rock types are granite, syenite, foyaite and carbonatite intruded in that order as confocal rings with the carbonatite at the centre.

The granite is intruded into Damara marbles and feldspathic quartzites and forms a discontinuous outermost zone enclosing abundant sedimentary xenoliths. It is holo-leucocratic, equigranular and consists of perthite and quartz. Fenitization in the form of replacement of quartz by aegirine-augite is conspicuous close to the syenite but shows a gradual decrease away from the contact.

Inside the granite is an incomplete ring of syenite consisting almost entirely of coarse perthite. Aegirine-augite metasomatism has intensely affected the syenite where foliated but is otherwise sparsely present.

Scattered outcrops of foyaite occur in the sandy flats on the inside of the syenite zone probably forming one continuous plug underneath the sand cover. The foyaite consists of perthite, primary aegirine-augite, nepheline, sodalite, biotite and accessory cancrinite, oligoclase, sphene, eudialyte, magnetite and pyrite. Judging from the compositions of the aegirine-augites in the foyaite, syenite and granite, fenitization of the syenite and granite took place during or shortly after the intrusion of the foyaite.

The carbonatite in the centre of the foyaite forms an oval hill approximately 2000 by 1500 m and rising 140 m above the surrounding plain. The carbonatite has a distinct flow-line pattern indicating a cone-shaped structure. It consists of a grey to brown sövite containing highly variable amounts of hematite-

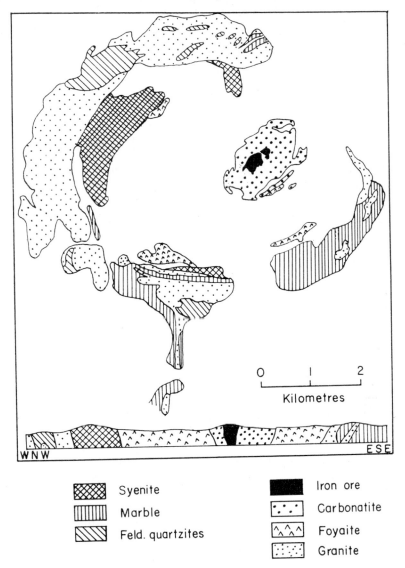

Syenite   Iron ore
Marble   Carbonatite
Feld. quartzites   Foyaite
Granite

Fig. 29.   Kalkfeld (after Van Zijl, 1962).

limonite, hydro-biotite and partly decomposed cloudy feldspar. A chemical analysis shows trace MgO and up to 0.84% SrO and 4.91% BaO. The feldspar consists of soda orthoclase or orthoclase perthite and occurs disseminated throughout the carbonatite oriented mainly in stringers parallel to the flow lines. The hydro-biotite is sparsely present but increases along the southwest side of the carbonatite mass to form a biotite glimmerite with interstitial hematite, limonite and calcite. Other accessory minerals within the carbonatite are aegirine-augite, melanite and a pale green mineral, probably ancylite. Within the carbonatite are several small xenoliths up to a foot in length of white limestone (early carbonatite?) and what appears to be altered fenitized granite.

Iron staining, disseminated iron ore and small iron ore veins are common features within the carbonatite. In the centre a large oval mass of iron ore 300×400 m and at least 65 m thick, exhibits a cone-shaped structure analogous to that found in the carbonatite. Judging from its structural and textural habit the iron ore appears to be of metasomatic origin. It consists chiefly of hematite and limonite, but in addition contains variable amounts of magnetite, siderite, goethite, pyrolusite and feldspar and trace amounts of barite and fluorite. The iron ore is slightly radioactive owing to the presence of an altered unidentified thorium mineral.

The last phase of magmatic activity was the intrusion of a variety of dikes and small stocks filling conical ring and radial fractures. These include tinguaite, bostonite, syenite aplite, minette, diorite and analcite-olivine-dolerite. Tinguaite, syenite aplite and dolerite dikes cut across the carbonatite whereas numerous minette veins and dikelets are found within the iron ore.

Martin, Mathias and Simpson, 1960.   van Zijl, 1959, 1962.
Stahl, 1930.   Verwoerd, *a*.

Osongombo (6)

Osongombo is the smallest of the South West Africa carbonatite complexes and is best described as a diatreme. The country rock is white calcite marble of the Damara System and irregular bodies of Salem granite.

The complex has an irregular outline with an average diameter of 500 m. It consists mainly of volcanic breccia but about one third of its surface area is occupied by beforsite containing scattered outcrops of radioactive iron ore. The beforsite forms a central zone except in the north west where it cuts across the breccia and sends an apophysis into the surrounding marble. There is no sharp contact between volcanic breccia and carbonatite since the latter often contains numerous fragmentary inclusions. The main constituents of the breccia are fragments of reddish fine-grained granite and fenitized granite with subordinate quartzite, micaceous carbonate rock and highly altered basic lava or greenstone. There is no well-defined aureole of fenitization but the granite is locally deprived of quartz, enriched in apatite or traversed by cracks filled with aegirine. Infiltration of iron along joints also took place in Damara marble. A few inconspicuous dolerite dikes cut through the plug in north easterly directions.

Petrographically, the beforsite and iron ore are similar to the corresponding rock types at Ondurakorume. The principal carbonate is manganiferous ankerite which weathers deep brown. Apatite is present as prismatic crystals but occurs mainly in the form of microcrystalline aggregates of low birefringence. These aggregates form a network of irregular veinlets in the beforsite and stand out on weathered surfaces revealing the flow structure where present; locally they swell into apatite-rich bodies a foot or more across. Pyrochlore is an accessory in the beforsite, occurring as microscopic yellowish octahedra disseminated in apatite-rich patches. Barite is fairly common in thin sections while quartz, plagioclase, calcite and rutile have also been encountered.

Verwoerd, *a*.

Brukkaros (*Gross Brukkaros*) (7)

Brukkaros is a considerably eroded volcano with a crater-like rim rising 550 m above the surrounding plain. It is approximately 3 km in diameter and owes its shape to central subsidence and/or differential erosion. The rim consists of inward-dipping layers of gritty tuff and pyroclastic breccia, thus affording a structural analogy with the basin-shaped carbonatite-type volcanoes of the Transvaal. In several other respects (e.g. the arching up of the otherwise horizontal strata 1.5 to 2 km away from the volcano, the occurrence of barite, satellitic breccia bodies, carbonatite dikes and associated ultrabasic rocks), Brukkaros shows a close resemblance with Salpeterkop.

Carbonates are not much in evidence at the present level of erosion of the volcano itself. The central part of the basin is obscured by detritus with no exposures of bedrock. The designation of Brukkaros as a carbonatite-type volcano rests mainly on the fact that thin beforsite dikes radiate from it, mainly in northeasterly and westerly directions. In the former direction they extend for distances up to 90 km. Around the mountain there are about fifty breccia bodies, either with beforsite as matrix or cut by irregular beforsite intrusions. These satellites measure 40 to 100 m in diameter.

Brukkaros volcano is post-Karroo in age and may possibly be related to the late-Cretaceous period of kimberlite eruptions. Several features indicate a genetic connection between these two phenomena. The main concentration of kimberlite pipes in South West Africa (46 pipes and 16 fissures have been mapped) is situated within 90 km north of Brukkaros in the Gibeon district. Many of the kimberlites are carbonatized and are also associated with carbonatized dikes. The altered ultrabasic rock is often difficult to distinguish from carbonatite.

Janse, 1962, 1963, 1964.   Verwoerd, *a*.

Chamais (*8*)

This is a small carbonatite plug in a normally inaccessible area north of the Orange River mouth. The locality is 100 km NW of Oranjemund, scarcely 1 km from the coast, in the desert waste of the southern Namib.

The plug forms a spur of an east-facing escarpment some 30 m high. It is elongated in plan, measuring about 100 m by 50 m. It intrudes chlorite schist, probably of the Archaean Grootderm Series, and has an irregular outline with numerous apophyses in the country rock. Large blocks of schist are also included in the carbonatite. In places the plug is crammed with angular and unsorted country rock fragments, including quartzite which must have been derived from depth. Irregular bodies of siliceous carbonatite and drusy quartz veinlets are also present.

The carbonatite is a medium-grained beforsite containing euhedral rhombo-hedra of magnesio-dolomite that stand out on weathered surfaces. Ankerite occurs interstitially and as reaction rims around magnesio-dolomite, replacing the latter to a limited extent. Miarolitic structure is characteristic of most speci-mens. Accessory minerals in the samples studied were quartz, feldspar, amphi-bole, biotite, pyrite and minute disseminated rutile.

The age is quite uncertain but one is tempted to link it either with the foyaite stocks of Granitberg and Pomona or the phonolites of the Klinghardt Mount-ains. Cretaceous to Tertiary ages have been assigned to these various occurrences but Dr. M. H. Martin considers it more likely that the foyaite stocks belong to the late-Stormberg (lower Jurassic) period of volcanism.

Verwoerd, *a*.

Tanganyika (now part of Tanzania)

The carbonatites of Tanganyika are conveniently grouped geographically under the headings Northern, Eastern and South Western. A number of vol-canic mountains such as Sadiman, Essimingor and Oldoinyo Lengai are con-fidently listed as carbonatite-type volcanoes but others in the same general area, although possessing some alkaline lavas are generally considered to be of con-tinental olivine basalt type rather than carbonatite. The extent to which car-bonatite activity may have modified the basaltic magma, however, renders the true parental association of some of these occurrences in doubt. Thus Harkin (1960) considers that the Rungwe volcanics have been modified by carbonatite activity but these rocks are not listed with the carbonatites. Some of the descriptions are taken from an unpublished typescript prepared by Dr. D. McKie and Dr. J. B. Dawson.

Northern
1. Mosonik
2. Oldoinyo Lengai
3. Kerimasi
4. Sadiman
5. Oldoinyo Dili
6. Essimingor
7. Burko
8. Monduli-Arusha carbonate tuff cones
9. Meru
10. Basotu Craters
11. Hanang and Balangida

Eastern
12. Ufiome (Kwaraa, Galappo)
13. Wigu Hill
14. Maji Ya Weta
15. Luhombero and Pangani Gorge

South Western
16. Sangu (Sango)
17. Ngualla
18. Musensi
19. Songwe Scarp
20. Panda Hill and Sengeri Hill
21. Nachendazwaya

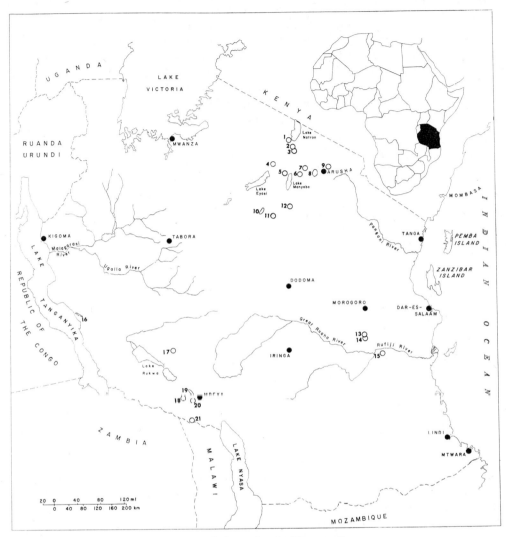

Fig. 30. Carbonatites in Tanganyika.

Mosonik (1)

This is a highly dissected volcano on the plateau on the upthrow side of the western escarpment of the Gregory Rift. The western side of the volcano has been blown away by an eruption and all that is now left is a crescent-shaped crater open to the west. The volcano is younger than the rift faulting. Lavas are nephelinites and phonolites. In the crater a sövite plug surrounded by arcuate sövite outcrops covers about 1.5 sq miles.

Guest, 1953.   James, 1958a.

Oldoinyo Lengai (2)

This is an active volcano 6400 ft high, cutting the Precambrian basement rocks and the overlying alkaline volcanics of the Crater Highlands. The cone is built of tuffs, agglomerates and lava flows. The pyroclastics are ijolitic and nephelinitic in beds 4–20 ft thick and are interbedded with nephelinite and phonolite flows. The most recent lava extruded into the summit crater is almost monominerallic carbonatite composed of Nyereite, a new sodium-calcium carbonate. The lavas contain about 30 per cent Na_2O and were observed being erupted from the main vent. Among the ejected blocks, although not found *in situ*, are urtite, ijolite, melteigite, jacupirangite, wollastonite ijolite, biotite pyroxenite, calcitic carbonatite and fenites.

Dawson, 1962*a*, *b*.

Dawson and Sahama, 1963.

DuBois, *et al.*, 1963.

Guest, 1935, 1956, 1963.

Hobley, 1918.

James, 1956*c*.

von Knorring, 1962.

Poole, 1963.

Reck, 1914.

Richard, 1942.

Uhlig, 1907.

Kerimasi (3)

This is a volcanic pile made up of lavas and pyroclastics completely sheathed in carbonatite tuff and/or lava and with carbonatite intrusive into the crater. It lies astride the western scarp of the Gregory Rift and rises 5000 ft above the plain except on the west where its volcanics spread out on to the plateau. The eruptive history is complex with a newer cone superimposed on an older one. The pile consists of tuffs, agglomerate, nephelinite and olivine nephelinite, the agglomerate containing blocks of the ijolite–urtite suite and biotite pyroxenite as well as country rocks. The entire cone is sheathed in carbonatite 4–6 ft thick made up of medium-grained grey carbonatite with rounded grains of magnetite, vermiculite and hornblende, and of brown-grey foliated carbonatite with isolated larger grains of calcite. The rock contains perovskite, apatite, sphene, forsterite, baddeleyite, melanite, aegirine and biotite as accessory minerals. The crater floor is covered with thick red-brown soil except for an outcrop of grey sövite with vertical banding. Blocks of carbonatite on the soil surface include grey sövite veined by light yellow sövite, pumiceous cream-coloured sövite, streaky brown sövite with breccia veins, and cataclastic feldspar-calcite rock. In the crater wall are sövite breccia and both dolomitic and calcitic carbonatite with foliation parallel to the periphery of the crater. Opinions are divided as to whether the flank carbonatite represents a carbonatite ash fall or lava flows.

Dawson, 1964*c*.

James, 1956*c*, *d*, 1958*b*.

Sadiman (4)

This is one of the volcanoes thought to be part of a carbonatite complex although no carbonatite is exposed. The cone consists of pyroclastics and lava flows. Pyroclastics are nephelinitic tuffs and agglomerates, some containing carbonates; lavas are phonolitic nephelinite, melilite nephelinite, phonolitic trachyte, sodalite phonolite and nephelinite. These are rock types frequently associated with carbonatites.

Pickering, 1962.

Oldoinyo Dili (5) (p. 263, Fig. 1)

Oldoinyo Dili is deeply eroded with relief of about 1000 ft and has been intruded into Archean gneisses, amphibolite and quartzite close to the west scarp of the Gregory Rift. It is an intimate complex of lenticular, sub-arcuate sövite outcrops separated by rafts and screens of fenite; the sövite has steeply dipping mineral banding. A common marginal variety is actinolite sövite (actinolite-aegirine-biotite-magnetite-apatite-calcite). Farther from the marginal zone is biotite sövite with abundant magnetite, limonite, hematite and siderite; this passes into magnetite sövite, and a rarer type is magnetite-biotite-pyrochlore sövite. Much of the complex is composed of sövite with only minor amounts of actinolite, aegirine, biotite, magnetite, pyrochlore, apatite and pyrite. Occasional carbonatite dikes occur between Oldoinyo Dili and the rift escarpment.

James, 1956*b*, *c*, 1958*b*.

Essimingor (6)

This is a large volcano 12 miles in diameter with a central cone made up of nephelinitic, phonolitic and ijolitic tuffs and agglomerates. These contain blocks of nephelinite, phonolite, ijolite, nepheline syenite and melteigite. Two phonolite lava flows are interbedded with the pyroclastics, and lavas form a thin outer covering to the volcano. The principal rock types are nephelinite, phonolite, phonolitic trachyte, analcitite and augitite. These occur both as lava flows and dikes and there are also dikes of monchiquite and fourchite. No carbonatite is exposed but these rock types are usually associated with carbonatites. Essimingor is thus grouped with the carbonatites.

Burko (7)

Burko is a smaller cone, 4.5 miles in diameter, composed of an inner cone of pyroclastics of the same types found on Essimingor. Lavas are nephelinite, melanephelinite and phonolite. It is also believed to be related to carbonatite although no carbonatites are observable.

Monduli-Arusha carbonate tuff cones (8)

These are a series of cones of very recent age. They are built principally of lapilli and welded scoria but some consist of carbonate-rich pyroclastics with ejected blocks of igneous rocks.

Lashaine is a volcanic cone 700 ft high. The building of a cone of red welded scoria was followed by an explosive phase that produced tuff and agglomerate containing up to 70 per cent calcite. Included are blocks of olivine basalt, red scoria, Basement gneiss and ultrabasic igneous rocks. The commonest minerals are olivine and pyroxene from the disruption of the ultrabasic nodules. Blocks are rarely more than 1 in. in diameter and are usually rounded; the commonest type is a garnet peridotite similar to that found as xenoliths in kimberlite pipes.

Lemugur is a 250-ft high tuff ring surrounding a broad flat crater that lies 50 ft below the plain. The pyroclastics are mainly basalt fragments but there is an outer layer of calcite-rich tuffs containing granulite blocks.

Loljoro is a 400-ft high tuff ring surrounding a 150-ft deep crater. Pyroclastics are olivine basalt fragments and a few granulite blocks in a calcite matrix.

Cameron's Crater is 3500 ft across and 680 ft deep. Calcite-cemented agglomerates and volcanic breccia contain fragments of olivine basalt, small rounded blocks of granulite, and rounded blocks of gneiss up to 2 ft across.

Mutelelu and Loiwilokwin Hills are small, rounded hills of calcitic tuffs containing fragments of olivine, orthopyroxene and basalt blocks.

Oldoinyo Eloriri is a hill of poorly welded and unwelded lapilli of black, glassy lava with phenocrysts of magnesian olivine and titanaugite, and an olivine tephrite flow. These are cut by carbonate dikes with glassy lava fragments.

All these cones and craters are believed to be due to explosive volcanism associated with carbonatite magma. There are irregular outcrops of limestone on the plain surrounding the vents; these contain pyroclastic fragments and in placcs can be traced back to the carbonate tuffs of the cones. It is thus assumed that carbonate ashes also settled on the plains. Carbonatitic tuffs of unknown source are also widely distributed on the plains in the Arusha–Longido area. (Longido is north of Mount Meru.)

Dawson, 1964*b, c.*

Meru (9)

This is an active volcano; carbonatite is not known on the volcano itself but the more than one hundred parasitic cones, some of which are carbonatitic (Longido area) suggest that it is a carbonatitic volcano. It has two lava series: trachyte-phonolite and tephrite-nephelinite-nepheline basalt.

Guest and Leedal, 1956.   Sturdy, Calton and Milne, 1933.
Oates, 1934.   Wilkinson, 1966.

Basotu Craters (10)

These are a group of about thirty craters in an area of about 20 sq miles. They lie along two parallel NNE–SSW lines about 2 miles apart and penetrate the Precambrian Basement which is covered by sediments, tuff and agglomerate. There are two types: one consists of a rim surrounding a crater, and the other comprises a single cone as much as 200 ft high with more than one crater. The cones are pyroclastic and made up of fragments of the Basement and the dikes cutting it and of fine-grained carbonate rock. The matrix is either a calcite-dolomite mixture or magnesian calcite. The cones have alternating coarser and finer deposits and are thought to be due essentially to gas explosions overlying a nephelinitic magma undergoing fractionation to carbonatite. They are probably of Quaternary age and partly filled by recent sediments.

Dawson, (in press).   Downie and Wilkinson, 1962.

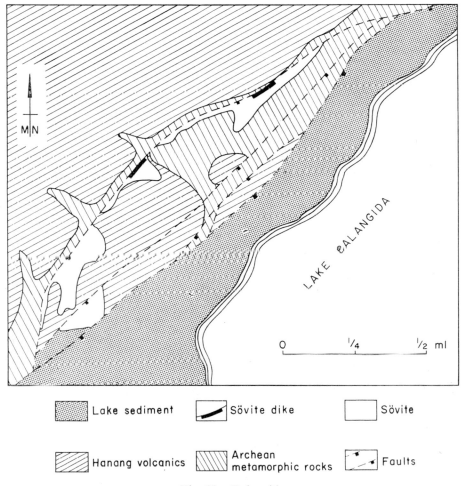

Fig. 31.   Balangida.

Hanang and Balangida (11) (Fig. 31)

This is a considerably eroded volcanic pile rising 6000 ft above the surrounding plain and composed of nephelinite lava and nephelinite tuff and agglomerate. There is no carbonatite in the central crater but small bodies of magnetite sövite intrude the pyroclastics of the lower western flanks. A zone of explosion vents extends for a 15 mile radius around the volcano. Some have tuff-lapilli and crystal tuffs of euhedral pyroxene, mica and magnetite but the amount of ejectamenta is small suggesting predominantly gas eruptions.

Balangida lies 5 miles WNW of Hanang where the western boundary fault of the Gregory Rift divides into a complex of sub-parallel fractures. In the vicinity of these fractures there are carbonatite dikes and extensive carbonation of the Archean rocks. Carbonated hornblende–biotite gneiss has magnetite–vermiculite–pyrochlore in its more calcitic patches.

James, 1956*c*, *d*, 1958*a*, *b*.

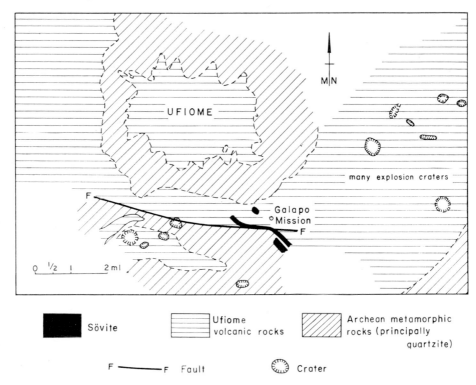

Fig. 32.   Ufiome.

Ufiome (*Kwaraa, Galappo*) (*12*) (Fig. 32)

The volcano Ufiome is superimposed on a symmetrically updomed area of Precambrian quartzites at least 2000 ft high and 5 miles across. The lavas comprising the volcanic pile are nephelinite and phonolite. A sheet of sövite dips gently away from the volcano and overlies similarly dipping pyroclastics. It contains accessory magnetite, pyrochlore, apatite and quartz. Explosion vents largely from gas eruptions surround the volcano out to 6 miles.

Bassett, 1956*a*.   James, 1956*c*, *d*, 1958*b*.

Wigu Hill (13)

Wigu Hill appears to be a complex of intersecting dolomitic dikes and brecciated, carbonated fenite, together with explosion vents of carbonatite- and fenite-breccia in carbonate matrix. There does not appear to be any single carbonatite intrusion. The complex has been emplaced in Archean gneisses and has a fenitized aureole. The carbonatite dikes are principally coarse-grained dolomite rich in rounded xenoliths of fenite but a few sövite dikes are present. The rare earth minerals occur as probable pseudomorphs after aragonite and appear to have been introduced metasomatically into the carbonatites along with strontium. The principal features of the complex are: (1) dominance of dolomite over calcite; (2) association of high concentrations of rare earths with strontium enrichment; (3) occurrence of rare earth minerals as pseudomorphs. These features are common to Kangankunde (Malawi) and Nkombwa (Zambia) as well.

James, 1956c, 1958a, b.   Sampson, 1958.
James and McKie, 1958.

Maji Ya Weta (Madji Ya Weta) (14)

This is a group of poorly-known minor intrusions in which a ring structure is discernible. There are dikes of carbonated nepheline rocks, breccia with carbonate matrix, and magnetite-melanite-pyroxene sövite. Some of the sövite has pyrochlore.

Bornhardt, 1900.   James, 1956b.

Luhombero and Pangani Gorge (Mkindu) (15)

The Karroo sediments are cut by several dikes and breccia-filled vents. The dikes are phonolite and biotite pyroxenite; the breccia is composed of Karroo sandstone cemented by brown carbonate or by an igneous-looking rock with large crystals of biotite, augite and olivine. There are also veins of carbonatite with small crystals of magnetite and vermiculite and pyrochlore-apatite. Near the intrusions the sediments are updomed and impregnated with calcite.

On the Rufiji River below the Pangani Gorge there is an explosion vent. A small plug of carbonatite contains fragments of altered Karroo country rocks (sandstones and mudstones).

James, 1956a, 1958b.   Stockley, 1943.
Spence, 1957.

Sangu (Sango) (16) (Fig. 33)

The Sangu complex consists of three elongate intrusions (Ikola, middle carbonatite and Ikamba) aligned on a north-westerly trend over a distance of 16 miles. The largest body (Ikamba) is 11.4 miles long with a maximum surface width of 1 mile. These carbonate rocks are discordant to the Basement and intrude post-Basement sediments.

Individual carbonatite bodies consist of dolomitic and white and red calcitic

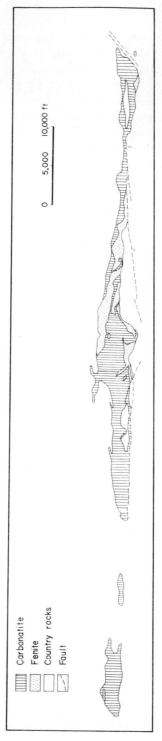

Fig. 33.   Sangu (after Coetzee, in press).

carbonatite. There is also an area of quartz-carbonate rock cut by carbonatite breccia. Minor or accessory minerals include apatite, magnetite, ilmenite, phlogopite-chlorite, soda amphibole, zircon, baddeleyite, pyrochlore and rutile. All calcitic carbonatites show exsolution of dolomite from magnesian calcite. The carbonatites are banded owing to the alignment of accessory minerals and carbonate lenses and bands. Albitite and albite-aegirine rock, closely associated with the carbonatite bodies, are interpreted as fenitized leucocratic and melanocratic country rock respectively.

The Sangu carbonatites are strongly enriched in strontium, niobium and lanthanides in relation to carbonate metasediments.

There are no alkalic igneous rocks.

Coetzee, 1963, (in press).   Schofield and Haskin, 1964.

Ngualla (17)

This is an almost circular carbonatite mass 2 miles in diameter intruded into grey porphyritic felsite and easterly striking Precambrian gneisses and quartzites. No volcanic rocks are preserved and there are no associated syenites. A fenitized zone 400–1200 yd wide surrounds the carbonatite, and the contact with the carbonatite is brecciated. The carbonatite consists roughly of three zones. The outer zone is sövite with poor flow banding and no magnetite but biotite, apatite, muscovite, quartz and chlorite as accessory minerals. The intermediate zone is a similar sövite but shows good flow banding with euhedral magnetite. Both zones are cut by dolomite and ankerite veins in random orientation and by melanocratic dikes. Probably related to the veins are small areas of sövite breccia. The central zone is white sövite with little flow texture and fluorite, biotite and parisite as accessory minerals. The final episode was the injection of quartz-calcite veins with minor chalcopyrite, galena and barite. These cut all other rock types.

James, 1956b, c, 1958b.   James and McKie, 1958.

Musensi[1] (Musense)[2] (18) (Fig. 34)

Musensi is a conical hill about 1 mile in diameter rising 900 ft above the plain and surrounded by Basement gneisses. Exposures are poor but the predominant type appears to be a potash feldspar rock composed of coarse, euhedral to sub-rounded phenocrysts of potash feldspar in a finer-grained feldspar matrix with occasional large biotites. There is one outcrop of nepheline tephrite. Drilling has indicated the presence at depth of carbonatized and feldspathized biotite pyroxenite. A swarm of feldspathic dikes suggests a poorly developed ring structure; they are composed largely of potash feldspar, quartz and iron oxides with trachytic texture in some. Small plugs of breccia consisting mainly of country rock fragments are found up to several miles from the complex.

James, 1956c, 1958b.   Miller and Brown, 1963.

[1] Condensed from a description furnished by Dr. P. E. Brown.
[2] Mbulu, a name sometimes associated with Musensi is a hill on the same complex.

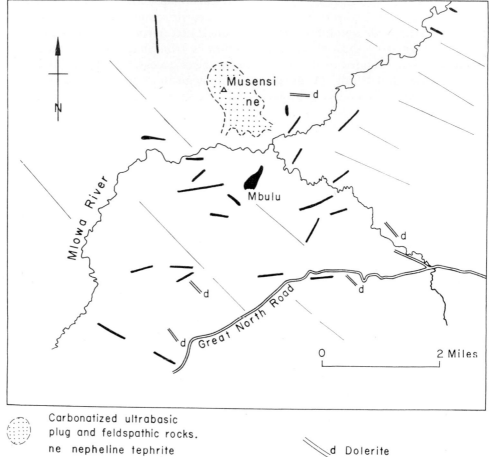

Carbonatized ultrabasic
plug and feldspathic rocks.
ne nepheline tephrite

Potassium feldspar dikes
and intrusive breccias

d Dolerite

Generalized strike of
granulite facies gneisses

Fig. 34.   Musensi (figure supplied by P. E. Brown, Univ. Sheffield).

Songwe Scarp[1] (*19*)

The Songwe Scarp carbonatite is a dike-like body about 12 miles long possibly
in discontinuous lenses that was intruded along a rift fault at the base of the
Songwe Scarp which bounds the Mbeya Range and delimits the Rukwa Trough.
The fault was active before and after carbonatite emplacement. It is a sheet
20–100 ft thick that is broadly conformable with the surrounding Precambrian
schists but in detail often is cross-cutting. The carbonatite is light to dark grey,
sometimes bluish, fine-grained with a splintery or conchoidal fracture and
typically ankeritic with no evidence of flow banding. The texture commonly is
fragmentary or brecciated with blocks of feldspathized and carbonated country

[1] Not to be confused with either the Songwe Vent, Malawi (see p. 433), or the Songo ijolite body in
Sierra Leone which does not appear to be a carbonatite complex.

rock. No rare accessory minerals have been observed but the rock is enriched in strontium, niobium and lanthanides. The carbonatite is intensely silicified by late stage veinlets of quartz. Adjacent to the carbonatite is a dike-like body about 30 ft thick of intrusive breccia made up of Basement fragments in a red matrix of quartz and iron oxide. There has been extensive potassic feldspathization of the country rocks in the vicinity of the carbonatite, and in parallel belts up to 100 ft wide by 1 mile in length as much as 8 miles from the carbonatite. Many of these are injected and brecciated by carbonatite veins.

Brown, 1964.

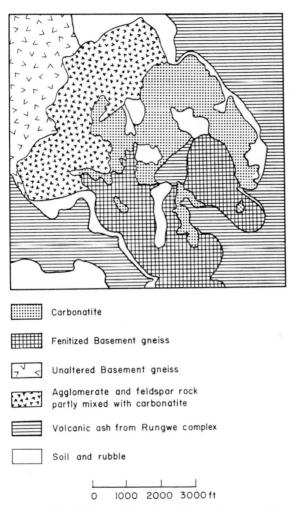

Carbonatite

Fenitized Basement gneiss

Unaltered Basement gneiss

Agglomerate and feldspar rock partly mixed with carbonatite

Volcanic ash from Rungwe complex

Soil and rubble

L___I___I___J
0   1000 2000 3000 ft

Fig. 35.   Panda Hill (Mbeya) (after Fawley and James, 1955, Fick and Van der Heyde, 1959).

Panda Hill (Mbeya) and Sengeri Hill (20) (Fig. 35)

Panda Hill is irregularly shaped with a maximum diameter of 6000 ft and rises 1000 ft above the floor of the Rukwa Rift. The carbonatite mass was emplaced in Precambrian gneisses and is surrounded by a fenitized zone. It is a white sövite with well-defined flow features marked by apatite-rich and magnetite-rich streaks, having a steep inward dip. There are minor segregations of dolomites, ankerite, siderite and possibly manganese carbonate, but only dolomite is in significant amounts. At the eastern contact many xenoliths of Precambrian country rocks are immersed in the carbonatite. Flow features bend around these xenoliths which are altered to fine-grained feldspar in a phlogopite-calcite matrix. At the northern and western contacts the carbonatite is separated from the gneisses by feldspathic agglomerate. Local late-stage iron metasomatism has produced limonitic sövite. There are concentrations in the sövite of magnetite-apatite-pyrochlore and of pyrochlore in other parageneses. Both dolomitic and calcitic carbonatite dikes are believed to be conically arranged within the main carbonatite mass.

Sengeri Hill is 4 miles NW of Panda Hill. Two large and numerous small dikes strike NE–SW. These are dolomitic, the principal accessory minerals being pyrite, magnetite, pyrochlore and barite. The adjacent country rock is fenitized. There are numerous dikes of the carbonatite suite between Sengeri Hill and Panda Hill and to the southeast of Panda Hill. They are less than one metre wide, have chilled margins and are flow banded parallel to their walls. In the same area as the dikes there are small explosion vents along a NW-trending line parallel to the main rift faulting. These are tilted with a breccia made up of highly altered angular and rounded fragments of the Basement in a carbonate matrix.

Bassett, 1956a.
Ebbinge and Krol, 1957.
Fawley and James, 1955.
Fick and van der Heyde, 1959.
Jager, Niggli and van der Veen, 1959.
James, 1956b, c, 1958.

James and McKie, 1958.
Miller and Brown, 1963.
Schofield and Haskin, 1964.
Snelling, 1965.
Veen, 1960.

Nachendazwaya (*21*) (Fig. 36)

This is an alkaline-carbonatite complex 1300 by 500 yd with its long axis parallel to the strike of the enclosing Precambrian metagabbro and amphibolite. It comprises three small hills, the outer two being entirely of foyaite and the inner of carbonatite. The whole complex is cut by dolerite dikes. Foliation within the carbonatite and foyaite parallels the long axis of the intrusion. The carbonatite is mainly sövite with small dolomitic areas. Accessory minerals are apatite, biotite, plagioclase, iron oxides, hornblende and epidote. Quartz, cancrinite and aegirine are found where the carbonatite has been brecciated. The highest Nb_2O_5 value obtained was 0.03 per cent. The complex appears to be related genetically to the Ilomba Hill Complex 1.5 miles to the south in Malawi.

Horne, 1961.

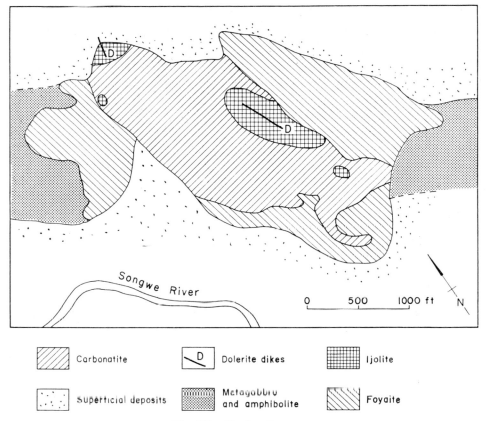

Carbonatite

Superficial deposits

D Dolerite dikes

Metagabbro and amphibolite

Ijolite

Foyaite

Fig. 36.   Nachendazwaya.

Possible carbonatite tuff cones at Igwisi

Three craters at Igwisi[1] are 200 to 400 yd in diameter with near perpendicular inner walls and flat floors. The hills are composed of tuff and lava and one crater has a lava flow. The tuff is composed of forsterite olivine grains set in a matrix of carbonate with rounded brown pebbles. The lavas vary from fine-grained non-vesicular to coarse-grained vesicular and consist of nodules of forsterite and fragments of calcite in a matrix of glass and carbonate with magnetite and perovskite as accessories. Some of the vesicles contain calcite, and the lava contains partly digested xenoliths of granite. Pyrochlore is found in the soil. It appears that Igwisi might be a carbonatite tuff cone occurrence, perhaps with a carbonatite lava flow.

Sampson, 1956.   Fozzard, 1958.

[1] 4° 52′ S, 31° 55′ E.

Uganda

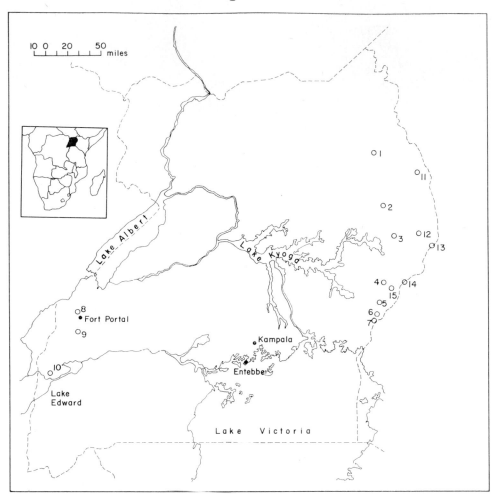

Fig. 37.   Carbonatites in Uganda.

With the exception of Lolekek the summaries of eastern Uganda carbonatites are condensed from material prepared by King and Sutherland originally as part of their Chapter, 'The Carbonatite Complexes of Eastern Uganda'.

1. Toror	PROBABLE CARBONATITES
2. Napak (Lokupoi)	9. Lake Kyekora
3. Lolekek	10. Katwe-Kikorongo
4. Budeda	11. Moroto
5. Bukusu	12. Kadam
6. Tororo	13. Kokipie
7. Sukulu	14. Mt. Elgon
8. Fort Portal area	15. Sekululu

Toror (1) (p. 113, Fig. 17)

The Toror Hills are a dissected volcano in which the volcanics have been removed by erosion. The initial intrusive activity consisted of the emplacement of trachyte dikes into the granitic gneisses of the Basement Complex, and the formation of a vent of brecciated trachyte. At the centre of the complex is an elliptical mass of agglomerate and breccia about three quarters of a mile in length and cut by phonolite intrusions. Fragments are earlier phonolite and tinguaite up to 2 in. across in a matrix of fine-grained volcanic material with calcite and zeolites. Carbonatite encircles the agglomerate as a ring intrusion about 2 miles across. It is usually brown with local magnetite enrichment in vertical bands and includes sövite, dolomitic sövite, ferruginous carbonatite and feldspathic carbonatite. The last intrusive phase consists of plugs, sheets and dikes of phonolite and tinguaite. Fenitization around the complex is only slight but brecciation is fairly extensive and belongs to several phases both preceding and following emplacement of the carbonatite ring. Late stage silicification has affected both the breccias and the carbonatite.

Bisset, 1935.   Hytonen, 1959.
DuBois, 1956.

Napak (Lokupoi) (2) (p. 97, Fig. 12; p. 99, Fig. 13)

Napak is the eroded remnant of a volcano originally 20 miles in diameter resting on updomed Basement gneisses and granites. The original volcanics have been removed over a central area 8 miles in diameter and the site of the main vent is marked by a circular group of hills (Lokupoi) formed of ijolites with a central carbonatite plug and surrounded by fenitized Basement gneisses. Lava flows are thought to represent not more than 3 per cent of the volcanics; the remainder consists of pyroclastics, chiefly agglomerates. Lava flows (10–30 ft thick) are mostly nephelinites and melanephelinites. The central intrusive complex is about 2 miles in diameter and composed of ijolite–urtite cut by occasional nephelinite dikes. At its centre is a carbonatite plug 0.25 mile in diameter; this is principally sövite with a variable amount of dolomitic carbonatite and abundant magnetite. Pyrochlore and baddeleyite are accessories. Occasional small masses of agglomerate (carbonatite fragments in a ferruginous matrix) cut the carbonatite which is brecciated in places.

Bisset, 1935.   King, 1949.

Lolekek (3)

Lolekek Hill is a carbonatite plug about a quarter of a mile in diameter and rises 500 ft above the plain. The carbonatite is a medium- to coarse-grained sövite with some siderite and dolomite. Conspicuous concentric banding consists of magnetite trains, colour and textural variations and boudins of finer, structureless carbonatite. Outcrops around the hill are poor but indicate a ring of ijolite, nepheline syenite and olivine melteigite. A few small surrounding hills may be remnants of the original volcanic cone although some may be intrusive. They comprise phonolite, nephelinite and agglomerate.

Trendall, 1962.

Budeda (4) (p. 76, Fig. 3)

The Budeda Complex is less than half a mile across and was intruded into the granitic Basement which has been extensively fenitized. There is an aureole of syenitic fenite containing some nepheline-bearing syenitic fenite. The central part of the complex is an arcuate mass ranging in composition from pyroxenite or melteigite to ijolite and urtite. Cancrinite syenite occurs locally along the outer edge. Within the 'ijolite' mass are two areas of carbonatite less than 40 ft across which appear to be replacements of the silicate rock. They are calcitic with apatite as an accessory. Later dikes of nepheline syenite and cancrinite syenite cut the 'ijolite' mass and surrounding rocks.

Davies, 1956.

Bukusu (5) (p. 75, Fig. 2)

Bukusu is a rather poorly exposed occurrence about 4 miles in diameter consisting of a central mass of carbonatite which is partly separated from a discontinuous ring of carbonatite by pyroxenites and ijolites. Similar silicate rocks enclose the outer carbonatites, while the complex is surrounded by an extensive zone of fenitized granite. The central carbonatite is partly covered by tuffs from Mt. Elgon. Arcuate shears and faults cut the enclosing granites and dip steeply inwards. Carbonatite is sövite with magnetite, phlogopite and apatite.

Broughton, Chadwick and Deans,   Davies, 1947, 1956.
   1950   Taylor, 1955.

Tororo (6) (p. 89, Fig. 7)

Tororo Rock is a conspicuous carbonatite hill rising nearly 1000 ft above the surrounding plain. A separate carbonatite mass has intruded a mixed assemblage of syenitic fenites, nepheline syenites and ijolites. These silicate rocks have been brecciated at one locality and the fragments mixed in a coarse agglomerate which has been intensively feldspathized prior to emplacement of the carbonatite. Agglomerate dikes up to 40 ft thick also cut the carbonatite. The main mass is pear-shaped, about three quarters of a mile in length and composed of a series of separately intruded sheets around a central plug 10 ft in diameter. The first ring dips steeply inwards and the dip of successive rings decreases away from the centre. The separate mass is elongate, about a quarter of a mile long and contains xenoliths of the silicate rocks. All the carbonatites are cut by veins of carbonatite from a fraction of an inch to several inches wide. These are demonstrably dilational.

Bisset, 1935.   Davies and Bisset, 1947.
Davies, 1947, 1956.   Williams, 1952.

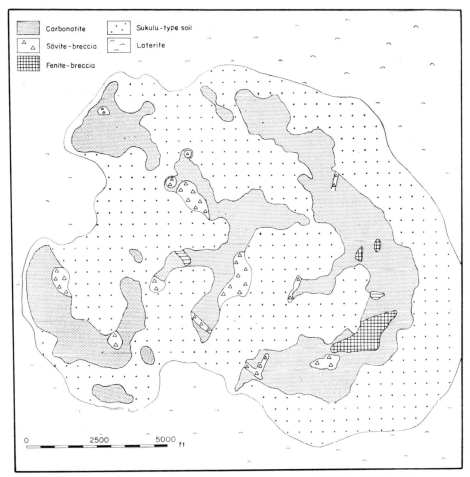

Legend:
- Carbonatite
- Sövite-breccia
- Fenite-breccia
- Sukulu-type soil
- Laterite

0   2500   5000 ft

Fig. 38.   Sukulu (after *Uganda Geol. Surv.* map 1697 by Williams).

Sukulu (7) (Fig. 38)

This circular group of hills about 2.5 miles across consists almost entirely of carbonatite which forms a complex pattern of concentric structures related to a number of centres and is cut by essentially radial faults and dikes. Carbonatite is principally sövite but irregular patches of beforsite are recognizable by their finer texture. It is generally a coarse-aggregate of crystals up to 0.5 in. across and generally white, but may be brownish owing to the presence of dispersed iron oxides. Lenses of clear crystalline calcite are common. A prominent linear or planar structure is caused by streaks of magnetite, apatite, micas, tremolite, zircon and pyrochlore. The carbonatite appears to be surrounded by fenitized granite and a narrow ring of alkali syenite not more than 400 yd across. Traversing the carbonatites are occasional dikes of tinguaite and numerous lines of fault breccia and veins of agglomerate.

Davies, 1947, 1956.   Williams, 1950, 1959.
Sinclair, 1955.

Fort Portal area (8)

Carbonatitic lavas are found at Kalyango volcano. These were originally described as 'carbonated' lavas by Holmes in 1956. They are vesicular with inclusions of Basement rocks and possibly eclogite. The groundmass is dense and composed of minute grains of pyroxene, olivine, biotite, magnetite, apatite and calcite. The other rocks making up the lava fields of the Fort Portal area are potassic ultrabasic rocks often with leucite.

Combe, 1939.   Holmes and Harwood, 1932.
Holmes, 1956.   von Knorring and DuBois, 1961.

PROBABLE CARBONATITE COMPLEXES

Lake Kyekora (9)

Rocks at Lake Kyekora are similar to those of the Fort Portal area and are probably also carbonatitic lavas.

Combe, 1939.   von Knorring and DuBois, 1961.
Holmes and Harwood, 1932.

Katwe-Kikorongo (10)

Lavas described by Holmes as 'carbonated ankaratrite' appear to be the same as the carbonatitic lavas of the Fort Portal area. Combe described rocks from Middle Mbuga crater as 'limestone with the appearance of a pumiceous lava'. The associated lavas are potassic ultrabasic rocks including leucite-bearing varieties, with ejected blocks of biotite pyroxenite.

Combe, 1939.   Holmes, 1952, 1956.

Moroto (11), *Kadam* (12), *Kokipie* (13), *Mt. Elgon* (14)

Carbonatite plugs are not exposed at any of these dissected volcanoes but the correspondence with the volcanic rocks of Napak make it reasonably certain that sufficient erosion would reveal carbonatite. Davies (1952) believes that the removal of the upper 10,000 ft of Mt. Elgon would reveal a carbonatite core. All are composed largely of agglomerate and tuff. The fragments are predominantly lavas resembling those of the flows which, in the case of Mt. Elgon, are trachyte, phonolitic trachyte, phonolite, nephelinite, ankaratrite and related types. Mt. Elgon has fragments of ijolite, and Kokipie has ijolites and melteigites in the vent.

Moroto: Macdonald, 1961.   Mt. Elgon: Davies, 1952;
Kadam: Trendall, 1961.   Ödman, 1930.
Kokipie: Trendall, 1962.

Sekululu (15)

This is merely an occurrence of fenitized granite with arcuate shear zones that appears beneath an outlier of the Mt. Elgon volcanics. There is probably a carbonatite plug at depth.

Davies, 1956.

Urundi (Burundi)

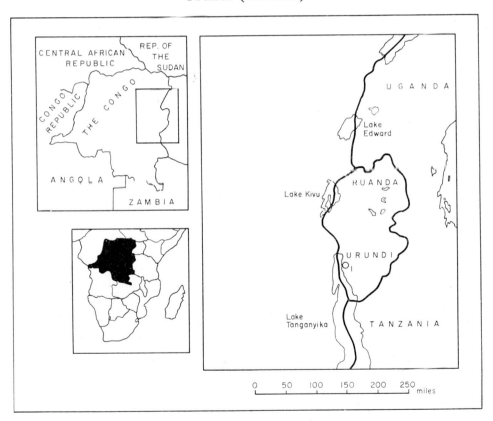

Fig. 39. Carbonatite in Urundi (Burundi).

Karonge (1)

This is a bastnaesite vein deposit believed related to a carbonatitic parent. (Thoreau, *et al.*, 1958.)

Zambia (formerly Northern Rhodesia)

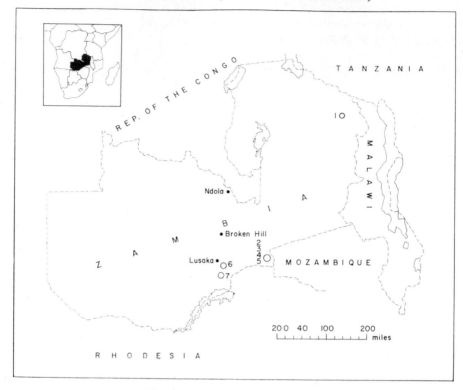

Fig. 40.   Carbonatites in Zambia.

General structural setting; Bailey, 1961*a*.

1. Nkombwa (Nkumbwa)
2. Kaluwe
3. Nachomba
4. Mwambuto
5. Chasweta
6. Mkwisi
7. Keshya

Nkombwa (Nkumbwa) (1)

Nkombwa Hill is a prominent ridge about 1.25 miles long by 0.5–0.75 miles wide rising 1000 ft above the surrounding plain. It has intruded Precambrian biotite gneiss, hornblende gneiss and granite. The complex consists of an outer ring of concentrically banded phlogopite breccia about 250 yd wide, an intermediate zone of mixed brown and white ankeritic carbonatite, and an inner area of silicified carbonatite at the top of the hill. There are also minor amounts of manganiferous carbonatite. There are no alkalic igneous rocks. Pyrochlore, monazite, isokite and apatite occur in the carbonatite. Pyrochlore is in pale yellow octahedra from 1 mm to less than 10 microns across.

Deans and McConnell, 1955.
Phillips, 1955.

Reeve, 1963.
Reeve and Deans, 1954.

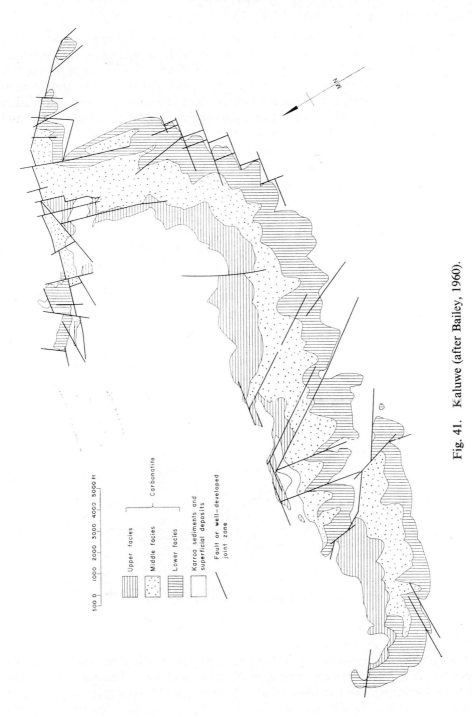

Fig. 41. Kaluwe (after Bailey, 1960).

Kaluwe (2) (Fig. 41)

This is a tilted synclinal mass up to 800 ft thick outcropping as a low curving scarp 8 miles long and essentially conformable with the enclosing Karroo sandstone. It is made up of layers of fragmental sövite from a few inches to tens of feet thick with a very variable fragment size. The principal fragments are rounded to sub-rounded sövite, but in the lower layers angular quartz occurs in addition and the upper layers also contain angular fragments of Karroo sandstone and conglomerate. The middle group contains apatite, martite and pyrochlore. Some of the apatite has been pseudomorphed by calcite and transfer of the phosphorus to the upper zone is indicated by an erratic fluctuation of the apatite content of this zone. The upper and lower groups contain less pyrochlore than the middle group. There are no alkalic igneous rocks.

Bailey, 1958, 1959, 1960.

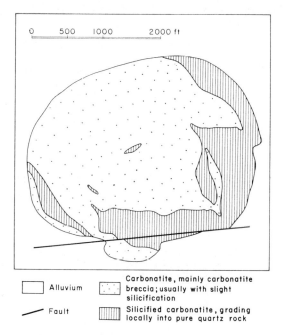

Fig. 42.   Nachomba (after Bailey, 1960).

Nachomba (3) (Fig. 42)

Nachomba is an isolated hill in the northern part of the Uma—a circular depression 3.5 miles in diameter ringed by Karroo sandstone. The peripheral rocks are very similar to those at Mwambuto. Nachomba Hill is largely composed of silica-iron oxide rock formed by alteration of carbonatite. Remnants of unaltered carbonatite consist of a breccia of brown and grey ankeritic carbonatite net-veined by buff ankeritic breccia and contain martite, barite and pyrochlore.

Most of the carbonatite is cut by thin quartz veins with silicified areas in between. There are no alkalic igneous rocks.

Bailey, 1958, 1959, 1960.

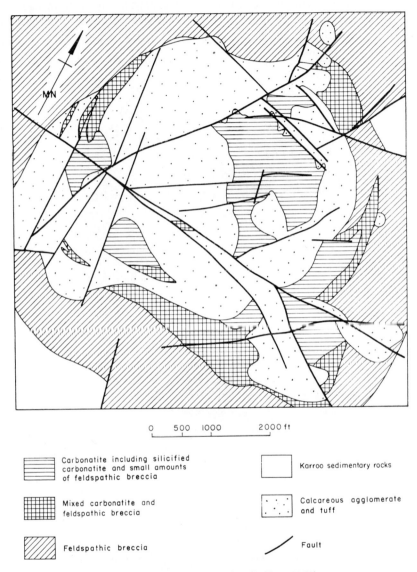

Fig. 43. Mwambuto (after Bailey, 1960).

Mwambuto (4) (Fig. 43)

An outer ring of hills 3 miles in diameter composed of metasomatized Karroo mudstone surrounding a collar of feldspathic breccia encircles a depression

1 mile in diameter that is underlain by carbonatite and carbonatite volcanics. The Karroo sediments surrounding the complex are updomed. Small satellite vents filled with carbonatite pyroclastics occur at the foot of the ring of hills on their outer side. The feldspathic breccia, thought to be feldspathized country rock, passes inwards through a mixed zone into carbonatite containing streaked-out masses of breccia. The carbonatite is very variable but is dominantly fine-grained ankerite with martite, barite and pyrochlore as accessories. The rock is

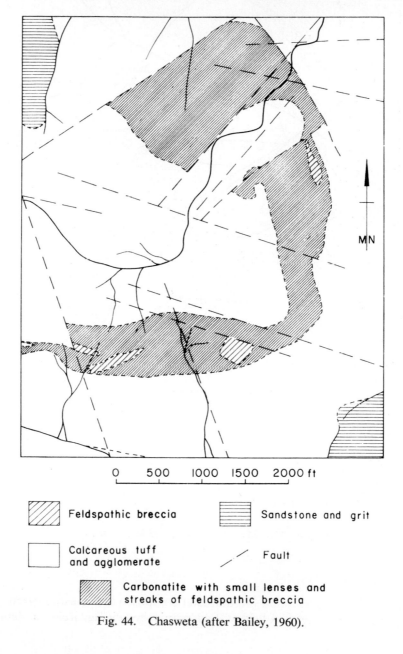

MN

0   500   1000   1500   2000 ft

Feldspathic breccia

Sandstone and grit

Calcareous tuff
and agglomerate

Fault

Carbonatite with small lenses and
streaks of feldspathic breccia

Fig. 44.   Chasweta (after Bailey, 1960).

variously silicified. The intrusive carbonatite plug has been cut and disrupted by eruptions of carbonatite pyroclastics. These volcanics are themselves cut by cone sheets one or two feet thick of buff carbonatite and by veins and dikes of fine carbonatite and tuffisite. There are no alkalic igneous rocks.

Bailey, 1958, 1959, 1960.

Chasweta (5)

Chasweta is the eroded relic of a twin volcano with part of the cone remaining. This is pyroclastic and composed of carbonatite fragments and carbonated Karroo fragments. Small satellite vents north and east of the main centre occur as circular hollows or small cones; one hollow is filled with well-rounded pyroclasts. The carbonatite cone is calcitic, medium-grained to fine-grained, with a colour range of pale grey, buff, brown, pink and black due to disseminated oxides of iron and manganese. Principal accessory minerals are martite, barite and pyrochlore. Xenoliths of country rock, generally well-carbonated, are common. Concentric banding, usually wavy and in places contorted, dips steeply inwards and outwards in an erratic manner. Individual bands are a few inches to several feet thick and vary unpredictably in grain size, colour and content of accessory minerals and xenoliths. The margin of the carbonatite plug is fine-grained pink carbonatite and may be a border phase or a peripheral tuff intrusion. Late stage effects are local silification, and veining of the carbonatite by red jaspillite. Carbonatite dikes are found up to three miles from the main plug and concentric with it.

Bailey, 1958, 1959, 1960.

Mkwisi (6)

The Mkwisi 'intrusive limestone' occurs in tightly folded and faulted metasediments. It consists of brecciated limestone with chloritic interstitial material and xenoliths of country rock metasediments and some granitic gneiss. The limestone displays little or no flow structure. As at Keshya there are no alkalic rocks. Some controversy over whether this is a carbonatite is created by the discovery (Cairney, 1964) of a thick sedimentary limestone bed underlying the Mkwisi area at shallow depth.

Bailey, 1959, 1961a, b.   Cairney, 1964.

Keshya (7) (Fig. 45)

The Keshya 'intrusive limestone' occurs in Basement gneiss as two irregularly-shaped areas of coarse marble containing xenoliths and breccia, the bulk of which consists of granitic country rock fragments in a calcite cement. The marble is a coarse-grained white calcite with minor chloritic material between the grains giving it a blotchy appearance. The commonest accessory mineral is magnetite or martite, usually as octahedra up to 2 mm across; in places these occur as streaks or trains. Less common accessories are mica, pyrite, blue-green amphibole, quartz, apatite, rutile, monazite (containing thorium), xenotime and ilmenite. Some masses of magnetite several feet across occur. The limestone is largely structureless with little or no evidence of plastic flow. Hematite is a common late-stage mineral, and the marble in places is cut by veins of albite-specularite–(apatite) rock. No alkalic or other silicate rocks are present.

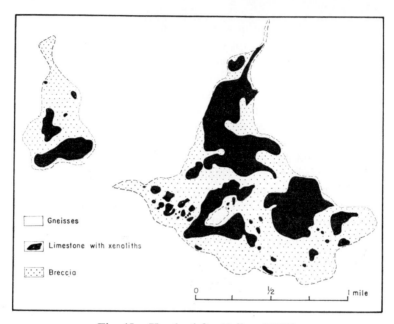

Fig. 45. Keysha (after Bailey, 1961b).

There is some doubt as to whether this really is a carbonatite (see further under Mkwisi). Hamilton and Deans (1963) on the basis of strontium isotope ratios believe that it is derived from a sedimentary limestone or that if it is carbonatitic that there has been assimilation of granitic or sedimentary rocks. Bailey (1964) seems prepared to accept the latter possibility. Further doubt is cast on the carbonatitic origin by the finding (Cairney, 1964) of a thick limestone bed below the Mkwisi 'intrusive' limestone.

Bailey, 1959, 1961a, b, 1964a.   Hamilton and Deans, 1963.
Deans, 1964.   Powell, 1965a.
Hamilton 1964.

EUROPE AND ASIA
Germany (West)

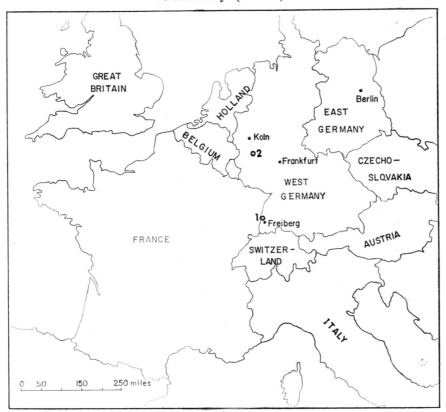

Fig. 46. Carbonatites in Germany (West).

Kaiserstuhl (1) (p. 184, Fig. 1; p. 187, Fig. 2).

The Kaiserstuhl is an eroded volcano that rises about 350 m above the plain and is somewhat oval in shape (16 × 12.5 km). It has pierced Oligocene calcareous sandstone, marl and clay that overlies Mesozoic deposits and a basement of pre-Hercynian granites and gneisses, and is surrounded by a contact metamorphic aureole about 100 m wide. The main remnant of the cone is a horseshoe-shaped ridge of alternating tuff and lava. The lavas are leucite tephrite, olivine tephrite, limburgite, nephelinite and phonolite; tuffs are of similar composition and contain fragments of fenite and carbonatite. Inside the tuff-agglomerate eroded cone is a central area of essexite-theralite rocks including limburgite, foyaite, sodalite syenite and hauyne-rich rocks. This is cut by innumerable dikes of the same composition. At the centre is the main carbonatite plug about 1 sq mile in area. The rock has very variable texture and composition and a distinct layering due to the non-carbonate minerals, principally micas, apatite, forsterite, monticellite, melilite, magnesioferrite and magnetite, with accessory pyrochlore. Grain size ranges from 0.01 mm to more than 10 cm with some individual calcite crystals reaching 30 cm. Carbonatite dikes are common, some being dolomite-ankerite carbonatites with barite. The youngest rocks are dikes of monchiquite, phonolite, tinguaite, etc. Phonolite also appears as several small plugs.

Cissarz, 1931.
Daub, 1912.
Deutzmann, 1964.
Eigenfeld, 1948.
Fischer, 1945.
Graeff, 1892, 1900.
Gruss, 1905.
Hubaux, 1964.
Hugel, 1912.
Keller, 1964.
Kiefer, 1932.
Kirchheimer, 1957, 1959.

Leibrand, 1948.
Metschke, 1938.
Omenetto and Weber, 1964.
Pfannenstiel, 1933.
Rein, 1950.
Schneiderhöhn, 1948.
Soellner, 1912a, b, c, 1913a, b, c, d,
    1915a, b, 1927a, b, 1928, 1939.
Wambeke, 1964a, b, (in press b).
Wambeke *et al.*, 1964.
Wimmenauer, 1957, 1959a, b, c,
    1962a, b, 1963a, b, 1964, (in press).

Laacher See (2)

Laacher See is a volcanic explosion vent that almost certainly has carbonatitic affinities but there is no modern published study to verify this.

Brauns and Brauns, 1925.   Brauns, 1922, 1926b, 1927, 1937.

Union of Soviet Socialist Republics

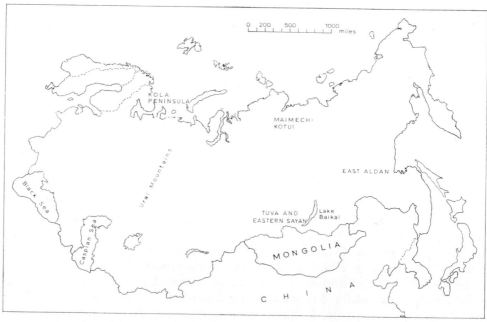

Fig. 47.   Carbonatite regions in the Union of Soviet Socialist Republics.

This section dealing with the U.S.S.R. is the least satisfactory. It is very difficult to obtain exact locations of most of the complexes, and the relative inaccessibility of some of the literature makes it difficult to check individual occurrences. Tomkeieff (1961) has compiled most of the Kola Peninsula occurrences and his notes have been combined with manuscripts kindly made available by Borodin, Pozharitskaya and Epshtein. The principal carbonatite areas are:

Kola Peninsula   Tuva and Eastern Sayan
Vishnevyye Mountains (Urals)   East Aldan Region
Maimech-Kotui

These are shown in Fig. 47. An index map of localities is given for the Kola Peninsula, but too little information is available to make this possible for the other regions. Only known carbonatite complexes are listed. Other alkalic complexes, of which there are several, have been omitted.

KOLA PENINSULA

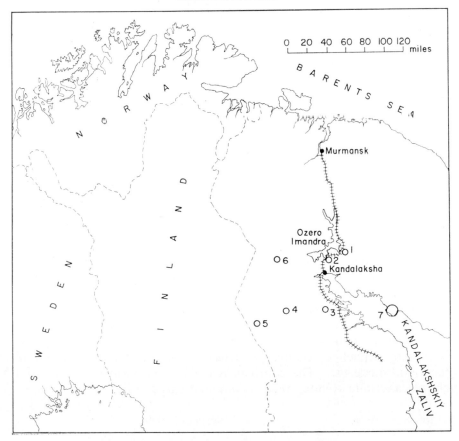

Fig. 48. Carbonatites of the Kola Peninsula.

1. Ozernaya Varaka	5. Salanlatvinsky (Salanlatva)
2. Afrikanda	6. Kovdorozero[1]
3. Kovdozero[1]	7. Turyi (Turja)
4. Vuori-Yarvi (Vuorijarvi)	Seblyarvi (not shown)

General references: Sergeev, 1959, 1962. Tomkeieff, 1961. Zlatkind, 1945.

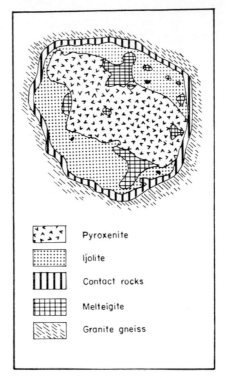

Fig. 49.   Ozernaya Varaka (figure supplied by L. S. Borodin, U.S.S.R.).

Ozernaya Varaka (*1*) (Fig. 49)

This is a circular complex about 1 km in diameter intruded into Archean gneisses that have been fenitized in a zone 10 to 600 m wide. The central part of the complex is alkali pyroxenite with pegmatitic patches containing amphibole, apatite, sphene and titaniferous magnetite. This is surrounded by an incomplete ring of ijolite and several small bodies of melteigite. The ijolite contains several very small urtite bodies. In places the ijolite grades with increasing feldspar content into nepheline syenite. Varieties of melteigite include melanite and wollastonite melteigite. The complex is cut by veins and dikes, up to 1.5 m thick, of cancrinite syenite, mica syenite and carbonatite.

Afanasyev, 1939.   Sergeev, 1959.

[1] Kovdozero and Kovdorozero are reversed on the map of Tomkeieff (1961).

Afrikanda (2)

This summary is condensed from Tomkeieff (1961). Afrikanda is a ring complex with an area of about 7 sq km surrounded by fenitized Precambrian biotite gneisses. There is an incomplete outer ring about 500 km in diameter of pyroxenite and melteigite. Towards the centre these become fine-grained and then change into coarse-grained magnetite pyroxenite characterized by uneven distribution of magnetite and schlieren of titaniferous magnetite and knopite. The central part of the intrusion is magnetite olivinite breccia cemented by coarse-grained pyroxenite and vibetoite. The whole complex is cut by dikes of knopite-schorlomite-nepheline, pyroxene-nepheline and carbonatite.

Bagdasarov, 1959.
Chirvinsky, Afanasyev
   and Ushakova, 1940.
Eliseev, 1958.

Florovskaya, 1939.
Gerling and Starik, 1942.
Kupletsky, 1937, 1938a, b.
Sergeev, 1959.

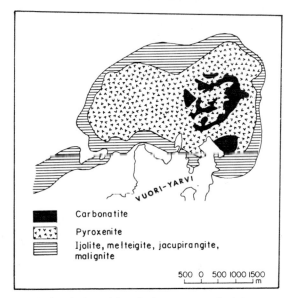

Fig. 50. Vuori-Yarvi (vuori-järvi) (figure supplied by L. S. Borodin, U.S.S.R.).

Kovdozero (3)

The Kovdozero Complex covers about 37.5 sq km. It is a slightly distorted ellipse with its long NW axis about 8 km and the short axis 5.5 km. The country rocks are Archean gneiss and granitic gneiss and are fenitized adjacent to the complex. The central part of the intrusion is olivinite, pyroxenite and peridotite; the latter two form incomplete rings, and the outer part consists of ijolite, melteigite and jacupirangite.

The central part consists of ultrabasic rocks; a dunite plug is surrounded by incomplete rings of pyroxenite and peridotite. The outer part is made up of incomplete rings of basic alkaline rocks—ijolite, melteigite and jacupirangite dipping inward at 70–80°. Between the ultrabasic and the alkaline rocks are two bodies of turjaite (melilite-rich rocks) also in the form of an incomplete ring together with many smaller lenticular bodies. In the southwest part of the complex is a body of apatite-olivine rock and magnetite. Inward-dipping dikes and lenticular bodies of carbonatite up to 400 by 100 m cut both the complex and the surrounding Archean gneisses and are concentrically banded. They are calcitic and contain accessory magnetite, phlogopite, apatite, and occasional forsterite.

Zlatkind, 1945, 1948.   Zlatkind and Shailov, 1946.

Vuori-Yarvi (*Vuorijärvi*) (4)[1] (Fig. 50)

This is a somewhat elliptical ring complex, elongated east and west, about 19.5 sq km in area. It was intruded into Archean gneiss and gneissic granite which have been fenitized in a peripheral zone. The central part of the complex is a mass of pyroxenite with inward dip of 65–80°. Within it are arcuate, inward-dipping lenses and bodies 2–40 m thick and 150–180 m (occasionally 350 m) long of apatite-olivine, and apatite-olivine-calcite rocks together with zones of perovskite and titaniferous magnetite. The central pyroxenite is also cut by veins, dikes, lenses and irregular bodies of carbonatite up to 100 m in length. These have produced at the contact with pyroxenite a tremolite-mica carbonate rock. The principal carbonatite is a light yellow, occasionally pinkish yellow rock made up of 85–90% calcite with some dolomite in solid solution and containing magnetite and phlogopite. They are often banded. Surrounding the central pyroxenite is a complete ring of ijolite, melteigite, jacupirangite and malignite, 100–140 m thick. Smaller bodies of similar rocks occur outside the complex towards the northwest.

Borodin, 1959, 1962.   Volotovskaya and Fizhenko, 1960.
Volotovskaya, 1958.

Salanlatvinsky (*Salanlatva*) (5) (Fig. 51)

This is a circular body about 3 km in diameter intruded into Precambrian metadiabase that shows development of albite, zeolite and chlorite in a zone adjacent to the complex. A central core of carbonatite somewhat elliptical in shape and made up of fine- and medium-grained sövite, calcite-dolomite carbonatite and barite-dolomite carbonatite in zones is surrounded by a narrow zone of vermiculite-magnetite-carbonate rock containing screens of metasomatized country rock diabase. Carbonatites are light to dark grey, with massive texture except in the border zone where an indefinite concentric streaking has vertical dip. Surrounding this is a complete ring of ijolite and ijolite-urtite followed by a semi-ring of melteigite. Poorly developed foliation in the alkaline rocks dips inward at 45–50°.

Serba, 1963.

[1] The Vuori-Yarvi (Vuorijärvi) complex is near the village of Vuori-Yarvi which is within the confines of the Kuolajärvi commune.

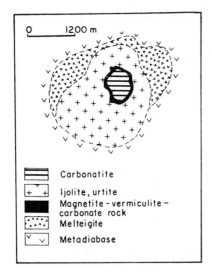

Fig. 51 (above). Salanlatvinski (Salanlatva) (after Serba, 1963).

Fig. 52. Kovdozero (figure supplied by L. S. Borodin, U.S.S.R.).

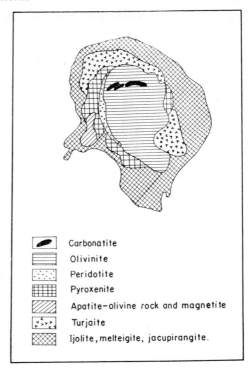

Kovdorozero (6) (Fig. 52)

No description is available except that it is a complex of alkalic syenite, ijolite and carbonatite.

Ivensen, 1941.   Zlatkind, 1948.
Koshitz, 1934.   Zlatkind and Shailov, 1946.

Turyi (*Turja*) (7)

This is essentially a set of dikes intrusive into sandstone and quartzite. The rock types are monchiquite, alnöite, calcitic eruptive breccia, ijolite, turjaite (nepheline-biotite melilitite) turjite (calcite-analcite-melanite-biotite), aegirine syenite, pyroxenite, nephelinite and carbonatite.

Belyankin and Vlodavetz, 1932.   Ramsay, 1921.
Kranck, 1928.

Seblyarvi

This is a newly reported carbonatite on the Tulona River.

VISHNEVYYE MOUNTAINS (URALS)

Carbonatite is mentioned among the descriptions of other alkalic rocks in part of the Ural Mountains but there seems to be very considerable doubt about the validity of this occurrence.

Eskova and Ganseev, 1963.   Zhabin, 1959.
Ronenson, 1959, 1963.   Zhadin *et al.*, 1960.
Vorobyeva, 1947.

MAIMECH-KOTUI

At least twenty alkalic ultrabasic and carbonatite complexes are said to cut thick Lower Paleozoic limestones. Individual complexes include; Bor-Uryakh, Changit, Gulinski, Kugda, Magan (?), Nemakit, Odikhincha, Saizhinski.

Butakova, 1956.   Epshtein, Anikeeva and Mikhailova,
Butakova and Egorov, 1962.   1961.
Egorov, 1957.   Ivanov and Safranov, 1959.
Egorov, Goltburt and Shikhoria,   Konev, 1958, 1960a, 1962.
  1959.   Moore, 1957, 1959.
Egorov and Surina, 1958, 1961.   Moore and Sheinman, 1946.
Epshtein, 1959.   Motychko, 1957.
                                  Sheinman, 1947.

TUVA AND EASTERN SAVAN

Individual complexes include Chinka and Belaja Zima.

Gaidukova, 1960.   Lavrenev, 1960.
Ivanova, 1959.   Lavrenev and Pozharitskaya, 1960a.
Konev, 1960b.   Leontyev, 1956.
Kononova, 1957, 1961.   Pozharitskaya, 1960.
Kuznetsov and Pinus, 1949.   Yashina, 1953, 1957.

EAST ALDAN REGION

One known carbonatite is Azbazastach.

Zdorik and Runov, 1961.   Zlenko, 1961.

What appears to be an additional carbonatite region has been reported in North Kazakhstan. A carbonatite complex is said to occur near the town of Kokchetav. This is one of the established regions of alkalic rocks in Russia but carbonatites have not previously been described. There is not yet any published documentation of the occurrence.

In addition to these there are two complexes for which the region of occurrence is uncertain: Mount Chavida in Siberia: Dmitriev, 1959. Konderski: Elyanov, 1961.

A useful grouping of alkalic provinces in the U.S.S.R. although omitting reference to carbonatite complexes is given by Vorobyeva, 1960.

Sweden

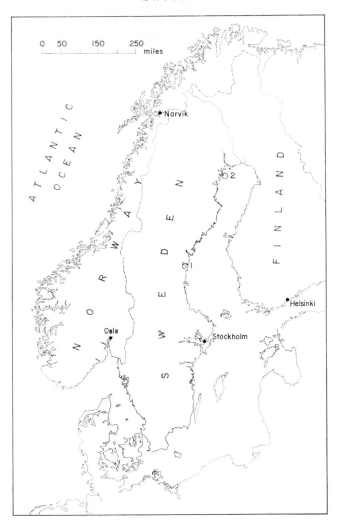

Fig. 53.   Carbonatites in Sweden.

1. Alnö Island
POSSIBLE CARBONATITE
2. Kalix

Alnö Island (1)

Alnö is a complex about 4 km in diameter of ring dikes, cone sheets and fenite zones around a central core of sövite that is largely covered by the waters of the

Baltic Sea but which outcrops on a few islands. Cone sheets are found up to 12 km from the sövite core and radial dikes up to 25 km. The country rocks are Precambrian migmatites, pegmatites, porphyry and dolerite dikes and these have been extensively fenitized such that their strike gradually becomes concentric with the ring complex. There is a generally concentric arrangement of granulated and fractured migmatite, quartz-syenitic fenite, syenitic fenite, leucocratic and melanocratic nepheline-syenitic fenite. Within these are incomplete arcuate bodies of urtite, juvite, ijolite, foyaite, melteigite, malignite, jacupirangite and tinguaite. The entire sequence is cut by a wide variety of rock types such as alnöite, melilitite, and kimberlite and variants of these together with calcitic and dolomitic carbonatites. Varieties of sövites include apatite sövite, biotite and pyroxene sövite and those containing all these minerals. Beforsite dikes (dolomitic carbonatite) include biotite beforsite, olivine beforsite, melilite beforsite and apatite beforsite. A number of composite dikes represent multiple intrusion of olivine melilitite and kimberlite into carbonatite. Barium, strontium and fluorine appear to have accumulated in the last stages of crystallization. All the carbonatites are cone sheets but the inward dips are of various orders and by plotting the foci of the various types of cone sheet v. Eckermann has concluded that four centres can be recognized at different depths. Each of these eruptive centres has given rise to carbonatites as well as kimberlites, melilitites and ouachitites. The deepest centre is that of dolomitic carbonatite, the next highest that of magnesian calcitic carbonatites, the third that of calcitic carbonatites and the highest that of the main sövite core and sövite breccia. The sövite displays distinct flow structure.

Berwerth, 1893, 1895.
v. Eckermann, 1928, 1939a, b, 1942, 1946, 1948a, b, c, d, 1950, 1951, 1958, 1960a, b, c, d, 1961a, b, c, 1962, 1963a, b, c, 1964a, b, (in press).
v. Eckermann, Ubisch and Wickman, 1952.

v. Eckermann and Wickman, 1956.
Eichstädt, 1884.
Högbom, 1892, 1895, 1909, 1910.
Holmquist, 1893, 1894, 1896.
Sahlböm, 1897.
Törnebohm, 1882, 1883.

POSSIBLE CARBONATITE

Kalix (2)

Dikes of carbonate-rich alnöite and kimberlite are found on a number of islands in the Baltic Sea between Lulea and Kalix in northern Sweden and may be related to a possible carbonatite-alkaline complex under that part of the Baltic lying to the east and known as the Malören Deep.

Geijer, 1928.   Larsson, 1943.

Norway

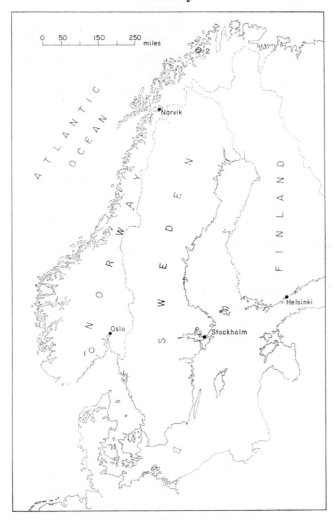

Fig. 54.   Carbonatites in Norway.

1. Fen

POSSIBLE CARBONATITE
2. Stjernøy (*and Sørøy*)

Fen (1) (p. 225, Fig. 1)

   Although Fen was one of the first carbonatite complexes to be recognized and studied it is rather poorly exposed. It was intruded into granitic gneisses of the Archean Basement which have been fenitized in an aureole surrounding the complex. Several bodies of granitic breccia pierce the fenitized country rock and probably represent an early explosive phase in the evolution of the complex. Alkalic rocks are mostly the basic, feldspar-free varieties ijolite and melteigite with some urtite. These form an irregularly shaped body in the south-western part of the complex. Mixed calcite-silicate rocks (hollaite) form an incomplete ring enclosing the carbonatite core. Carbonatite is of three types: sövite, ankerite carbonatite (rauhaugite) and hematite-carbonate rock. Magnetite, apatite and pyrochlore are accessories in the sövite. Commoner minerals include phlogopite, biotite, aegirine and amphibole but not all in the same rock. The main sövite mass (2 km across) has a marked banding with steep inward dip and consists of a series of sövite arcs separated by screens of brecciated and carbonated melteigite, fenite, etc. There are concentric cone sheets of sövite outside the main central mass. In parts the sövite is brecciated. Rauhaugite is principally ankerite with accessory chlorite, biotite and magnetite except that magnetite may become concentrated locally. There are no flow lines. Irregularly shaped intrusions together with pipes, breccias and dikes of damkjernite (variety of kimberlite) occur within the complex with diffuse borders and outside the complex with sharp contacts. They contain inclusions of gneiss, fenite, urtite-jacupirangite, sövite, raughaugite, peridotite, pyroxenite and hornblendite both angular and spheroidal. Dikes, plugs and irregular patches of tinguaite are found throughout the Fen vicinity.

Bergstöl, 1960, (in prep.).

Bergstöl and Svinndal, 1960a, b, c.

Bjorlykke, 1934, 1953, 1955.

Bjorlykke and Svinndal, 1960.

Bowen, 1924, 1926a, b.

Brauns, 1926a.

Brögger, 1921.

Conradi, 1953.

Faul, Elmore and Brannock, 1959.

Neumann and Rosenquist, 1940.

Ramberg, 1964.

Saether, 1948a, b, 1957.

Sørum, 1955.

POSSIBLE CARBONATITE

Stjernøy (2) (and Sørøy)

This is part of the Seiland petrographic province. The earliest intrusions of the complex suffered metamorphism in the granulite facies, together with intense folding, during the Caledonian orogeny and even the youngest rocks have been folded. The distribution of rock types, within the complex, which is not a ring intrusion, is rather complex. The earliest rocks are gabbros, gabbto gneisses and layered gabbros, all metamorphosed. Peridotite may have been emplaced before or after the metamorphism and contains xenoliths of the gabbro. Hornblendite shows all gradations to gabbro. Carbonatite covers about 4 sq km and is a calcite rock with biotite-rich bands. It contains apatite (1–10%) and magnetite (up to 5%) but no rare earth or niobium minerals. It does appear, however, to be enriched in Ba and Sr. Hornblende is present near the contact with hornblendite. Nepheline syenite is in contact with the carbonatite on the south side and separated from it by a zone of nepheline-bearing skarn gneiss. Bands of nepheline syenite and nepheline-albite-biotite pegmatite are found within the carbonatite and have been boudinaged by later deformation.

A similar group of rocks has recently been described on neighbouring Sørøy.

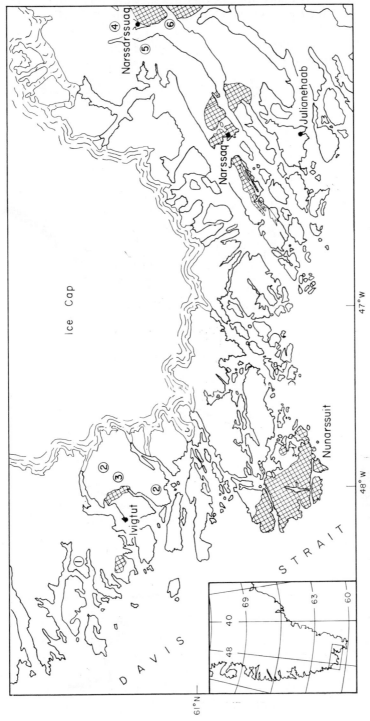

Fig. 55.   Carbonatites in Greenland (figure supplied by C. H. Emeleus, Univ. Durham).

If Stjernøy and Sørøy really are carbonatites they are very unusual. The description is reminiscent of part of the Canadian Grenville Province.

Heier, 1961, 1962, 1964.   Strand, 1952.
Sturt and Ramsay, 1965.

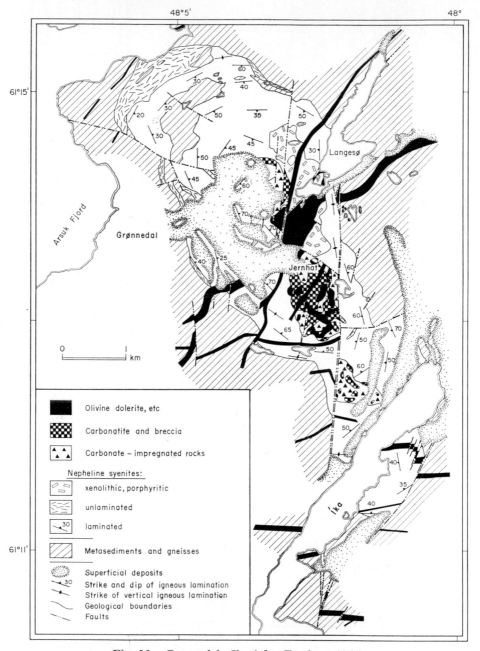

Fig. 56.   Grønnedal—Ika (after Emeleus, 1964).

Greenland

1. Gronnedal-Ika

POSSIBLE CARBONATITES

2. Kuanit–Tigssaluk Fjords
3. Arsuk Fjord–Kornoq area

4. Tunugdliarfik Fjord–Kiagtut Glacier
5. Qagssiarssuk Village
6. Igaliko Complex

The following summary and notes were prepared by Dr. C. H. Emeleus, Durham University, England.

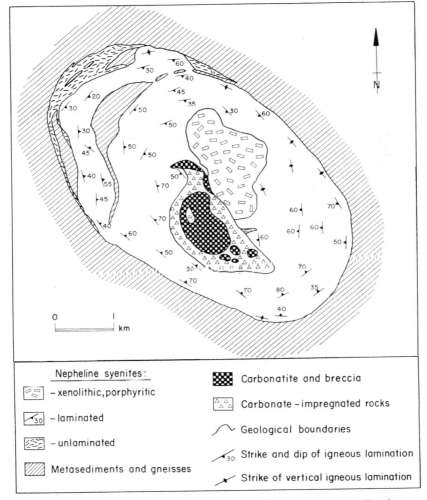

Fig. 57. Reconstruction of the Grønnedal—Ika complex (after Emeleus, 1964).

Gronnedal-Ika (*1*) (Figs. 56, 57)

The igneous complex of Gronnedal-Ika, near Ivigtut, southern Greenland is one of the pre-Gardar intrusions and consists of several nepheline syenites and later carbonatites. The complex is cut by numerous dikes including thin trachytes, phonolites and porphyritic basalts, and several thick olivine dolerites; it has been severely faulted at a late stage during the period of dike intrusion. The complex is emplaced in gneisses and metasediments of the Ketilidian cycle and shows well defined, steep and transgressive contacts with the country rocks; there is only a very limited amount of fenitization.

After allowance has been made for distortion due to the later dikes and faulting, the complex is found to have consisted of two groups of dominantly foyaitic syenites with centrally-inclined, confocal lamination and occasional weak concordant mineral layering, cut by a later stock of xenolithic porphyritic nepheline syenite and by a central body of carbonatites.

The carbonatites are intrusive into the syenites; they occur as dike-like masses in altered syenites and are highly xenolithic with fragments generally derived from adjacent syenites, but sometimes originating from structurally lower levels within the syenite complex. Where laminated syenites are brecciated by carbonatites the fragments are demonstrably displaced relative to one another. Fluxion structures parallel to the margins of the carbonatites and wrapping around xenoliths are common; these are brought out by slight differences in mineralogy or concentration of small xenoliths.

In the xenoliths and syenites adjacent to carbonatites alkali feldspar is usually the only original mineral recognizable; the mafic minerals and nepheline are replaced by an aggregate of micaceous minerals and occasional cancrinite.

There is some mineral zonation in the carbonatites. The outer parts are mainly a calcite carbonatite; inwards the proportion of siderite increases until it becomes an important constituent in the central parts where minor quantities of rhodochrosite, barite, sphalerite, apatite, pyrite and fluorite appear. A thick dike of olivine dolerite cuts the central carbonatites with the formation of abundant magnetite along its contact with the carbonatite.

Callisen, 1943.   Emeleus, 1964.

POSSIBLE CARBONATITES

2. Thin dikes (20 cm–1 m thick) in gneisses between Kuanit and Tigssaluk Fjords; also numerous loose boulders.

3. Thin dikes associated with lamrophyre dikes, cutting gneisses between Arsuk Fjord and Kornoq.

4. Group of thin dikes and plugs (latter to 500×100 m) in pre-Gardar country rocks between the northern arm of Tunugdliarfik Fjord and Kiagtut Glacier.

5. Plugs and sheets in pre-Gardar and Gardar supracrustal rocks at Qagssiar-ssuk Village.

6. Occasional thin dikes cutting nepheline syenites of the Igaliko Complex.

India

Amba Dongar (1)

This is a ring complex 4 miles in diameter that was intruded into Cretaceous sandstones and limestones and has domed and albitized overlying Deccan basalts. It is partly covered by younger basalts. The central part of the complex,

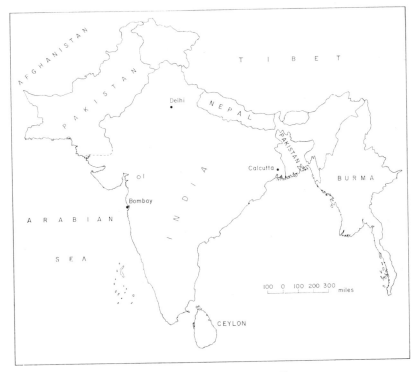

Fig. 58. Carbonatite in India.

marked by the domed-up basalts has been dropped on a ring fracture and is surrounded by a cone sheet of carbonatite which is in turn surrounded by a ring of ijolite. The carbonatite contains the following varieties: coarse white martite sövite, aphanitic brown barite-fluorite carbonatite (radioactive), fluorite masses, silicified carbonatite, and fluorite veins. On the southern side of the complex the outermost rock is a breccia with fragments of sandstone, basalts, and foliated sövite in a matrix of nepheline-aegirine-orthoclase-calcite rock. The complex is cut by a variety of alkalic dikes. Four large parallel breccia dikes lie outside the complex. A very substantial tonnage of fluorite ore has now been proved.

Subramanium and Parimoo, 1964.   Sukkeswala, Udas and Heinrich, 1965
Sukkeswala and Udas, 1963.

NORTH AMERICA
Canada

QUEBEC
1. Oka
ONTARIO
2. Calander Bay

3. Manitou Islands
4. Iron Island
5. Seabrook Lake
6. Lackner Lake

7. Borden
8. Nemegosenda Lake
9. Cargill
10. Clay-Howells
11. Firesand
12. Prairie Lake
13. Chipman Lake
14. Schryburt Lake

15. Big Beaverhouse
BRITISH COLUMBIA
16. Ice River
POSSIBLE CARBONATITES
17. Verity
18. Lonnie
19. Aillik
20. Ottawa Region

Fig. 59.   Index map of Canadian provinces.

QUEBEC

Oka (1)

This is a rather poorly exposed double-ring complex with an oval outline 4.5 × 1.5 miles and a NW trend. It is marked by a shallow depression filled with Pleistocene sediments and ringed by the Oka Hills that rise 400 to 700 ft above the surrounding plain. The hills are composed of the Precambrian anorthosite and gneisses that surround the complex.

The Oka Complex comprises two carbonatite plugs cut by arcuate dikes of ultramafic alkaline rocks largely in the rim zone around the perimeter of the plugs. The country rocks are fenitized, and nepheline-bearing syenites within 200 ft of the complex are interpreted as mobilized fenites. Carbonatites of various types underlie more than half the surface area. They are mainly medium- to coarse-grained sövites, although dolomitic carbonatite does occur, and have a prominent banding essentially concentric to the margins of the complex and dipping outward, composed of layers, lenses, boudins and inconsistent bands of minor and accessory minerals. Individual carbonatite types occur as arcuate tabular bodies within other types of carbonatites.

Carbonatite varieties.

1. Coarse-grained banded sövite with minor magnetite, apatite and biotite and accessory forsterite, soda-pyroxene and pyrochlore. This type forms the bulk of the rim zone carbonatites.

2. Coarse-grained banded aegirine-apatite-biotite-magnetite sövite, occurring locally in bands and lenses within the coarse-grained sövites. Red-brown pyrochlore is the main accessory mineral.

3. Medium- to coarse-grained monticellite (20–50%) is accompanied by accessory biotite, perovskite, magnetite, apatite and pyrochlore.

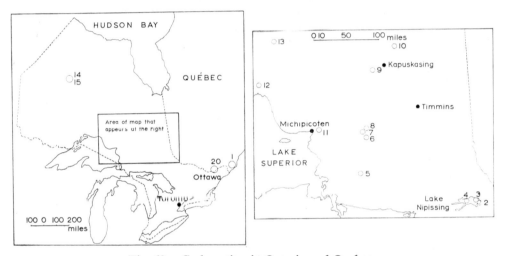

Fig. 60. Carbonatites in Ontario and Quebec.

4. Very coarse-grained sövite with sparse magnetite, pyrochlore and tremolite occurring mainly as a thick band in the southern ring.

5. Fine-grained grey banded dolomitic carbonatite with minor apatite, calcite and magnetite, and accessory pyrochlore; massive, coarse-grained buff dolomitic carbonatite. These occur mainly in the northern part of the complex. Thin, dolomite-magnetite dikes and veins are probably related to this type.

6. Melilite sövite with 30–50% melilite and accessory apatite. This occurs as thin bands and pods.

7. Niocalite sövite as two bands 60 ft and 15 ft thick. Accessory minerals include apatite, melitite, magnetite, melanite and biotite.

8. A thin sideritic band marginal to pyrite-pyrrhotite veins; veins of fine-grained calcite and dolomite with accessory melanite and magnetite; sövite rich in magnetite and apatite.

The ultramafic alkaline rocks comprise the okaite and jacupirangite series, ijolite—melteigite—urtite series, alnöite, and various dike rocks.

Okaite and jacupirangite series. Rocks of this series vary from melilite-magnetite rocks through melilitite and melilite-nepheline rocks (okaite), melilite-hauyne and melilite-nepheline-titanaugite rocks to nepheline-titanaugite and titanaugite-rich rocks (jacupirangites). These rocks form a crescentic body and six arcuate dikes in the northern ring. Melilite rocks are not found in the southern ring.

Ijolite—melteigite—urtite series. The bulk of the silicate rocks in the complex are of this type consisting essentially of nepheline and soda-pyroxene. They include malignite, urtite, micro-urtite, melanite urtite, ijolite, micro-ijolite, wollastonite-melanite-melteigite and transitional varieties. They occur principally as arcuate dikes in the rim zone. Biotite replacement zones with steep inward dip are found within the silicate rocks.

Alnöite. Plugs and dikes of alnöite and alnöite breccia intrude both the complex and the country rocks around the complex. Dikes of kersantite, minette, ijolite, monchiquite, fourchite and carbonatite are aligned preferentially in E-W, N-S and NE-SE directions. Sulphide- and fluorite-bearing veins appear to follow joint planes associated with minor faults.

The carbonatite bodies appear to have been emplaced as a series of ring dikes. The silicate rocks in the southern ring and the melilite rocks of the northern ring also appear to be ring dikes but the ijolites of the northern ring are probably cone sheets.

Interpretation of the geology was aided by extensive drilling, open-pit mining and geophysical surveys and is due largely to the work of Gold. The Oka Complex appears to be part of the Montergian petrographic province of alkaline rocks which comprises nine plutons together with dikes, sills and breccia plugs in a broad E-W belt across the St. Lawrence lowlands from Oka to the Appalachian Mountains.

Bowen, 1922.

Davidson, 1963.

Gold, 1962, 1963a, (in press, b).

Hogarth, 1961.

Howard, 1922.

Hughson and Sen Gupta, 1964.

Maurice, 1956, 1957.

Nickel, 1956, 1960, 1964.

Nickel and McAdam, 1963.

Nickel, Rowland and Maxwell, 1958.

Perrault, 1959.

Rowe, 1955, 1958.

Stansfield, 1923.

ONTARIO

Calander Bay (2)

This is a probable carbonatite complex under the waters of the almost circular Calander Bay at the east end of Lake Nipissing. No carbonatite is exposed but nepheline syenite occurs on the shore and as recognizable ring dikes. Basic dikes cut the Precambrian gneisses for some distance around the bay.

Manitou Islands (3) (Fig. 61)

The complex consists of five islands in an approximate ring about 2 miles across, rising above the waters of Lake Nipissing. The country rocks are Precambrian granitic gneisses and the ring represents the fenitized margin of the complex composed of potash feldspar-soda pyroxene-quartz rocks followed inward by similar rocks but without quartz, and in which small areas of carbonatite occur. The inner part of the complex is submerged and hence largely unknown, but appears to consist of altered pegmatitic soda pyroxene syenite. Carbonatite varies from very fine to coarse-grained and massive to foliated with

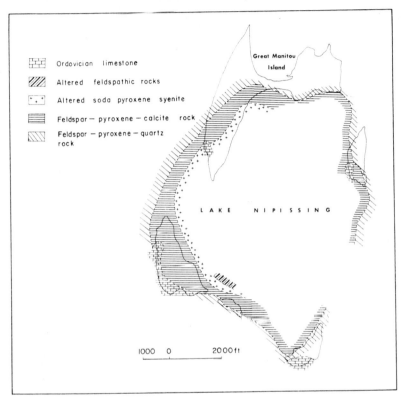

Fig. 61. Manitou Islands (after Rowe, 1958).

streaks of soda pyroxene, soda amphibole, magnetite, apatite, biotite and minor pyrochlore. Nothing further is known of the complex. The SW flank has been investigated by a 400-ft shaft and several hundred feet of cross cuts, but the workings are now flooded. Numerous dikes of lamprophyre and feldspar porphyry cut the rocks of the outer part. Carbonatite has been found on Burrit Island 8 miles west of the Manitou Islands and probably represents another carbonatite complex.

Barlow, 1908.   Rowe, 1954, 1956, 1958.
Gill and Owens, 1957.

Iron Island (4)

The complex is exposed on Iron Island and several small neighbouring islands in Lake Nipissing. It intrudes Precambrian granitic gneisses but no published description is available.

Seabrook Lake (5) (Fig. 62)

This is a roughly circular intrusion about 0.5 mile across with a tail extending about 0.75 mile to the south, the whole complex being surrounded by fenitized granitic gneisses. The central carbonatite is sövite with strongly concentric foliation marked by pyroxene, amphibole and magnetite. This is surrounded by mafic

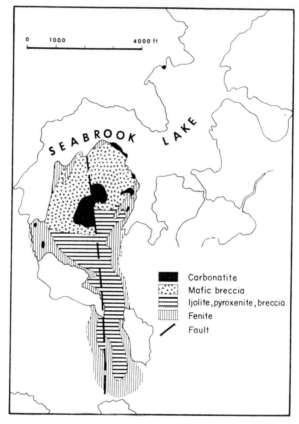

Fig. 62.   Seabrook Lake (after Parsons, 1961).

breccia composed largely of carbonate, biotite and pyroxene, but lacking nepheline or feldspar. Magnetite and fluorite are also present. The breccias are cut by many foliated carbonatite dikes and grade outward into fenitized granitic breccia. On the south side an appendage of ijolite and pyroxenite extends outward from the mafic breccia and is surrounded by fenitized granite. There are in addition dikes of mafic alkaline rocks of lamprophyre-type some of which may extend for several miles. Pyrochlore is an accessory mineral in the carbonatite.

Harding, 1950.   Parsons, 1961.

Lackner Lake (6) (Fig. 63)

This is a circular complex nearly 4 miles across, emplaced in Precambrian granitic gneisses; a satellite intrusion of ijolite adjoins the complex on the north east. It consists essentially of a series of concentric, inward-dipping zones of foliated ijolite, malignite and syenite enclosed in nepheline syenite. Most of the

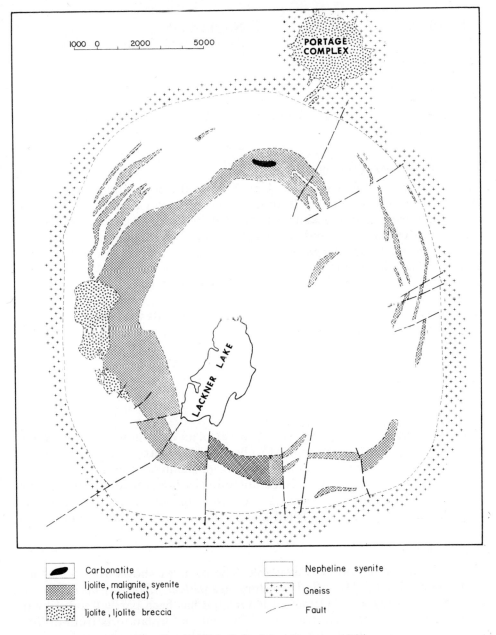

	Carbonatite		Nepheline syenite
	Ijolite, malignite, syenite (foliated)		Gneiss
	Ijolite, Ijolite breccia		Fault

Fig. 63. Lackner Lake (after Parsons, 1961).

ijolitic rocks contain calcite and are cut by carbonatite dikes. These are pyroxene-
and biotite-sövites with apatite, magnetite and pyrochlore. Fine-grained mafic
alkaline dikes cut both the complex and the Precambrian gneisses. The gneisses
around the complex have been fenitized.

A number of magnetite-apatite bodies containing pyrochlore occur within
the ijolites.

Haanel, 1909.   Neczkar, 1958.
Hewitt, 1961.   Parsons, 1961.
Hodder, 1958, 1959.

Borden (7)

No description is available. The complex shows as a prominent circular aeromagnetic anomaly.

Nemegosenda Lake (8) (Fig. 64)

The complex is elliptical about 4 × 3 miles and is mostly covered by the
waters of Nemegosenda Lake. It appears to consist of a central core of juvite,
malignite, foyaite and pulaskite surrounded by successive zones of syenitic
breccia, pyroxenitic fenite and red alkaline fenite. The country rocks are Precambrian granitic and dioritic gneisses intruded by gabbro and biotite pyroxenite. Carbonatite occurs as lenticular masses within the fenites and is mostly
biotite sövite sometimes with pyroxene and apatite. Concentric zones of malignite and jacupirangite occur within the fenites and contain segregations of
magnetite and apatite with pyrochlore. Dikes of mafic alkaline type and feldspar
porphyry cut the complex.

Bell, 1883.   Parsons, 1957, 1961.
Hewitt, 1961.

Cargill (9)

This is extremely poorly exposed on a flat plain and shows as three intense
aeromagnetic anomalies. It appears to be largely an intrusion of highly titaniferous biotite pyroxenite containing sphene, magnetite and minor chalcopyrite
and pyrite, that is cut by fine-grained dolomitic carbonatite and coarse-grained
sövite. No alkaline igneous rocks can be seen in the less than 1 per cent of the
complex that is exposed. It is listed tentatively as a carbonatite complex.

Clay-Howells (10)

No published description is available. The complex shows as two magnetic
anomalies in Clay and Howells Townships on a perfectly flat plain at the junction
of the Kapuskasing and Mattagami Rivers and has been partly flooded by the
construction of a hydro-electric dam. The only information is from drilling:
carbonatite, alkaline rocks and rare earth mineralization are reported.

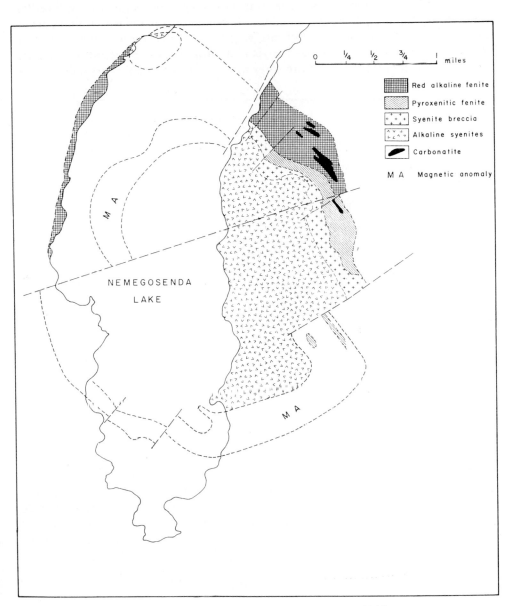

Fig. 64.   Nemegosenda Lake (after Parsons, 1961).

Firesand (11) (Fig. 65)

The complex was intruded into Precambrian greenstones (andesites or basalts) and possibly dacites and quartz syenites. There is some evidence of fenitization but exposures are too poor to indicate whether a fenite aureole exists. It is a circular complex about 1.5 miles across consisting of a central dolomitic carbonatite core surrounded by sövite rings interzoned with mafic carbonate rocks

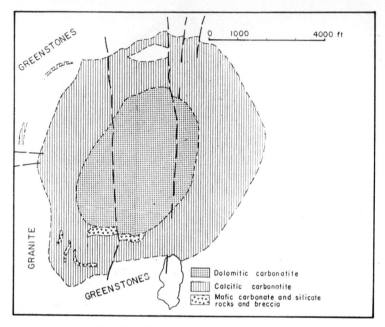

Fig. 65.   Firesand (after Parsons, 1961).

and mafic silicate rocks that are probably metasomatized greenstone. Dolomitic carbonatite is fine- to medium-grained with a variable chlorite content. Quartz and brecciated quartz are common and barite is reported. Sövite is either a ring intrusion with screens of mafic rocks and greenstones or a number of ring intrusions. It is coarse-grained with biotite, apatite, magnetite, pyrrhotite, aegirine and pyrochlore. Part of the sövite is porphyritic. Basic alkaline dikes with chilled margins cut the complex and the country rocks.

Moore, 1932.   Parsons, 1961.

Prairie Lake (12)

No published report is available. The complex shows as a ring of hills 200 to 300 ft high, but is poorly exposed. It appears to be a circular area of ijolitic rocks cut by carbonatite ring dikes and surrounded by fenitized gneisses. Fragmental rocks near the centre may be intrusive breccias, and one outcrop of juvite occurs. Other rock types include biotite-pyroxene-calcite rocks and pyroxene-apatite rocks. Carbonatite is a magnetite sövite. Traces of niobium are present.

Chipman Lake (13)
Schryburt Lake (14)
Big Beaverhouse (15)

No published descriptions are available for any of these complexes but they have been definitely established as carbonatite complexes by mining companies.

Duffell, MacLaren and Holman, 1963 (14, 15).

BRITISH COLUMBIA

Ice River (16)

   Ice River is a well known alkaline complex in the Canadian Rocky Mountains and was intruded into Cambro-Ordovician limestone and shale. The complex comprises sodalite syenite and nepheline syenite, urtite, ijolite and pyroxenite that are largely gradational into one another, and a mass of carbonatite 2 miles

Fig. 66.   Carbonatites in British Columbia.

S

long by 900 ft wide. The outer boundary of the complex is marked by a narrow fenite zone and contorted marble or by a skarn and hornfels zone up to several hundred feet wide.

The dominant carbonatite is ankeritic with some calcite, and becomes increasingly ankeritic towards the centre of the mass. Accessory minerals include feldspar, sodic pyroxenes and pyrochlore. The carbonatite mass is cut by siderite veins and dikes. The contact of the carbonatite with the ijolites and pyroxenite is intensely fractured and brecciated and merges into foliated and carbonatized aegirine-feldspar fenites. A wide variety of lamprophyric rocks is found.

Allan, 1910, 1911, 1912, 1914.   Jones, 1955.
Barlow, 1902.   McConnell, 1886.
Bonney, 1902.   Rapson, (in press).
Campbell, 1961.   Warren, Allen and Connor, 1917.
Dawson, 1885.

POSSIBLE CARBONATITES

Verity (17)

Verity is a probable carbonatite-alkaline complex, but is not well-known geologically. It consists of bands and lenses of carbonate rock up to 150 ft thick

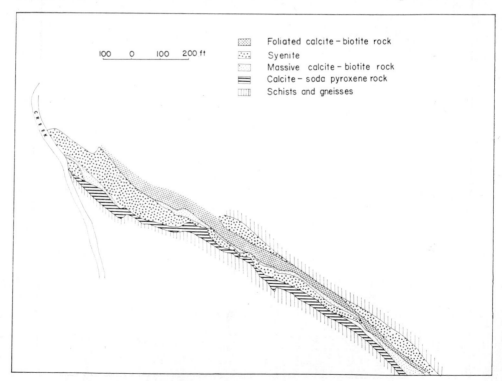

Fig. 67.   Lonnie (after Rowe, 1958).

that appear to be conformable with the enclosing quartz-mica and hornblende gneisses. Dikes and sills made up mostly of plagioclase cut both the carbonate rock and country rock and sodalite syenite outcrops close by. The carbonate rock is fine- to coarse-grained and appears to be largely dolomite. Accessory minerals include vermiculite, olivine, ilmenite, amphibole, zircon, biotite, muscovite, pyrochlore and columbite.

McCammon, 1951, 1953, 1955.   Rowe, 1958.

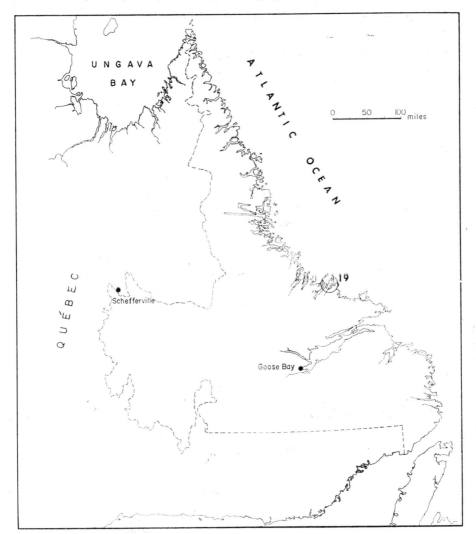

Fig. 68.   Possible carbonatite in Labrador.

Lonnie (*Manson Creek*) (*18*) (Fig. 67)

This also is a possible carbonatite complex. It is 2000 ft long and 300 ft across at its widest part, consisting of bands of calcite-soda pyroxene rock, syenite,

s 2

massive calcite-biotite rock and foliated calcite-biotite rock. The country rocks are schists and gneisses and have been fenitized adjacent to the complex. Accessory minerals include columbite and pyrochlore. Nothing further is known of the complex, but it is clearly alkalic.

Holland, 1955.   Rowe, 1958.

Aillik (*19*)

Alnöite dikes and cone sheets, nepheline lamprophyres and at least one carbonatite dike are found on the mainland of the Labrador coast and on several off-shore islands, and appear to be related to an alkaline ring complex. An analysis of the carbonatite dike is given in the 6th Annual Report of the University of Leeds Research Institute of African Geology (p. 55, no. 475).

Kranck, 1953.

Ottawa Region (*20*)

Dikes of what appear to be carbonatite with inclusions of the Precambrian basement or of related alkali rocks cut Paleozoic limestone at Eastview, a suburb of Ottawa. A possible carbonatite complex is reported by Hogarth (Ottawa Univ.) roughly 15 miles north of Ottawa. Intrusive (?) dolomitic bodies are found within a circular aplite body that is surrounded by syenite. Calcite veins and breccias are found in both the aplite and the syenite. Calcite rock is enriched in strontium and there are calcite-barite veins. The calcitic bodies are bordered by greenish biotite and arfvedsonite and dolomitic bodies by biotite and actino-lite. Fluorapatite is common, magnetite is locally abundant, and betafite (niobium-rich) occurs in calcitic types.

A probable carbonatite occurs in Township 107 (35 miles ENE of Sudbury). No description is available but carbonate rock and nepheline syenite are present in a ring structure. Guillet (1962) mentions vermiculite.

In addition to the Canadian complexes listed, there are a number of strong circular aeromagnetic anomalies in Ontario that might be carbonatite complexes. Several of these occur along lines joining known carbonatites and others show no obvious relationship. Many of these are being investigated at the present time (1965) and some are being drilled. It seems likely that many more car-bonatite complexes will be found in Canada.[1]

United States of America

CALIFORNIA
1. Mountain Pass
MONTANA
2. Rocky Boy

COLORADO
3. Gem Park and McClure Mountain
4. Powderhorn (Iron Hill)
ARKANSAS
5. Magnet Cove

[1] Two more at least have been located on the James Bay Lowlands of Ontario by drilling (August 1966).

Fig. 69. Carbonatites in the United States of America.

CALIFORNIA

Mountain Pass (1)

The Mountain Pass district lacks the form and several of the features of a typical carbonatite complex, yet it does appear to have carbonatitic affinities. It consists of a carbonate rock body and seven plugs and masses 300–1800 ft wide of potassic silicate igneous rocks—granite, syenite and shonkinite, together with numerous dikes of all these rock types, intrusive into a Precambrian gneissic complex. The area involved is about 7.5 × 1.5 miles. Most of the dikes are concentrated near the larger bodies; several hundred of them cover all gradations from granite through syenite to shonkinite. They tend to be finer-grained than the larger bodies and porphyritic varieties are abundant. Shonkinite is composed of biotite, augite and microline.

Augite and biotite are very variable but biotite shonkinite is the commonest variety. Altered leucite may be present. Similarly biotite syenite is commoner than augite syenite, and the granite is unusually potassic. Among the dikes is a biotite-aegirine-feldspar-carbonate rock. There is a suggestion of fenitization adjacent to the dikes. There is one large carbonate body, 2400 ft long and ranging from 700–200 ft wide, known as the Sulphide Queen, together with numerous dikes and veins from 1 inch to 20 ft in width, and carbonate-rich shear zones up to 20 ft wide and 600 ft long. The four principal varieties of carbonate rock are calcite, ankerite, dolomite and siderite with various amounts of barite, strontian barite, barian celestite, quartz, parisite and bastnaesite. An average composition is: carbonate 60%, barite 20%, rare earth fluorcarbonates 10% and silicates 10%. The Sulphide Queen carbonate body has sharp contacts that are in places discordant; apophyses extend into the surrounding Precambrian gneisses and satellite carbonate bodies up to 200 ft long occur close to the main mass. The border zone contains xenoliths of gneiss and igneous rocks, many of them brecciated. The carbonate rock body consists of three types: brown, ferruginous dolomite; grey calcite–pink barite; and silicified carbonate rock containing up to 60% bastnaesite. Foliation parallels the contacts and bends around xenoliths; it is due to barite, crocidolite, phlogopite, etc. Faults and shears are numerous in the area and one of them brecciates the Sulphide Queen body. The entire area is cut by late andesitic dikes.

Olson, *et al.*, 1954.   Sharp and Pray, 1952.

MONTANA

Rocky Boy (2)

   The Rocky Boy stock with an area of 12 sq miles consists of porphyritic potassic syenite, nepheline syenite, monzonite, shonkinite and biotite pyroxenite. One area of nepheline syenite, at Big Sandy Creek, forms a ring or collar around an oval area of sericitized porphyritic cancrinite syenite that is thought to be a volcanic neck. Dikes equivalent to the cancrinite syenite cut the nepheline syenite. Within the neck are pegmatites veins and vein dikes up to 50 ft thick composed of orthoclase, biotite, calcite, pyrrhotite and pyrite with accessory aegirine, apatite, zircon, uranium-rich pyrochlore, rare earth carbonates, barite and ilmenite. They have random orientation and are complexly bifurcated. A few cut the surrounding monzonite and shonkinite. Those of the central most sericitized core are richer in orthoclase and biotite while the more carbonate-rich veins are in the less altered periphery. There are two varieties of calcite— one is strontian and the other, although optically homogeneous is thought to be calcite with exsolved strontianite. Rare earth minerals include burbankite, calkinsite, ancylite, lanthanite and bastnaesite.

   Pecora suggests that the extensive sericitization has tied up a lot of otherwise available carbonate, and hence there is no central carbonatite plug, but rather a ramifying network of veins.

The stock is part of the larger alkaline petrographic province of central Montana.

Larsen, 1940.   Pecora and Kerr, 1953.
Pecora, 1942, 1956, 1962.   Pecora, *et al.*, 1957.
Pecora and Fisher, 1946.

COLORADO

Gem Park and McClure Mountain (*Arkansas River area*) (*3*) (Fig. 70)

Three alkalic intrusives intrude Precambrian metasediments and two of them have carbonatite dikes and sills: the McKinley Mountain syenite stock, the Gem Park alkalic gabbro and nepheline syenite stock, and the McClure Mountain-Iron Mountain complex of gabbro, peridotite, hornblende syenite, ijolite, nepheline syenite and alkalic dikes. Both the Gem Park and McClure Mountain-Iron

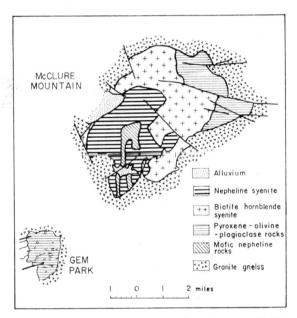

Fig. 70.   Gem Park, Colorada (after Parker, 1963).

Mountain complexes have fenite aureoles. Carbonatite dikes and sills occur in the marginal parts, in the fenites and, in the case of the McClure Mountain body, in the surrounding metamorphic rocks up to 15 miles away. They vary from less than 1 ft to more than 10 ft in width and where they cut the metamorphic rocks they have fenitized walls. Three major types are distinguished: unzoned calcitic or dolomitic carbonatite with apatite, magnetite, ilmenite, feldspar, vermiculite, sodic amphibole, lueshite and bastnaesite; zoned, silicate carbonatites usually with feldspathic walls and carbonatitic cores; Ba-F-rich carbonatite characterized by barite and fluorite and in one deposit by the assemblage cryolite, weberite, ralstonite, prosopite and pachnolite. One of the carbonatites has been named the Goldie carbonatite.

Christman, Brock, Pearson and
    Singewald, 1959.
Heinrich and Anderson, 1965.

Heinrich and Dahlem, (in press).
Parker, Adams and Hildebrand, 1962.
Parker and Hildebrand, 1963.

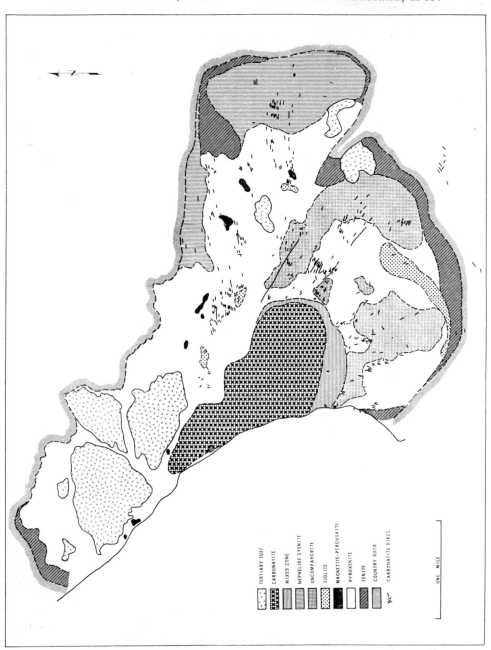

Fig. 71. Powderhorn (Iron Hill) (after Temple and Grogan, 1965).

Powderhorn (Iron Hill) (4) (Fig. 71)

The Powderhorn complex, perhaps better known as Iron Hill, is roughly pear-shaped and about 6 miles in length, covering an area of approximately 12 sq miles. About 70% of the complex is underlain by pyroxenite which is intruded and/or replaced by incomplete rings of nepheline syenite, ijolite, uncompahgrite, magnetite-perovskite bodies and biotite-rich zones around a central core of carbonatite. The surrounding Precambrian Powderhorn granite is partly fenitized adjacent to the complex. The carbonatite core rises nearly a thousand feet above the rest of the complex and is characterized by steeply inward-dipping banding. The principal varieties are granular, brown, foliated, ankerite-dolomite carbonatite; white coarsely crystalline dolomitic carbonatite occurring as elongate masses within the foliated variety and as narrow, cross-cutting dikelets; magnetite-bearing sideritic carbonatite and zones of altered carbonatite enriched in barium and rare earths and occurring with jasper dikes and jasperized areas of carbonatite. Pyrochlore is found principally in the brown foliated carbonatite along with apatite, magnetite, ilmenite, pyrite, rutile, zircon, monazite and fluorite. Inclusions and streaks of biotite-rich rock are common. The central carbonatite is partly surrounded by a zone of mixed rocks intermediate in composition between carbonatite and pyroxenite and passing gradationally into both. The rock is characterized by an abundance of biotite and sodic amphibole. Uncompahgrite consists primarily of melilite with lesser amounts of pyroxene, magnetite and perovskite. The pyroxenite is typically an aegirine-augite rock with about 10% sphene and accessory magnetite and apatite. Other varieties include pegmatitic pyroxenite, biotitite, and potash feldspar-bearing pyroxenite. The main mass is cut by narrow dikes of pyroxenite. The southern half of the complex and surrounding country rocks are cut by numerous carbonatite dikes.

Hedlund and Olson, 1961.　　　　　Olson and Wallace, 1956a, b.
Larsen, 1942.　　　　　　　　　　Rose and Shannon, 1960.
Larsen and Goransen, 1932.　　　　Temple and Grogan, 1965.

ARKANSAS

Magnet Cove (5) (Fig. 72)

This is a somewhat elliptical body about 3 × 2.5 miles intruded into folded and faulted Paleozoic sediments (largely shales and sandstones) and surrounded by a thermal metamorphic aureole from 1000–2500 ft wide. A central core of ijolite and carbonatite is surrounded by successive ring dikes of phonolite, melteigite, jacupirangite, and various types of nepheline syenite. In addition there are two masses of jacupirangite, one on the western flank and the other on the north east. Smaller ring dikes and radial dikes of tinguaite, trachyte porphyry, nepheline syenite and various other rock types are widespread. Carbonatite forms irregularly shaped bodies in the core and consists largely of sövite with apatite, magnetite, monticellite, perovskite, kimzeyite and pyrite. Veins are common within and outside the complex and include quartz-brookite-rutile

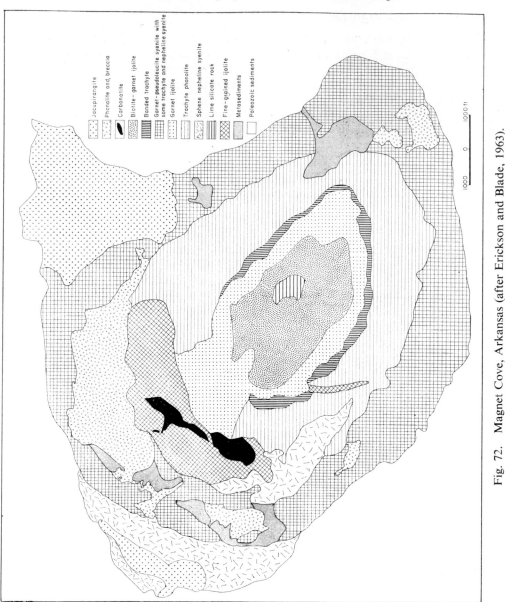

Fig. 72. Magnet Cove, Arkansas (after Erickson and Blade, 1963).

veins, feldspar-carbonate veins, feldspar veins, quartz-feldspar veins and fluorite veins. Late quartz veins, molybdenite, and apatite veins occur in the carbonatite. Niobium is found principally in titanium minerals and rare earths in apatite and perovskite.

Bramlette, 1936.

Dana, 1886.

Erickson and Blade, 1963.

Foshag, 1923.

Fryklund, 1949.

Fryklund, Harner and Kaiser, 1954.

Fryklund and Holbrook, 1950.

Glass, 1937.

Harker, 1902.
Holbrook, 1947, 1948.
Keller and Henderson, 1949.
Kinney, 1949.
Kunz, 1886.
Landes, 1931.
Mar, 1890.
McConnell and Gruner, 1940.
Melville, 1892.
Milton and Blade, 1958.
Miser and Glass, 1941.
Miser and Stevens, 1938.
Nieberlein, Fine, Calhoun and
 Parsons, 1954.

Padon, 1851.
Parks and Branner, 1932.
Penfield, 1894.
Purdue and Miser, 1923.
Rath, 1876.
Reed, 1949a, b.
Rose, Blade and Ross, 1958.
Ross, 1938.
Sleight, 1941.
Spencer, 1946.
Teschamacher, 1849.
Washington, 1900, 1901.
Williams, 1891.

Fig. 73. Carbonatite in Bolivia.

SOUTH AMERICA

Cerro Sapo (1)   **Bolivia**

This is a nepheline syenite intrusion that has been known for many years. In 1961 one of the editors (J. G.) suggested to F. Ahlfeld that the occurrence might be a carbonatite on the basis of sodalite-ankerite-barite veins described there. Ahlfeld has subsequently confirmed the presence of 'albite-rich limestone' and 'limestone with phlogopite' and expresses the belief that it is a carbonatite complex. The intrustion cuts Devonian shales. It is listed tentatively until confirmed by more detailed mapping.

Ahlfeld and Mosebach, 1935.   Brendler, 1932, 1934.
Ahlfeld and Wegner, 1931.

Brazil

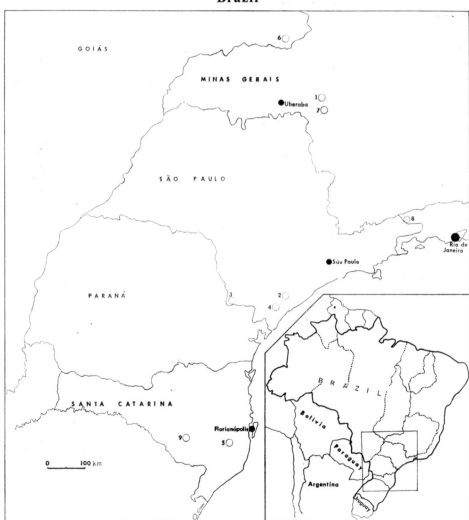

Fig. 74.   Carbonatites in Brazil.

1. Araxá (Barreiro)
2. Serrote (Juquia, Guaviruva)
3. Itapirapuã
4. Jacupiranga
5. Anitápolis

PROBABLE CARBONATITES
6. Catalão
7. Tapira
8. Itatiaia
9. Lages

These summaries are condensed from manuscripts prepared by Dr. G. C. Melcher, J. M. V. Coutinho and C. B. Gomes.

Araxá (Barreiro) (1)

The complex is circular with a diameter of about 6 km. Because of the extremely deep weathering, few fresh outcrops are seen and neither the outer contact nor the distribution of different rock types within the complex can be mapped accurately. However, the topographic expression of the alkalic rocks clearly indicates the approximate contact with the surrounding Precambrian quartzite and phyllite. There is also a marked decrease in radioactivity at the contact. The quartzites are cut by veins containing barite, magnetite, calcite, and altered amphiboles and pyroxenes. Carbonatite was pierced by several drill holes and contains calcite, apatite, magnetite, phlogopite, barite, perovskite, zircon and uranoan phosphates. The size of the body has not been determined. Among the alkaline rocks are jacupirangite, limburgite, foyaite and tinguaite. A large body of apatite-magnetite-biotite-barite rock constitutes a potential phosphate ore body. Large tonnages of niobium ore are also present.

Andrade Junior, 1925.   Leonardos, 1956a, b.
Barbosa, 1937a, b.   Oliveira, 1936.
Guimaraes, 1925, 1946, 1957.

Serrote[1] (Juquia, Guaviruva) (2) (Fig. 75)

The thick weathering mantle and the surrounding swamps have impeded detailed geologic investigation of the area. The alkalic intrusion seems to be roughly circular with a diameter of about 3 km. The red, iron-rich soils were probably derived from peridotites and pyroxenites which may be observed at a few outcrops. They contain olivine, augite, biotite, nepheline, magnetite and ilmenite in varying proportions. Ijolites and biotite-ijolites also occur in the area. The nepheline syenites are made up of orthoclase, aegirine, nepheline, biotite, apatite, magnetite and ilmenite, sphene, zircon, pyrrhotite and calcite. The carbonatite of Morro do Serrote, a rounded hill rising 200 m above the swamps, ranges from fine-grained ferruginous carbonate rock to coarse-grained white marble. The carbonates are mainly dolomite and subordinate calcite. Apatite, biotite and magnetite are the common accessories. Many barite veins cut the carbonatite. No niobium or rare earth minerals have been reported. Large bodies of magnetite-apatite rock constitute mineable phosphate ore.

Knecht and Felicissimo Junior, 1939.   Maciel, 1952.
Leonardos, 1956a, b.

[1] Referred to by Heinrich (1958) as Registro.

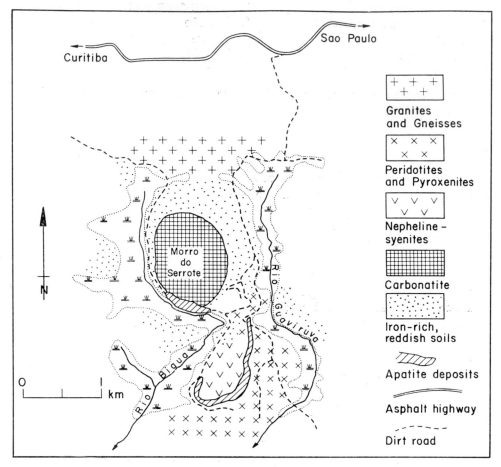

Fig. 75.   Serrote (figure supplied by G. E. Melcher, Univ. São Paulo).

Itapirapuã (3)

The rocks of the region are Precambrian granites which intrude metasediments. The granites, which locally contain some mica schist, hornfels and amphibolite roof pendants or xenoliths, are cut by alkalic rocks which crop out in a circular area with a diameter of about 3 km. Near the contact, fenitization of the granite is shown by the appearance of sodic amphibole and a decrease in quartz content. The main rock type of the alkalic stock is foyaite, which contains soda orthoclase, nepheline, aegirine and minor sodalite and cancrinite. Tinguaite dikes cut the surrounding Basement rocks.

Carbonatite outcrops within the alkalic rock area, but its size and exact relationship with the surrounding rocks are still unknown. The carbonatite is medium-grained and is composed of calcite, soda orthoclase and apatite. Magnetite and zircon occur as accessories.

A strongly radioactive carbonate vein, about 0.5 m thick, cuts the granite at a distance of 1 km from the foyaite contact. The rock contains calcite, magnetite, pyrrhotite, galena, bastnaesite, apatite, fluorite, barite and an extremely fine-grained, unidentified thorium mineral. Chemical analysis of one vein rock sample showed 0.67% thorium oxide and 9.1% rare earth elements. The existence of other similar veins or dikes is indicated by eluvial boulders of limonite-fluorite-barite rock which is also strongly radioactive.

Jacupiranga (4) (p. 171, Fig. 2)

The Jacupiranga complex is oval with an area of about 65 sq km and is intrusive into Precambrian granodiorites and mica schists which are fenitized for some distance from the complex.

There appear to be two intrusive centres. A peridotite plug is surrounded by a ring intrusion of pyroxenite. South of this and partly cutting it is an almost circular jacupirangite plug enclosing a crescentic body of ijolite. Carbonatite intrudes the jacupirangite as two plugs, one partly cutting the other. The whole complex is surrounded by leucocratic alkalic rocks that may be remobilized fenite. The carbonatite is principally sövite with some dolomite, apatite, magnetite, forsterite, serpentine, phlogopite, sulphides, ilmenite, spinel, pyrochlore, baddeleyite, barite and perovskite concentrated in bands or irregular clusters. Magnetite-apatite concentrations are particularly common. Faults within the carbonatite do not extend into the adjacent rocks and are filled with apatite and magnetite or with carbonatite breccia. The carbonatite body has steeply outward-dipping contacts with the jacupirangite and is cut by numerous vertical dikes composed of carbonates, apatite, phlogopite and magnetite oriented parallel to the dike walls. The rocks of the complex and the country rocks for a few kilometres are cut by dikes of phonolite, essexite, ijolite, monchiquite and tinguaite. Thick residual soil 1–10 m thick covering much of the complex is enriched in apatite and magnetite and constitutes mineable phosphate ore.

Bauer, 1877. Knecht, 1939, 1940, 1948.
Derby, 1887, 1891a, b. Melcher, 1954.
Hussak, 1892, 1895, 1904.

Anitápolis (5) (Fig. 76)

A small alkalic intrusion 10 km NW of Anitápolis, was described briefly by Moraes Rego and Guimaraes (1926), who observed nepheline syenites and pyroxenites which cut Precambrian granite. Crystalline limestone was found in contact with the alkalic rocks and was interpreted to be the result of contact metamorphism. Leonardos (1956) suggested that it might be a carbonatite.

Pyroxenites outcrop in the central part of the area on both sides of Rio Pinheiros, which flows in a deep valley, 400 m below the surrounding granite peaks. Fenites and nepheline syenites occur between the basic igneous rocks and the unaltered granite. One single carbonatite outcrop may be observed in the river bed. Several nephelinite dikes cut the granite a few kilometres from the central plug.

The pyroxenites contain mainly aegirine-augite and a high proportion of biotite. The carbonatite is a medium- to coarse-grained rock, composed of calcite, apatite, magnetite, phlogopite, and partly serpentinized olivine. The region is an excellent example of fenitization and several stages of the gradual alteration of granite to nepheline syenites may be recognized. Near the outer border of the fenite area the quartz content of the rocks decreases rapidly and

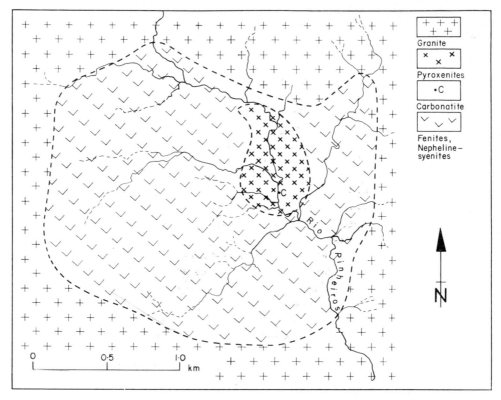

Fig. 76.   Anitápolis (figure supplied by G. E. Melcher, Univ. São Paulo).

abundant aegirine appears between the feldspar crystals, and also in irregular veins. Towards the centre of the area, feldspars are completely altered to soda orthoclase, quartz is absent and some nepheline appears. Aegirine needles up to 10 cm long occur in many veins and in irregular masses. In the last stage, the rocks become nepheline syenites, which contain soda orthoclase, aegirine and nepheline, with apatite and calcite as abundant accessories.

Moraes Rego and Guimaraes, 1926.   Leonardos, 1956a, b.

PROBABLE CARBONATITES

Melcher (this volume, p. 169) expresses the view that carbonatite probably occurs at the following alkalic rock localities, but is obscured by the deep weathering: Catalão (6), Tapira (7), Itatiaia (8), Lages (9).

NOTE ADDED IN PROOF

Carbonatite complexes have recently been reported from the Cape Verde Islands. The particular islands are Sal (Heinrich, in press), Brava, Fogo and São Vicente.

If the Cape Verde Islands are truly oceanic and not a remnant of the continental crust this is the first known example of a non-continental carbonatite complex. If this be the case it is tempting to suggest that some other islands of feldspathoidal rocks might be re-examined for carbonatite. Candidates that suggest themselves are the Fernando Poo–Principe–São Tomé–Annobon chain in the Gulf of Guinea and perhaps Kerguelen in the Southern Ocean.

Tchivira (Chivira) in Angola is now confirmed as a carbonatite complex.

BIBLIOGRAPHY OF THEORETICAL, EXPERIMENTAL AND GENERAL WORKS

Ambs and Paulitsch, (in press)
Baertschi, 1951, 1957
Bailey, 1964a, b, c, (in press)
Bassett, 1956a, b
Biggar, 1962
Biggar and Wyllie, 1962
Borodin, 1957, 1958a, b, 1960, 1961
Borodin and Barinski, 1960, 1961
Borovko, 1961
Bowden, 1962
Butakova, 1959
Cox, Vail, Monkman and Johnson, 1961
Cox, Johnson, Monkman, Stillman, Vail and Wood, 1965
Daly, 1910, 1914, 1925, 1933
Dawson, 1964a, (in press)
Deans, 1964
Deans, Snelling and Rapson, (in press)
Dmitriev, 1959
v. Eckermann, 1948a, b, 1951, 1964a
v. Eckermann and v. Ubisch, 1952
Egorov, 1960a, b, 1964
Epshtein, Anikeeva and Mikhailova, 1961
Eskova and Ganzeev, 1963
Franz, 1965
Franz and Wyllie, 1966
Frolov, 1960
Frolov and Epshtein, 1962
Gaidukova, 1960
Garson, 1955a, 1959a
Gellatly, 1964
Gittins and Tuttle, 1964, (in press)
Glagolev, 1962
Gold, 1963, (in press)
Goldsmith, Grof, Witters and Northrop, 1962
Goldsmith and Heard, 1961
Gonfiantini and Tongiorgi, 1964
Hamilton, 1964
Hamilton and Deans, 1963
Harker, 1909
Harker and Tuttle, 1955
Harkin, 1960
Hayatsu, York, Farquar and Gittins, 1965
Heier, 1962
Higazy, 1954
Holmes, 1950, 1952, 1956
Ivanov, 1959
James, 1956c, 1958b

James and McKie, 1958
Khitarov and Malinin, 1958
King, 1965
King and Sutherland, 1960
Kirilov, 1963
von Knorring, 1962
Kononova, 1957, 1961
Koster, van Groos and Wyllie, 1963, (in press)
Kranck, 1928
Kukharenko and Dontsova, 1962, 1964
deKun, (in press)
Lavrenev and Epshtein, 1962a
Lombard, 1955
Meyer, 1958a
Pecora, 1956
Powell, 1962, (in press)
Powell, 1965a, b, c
Powell, Hurley and Fairbairn, 1962
Pozharitskaya, 1962
Pozharitskaya and Epshtein, 1962
Quon and Heinrich, (in press)
Saether, 1948a
Saggerson and Williams, 1963, 1964
Schröcke, 1955
Schuling, 1961
Serba, 1959
Shand, 1950
Sobolev, 1959
Smith, 1956
Tomkeieff, 1961
Vainshtein, Pozharitskaya and Turanskaya, 1961
Volotovskaya and Kukharenko, 1959
Walter, Wyllie and Tuttle, 1962
Wambeke, 1964a, b, (in press)
Wambeke and Wimmenauer, 1964
Waters, 1955
Watkinson, 1965
Watkinson and Wyllie, 1964
Williams, 1956
Workman, 1911
Wright, 1963
Wyllie, 1965, (in press)
Wyllie and Biggar, (in press)
Wyllie, Cox and Biggar, 1962
Wyllie and Haas, 1965, (in press)
Wyllie and Raynor, (in press)
Wyllie and Tuttle, 1959a, b, 1960a, b, 1962, 1963

REFERENCES

Afanasyev, W. A., 1939, Alkaline rocks of the Ozernaya Varaka of the Khabozero region (south-west Kola Peninsula): *Doklady Akad. Nauk SSSR*, v. **25**, pp. 508–512 (in English).

Agard, J., 1956a, Les roches à carbonates et silicates associés de l'oued Archakhchakh, massif du Tamazert, Haut Atlas de Midelt: *Arch. Serv. et gîtes minér.*, Rabat.

Agard, J., 1956b, Les gîtes minéraux associés aux roches alcalines et aux carbonatites: *Science de la Terre*, v. **4**, Nos. 1–2, pp. 103–151.

Agard, J., 1958, Les ankaratrites et le volcanisme récent de la région de Zebzat (Haut Atlas de Midelt): *Notes Serv. géol. Maroc.*, v. **15**, No. 135 for 1956, pp. 109–117.

Agard, J., 1959, Les carbonatites et les roches à silicates et carbonates associés du massif de roches alcalines du Tamazert (Haut Atlas de Midelt, Maroc) et les problèmes de leur genèse: *Arch. Serv. et gîtes minér.* No. 646, Rabat.

Agard, J., 1960, Les carbonatites et les roches à silicates et carbonates associés du massif de roches alcalines du Tamazert (Haut Atlas de Midelt, Maroc) et les problèmes de leur genèse: *Int. Geol. Congr., 21st sess.*, Pt. 13, pp. 293–303.

Agard, J., and Menyr, B., 1958, Les carbonatites de l'oued Tamazert, massif du Tamazert, Haut Atlas de Midelt: *Arch. Serv. et gîtes minér.*, Rabat.

Ahlfeld, F., and Mosebach, R., 1935, Uber alkaligesteine in der bolivianischen Ostkordillere: *Neues Jb. Min., A*, v. **69**, pp. 388–414.

Ahlfeld, F., and Wegner, R., 1931, Uber die herkunst der im bereich altperuanischer kulturen gefundenen schumuckstücke aus sodalith: *Zeitschr. f. Ethnologie*, v. **63**, pp. 288–296.

Allan, J. A., 1910, Geology of the Ice River District, British Columbia: *Canada Geol. Surv. Summ. Rept.*

Allan, J. A., 1911, Geology of Field District and Vicinity, British Columbia: *Canada Geol. Surv. Summ. Rept.*

Allan, J. A., 1912, *Geology of the Ice River District:* Thesis, Massachusetts Inst. Technology, Boston, U.S.A.

Allan, J. A., 1914, Geology of Field Map Area, British Columbia and Alberta: *Canada Geol. Surv., Mem.*, v. **55**.

Ambs, H., and Paulitsch, P. (in press), Carbonatites, their fabric, chemistry and their genesis: *Int. Mineral. Assoc.*, 1964 meeting, India.

Andrade Junior, J. F. de., 1925, Reconhecimento geológico dos arredores de Araxá e outros pontos de ocorrência de águas minerais: *Geol. e Min. do Brasil, Bol.*, v. **9**.

Aubert, F., 1947, Identifisering av de Nb-Ta- förende mineraler i sövit og forsök på deres magnetiske separasjon: *Tidsskr. Kjemi Bergvesen og metall.*, v. **7**, p. 169.

Baertschi, P., 1951, Relative abundance of oxygen and carbon isotopes in carbonate rocks: *Nature*, v. **168**, pp. 288–289.

Baertschi, P., 1957, Messung und deutung relativer Haufigkeits variationen von ^{18}O unde ^{13}C in karbonatgesteinen und-mineralien: *Schweiz. Min. Petr. Mitt.*, v. **37**, pp. 73–152.

Bagdasarov, E. A., 1959, Alkaline pegmatites of the Afrikanda massif: *Zapiski Vses. Mineralog.*, v. **88**, pp. 271–274 (in Russian). English transl., *Int. Geol. Rev.*, v. **3**, pp. 463–473.

Bagdasarov, E. A., and Kukkarenko, A. A., 1959, Vesuvianites of Afrikanda: In 'The Mineralogy of postmagmatic processes,' Leningrad (in Russian).

Bailey, D. K., 1958, Carbonatites in the Rufunsa Valley: *N. Rhodesia Geol. Surv.*, Rec. for 1956, pp. 35–42.

Bailey, D. K., 1959, *Carbonatites and intrusive limestones in the Central Province of Northern Rhodesia:* Ph.D. thesis, Univ. of London, England.

Bailey, D. K., 1960, Carbonatites of the Rufunsa Valley, Feira District: *N. Rhodesia Geol. Surv., Bull.*, **5**.

Bailey, D. L., 1961a, The Mid-Zambezi–Luangwa rift and related carbonatite activity: *Geol. Mag.*, v. **98**, pp. 275–284.

Bailey, D. K., 1961b, Intrusive limestones in the Keshya and Mkwisi Valleys, Northern Rhodesia: *Geol. Soc. London Quart. Jour.*, v. **117**, pp. 419–446.

Bailey, D. K., 1964a, Isotopic composition of strontium in carbonatites: *Nature*, v. **201**, p. 599.

Bailey, D. K., 1964b, Crustal warping—a possible tectonic control of alkaline magmatism: *Jour. Geophys. Res.*, v. **69**, pp. 1103–1111.

Bailey, D. K., 1964c, Temperature and vapor composition in carbonatite and kimberlite: *Carnegie Inst. Wash. Year Book*, v. **63**, pp. 79–81.

Bailey, D. K. (in press), Potash feldspar and phlogopite as indices of temperature and partial pressure of CO_2 in carbonatite and kimberlite: *Int. Mineral. Assoc.*, 1964 meeting, India.

Baker, B. H., 1953, The alkaline igneous complex at Jombo: in Caswell, P. V., *Kenya Geol. Surv., Rept.*, **24**, pp. 32–48.

Barbosa, O., 1937a, Geologia do Municipio de Araxá, Minas Gerais: *Min. Metal.*, v. **2**, pp. 247–248.

Barbosa, O., 1937b, Resumo da geologia do Estado de Minas Gerais: *Serv. Geologico, Minas Gerais, Bol.* **3**, Belo Horizonte.

Barlow, A. E., 1902, Nepheline rocks of Ice River, British Columbia: *Ottawa Naturalist*, pp. 70–76.

Barlow, A. E., 1908, Report on the geology and natural resources of the area included by the Nipissing and Timiskaming map-sheets comprising portions of the District of Nipissing, Ontario, and the County of Pontiac, Quebec (2nd edition): *Canada Geol. Surv.*, Pub. 962.

Barrere, J., 1961, Rapport de Fin de Campagne dans l'Adrar des Iforas, 1958–1959: *Serv. de Géol. et de Prospection minière.*

Bassett, H., 1956a, The isolation of the insoluble constituents of impure limestones: *Tanganyika Geol. Surv.*, Rec. for 1953, v. **3**, pp. 86–92.

Bassett, H., 1956b, The carbonatite problem: *Tanganyika Geol. Surv.*, Rec. for 1954, v. **4**, pp. 81–92.

Bauer, H. E., 1877, As minas de ferro de Jacupiranga: *Revista de Engenharia*, p. 213.

Bell, R., 1883, *Canada Geol. Surv., Rept.* of progress for 1880–1–2, pt. c. sec. 1 (map 159).

Belyankin, D. S., and Vlodavetz, V. I., 1932, The alkalic complex of the Turja Peninsula: *Trans. Petr. Inst. Akad. Nauk SSSR*, v. **2**, pp. 45–71 (in Russian).

Bergstöl, S., 1960, *Undersökelse av bergartene rundt Fensfeltet:* thesis, Univ. of Oslo, Norway.

Bergstöl, S. (in prep.), Tinguaite dikes related to the Fen circular complex.

Bergstöl, S., and Svinndal, S., 1960a, The carbonatite and per-alkaline rocks of the Fen area: *Geology of Norway, Norg. geol. Unders.*, No. **208**, pp. 99–105.

Bergstöl, S., and Svinndal, S., 1960b, Søve niobium mine, Fen area: *Int. Geol. Congr., 21st sess.*, Excursion Guide C 10.

Bergstöl, S., and Svinndal, S., 1960c, The per-alkaline rocks of the Fen area: *Int. Geol. Congr., 21st sess.*, Excursion Guide A 12, C 8.

Berwerth, Fr., 1893, Uber alnöit von Alnö: *Ann. K.K. naturhist. Hofmuseum, Vienna*, v. **8**, p. 440.

Berwerth, Fr., 1895, Uber alnöit von Alnö: *Ann. K.K. naturhist. Hofmuseum, Vienna*, v. **10**, p. 76.

Bésaires, H., 1954, Les recherches récentes de niobium en Afrique Noire (granites et carbonatites). Possibilités à Madagascar: *Doc. Bur. Geol., Tananarive*, No. **90**.

Bethune, P. de, 1952, Etudes petrographiques dans les Monts Ruindi (Kivu, Congo Belge): *Mém. de l'Inst. Géol. de l'Univ. de Louvain*, v. **16**, pp. 221–299.

Bethune, P. de, 1956, Caractères petrographiques des carbonatites de la Lueshe (Kivu, Congo Belge): *Ann. Soc. géol. Belgique*, v. **80**, pp. 63–66.

Bethune, P. de, 1957, La busorite, une roche feldspathoidale nouvelle de Kivu: *Bull. Soc. belge géol.*, v. **65**, No. 3 for 1956, pp. 394–399.

Bethune, P. de, and Meyer, A., 1956, Les carbonatites de la Lueshe (Kivu, Congo Belge): *Acad. Sci. Paris Comptes rendus*, v. **243**, pp. 1132–1134.

Bethune, P. de, and Meyer, A., 1957, Carbonatites in Kivu: *Nature*, v. **179**, pp. 270–271.

Biggar, G. M., 1962, *High pressure–high temperature phase equilibrium studies in the system* $CaO–CaF_2–P_2O_5–H_2O–CO_2$ *with special reference to the apatites:* Ph.D. thesis, Univ. of Leeds, England.

Biggar, G. M., and Wyllie, P. J., 1962, Solid–liquid–vapour phase relationships at high pressures in parts of the system $CaO–CaF_2–CO_2–H_2O–P_2O_5$: *Jour. Geophys. Res.*, v. **67**, pp. 3542–3543.

Binge, F. W., 1962, Geology of the Kericho area: *Kenya Geol. Surv.*, Rept. 50.

Bisset, C. B., 1935, Notes on the volcanic rocks of Central Karamoja: *Uganda Geol. Surv., Bull.*, **2**, pp. 40–44.

Björlykke, H., 1934, Norwegische mikrolithmineralien: *Norsk Geol. tidsskr.*, v. **14**, pp. 145–161.

Björlykke, H., 1953, Utnytting av sövemalm: *Tidsskr. Kjemi og Bergvesen*, v. **13**, p. 47.

Björlykke, H., 1955, The niobium deposits at Söve, southern Norway: *Min. Jour.*, v. **244**, pp. 412–413.

Björlykke, H., and Svinndal, S., 1960, The carbonatite and per-alkaline rocks of the Fen area. Mining and exploration work: *Geology of Norway. Norg. geol. Unders.*, No. 208, pp. 105–110.

Bloomfield, K., 1965, The Geology of the Zomba area: *Malawi Geol. Surv., Bull.* **16**.

Bloomfield, K., and Garson, M. S., 1965, The geology of the Kirk Range—Lisungwe Valley area: *Malawi Geol. Surv., Bull.* **17**, pp. 139–175.

Bonney, T. G., 1902, On a sodalite syenite (Ditroite) from Ice River Valley, Canadian Rocky Mountains: *Geol. Mag.*, v. **9**, pp. 199–206.

Bornhardt, W., et al., 1900, Zur Oberflächengestaltung und geologie Deutsch-Ostafrikas: *Deutsch-Ost-Afrika*, v. **7**, p. 595, S. Dietrich Reimer, Berlin.

Borodin, L. S., 1957, Types of carbonatite deposits and their relationship to massifs of ultrabasic alkaline rocks: *Izvest. Akad. Nauk SSSR, Geol. Ser.*, No. 5, pp. 3–16 (in Russian). French transl., BRGM No. 2048.

Borodin, L. S., 1958a, The chemistry of aegerinization and nephelinization of pyroxene in the formation of metasomatic nepheline-pyroxene rocks (ijolites): *Geokhimiya*, No. **5**, pp. 501–502. English transl., *Geochemistry*, v. **5**, pp. 637–640.

Borodin, L. S., 1958b, On the process of nephelinization and aegirinization or pyroxenites in connection with the problem of the genesis of alkaline rocks of the ijolite-melteigite type: *Izvest. Akad. Nauk SSSR, Geol. Ser.*, No. 6, pp. 48–57 (in Russian).

Borodin, L. S., 1959, On perovskite mineralization in the Vuori–Yarvi massif: *Geology of ore deposits*, v. **5**, pp. 21–30 (in Russian).

Borodin, L. S., 1960, Genesis of carbonatite deposits and their geological relationship to massifs of ultrabasic alkaline rocks: in '*Genetic problems of ores*', Moscow (in Russian).

Borodin, L. S., 1961, Nephelinization of pyroxenites and paragenesis of rock-forming ijolite minerals from massifs of ultrabasic alkaline rocks: *Symposium on physico-chemical problems of the formation of rocks and ores*, **1**, Akad. Nauk SSSR, Moscow (in Russian, English abstract).

Borodin, L. S., 1962, The petrography and genesis of the Vuori-Yarvi massif: in '*Rare elements in massifs of alkaline rocks*', Inst. Min., Geochem., *Crystal-chemistry of rare elements*, No. 9 (in Russian).

Borodin, L. S., and Barinski, R. L., 1960, Rare earths in perovskites (knoppites) from massifs of ultrabasic alkaline rocks: *Geokhimiya*, v. **4**, pp. 291–291 (in Russian, English abstract).

Borodin, L. S., and Barinski, R. L., 1961, The composition of rare earths in pyrochlore from massifs of ultrabasic alkaline rocks and carbonatites: *Geochemistry*, v. **6**, p. 517, trans. from *Geokhimiya*, v. **6**, pp. 486–492.

Borodin, L. S., and Kapustin, Yu. L., 1962, Burbankite—first discovery in USSR: *Doklady Akad. Nauk SSSR*, v. **147**, No. 2 (in Russian).

Borovko, N. N., 1961, The relation between the contents of niobium, tantalum, uranium, and thorium in rare metal carbonatites: *Zapiski Vses. Mineralog.*, v. **90**, pp. 637–642 (in Russian).

Bowden, P., 1962, Trace elements in Tanganyika carbonatites: *Nature*, v. **196**, p. 570.

Bowen, N. L., 1921, Preliminary note on monticellite alnöite from Isle Cadieux, Quebec: *Washington Acad. Sci. Jour.*, v. **13**, pp. 278–281.

Bowen, N. L., 1922, Genetic features of alnöitic rocks at Isle Cadieux, Quebec: *Am. Jour. Sci.*, v. **34**, pp. 1–34.

Bowen, N. L., 1924, The Fen area in Telemark, Norway: *Am. Jour. Sci.*, v. **8**, pp. 1–11.

Bowen, N. L., 1926a, The carbonate rocks of the Fen area in Norway: *Am. Jour. Sci.*, v. **12**, pp. 499–502.

Bowen, N. L., 1926b, Die carbonatgesteine des Fengebietes in Norwegen: *Centralblatt f. Min.*, A, No. 8, pp. 241–245.

Bramlette, M. N., 1936, Geology of the Arkansas Bauxite region: *Arkansas Geol. Surv., Inf. Circ.*, v. **8**.

Brasseur, H., Herman, P., and Hubaux, A., 1962, Apatites de l'est du Congo et du Ruanda: *Ann. Soc., géol. Belgique*, v. **85**, pp. 61–85.

Brauns, A., and Brauns, R., 1925, Ein Carbonatit aus dem Laacher Seegebiet: *Centralblatt f. Min.*, A, pp. 97–101.

Brauns, R., 1899, Ein neues kontaktgesteine aus dem Kaiserstuhl: *Dies. Jahrb.*, v. **1**, p. 79.

Brauns, R., 1922, Die phonolitischen Gesteine des Laacher Seegebietes und ihre Beziehung zu anderen Gesteinen dieses Gebietes: *Neues Jb. f. Min.*, v. **46**, pp. 1–116.

Brauns, R., 1926a, Primärer calcit in tiefengesteinen oder verdrängung der silikate durch calcit?: *Centralblatt f. Min.*, A, No. **1**, pp. 1–8.

Brauns, R., 1926b, Die Bedeutung dea Laacher Sees in mineralogischer und geologischer Heinsicht: *Aus Natur und Heimat*, v. **1**, pp. 15–41.

Brauns, R., 1927, Die Chemische Zusammensetzung der Basaltlaven des Laacher Seegebietes: *Neus Jb. f. Min.*, v. **56**, Abt. A, pp. 468–498.

Brauns, R., 1937, Die Geologisch—mineralogisch Durchforschung des Laacher Seegebietes in ihrer geschichtlichen Entwicklung dargestellt: Sonderabdruck aus dem 2 proteusband Abhandlungen und Verhandlungsberichte der "Rheinischen Ges. F. Geschichte der Naturw., Med. u. Technik." von Paul Diergart in Bonn. Selbstverlag, pp. 83–92.

Brendler, W., 1932, Uber sodalith von Cerro Sapo, Bolivien: *Centralblatt f. Min.*, A, No. **2**, pp. 42–46.

Brendler, W., 1934, Sodalite from Bolivia: *Am. Mineralogist*, v. **19**, pp. 28–31.

Brinck, J. W., 1964, *Results of a geochemical soil survey for niobium on the carbonatites of the Kaiserstuhl:* EURATOM publication EUR, 1827, d, f, e, pp. 201–209.

Brögger, W. C., 1921, Die eruptivgesteine des Kristianiagebietes, IV, Das Fengebiet in Telemark, Norwegen: *Norsk. Vidensk. Selsk. Skifter. I, Math. Naturv. kl.*, (1920), No. **9**, pp. 1–408.

Broughton, H. J., 1950, Iron and titanium ores from the Bukusu Hill alkaline complex, Uganda: *Colon. Geol. and Mineral Resources*, v. **1**, pp. 262–266, London.

Brown, P. E., 1964, The Songwe scarp carbonatite and associated feldspathization in the Mbeya Range, Tanganyika: *Geol. Soc. London Quart. Jour.*, v. **120**, pp. 223–240.

Butakova, E. L., 1956, The petrology of the Maimech-Kotui complex of ultrabasic and alkaline rocks: *Inst. Geol. Arctic*, v. **89**, No. 6 (in Russian).

Butakova, E. L., 1959, The role of metasomatism in the formation of alkaline rocks: *Mineralog. Symposium, Lvov Geol. Soc.*, No. 13, pp. 283–290 (in Russian). English transl., *Int. Geol. Rev.*, v. **3**, pp. 187–194.

Butakova, E. L., and Egorov, L. S., 1962, The Maimech-Kotui complex of alkaline ultrabasic rocks: *Petrography of Eastern Siberia*, v. **1**, Akad. Nauk SSSR, Moscow (in Russian).

Cairney, T., 1964, A re-assessment of the origin of the Mkwisi intrusive limestone, Northern Rhodesia: *Univ. of Leeds Res. Inst. African Geol.*, 8th Ann. Rept., 1962–1963, pp. 25–26.

Callisen, K., 1943, Igneous rocks of the Ivigtut region, Greenland: *Medd. om Grønland*, v. **131**, No. 8.

Campbell, F. A., 1961, Differentiation trends in the Ice River complex, British Columbia: *Am. Jour. Sci.*, v. **259**, pp. 173–180.

Caswell, P. V., 1953, Geology of the Mombasa-Kwale area. Degree sheet 69: *Kenya Geol. Surv.*, Rept. 24.

Chaignau, M., Tazieff, H., and Fabre, R., 1960, Composition des gaz volcaniques du lac de lave permanent du Nyiragongo (Congo): *Acad. Clerm.-Ferrand Comptes rendus*, v. **250**, pp. 2482–2485. *Centre National de Volcanologie*.

Chirvinsky, P. N., Afanasyev, M. S., and Ushakova, Z. G., 1940, Massif of ultrabasic rocks at the Afrikanda railroad station on the Kola Peninsula: *Trans. Kola Base Akad. Nauk SSSR*, No. 5 (in Russian).

Christman, R. A., Brock, M. R., Pearson, R. C., and Singewald, Q. D., 1959, Geology and thorium deposits of the Wet Mountains, Colorado; A progress report: *U.S. Geol. Survey, Bull.*, **1072**-H, pp. 491–533.

Cissarz, A., 1931, Der gesteinsinhalt der schlotbreccie im gewann nonnensohl in der gemarkung oberschaffhausen, Kaisterstuhl: *Ges. Freiburg i. Br.*, v. **31**, pp. 273–286.

Coetzee, G. L., 1963, *The origin of the Sangu carbonate complex and associated rocks, Karema depression, Tanganyika Territory, East Africa:* Ph.D. thesis, Univ. of Wisconsin, U.S.A.

Coetzee, G. L. (in press), Carbonatites of the Karema Depression, Western Tanganyika: *Geol. Soc. S. Africa Trans.*

Coetzee, G. L., and Edwards, C. B., 1959, The Mrima Hill carbonatite, Coast Province, Kenya: *Geol. Soc. S. Africa Trans.*, v. **62**, pp. 373–397.

Combe, A. D., 1939, The Katwe–Kikorongo Area: *Uganda Geol. Surv., Ann. Rept.*, 1938, pp. 17–19.

Conradi, L. A., 1953, Utnytting av Søvemalmene: *Tiddskr. Kjemi Bergvesen og metall.*

Cox, K. G., Johnson, R. L., Monkman, L. J., Stillman, G. J., Vail, J. R., and Wood, D. N., 1965, The geology of the Nuanetsi igneous province: *Roy. Soc. London Phil. Trans.*, ser. *A.*, v. **257**, pp. 71–218.

Cox, K. G., Vail, J. R., Monkman, L. J., and Johnson, R. L., 1961, Karroo igneous activity and tectonics in south-east Southern Rhodesia: *Nature*, v. **190**, pp. 40–77.

Daly, R. A., 1910, Origin of the alkaline rocks: *Geol. Soc. America Bull.*, v. **21**, pp. 87–118.

Daly, R. A., 1914, *Igneous Rocks and Their Origin:* McGraw-Hill, New York.

Daly, R. A., 1925, Carbonate dikes of the Premier Diamond Mine, Transvaal: *Jour. Geol.*, v. **33**, pp. 659–684.

Daly, R. A., 1933, *Igneous rocks and the depths of the earth:* McGraw-Hill, New York.

Dana, E. S., 1886, On the brookite from Magnet Cove, Arkansas: *Am. Jour. Sci., 2nd ser.*, v. **32**, pp. 314–317.

Daub, R., 1912, Beiträge zur Kenntnis der Kontaktmineralien aus dem körnigen kalke des Kaiserstuhls: *Inaugural dissertation, Freiburg i. Br.*

Davidson, A., 1963, *A study of Okaite and related rocks near Oka, Quebec:* Unpubd, M.Sc. thesis, Univ. of British Columbia, Canada.

Davies, K. A., 1947, The phosphate deposits of the Eastern Province, Uganda: *Econ. Geology*, v. **42**, pp. 137–146.

Davies, K. A., 1952, The building of Mount Elgon (East Africa): *Uganda Geol. Surv., Mem.*, 7.

Davies, K. A., 1956, The geology of part of south-east Uganda with special reference to the alkaline complexes: *Uganda Geol. Surv., Mem.*, 8.

Davies, K. A., and Bisset, C. B., 1947, The geology of the mineral deposits of Uganda: *Imp. Inst. London, Bull.*, v. **45**, pp. 161–180.

Dawson, G. M., 1885, Physical and geological features of that portion of the Rocky Mountains between lat. 49° and 51° 31′; *Canada Geol. and Nat. Hist. Surv., Ann. Rept.*, 1, Pt. B.

Dawson, J. B., 1962a, Sodium carbonate lavas from Oldoinyo Lengai, Tanganyika: *Nature*, v. **195**, pp. 1075–1076.

Dawson, J. B., 1962b, The geology of Oldoinyo Lengai: *Bull. Volcanol.*, v. **24**, pp. 349–387.

Dawson, J. B., 1962c, Brief explanation of the geology—Quarter degree sheet 54, Monduli: *Tanganyika Geol. Surv.*, unpubd. rept. JBD 6.

Dawson, J. B., 1962d, Basutoland Kimberlites: *Geol. Soc. America Bull.*, v. **73**, pp. 545–559.

Dawson, J. B., 1964a, Reactivity of the cations in carbonate magmas: *Geol. Assoc. Canada Proc.*, v. **15**, pp. 103–113.

Dawson, J. B., 1964b, Carbonate tuff cones in northern Tanganyika: *Geol. Mag.*, v. **101**, pp. 129–137.

Dawson, J. B., 1964c, Carbonatitic volcanic ashes in northern Tanganyika: *Bull. Volcanol.*, v. **27**, pp. 1–11.

Dawson, J. B. (in press), The Kimberlite-carbonatite relationship: *Int. Mineral. Assoc.*, 1964 meeting, India.

Dawson, J. B., and Sahama, Th. G., 1963, A note on parawollastonite from Oldoinyo Lengai, Tanganyika: *Schweiz. Min. Petr. Mitt.*, v. **43**, pp. 131–133.

Deans, T., 1955, Carbonatite investigations in America: *Colon. Geol. and Min. Resources*, v. **5**, pp. 336–339.

Deans, T., 1964, Reply to a letter by Bailey in Nature: *Nature*, v. **201**, p. 599

Deans, T., and McConnell, J. D. C., 1955, Isokite $CaMgPO_4$ F, a new mineral from Northern Rhodesia: *Min. Mag.*, v. **30**, pp. 681–690.

Deans, T., Snelling, N. J., and Rapson, J. E. (in press), Strontium isotopes and trace elements in carbonatites and limestones from Ice River, British Columbia: *Nature*.

Denaeyer, M. E., 1960, Composition de la lave actuelle du Nyiragongo et de quelques laves similaires de ce volcan: *Acad. Roy. Sci. d'Outre Mer Bull.*, Bruxelles, v. **6**, pp. 999–1013.

Denaeyer, M. E., 1965, La rushayite lave ultrabasic nouvelle du Nyiragongo (Virunga, Afrique centrale): *Acad. Sci. Paris Comptes rendus*, v. **261**, pp. 2119–2122.

Denaeyer, M. E., and Tazieff, H., 1957, Nature de la lava actuelle et de quelques lavas plus anciennes de la caldere du Nyiragongo (Kivu): *Acad. Sci. Paris C.R.*, v. **244**, pp. 218–221.

Denaeyer, M. E., and van Wallendael, 1961, Les enclaves enallogènes du Nyiragongo et du Nyamuragira (Kivu) (Note préliminaire): *Bull. des scéances de l'A.R.S.O.M.*, v. **7**, pp. 460–467, *Centre National de Volcanologie*, No. 15.

Derby, O. A., 1887, On nepheline rocks in Brazil: *Geol. Soc. London Quart. Jour.*, v. **43**. pp. 445–473.

Derby, O. A., 1891a, On nepheline rocks in Brazil: *Geol. Soc. London Quart. Jour.*, v. **47**, pp. 251–265.

Derby, O. A., 1891b, Magnetite ore districts of Jacupiranga and Ipanema, São Paulo, Brazil: *Am. Jour. Sci.*, v. **41**, pp. 311–321.

Deutzmann, W., 1964, *Erzmikroskopische Untersuchungen an Gesteinen des Kaiserstuhls Breisgau:* EURATOM publication EUR, 1827, d, f, e, pp. 47–64.

Dias, M. de B., 1961, Geologia do Monte Muambe: *Estudos, notas and trabalhos dos Serv. de Geol. Minas. Bull.*, Mozambique, v. **27**, pp. 37–88.

Dixey, F., 1930, The Chilwa igneous complex: *Nyasaland Geol. Surv.*, Ann. Rept., 1929, p. 8.

Dixey, F., 1946, Carbonate pipes and ring structures: *Geol. Mag.*, v. **83**, pp. 289–291.

Dixey, F., Smith, W. C., and Bisset, C. B., 1937, revd. 1955, The Chilwa Series of Southern Nyasaland: *Nyasaland Geol. Surv., Bull.*, 5.

Dmitriev, Y. L., 1959, Metasomatic carbonate rocks of Mount Chavida: *Inst. Geol. Ore Deposits, Petrog., Mineralog. Geochem., Akad. Nauk. SSSR, pp.* 360–379 (in Russian).

Downie, C., and Wilkinson, P., 1962, The explosion craters of Basotu, Tanganyika Territory: *Bull. Volcanol.*, v. **24**, pp. 389–420.

DuBois, C. G. B., 1956, *The Geology of the Toror Hills, Central Karamoja, Uganda:* Ph.D. thesis, Univ. of London.

DuBois, C. G. B., 1959, The Toror Hills alkaline complex, Central Karamoja, Uganda: *Int. Geol. Congr., 20th sess., Assoc. Serv. géol. Africains*, pp. 303–308.

DuBois, C. G. B., Furst, J., Guest, N. J., and Jennings, D. J., 1963, Fresh natro carbonatite lava from Oldoinyo L'Engai, *Nature*, v. **197**, pp. 445–446.

Duffell, S., Maclaren, A. S., and Holman, R. H. C., 1963, Red Lake, Lansdowne House Area, Northwestern Ontario: *Canada Geol. Surv.*, Paper 63–65.

Du Toit, A. L., 1931, The genesis of the pyroxenite–apatite rocks of Palabora, eastern Transvaal: *Geol. Soc. S. Africa Trans.*, v. **34**, pp. 107–127.

Du Toit, A. L., 1954, *Geology of South Africa:* Oliver and Boyd, Edinburgh, 3rd. ed.

Ebbinge, H., and Krol, G. L., 1957, De niobium a houdende carbonatiet van Panda Hill, Tanganyika: *Ingenieur*, Amsterdam, v. **69**, p. 37.

v. Eckermann, H., 1928, Dikes belonging to the Alnö formation in the cuttings of the East Coast Railway: *Geol. Fören. Förh.*, v. **50**, pp. 381–412.

v. Eckermann, H., 1939a, The 'baddelyite from Alnö'—an error: *Min. Mag.*, v. **25**, pp. 413–414.

v. Eckermann, H., 1939b, De alkalina bergarternas genesis i belysning av nya forskningsrön från Alnön: *Geol. Fören. Förh.*, v. **61**, pp. 142–151.

v. Eckermann, H., 1942, Ett preliminärt meddelande om nya forskningsrön inom Alnö alkalina område: *Geol. Fören. Förh.*, v. **64**, pp. 399–415.

v. Eckermann, H., 1946, Alnö alkalina intrusionstektonik och genesis i belysning av dess gångbergarter: *Geol. Fören. Förh.*, v. **68**, pp. 115–119.

v. Eckermann, H., 1948a, The distribution of barium in the alkaline rocks and fenites of Alnö Island: *Int. Geol. Congr.*, *18th sess.*, Pt. 2, pp. 46–48.

v. Eckermann, H., 1948b, The process of nephelinization: *Int. Geol. Congr.*, *18th sess.*, Pt. 3, pp. 90–93.

v. Eckermann, H., 1948c, The genesis of the Alnö alkaline rocks: *Int. Geol. Congr.*, *18th sess.*, Pt. 3, pp. 94–101.

v. Eckermann, H., 1948d, The alkaline district of Alnö Island: *Sverig. Geol. Undersök.*, Ser. Ca. No. 36.

v. Eckermann, H., 1950, A comparison between the parageneses of Fennoscandian limestone minerals and those of the Alnö alkalic rocks, associated with carbonatites: *Min. Mag.*, v. **29**, pp. 304–312.

v. Eckermann, H., 1951, The distribution of barium and strontium in the rocks and minerals of the syenitic and alkaline rocks of Alnö Island: *Arkiv. f. Mineral. Geol.*, v. **1**, pp. 367–375.

v. Eckermann, H., 1958, The alkaline and carbonatitic dikes of the Alnö formation on the mainland north-west of Alnö Island: *kgl. Swenska Vedensk. Akad. Handl.*, Ser. 4. v. 7, No. 2.

v. Eckermann, H., 1960a, Borengite. A new ultrapotassic rock from Alnö Island: *Arkiv. f. Mineral. Geol.*, v. **2**, pp. 519–528.

v. Eckermann, H., 1960b, Boulders of volcanic breccia at the Salskar shoals north of Alnö Island: *Arkiv. f. Mineral. Geol.*, v. **2**, pp. 529–537.

v. Eckermann, H., 1960c, Contributions to the knowledge of the alkaline dikes of the Alnö region, I–III: *Arkiv. f. Mineral. Geol.*, v. **2**, pp. 539–550.

v. Eckermann, H., 1960d, The Alnö alkaline region: *Int. Geol. Congr.*, *21st sess.*, Guide to excursion No. C 27.

v. Eckermann, H., 1961a, Contributions to the knowledge of the alkaline dikes of the Alnö region, IV: *Arkiv. f. Mineral. Geol.*, v. **3**, pp. 65–68.

v. Eckermann, H., 1961b, The petrogenesis of the Alnö alkaline rocks: *Geol. Inst. Uppsala Bull.*, v. **40**, pp. 25–36.

v. Eckermann, H., 1961c, The decomposition of Alnö alkaline dikes by percolating water: *Comptes Rendus de la Soc. de Finlande*, No. 33, pp. 244–254.

v. Eckermann, H., 1962, The economic geology of columbium (niobium) and of tantalum: *Econ. Geology*, v. **57**, p. 1133.

v. Eckermann, H., 1963a, Contributions to the knowledge of the alkaline dikes of the Alnö region V–VIII: *Arkiv. f. Mineral. Geol.*, v. **3**, pp. 259–275.

v. Eckermann, H., 1963b, Contributions to the knowledge of the alkaline dikes of the Alnö region: IX: *Arkiv. f. Mineral. Geol.*, v. **3**, pp. 397–402.

v. Eckermann, H., 1963c, Contributions to the knowledge of the alkaline dikes of the Alnö region X: *Arkiv. f. Mineral. Geol.*, v. **3**, pp. 403–406.

v. Eckermann, H., 1964a, Distribution of radioactivity in minerals and rocks of the Alnö alkaline area: *Arkiv. f. Mineral. Geol.*, v. **3**, pp. 479–488.

v. Eckermann, H., 1964b, Contributions to the knowledge of the alkaline dikes of the Alnö region XI–XII: *Arkiv. f. Mineral. Geol.*, v. **3**, pp. 521–535.

v. Eckermann, H. (in press), The pyroxenes of the Alnö carbonatite (sövite) and of the surrounding fenite: *Int. Mineral Assoc.*, 1964 meeting, India.

v. Eckermann, H., v. Ubisch, H., and Wickman, F. E., 1952, A preliminary investigation into the isotopic composition of carbon from alkaline intrusions: *Geochim. et Cosmochim. Acta*, v. **2**, pp. 207–210.

v. Eckermann, H., and Wickman, F. E., 1956, A preliminary determination of the maximum age of the Alnö rocks: *Geol. Fören. Förh.*, v. **78**, pp. 122–124.

Egorov, L. S., 1957, New carbonatite discoveries to the north of the Siberian Platform: *Inf. Bull. Inst. Geol. Arctic.*, No. 4 (in Russian).

Egorov, L. S., 1960a, The problem of nephelinization and iron-magnesium–calcium metasomatism in intrusions of alkaline and ultrabasic rocks: *Inst. Geol. Arctic.*, v. **114**, No. 14 (in Russian).

Egorov, L. S., 1960b, On the types of carbonatite deposits and their association with massifs of ultrabasic alkaline rocks: *Izvest. Akad. Nauk SSSR. Geol. Ser.*, No. 1, 1960, pp. 108–111 (in Russian).

Egorov, L. S., 1964, On the origin of carbonatites: *Izvest. Akad. Nauk SSSR. Geol. Ser.*, pp. 63–74 (in Russian).

Egorov, L. S., Goltburt, T. L., and Shikhoria, K. M., 1959, On the shape and mechanism of formation of the Gulinski intrusion: *Inst. Geol. Arctic.*, v. **107**, No. 12 (in Russian).

Egorov, L. S., and Surina, N. P., 1958, First discovery of carbonatites in sedimentary carbonate rocks: *Inf. Bull. Sci. Res. Inst. Geol. Arctic.*, No. 12 (in Russian).

Egorov, L. S., and Surina, N. P., 1961, Carbonatites from the region of the Changit intrusion to the north of the Siberian Platform: *Inst. Geol. Arctic.*, v. **125**, No. 17 (in Russian).

Eichstädt, Fr., 1884, Anomit från Alnö, Vesternorrlands Län: *Geol. Fören. Förh.*, v. **7**, pp. 194–196.

Eigenfeld, R., 1948, Über das Verhältnis des Marmors im zentralen Kaiserstuhl zum Eruptivgestein: *Mitt. Bl. bad. geol. Landesanst.*, pp. 36–39.

Eigenfeld, R., 1954, Zur genese von alkaligesteinen: *Ber. phys.-med. Ges. Würsburg*, v. **66**, pp. 95–115.

El-Hinnawi, Essam, E., 1964, Petrochemical characters of African volcanic rocks. Part II. East Africa: *Neues Jb. f. Min.*, v. **6**, pp. 166–187.

Eliseev, N. A., 1958, Afrikanda massif: in *Geology of the USSR*, v. **28**, pt. 1, *Murmansk District*, Moscow–Leningrad (in Russian).

Elyanov, A. A., 1961, Some characteristics of the carbonatites of the Konderski intrusive massif: VAGT, No. 7 (in Russian).

Emeleus, C. H., 1964, The Grønnedal–Ika complex, South Greenland. The structure and geological history of the complex: *Medd. om Grønland*, v. **172**, No. 3.

Epshtein, E. M., 1959, Carbonatites and their structural position in the Gulinski pluton: *Inst. Geol. Arctic.*, v. **107**, pp. 13–22 (in Russian).

Epshtein, E. M., Anikeeva, L. J., and Mikhailova, A. F., 1961, Metasomatic rocks and the phlogopite content of the Gulinski intrusion: *Inst. Geol. Arctic.*, v. **120** (in Russian).

Erickson, R. L., and Blade, L. V., 1963, Geochemistry and petrology of the alkalic igneous complex at Magnet Cove, Arkansas: *U.S. Geol. Surv.*, Prof. Paper 425.

Eskova, E. M., and Ganzeev, A. A., 1963, Variations in rare earth assemblages in pyrochlore from the Vishnevyye Mountains: *Geokhimiya*, No. 9, pp. 859–863 (in Russian), *Geochemistry*, v. **9**, pp. 891–896 (English transl.).

Faul, H., Eldmore, P. L. D., and Brannock, W. W., 1959, Age of the Fen carbonatite (Norway) and its relation to the Oslo region: *Geochim. Cosmochim. Acta.*, v. **17**, pp. 153–156.

Fawley, A. P., and James, T. C., 1955, A pyrochlore (columbium) carbonatite, southern Tanganyika: *Econ. Geology*, v. **50**, pp. 571–585.

Fick, L. J., and Van der Heyde, C., 1959, Additional data on the geology of the Mbeya carbonatite: *Econ. Geology*, v. **54**, pp. 842–872.

Fischer, R. P., 1945, The niobium deposit in the Kaiserstuhl: *Joint Intelligence Objectives Agency*, Rept. 16, Washington.

Florovskaya, V. N., 1939, On the mineralogy of the Knopite deposit of Afrikanda: *Zapiski Vses. Mineralog.*, v. **68**, pp. 562–574 (in Russian).

Fockema, R. A. P., 1953, The geology of the area around the confluence of the Elands and Crocodile Rivers: *Geol. Soc. S. Africa Trans.*, v. **55**, pp. 155–171.

Forster, I. F., 1958, Paragenetical ore mineralogy of the Loolekop–Phalaborwa carbonatite complex. Eastern Transvaal: *Geol. Soc. S. Africa*, v. **61**, pp. 359–363.

Foshag, W. F., 1923, Catapleiite from Magnet Cove, Arkansas: *Am. Mineralogist*, v. **8**, pp. 70–72.

Fozzard, P. M. H., 1958, Further notes on the volcanic rocks from Igwisi: *Tanganyika Geol. Surv.*, Rec. for 1956, v. **6**, pp. 69–75.

Freitas de, A. J., 1959, *A geologia de Mozambique*: Lourenzo Marques.

Franz, G. W., 1965, *Melting relationships in the system* $CaO–MgO–SiO_2–CO_2–H_2O$: *A Study of Synthetic Kimberlites:* Ph.D. thesis, Pennsylvania State University, U.S.A.

Franz, G. W., and Wyllie, P. J., 1966, Melting relationships in the system $CaO–MgO–SiO_2–SiO_2–H_2O$ at 1 kilobar pressure: *Geochim. et Cosmochim Acta*, v. **30**, pp. 9–22.

Frolov, A. A., 1960, Some questions on the detailed geological structural study of carbonatites: *Geology of Ore Deposits*, v. **5**, pp. 82–93 (in Russian).

Frolov, A. A., and Epshtein, E. M., 1962, Geological structure of carbonatite massifs: in the symposium, *Geology of Rare Element Deposits*, issue 17 (in Russian).

Fryklund, V. C., Jr., 1949, *The Titanium Ore Deposits of Magnet Cove, Hot Spring County, Arkansas:* Ph.D. thesis, Univ. of Minnesota.

Fryklund, V. C., Jr., Harner, R. S., and Kaiser, E. P., 1954, Niobium (columbium) and titanium at Magnet Cove and Potash Sulphur Springs, Arkansas: *U.S. Geol. Surv. Bull.*, 1015–B, pp. 23–56.

Fryklund, V. C., Jr., and Holbrook, D. F., 1950, Titanium ore deposits of Hot Spring County, Arkansas: *Arkansas Resources and Develop. Comm., Div. Geol. Bull.*, 16.

Furon, R., and Lombard, J., 1964, Geological Map of Africa (1/5,000,000) with explanatory note: *UNESCO* and *Assoc. Serv. Géol. Arricains*, Paris.*

Gaidukova, V. S., 1960, Columbite and fersmite after pyrochlore: *Zapiski. Vses. Mineralog.* v. **89**, pp. 460–464 (in Russian).

Gaidukova, V. S., and Zdorik, T. B., 1962, Minerals of rare elements in carbonatites: *Geology of Rare Element Deposits*, No. 17 (in Russian).

Garson, M. S., 1953a, The geology of Chilwa Island: *Nyasaland Geol. Surv., Ann. Rept.*, 1952, pp. 6–10.

Garson, M. S., 1953b, A note on the Nkalonje Vent, part map sheet 44/1: *Nyasaland Geol. Surv., Ann. Rept.*, 1952, pp. 21–22.

Garson, M. S., 1954, Investigation of carbonatites, Mlanje District: *Nyasaland Geol. Surv., Ann. Rept.*, 1953, p. 6.

Garson, M. S., 1955a, Flow phenomena in carbonatites in southern Nyasaland: *Colonial Geol. and Mineral Resources*, v. **5**, pp. 311–318.

Garson, M. S., 1955b, Investigation of carbonatites and new ring structures: *Nyasaland Geol. Surv., Ann. Rept.*, 1954, pp. 7–9.

Garson, M. S., 1956, Manganiferous rocks in Nyasaland: *Int. Geol. Congr., 20th sess., Manganese symposium*, v. **2**, Africa.

Garson, M. S., 1958, Investigation of carbonatites and ring structures: *Nyasaland Geol. Surv., Ann. Rept.*, 1957, pp. 7–11.

Garson, M. S., 1959a, Stress pattern of carbonatite and alkaline dikes at Tundulu ring structure, southern Nyasaland: *Int. Geol. Congr., 20th sess., Assoc. Serv. geol. Africains*, pp. 309–323.

Garson, M. S., 1959b, Investigation of carbonatites and ring structures: *Nyasaland Geol. Surv., Ann. Rept.*, 1958, pp. 9–13.

Garson, M. S., 1960, The geology of the Lake Chilwa area: *Nyasaland Geol. Surv., Bull.* **12**.

* The locations of carbonatite complexes in eastern and southern Africa supplied by Overseas Geological Surveys in London have been combined by the editors of the map with non-carbonatite alkaline complexes in some countries and with unconfirmed complexes in Ethiopia to produce a somewhat confused picture of carbonatite distribution.

Garson, M. S., 1961a, The geology of the Namangali Vent, Mlanje District: *Nyasaland Geol. Surv., Rec.*, 1959, v. **1**, pp. 51–62.

Garson, M. S., 1961b, *The Tundulu Carbonatite Ring Complex in Southern Nyasaland:* Ph.D. thesis, Univ. of Leeds, England.

Garson, M. S., 1962, The Tundulu carbonatite ring complex in southern Nyasaland: *Nyasaland Geol. Surv., Mem.* **2**.

Garson, M. S., 1963, The geology of the Nkalonje area, Mlanje District: *Nyasaland Geol. Surv., Rec.*, 1960, v. **2**, pp. 91–110.

Garson, M. S., 1965b, Carbonatite and agglomerate vents of the western Shire Valley: *Malawi Geol. Surv., Mem.* **3**.

Garson, M. S., 1965a, The geology of the area west of Lake Malombe, Fort Johnston, District: *Malawi Geol. Surv. Rec.*, 1961, v. **3**.

Garson, M. S., 1965c, Carbonatites in southern Malawi: *Malawi Geol. Surv., Bull.* 15.

Garson, M. S., and Smith, W. C., 1958, Chilwa Island: *Nyasaland Geol. Surv., Mem.* **1**.

Geijer, P., 1922, Problems suggested by the igneous rocks of Jotnian and Sub-Jotnian age: *Geol. Fören. Förh.*, v. **44**, pp. 411–443.

Geijer, P., 1928, Alnöitic dikes from the coast-region of Luleå and Kalix in northern Sweden: *Fennia*, v. **50**, No. 11.

Gellatly, D. C., 1962, A preliminary note on the Darkainle alkaline complex, Borama District, Somali Republic: *Univ. of Leeds Res. Inst. African Geol.*, 6th Ann. Rept., 1960–1961, pp. 22–23.

Gellatly, D. C., 1963a, *The Geology of The Darkainle Nepheline Syenite Complex, Borama District, Somali Republic:* Ph.D. thesis, Univ. of Leeds, England.

Gellatly, D. C., 1963b, Carbonatites of the Darkainle alkaline complex, Somali Republic: *Univ. of Leeds Res. Inst. African Geol.*, 7th Ann. Rept., 1961–1962, pp. 15–16.

Gellatly, D. C., 1964, Nepheline and feldspar orientations in nepheline syenites from Darkainle, Somali Republic: *Am. Jour. Sci.*, v. **262**, pp. 635–642.

Gerling, E. K., and Starik, I. E., 1942, Age of pyroxenite intrusions of Afrikanda and Ozernaya Varaka in the Kola Peninsula: *Doklady Akad. Nauk SSSR, Geol. Ser.*, v. **35**, pp. 153–154 (in English).

Gevers, T. W., 1949, Vermiculite at Lookekop, Palabora, North East Transvaal: *Geol. Soc. S. Africa Trans.*, v. **51**, pp. 133–173.

Gill, J. E., and Owens, O. E., 1957, Columbium–uranium deposits at North Bay, Ontario: *Canadian Inst. Min. Met., Trans.*, v. **60**, pp. 244–250.

Ginzburg, A. I., Nechaeva, E. A., Lavrenev, Yu. B., and Pozharitskaya, L. K., 1958, *Geology of Rare Element Deposits*, v. **1**, Rare Metal Carbonatites: Vims. Gosgeoltekhizdat, Moscow (in Russian).

Gittins, J., and Tuttle, O. F., 1964, The system CaF_2–$Ca(OH)_2$–$CaCO_3$: *Am. Jour. Sci.*, v. **262**, pp. 66–75.

Gittins, J., and Tuttle, O. F. (in press), Further evidence for the existence of carbonate liquids: *Canadian Mineralogist.*

Glagolev, A. A., 1962, Example of metasomatic zoning around the apatite-magnetite rocks and the carbonatites: *Doklady Akad. Nauk SSSR, Geol. Ser.*, v. **147**, No. 3 (in Russian).

Glass, J. J., 1937, Sodalite from Magnet Cove, Arkansas: *Washington Acad. Sci. Jour.*, v. **27**.

Gold, D. P., 1962, The Oka complex: *54th New England Inter-collegiate Geological Congress Guide Book, Montreal Meeting*, pp. 7–14.

Gold, D. P., 1963a, *The Relationship Between The Limestone and The Alkaline Igneous Rocks of Oka and St.-Hilaire, Quebec:* Ph.D. thesis, McGill Univ., Canada.

Gold, D. P., 1963b, Average chemical composition of carbonatites: *Econ. Geology*, v. **58**, pp. 988–991.

Gold, D. P. (in press a), The average chemical composition of carbonatites: *Int. Min. Assoc.*, 1964 meeting, India.

Gold, D. P. (in press b), Minerals from the Oka alkaline complex, near Montreal, Quebec, Canada: *Int. Min. Assoc.*, 1964 meeting, India.

Goldsmith, J. R., Graf, D. L., Witters, J., and Northrop, D. A., 1962, Studies in the system $CaCO_3$–$MgCO_3$–$FeCO_3$: *Jour. Geology*, v. **70**, pp. 659–688.

Goldsmith, J. R., and Heard, H. C., 1961, Sub-solidus phase relationships in the system $CaCO_3$–$MgCO_3$: *Jour. Geology*, v. **69**, pp. 45–74.

Gonfiantini, R., and Tongiorgi, E., 1964, *Composition isotopique des carbonatites du Kaiserstuhl:* EURATOM publication EUR, 1827, d, f, e, pp. 193–199.

Graeff, F., 1892, Zur geologie des Kaiserstuhlgebirges: *Mitteil. d. Bad. Geol. Landesant.*, v. **2**, p. 455.

Graeff, F., 1900, Petrographische und geologische notizen aus dem Kaiserstuhl: *Ber. ü. d., Vers. d. oberhein. geol. vereins, in Denausschingen*, v. **33**, pp. 50–51.

Graham, A. R., 1955, Cerianite, CeO_2 a new rare earth oxide mineral: *Am. Mineralogist*, v. **40**, pp. 560–564.

Gregory, J. W., 1921, *The rift valleys and geology of East Africa*: London, Seeley, Service and Co.

Groenveld, D. (no date), The geological environment of the copper deposits of the Union of South Africa: *CCTA*, No. 44, pp. 223–248.

Gruss, K., 1905, Beiträge zur kenntnis der gesteine des Kaiserstuhlgebirges. Tephritische stromund ganggesteine: *Mitteil. d. Bad. Geol. Landesant.*, v. **4**, p. 85.

Guest, N. J., 1953, *The geology and petrology of the Engaruka–Oldoinyo L'Engai–Lake Natron Area of Northern Tanganyika:* Ph.D. thesis, Sheffield Univ., England.

Guest, N. J., 1956, The volcanic activity of Oldoinyo L'Engai, 1954: *Tanganyika Geol. Surv., Rec. for 1954*, v. **4**, pp. 56–59.

Guest, N. J., 1963, Description of exhibit of fresh 'natro-carbonatite' from Oldoinyo Lengai, Tanganyika: *Geol. Soc. London Proc.*, No. 1606, pp. 54–57.

Guest, N. J., and Leedal, G. P., 1956, The volcanic activity of Mount Meru: *Tanganyika Geol. Surv., Rec. for 1953*, v. **3**, pp. 40–46.

Guillet, G. R., 1962, Vermiculite in Ontario: *Ontario Dept. Mines, Ind. Min. Rept.* **7**, pp. 18–20.

Guimaraes, D., 1925, Estudo de algumas rochas relacionadas com as fontes minerais de Araxá e outras: *Serv. Geol. & Min. do. Brasil, Bull.* **9**, Rio de Janeiro.

Guimaraes, D., 1946, Nota preliminar sobre a jazida de Barreiro, Munícípio de Araxá, Minas Gerais: *Inst. Tecnol. Industrial, Avulso* 2, Belo Horizonte.

Guimaraes, D., 1957, Relatório sobre a jazida de picocloro de Barreiro, Araxá. Minas Gerais: *Dep. Nac. Prod. Min. Bull.* **103**, Belo Horizonte.

Haanel, B. F., 1909, *Summary Report for 1909:* Mines Branch, Canada Dept. Mines, pp. 110–111.

Hall, A. L., 1912, The crystalline metamorphic limestone of Lulu Kop: *Geol. Soc. S. Africa Trans.*, v. **15**, pp. 18–25.

Hamilton, E. I., 1964, Reply to letter by Bailey in Nature: *Nature*, v. **201**, p. 599.

Hamilton, E. I., and Deans, T., 1963, Isotopic composition of strontium in some African carbonatites and limestone and in strontium minerals: *Nature*, v. **198**, pp. 776–777.

Hanekona, H. J., van Staden, C. M. v. H., Smit, P. J., and Pike D. R., 1965, The geology of the Palabora igneous complex: *S. Africa Geol. Surv., Mem.* **54**.

Harding, W. D., 1950, *Preliminary Report on the Geology along the Mississagi Road:* Ontario Dept. Mines, 1950–1956.

Harker, A., 1902, Reviews of papers on Magnet Cove, Arkansas: *Geol. Mag.*, v. **9**, pp. 177–180.

Harker, A., 1909, *The Natural History of Igneous Rocks:* Macmillan, New York.

Harker, R. I., and Tuttle, O. F., 1955, Studies in the system CaO–MgO–CO_2. Part I. The thermal dissociation of calcite, dolomite and magnesite: *Am. Jour. Sci.*, v. **253**, p. 209.

Harkin, D. A., 1956, The Rungwe volcanics: *Tanganyika Geol. Surv., Rec., for 1954*, v. **4**, p. 13.

Harkin, D. A., 1960, The Rungwe volcanics: *Tanganyika Geol. Surv., Mem.* **2**.

Harris, P. M., 1965, Pandaite from the Mrima Hill niobium deposit (Kenya): *Mineralog. Mag.*, v. **35**, pp. 277–290.

Hayatsu, A., York, D., Farquar, R. M., and Gittins, J., 1965, The significance of Sr isotope ratios in theories of carbonatite genesis: *Nature*, v. **207**, pp. 625–626.

Hedlund, D. C., and Olson, J. C., 1961, Four environments of thorium-, niobium-, and rare-earth-bearing minerals in the Powderhorn district of Southwestern Colorado: *U.S. Geol. Surv.*, Prof. Paper. 424 B, pp. 283–286.

Heier, K. S., 1961, Layered gabbro, hornblendite, carbonatite and nepheline syenite on Stjernøy, North Norway: *Norsk. geol. tidsskr.*, v. **41**, pp. 109–155.

Heier, K. S., 1962, A note on the U, Th and K contents in the nepheline syenite and carbonatite on Stjernøy, North Norway: *Norsk. geol. tidsskr.*, v. **42**, pp. 287–292.

Heier, K. S., 1964, Geochemistry of the nepheline syenite on Stjernøy, North Norway: *Norsk. geol. tiddskr.*, v. **44**, pp. 205–215.

Heinrich, E. W., 1958, *Mineralogy and Geology of Radioactive Raw Materials*: McGraw-Hill, New York.

Heinrich, E. W., and Anderson, R. J., 1965, Carbonatites and alkalic rocks of the Arkansas River area, Fremont County, Colorado 2. Fetid gas from carbonatite and related rocks: *Am. Mineralogist*, v. **50**, pp. 1914–1920.

Heinrich, E. W., and Dahlem, D. H. (in press), Carbonatites and alkalic rocks of the Arkansas River area, Fremont County, Colorado 1. General Features: *Int. Min. Assoc.*, 1964 meeting, India.

Heinrich, E. W., and Levinson, A. A., 1961, Carbonatic niobium–rare earth deposits, Ravalli Co., Montana: *Am. Mineralogist*, v. **46**, pp. 1424–1447.

Heinrich, E. W., (in press), *The Geology of Carbonatites*: Rand McNally, New York.

Herman, P., Wanderstrappen, R., and Hubaux, A., 1960, Sublimés du Nyiragongo (Kivu): *Bull. des scéances de l'A.R.S.O.M.*, v. **6**, pp. 961–971, *Centre National de Volcanologie*, No. 12.

Hewitt, D. F., 1961, Nepheline syenite deposits of southern Ontario: *Ontario Dept. Mines, Ann. Rept.*, v. **69**, Pt. 8.

Higazy, R. A., 1954, Trace elements of volcanic and ultrabasic potassic rocks of southwestern Uganda and adjoining parts of the Belgian Congo: *Geol. Soc. America Bull.*, v. **65**, pp. 39–70.

Hobley, C. W., 1918, A volcanic eruption in East Africa: *East Africa Nat. Hist. Soc. Jour.*, v. **6**, pp. 339–343.

Hodder, R. W., 1958, Alkaline rocks and niobium deposits near Nemegos, Ontario: *Canada, Geol. Surv.*, Paper 57–58.

Hodder, R. W., 1959, *Alkaline Rocks and Niobium Deposits near Nemegos, Ontario:* Ph.D. thesis, Univ. of California, Berkely, U.S.A.

Högbom, A. G., 1892, Syenitområdet på Alnön: *Geol. Fören. Förh.*, v. **14**, pp. 15–19.

Högbom, A. G., 1895, Uber das nephelinsyenit auf der Insel Alnö: *Geol. Fören. Förh.*, v. **17**, pp. 100–160, 214–256.

Högbom, A. G., 1909, The igneous rocks of Ragunda, Alnö, Rödö, and Nordingrå: *Geol. Fören, Förh.*, v. **31**, pp. 356–364.

Högbom, A. G., 1910, Precambrian geology of Sweden: *Geol. Inst. Upsala Bull.*, v. **10**, pp. 1–80.

Holbrook, D. F., 1947, A brookite deposit in Hot Spring County, Arkansas: *Arkansas Resources and Devel. Comm., Div. Geol., Bull.* 11.

Holbrook, D. F., 1948, Molybdenum in Magnet Cove, Arkansas: *Arkansas Resources and Devel. Comm., Div. Geol., Bull.* 12.

Holland, S. S., 1955, Lonnie property: *British Columbia, Rept. Minister Mines for 1954*, pp. 96–97.

Holmes, A., 1950, Petrogenesis of Katungite and its associates: *Am. Mineralogist*, v. **35**, pp. 772–792.

Holmes, A., 1952, The potash–ankaratrite–melaleucitite lavas of Nabugando and Mbuga craters, south-west Uganda: *Geol. Soc. Edinburgh Trans.*, v. **15**, Campbell Volume, pp. 187–213.

Holmes, A., 1956, The ejectamenta of Katwe crater, south-west Uganda: *Verh. konink. Nederland Geol. Mijnbouw, Genootschap, Geol. Ser.*, v. **16**, Brouwer Volume, pp. 139–166.

Holmes, A., 1958, Spitskop carbonatite, Eastern Transvaal: *Geol. Soc. America Bull.*, v. **69**, pp. 1525–1526.

Holmes, A., and Harwood, H. F., 1932, Petrology of the volcanic fields east and south-east of Ruwenzori, Uganda: *Geol. Soc. London Quart. Jour.*, v. **88**, pp. 370–442.

Holmquist, P. J., 1893, Pyrochlor från Alnön: *Geol. Fören. Förh.*, pp. 588–606.

Holmquist, P. J., 1894, Knopit, ett perowskit närstående, nytt mineral från Alnön: *Geol. Fören. Förh.*, v. **16**, pp. 73–95.

Holmquist, P. J., 1896, Synthetische studien über die perowskit und pyrochlormineralien: *Geol. Inst. Univ. Upsala Bull.*, v. **111**, pp. 181–260.

Holt, D. N., 1965, The Kangankunde rare earth prospect: *Malawi Geol. Surv., Bull.* **20**.

Horne, R. G., 1961, Nachendezwaya carbonatite: *Tanganyika Geol. Surv., Rec. for 1959*, v. **9**, pp. 37–39.

Howard, W. V., 1922, Some outliers of the Monteregian Hills: *Roy. Soc. Canada, Trans. ser. 3*, v. **16**, sec. 4, pp. 47–95.

Hubaux, A., 1964, *Structure des Carbonatites de Schelingen:* EURATOM publication EUR, 1827, d, f, e, pp. 31–35.

Hugel, E., 1912, Uber den dysanalyt von Vogtsburg in Kaiserstuhl: *Inaugural dissertation*, Freiburg i. Br., v. **54S**.

Hughson, M. R., and Sen Gupta, J. G., 1964, A thorium intermediate member of the britholite–apatite series: *Am. Mineralogist*, v. **49**, pp. 937–951.

Hussak, E., 1892, Ueber Brazilit, ein neues tantal (niob) mineral von der Eisenmine Jacupiranga: *Neues Jb. f. Min.*, v. **2**, pp. 141–159.

Hussak, E., 1895, Ueber den baddelyit (syn. brazilit) von der Eisenmine in Jacupiranga in São Paulo: *Tschermak's Min. Petr. Mitt.*, pp. 395–411.

Hussak, E., 1898, Uber ein neues vorkommen von baddeleyit als accessorischer gemengtheil der jacupirangitähnlichen basischen ausscheidungen des nephelinsyenits von Alnö, Schweden: *Neues Jb. f. Min.*, v. **2**, pp. 228–229.

Hussak, E., 1904, Ueber die microstruktur einiger brasilianischer titanmagneteisensteine: *Neues Jb. f. Min.*, v. **1**, pp. 94–113.

Hytönen, K., 1959, On the petrology and mineralogy of some alkaline volcanic rocks of Toror Hills, Mt. Moroto, and Morulinga, north-eastern Uganda: *Comm. Geol. Finlande Bull.*, v. **184**, pp. 75–132.

Ivanov, A. I., 1959, Basic features of the history of magmatic development of Tuva: *Soviet Geology*, v. **11** (in Russian).

Ivanova, T. N., and Safronov, V. P., 1959, The contact-metasomatic change of gabbro-dolerite, melilite rocks, and ijolite-melteigite of the Nemakit massif (right bank of the Kotui River): *Inst. Geol. Arctic.*, v. **65**, No. 13 (in Russian).

Ivensen, Y. P., 1941, On the alkaline rocks of the Kovdorozero region of the Kola Peninsula: *Doklady Akad. Nauk SSSR*, v. **30**, pp. 337–339 (in English).

Jäger, E., Niggli, E., and van der Veen, A. H., 1959, A hydrated barium–strontium pyrochlore in a biotite rock from Panda Hill, Tanganyika: *Mineralog. Mag.*, v. **32**, pp. 10–25.

James, T. C., 1953, An interim report on recent investigations in the Northern and Central Provinces: *Tanganyika Geol. Surv.*, unpubd. rept. TCJ/18.

James, T. C., 1956a, An occurrence of carbonatite at Maji ya Weta Hill, Morogoro District: *Tanganyika Geol. Surv., Rec. for 1953*, v. **3**, p. 31.

James, T. C., 1956b, Carbonatite investigations: *Tanganyika Geol. Surv., Rec. for 1954*, v. **4**, p. 20.

James, T. C., 1956c, Carbonatites and rift valleys in East Africa: *Tanganyika Geol. Surv.*, unpubd. rept. TCJ/34. Also *Int. Geol. Congr., 20th sess.* (abstract only). Sometimes referred to as James, T. C., 1959, *Int. Geol. Congr., 20th sess., Assoc. des Serv. Geol. Africains*, p. 325.

James, T. C., 1956d, Niobium, salt and natural gas deposits in northern Tanganyika: *Tanganyika Geol. Surv., Rec. for 1953*, v. **3**, pp. 17–20.

James, T. C., 1958a, Carbonatite investigation: a progress report: *Tanganyika Geol. Surv., Rec. for 1965*, v. **6**, p. 45.

James, T. C., 1958b, Summary of silicate rocks associated with carbonatite bodies in Tanganyika: *Tanganyika Geol. Surv.*, unpubd. typescript; also *CCTA* east-central, west-central and southern reg. comm., *Geology*, Leopoldville, 1958, pp. 307–308 (summary only).

James, T. C., and McKie, D., 1958, The alteration of pyrochlore to columbite in carbonatite in Tanganyika: *Mineralog. Mag.*, v. **31**, pp. 889–900.

Janse, A. J. A., 1962, Geology and petrology of the Gibeon kimberlite province and the Gross Brukkaros Mountain: *Univ. of Leeds Res. Inst. African Geol., 6th Ann. Rept., 1960–1961*, pp. 18–20.

Janse, A. J. A., 1963, Progress report on the geology and petrology of the Gibeon kimberlite province and the Gross Brukkaros Mountain: *Univ. of Leeds Res. Inst. African Geol., 7th Ann. Rept., 1961–1962*, pp. 17–19, 67.

Janse, A. J. A., 1964, Monticellite–peridotite from Mt. Brukkaros, South West Africa: *Univ. of Leeds Res. Inst. African Geol., 8th Ann. Rept.,* 1962–1963, pp. 21–24.

Jérémine, E., 1949, Études pétrographiques des roches éruptives et métamorphiques du massif de Bou Agrao: *Notes Serv. Géol. Maroc.*, v. **74**, pp. 119–147.

Jérémine, E., 1950, Sur quelques minéraux des syénites néphéliniques de Bou Agrao (Bou Aougra), Haut Atlas, Maroc: *Acad. Sci. Paris Comptes rendus*, v. **250**, pp. 110–111.

Jérémine, E., and Dubar, G., 1947, Note sur les syénites néphéliniques à eudialyte du massif éruptif du Bou Agrao (Haut Atlas, Maroc): *Acad. Sci. Paris Comptes rendus*, v. **224**, pp. 1022–1023.

Johannsen, A., 1931, *A descriptive petrography of the igneous rocks*, vol. 1, Introduction, textures, classifications and glossary: Univ. of Chicago Press, Chicago.

Johnson, R. L., 1961, The geology of the Dorowa and Shawa carbonatite complexes, Southern Rhodesia: *Geol. Soc. S. Africa Trans.*, v. **64**, pp. 101–145.

Jones, W. C., 1955, *Geology of the Garnet Mountain–Aquila Ridge area, Ice River, British Columbia:* M.Sc. thesis, Univ. of British Columbia, Canada.

Keller, F., Jr., and Henderson, J. R., 1949, Total intensity aeromagnetic map of Magnet Cove area, Hot Springs County, Arkansas: *U.S. Geol. Surv.*, Geophys. Inv., Prelim. Map.

Keller, J., 1964, Zur vulkanologie des Burkheim-Sponeck-Gebietes in westlichen Kaiserstuhl: *Ber naturforsch. Ges. Freiburg i. Br.*, v. **54**, pp. 107–130.

Kent, P. E., 1944, Age and tectonic relations of East African volcanic rocks: *Geol. Mag.*, v. **81**, pp. 15–25.

Khitarov, N. I., and Malinin, S. D., 1958, Phase equilibrium in the system CO_2–H_2O: *Geokhimiya*, v. **7** (in Russian).

Kiefer, H., 1932, Das alter der kontaktmetamorphen kalke im zentralen Kaiserstuhl: *Fortschr. Geol. Paläont.*, v. **11**, pp. 461–501.

King, B. C., 1949, The Napak area of southern Karamoja, Uganda: *Uganda Geol. Surv., Mem.* 5.

King, B. C., 1965, Petrogenesis of the alkaline igneous rock suites of the volcanic and intrusive centres of eastern Uganda: *Jour. Petrology*, v. **6**, pp. 67–100.

King, B. C., and Sutherland, D. S., 1960, Alkaline rocks of eastern and southern Africa, parts I–III: *Sci. Progress*, v. **48**, pp. 298–321, 504–524, 709–720.

Kinney, D. M., 1949, The Magnet Cove rutile company mine: *U.S. Geol. Surv.*, open file report.

Kirilov, A. S., and Rylov, V. S., 1963, Origin of magnesium in carbonatites: *Zap. Vses. Mineralog.*, v. **92**, pp. 228–231 (in Russian).

Knecht, T., 1934, Os minerais e minérios do Estado de São Paulo: *Bol. de Agricultura*, ser. 32, pp. 237–323.

Knecht, T., 1939, As ocorrencias de minérios de ferro e pirita no Estado de São Paulo: *Inst. Geogr. Geol. Bol.*, São Paulo, No. 25.

Knecht, T., 1940, Os minérais nao metálicos do Estado de São Paulo: *Inst. Geogr. Geol. Bol.*, São Paulo, No. 27.

Knecht, T., 1948, Novas ocorrencias nos municipos do Extremo Sudveste Paulista: *Min. e Met.*, Rio de Janeiro, v. **13**, No. 73.

Knecht, T., and Felicissimo Junior, J., 1939, Jazida de magnetita do Morro do Serrote: *Inst. Geogr. Geol. Bol.*, São Paulo, v. **23**.

Knorring, O. von., 1962, Geochemical characteristics of carbonatites: *Nature*, v. **194**, pp. 860–861.

Knorring, O. von., and DuBois, C. G. B., 1961, Carbonatitic lava from Fort Portal area in western Uganda: *Nature*, v. **192**, pp. 1064–1065.

Kolotukhina, C. E., Perukhina, A. E., and Pozhanez, A. B., 1964, *Geology of Afrikan Rare Element Deposits and Their Economic Importance*: Moscow, pp. 166–197 (in Russian).

Konev, A. A., 1958, Ijolites of Saizhinski and Gulinski plutons of alkaline and basic rocks (Vitminsk plateau): *Izvest. Akad. Nauk SSSR*, new series, v. **120**, No. 2 (in Russian).

Konev, A. A., 1960a, Alkaline and ultrabasic rocks of the Saizhinski and Gulinski plutons: *All-Union Mineralog. Soc.*, Eastern Siberia sect., No. 2 (in Russian).

Konev, A. A., 1960b, Ore-bearing perovskite pyroxenite intrusions in Eastern Sayan: *Doklady Nauk SSSR*, v. **133**, pp. 935–938 (in Russian). English transl., *Doklady Akad. Nauk SSSR*, 1961, v. **133**, pp. 835–837.

Konev, A. A., 1962, Carbonatites of the Saizhinsk alkalic-ultrabasic complex: *Zap. Vses. Mineralog.*, v. **91**, pp. 165–169 (in Russian).

Kononova, V. A., 1957, Urtite-ijolite intrusions in Tuva and the role of metasomatic processes in their formation: *Izvest. Akad. Nauk SSSR*, v. **5** (in Russian).

Kononva, V. A., 1961, Urtite-ijolite intrusives in south-east Tuva and their genesis: *Inst. Geol. Ore Deposits, Petrog., Mineralog., Geochem., Akad. Nauk SSSR*, No. 60 (in Russian).

Korzhinsky, D. S., 1951, Common properties of infiltration and metasomatic zoning: *Izvest. Akad. Nauk SSSR*, v. **28**, No. 1 (in Russian).

Korzhinsky, D. S., 1952, Granitization as a magmatic replacement: *Izvest. Akad. Nauk SSSR*, v. **2** (in Russian).

Korzhinsky, D. S., 1955, Outline of metasomatic processes: In *Basic Problems in The Teachings on Magmatogenic Ore Deposits*, Moscow (in Russian).

Korzhinsky, D. S., 1956, Dependence of activity of components upon the solution acidity and reaction sequence in postmagmatic processes: *Geochemistry*, v. **7**, pp. 643–652 (English transl.).

Korzhinsky, D. S., 1957a, Condition of acidity of postmagmatic solutions: *Izvest. Akad. Nauk SSSR, Geol. Ser.*, v. **12** (in English),

Korzhinsky, D. S., 1957b, Physiochemical basis of the analysis of the paragenesis of minerals: *Akad. Nauk SSSR* (in Russian). English transl. 1959, New York, Consultants Bureau.

Korzhinsky, D. S., 1960, The acidity-alkalinity during magmatic processes: In *Granite Gneisses*, Kiev (in Russian).

Koshitz, K. M., 1934, The alkalic rocks of the Ensk region and related ore formations: *Bull. Leningrad Geol. Trust*, No. 1, p. 13 (in Russian).

Koster van Groos, A. F., and Wyllie, P. J., 1963, Experimental data bearing on the role of liquid immiscibility in the genesis of carbonatites: *Nature*, v. **199**, pp. 801–802.

Koster van Groos, A. F., and Wyllie, P. J. (in press), Liquid immiscibility in the system $Na_2O-Al_2O_3-SiO_2-CO_2$ at pressures up to 1 kilobar: *Am. Jour. Sci.*

Kranck, E. H., 1928, On Turjaite and the ijolite stem of Turja, Kola: *Fennia*, v. **51**, No. 5, pp. 1–104.

Kranck, E. H., 1953, Bedrock geology of the seaboard of Labrador between Domino Run and Hopedale, Newfoundland: *Canada Geol. Surv., Bull.* **26**.

Kukharenko, A. A., and Dontsova, E. I., 1962, The problem of carbonatite genesis: *Ore Deposits*, v. **2** (in Russian).

Kukharenko, A. A., and Dontsova, E. I., 1964, A contribution to the problem of the genesis of carbonatites: *Economic Geology USSR*, v. **1**, Nos. 3–4, pp. 47–68 (in English).

Kun, N. de., 1961, Die niobkarbonatit von Afrika: *Neues Jb. f. Min.*, Mh. 6, pp. 124–135.

Kun, N. de, 1962, The economic geology of columbi (niobium) and of tantalum: *Econ. Geol.*, v. **57**, pp. 377–404.

Kun, N. de, 1965, *The Mineral Resources of Africa:* Elsevier, New York.

Kun, N. de (in press), *Geology of The World's Niobium and Tantalum Deposits:* Elsevier, New York.

558   References

Kunz, G. F., 1886, A pseudomorph of feldspar after leucite (?) from Magnet Cove, Arkansas:
    Am. Assoc. Adv. Sci., Proc., v. 34, pp. 243–246.
Kupletsky, B. M., 1937, The Afrikanda pyroxenite intrusion: Int. Geol. Congr., 17th sess.,
    Guidebook, Northern Excursion.
Kupletsky, B. M., 1938a, Chemical petrographic characteristics of the pyroxenite intrusion at
    the Afrikanda railway station, Kola Peninsula: Trans. Inst. Geol. Sci., Petrog., ser. I,
    No. 2, pp. 33–42 (in Russian).
Kupletsky, B. M., 1938b, The pyroxenite intrusion near Afrikanda station on the Kola
    Peninsula: Trav., Inst. Petr., No. 12, pp. 71–88 (in Russian).
Kuznetsov, V. A., and Pinus, G. V., 1949, Intrusive complexes of Tuva: Izvest. Akad. Nauk
    SSSR, new ser, v. 65, No. 1 (in Russian).
Landes, K. K., 1931, A paragenetic classification of the Magnet Cove Minerals: Am.
    Mineralogist, v. 16, pp. 313–326.
Larsen, E. S., 1940, Petrographic province of central Montana: Geol. Soc. America Bull.,
    v. 51, pp. 887–948.
Larsen, E. S., 1942, Alkalic rocks of Iron Hill, Gunnison County, Colorado: U.S. Geol. Surv.,
    Prof. Paper. 197A.
Larsen, E. S., and Goransen, E. A., 1932, The deuteric and later alteration of the uncompah-
    grite of Iron Hill, Colorado: Am. Mineralogist, v. 17, pp. 343–356.
Larsen, E. S., and Hunter, J. F., 1914, Melilite and other minerals from Gunnison County,
    Colorado: Washington Acad. Sci. Jour., v. 4, pp. 473–479.
Larsen, E. S., and Schaller, W. J., 1914, Cebollite, a new mineral: Wash. Acad. Sci. Jour.,
    v. 4, pp. 480–482.
Larsson, W., 1943, Zur Kenntnis der alkalinen ultrabasischen Ganggesteine des Kalixgebiets,
    nord–Schweden: Sverig. Geol. Undersök., Ser. C, No. 456.
Lavrenev, Yu. B., 1960, Some features of the ultrabasic alkaline formations of eastern
    Siberia: Sci. Res. Inst. Mineral Raw Materials, No. 1 (in Russian).
Lavrenev, Yu. B., and Epshtein, E. M., 1962a, Pre-carbonatitic metasomatic processes in
    ultrabasic alkaline massifs: in the symposium Geology of Rare Element Deposits, issue 17
    (in Russian).
Lavrenev, Yu. B., and Epshtein, E. M., 1962b, Geological structure of ultrabasic alkaline rock
    massifs and the pattern of their formation: in the symposium Geology of Rare Element
    Deposits, issue 17 (in Russian).
Lavrenev, Yu. B., and Pozharitskaya, L. K., 1960a, Carbonatites of Eastern Sayan: in Magma-
    tism and its Related Mineral Resources, Moscow, pp. 466–468 (in Russian).
Lavrenev, Yu. B., and Pozharitskaya, L. K., 1960b, Carbonatites and their related mineral re-
    sources: Papers of the 2nd All-Union conference GOSGEOLOZDAT (in Russian).
Le Bas, M. J., and Dixon, J. A., 1965, A new carbonatite in the Legetet Hills, Kenya: Nature,
    v. 207, p. 68.
Leibrand, F., 1948, Das vorkommen von niobmineralien im Kaiserstuhl: Mitteilungsblatt der
    Badischen Geologischen Landesanstalt, pp. 39–42.
Leonardos, O. H., 1956a, Carbonatitos com apatita e pirocloro: Dep. Nac. Prod. Min., Minis.
    da Agricultura, Rio de Janeiro, Avulso, v. 8, pp. 7–30.
Leonardos, O. H., 1956b, Carbonatitos com apatita e pirocloro no estrangeiro e no Brasil:
    Engenharia, Mineracao e metalurgia, Rio de Janeiro, pp. 157–163.
Leontyev, L. N., 1956, Short geological outline of Tuva: Akad. Nauk SSSR.
Lippolt, H. J., Gentner, W., and Wimmenauer, W., 1963, Altersbestimmungen nach der
    Kalium-Argon Methode an tertiären Eruptivgesteinen Südwestdeutschlands: Jh. Geol.
    Landesamt Baden-Würtemberg, v. 6, pp. 507–538.
Lombaard, A. F., Ward-Able, N. M., and Bruce, R. W., 1964, The exploration and main
    geological features of the copper deposit in carbonatite at Loolekop, Palabora Complex:
    in The Geology of Some Ore Deposits in Southern Africa, ed. S. H. Haughton, v. 2, pp.
    315–338, Pubd. by Geol. Soc. S. Africa, Johannesburg.
Lombard, J., 1955, Caractères généraux des occurrences de carbonatites. Minéraux associés:
    Chronique des mines coloniàles, Paris, v. 23, No. 234, pp. 310–316.

McCall, G. J. H., 1958, Geology of the Gwasi area, Kenya Colony: *Kenya Geol. Surv., Rept.* **45**.

McCall, G. J. H., 1959, Alkaline and carbonatite ring complexes in the Kavirondo Rift Valley, Kenya: *Int. Geol. Congr., 20th sess., Assoc. de serv. géol. Africains*, pp. 327–334.

McCall, G. J. H., 1963, A reconsideration of certain aspects of the Rangwa and Ruri carbonatite complexes in Western Kenya: *Geol. Mag.*, v. **100**, pp. 181–185.

McCammon, J. W., 1951, Verity: *British Columbia Dept. Mines, Ann. Rept. for 1950*, pp. 229–230.

McCammon, J. W., 1953, Verity, Paradise, etc.: *British Columbia Dept. Mines, Ann. Rept. for 1952*, p. 115.

McCammon, J. W., 1955, Verity, Paradise, etc.: *British Columbia Dept. Mines, Ann. Rept. for 1954*, p. 111.

McConnell, D., and Gruner, J. W., 1940, The problem of the carbonate-apatites, III, Carbonate-apatite from Magnet Cove, Arkansas: *Am. Mineralogist*, v. **25**, pp. 157–167.

McConnell, R. C., 1886, Geological structure of a portion of the Rocky Mountains accompanied by a section measured near the 51st parallel: *Canada Geol. Surv., Ann. Rept.*, v. **2**, Pt. D, pp. 1–41.

McKinlay, A. C. M., 1958, Kimberlite intrusions cutting Karroo sediments in the Ruhuhu Depression of south-west Tanganyika: *Tanganyika Geol. Surv., Rec. for 1955*, v. **5**, pp. 63–80.

Macdonald, R., 1961, Explanation of the geology of sheet 36 (Nabilatuk): *Uganda Geol. Surv., Rept.* **5**.

Machado, F. J. de S., 1958, The volcanic belt of Angola and its carbonatites: *CCTA*, Leopoldville, theme 7, Carbonatites, pp. 309–317.

Maciel, P., 1952, Nota sobre uma nova jazida de apatita no Sul do Estado de São Paulo: *Soc. Bras. Geol. Bol.*, v. **1**, pp. 3–14.

Mar, F. W., 1890, On the so-called perofskite from Magnet Cove, Arkansas: *Am. Jour. Sci.*, ser. 3, v. **40**, pp. 403–405.

Martin, H., Mathias, M., and Simpson, E. S. W., 1960, The Damaraland sub-volcanic ring complexes in South West Africa: *Int. Geol. Congr., 21st sess.*, Pt. 13, pp. 156–174.

Maurice, O. D., 1956, Geology of the Oka Hills: *Canadian Mining Jour.*, pp. 70–72.

Maurice, O. D., 1957, *Preliminary Report on Oka Area, Electoral District of Deux Montagnes*: Quebec Dept. Mines, PR 351.

Melcher, G. C., 1954, Nota sôbre o distrito alcalino de Jacupiranga, São Paulo: *Div. Geol. Min., Notas Prelim.*, Rio de Janeiro, No. 84.

Melville, W. H., 1892, Mineralogical notes. Natrolite from Magnet Cove, Arkansas: *U.S. Geol. Surv., Bull.* **90**.

Mennell, F. P., 1946, Ring structures with carbonate cores in Southern Rhodesia: *Geol. Mag.*, v. **83**, pp. 137–140.

Metschke, H., 1938, Koppitkarbonatit und kappitmarmor von Schelingen im Kaiserstuhl: *Ber. naturforschr. Ges Freiburg i Br.*, v. **36**, pp. 28–56.

Meyer, A., 1957, Un type particulier de roche carbonatée au Ruanda (Afrique Centrale): *Acad. Sci. Paris Comptes Rendus*, v. **245**, pp. 976–978.

Meyer, A., 1958, Carbonatites–quelques grand traits: *CCTA*, Leopoldville, Theme 7, Carbonatites, No. 44, pp. 295–301.

Meyer, A., and Bethune, P. de, 1958, La carbonatite Lueshe (Kivu): *Congo Belge Serv. Géol. Bull.* **8**, fasc. 5.

Meyer, A., and Bethune, P. de, 1960, The Lueshe carbonatite (Kivu, Belgian Congo): *Int. Geol. Congr., 21st sess.*, Pt. 13, pp. 304–309.

Miller, J. A., and Brown, P. E., 1963, The age of some carbonatite igneous activity in south-west Tanganyika: *Geol. Mag.*, v. **100**, pp. 276–279.

Milton, C., and Blade, L. V., 1958, Preliminary note on Kimzeyite, a new zirconium garnet: *Science*, v. **127**, p. 1343.

Miser, H. D., and Glass, J. J., 1941, Fluorescent sodalite and hackmanite from Magnet Cove, Arkansas: *Am. Mineralogist*, v. **26**, pp. 437–445.

Miser, H. D., and Stevens, R. E., 1938, Taeniolite from Magnet Cove, Arkansas: *Am. Mineralogist*, v. **23**, pp. 104–110.

Mohr, P. A., 1961, The geology, structure and origin of the Bishoftu explosion craters: *Geophys. Observ. Addis Ababa Bull.*, v. **2**, pp. 65–101.

Moore, G. G., 1957, Differentiated alkaline intrusives of the northern outskirts of the Siberian Platform (right bank of the lower reaches of the Kotui River): *Izvest. Akad. Nauk SSSR, Geol. Ser.*, No. 8, pp. 40–52 (in Russian).

Moore, G. G., 1959, The age relations of trap rocks and rocks of the alkaline-ultrabasic complex of the Siberian Platform: *Doklady Akad. Nauk SSSR*, v. **2–4**, pp. 387–389 (in Russian).

Moore, G., and Sheinman, G., 1946, Meimechite, a new rock from the northern border of the Siberian platform: *Doklady Akad. Nauk SSSR*, v. **51**, pp. 151–158 (in Russian).

Moraes Rego, L. F., and Guimarães, D., 1926, Jazida de magnetita Anitápolis: *Serv. Geol. Min. do Brasil, Bull.* **21**.

Motychko, V. F., 1957, Carbonatites of the Odikhincha massif and their genesis: *Inst. Geol. Arctic*, v. **107**, No. 12 (in Russian).

Neczkar, E., 1958, *Paragenesis of the Rock-forming Minerals of the Nepheline Syenite and Adjacent Wallrocks near Nemegos, Ontario*: M.A.Sc. thesis, Univ. of Toronto, Canada.

Neuman, H., and Rosenquist, I., 1940, On red, fluorescent calcite from the Fen Area near Ulefoss: *Norsk. Geologisk. Tidsskr.*, v. **20**, p. 267.

Nickel, E. H., 1956, Niocalite, a new calcium niobium silicate mineral: *Am. Mineralogist*, v. **41**, pp. 785–786.

Nickel, E. H., 1960, A zirconium-bearing garnet from Oka, Quebec: *Canadian Mineralogist*, v. **6**, pp. 549–556.

Nickel, E. H., 1964, Latrappite—a proposed new name for the perovskite-type calcium niobate mineral from the Oka area of Quebec: *Canadian Mineralogist*, v. **8**, pp. 121–122.

Nickel, E. H., and McAdam, R. C., 1963, Niobium perovskite from Oka, Quebec; a new classification for minerals of the perovskite group: *Canadian Mineralogist*, v. **7**, pp. 683–697.

Nickel, E. H., Rowland, J. F., and Maxwell, J. A., 1958, The composition and crystallography of niocalite: *Canadian Mineralogist*, v. **6**, pp. 264–272.

Nicolayson, L. O., Burger, A. J., and Johnson, R. L., 1962, The age of the Shawa carbonatite complex: *Geol. Soc. S. Africa Trans.*, v. **65**, pp. 293–294.

Nieberlein, V. A., Fine, M. M., Calhoun, W. A., and Parsons, E. W., 1954, Progress report on development of columbium in Arkansas for 1953: *U.S. Bur. Mines Rept. Inv.* 5064.

Oates, F., 1934, Collection of Tertiary lavas from the Northern Province: *Tanganyika Geol. Surv., Ann. Rept. for 1933*.

Ödman, O., 1930, Volcanic rocks of Mt. Elgon in British East Africa: *Geol. Fören. Förh.*, v. **52**, pp. 455–536.

Oliveira, A. I. de, 1936, Baritina em Araxá, Minas Gerais: *Dep. Nac. Prod. Min., Minis da Agricultura*, Rio de Janeiro, Avulso 10.

Olson, J. C., and Pray, L. C., 1954, The Mountain Pass rare earth deposits: *California Div. Mines Bull.* 170, Ch. 8, pp. 23–29.

Olson, J. C., Shawe, D. R., Pray, L. C., Sharp, W. N., and Hewett, D. F., 1954, Rare earth mineral deposits of the Mountain Pass District, San Bernadino County, California:. *U.S. Geol. Surv.*, Prof. Paper 261.

Olson, J. C., and Wallace, S. R., 1956a, Thorium and rare earth minerals in Powderhorn district, Gunnison County, Colorado: *U.S. Geol. Surv. Bull.* 1027–O.

Olson, J. C., and Wallace, L. C., 1956b, Thorium in the Powderhorn district, Gunnison County, Colorado: *Int. Conf. Peaceful Uses Atomic Energy, Proc.*, v. **6**, pp. 582–586.

Omenetto, P., and Weber, K., 1964, *Contribution a l'étude de quelques minéraux des carbonatites du Kaiserstuhl*: EURATOM publication EUR, 1827, d, f, e, pp. 37–45.

Padon, A., 1851, Arkansas minerals: *De Bow's Review*, v. **11**, pp. 406–407.

Parker, R. L., 1963, Preliminary report on alkalic intrusive rocks in the Northern Wet Mountains, Colorado: *U.S. Geol. Surv.*, Prof. Paper 450–E, article 181, pp. E 8–E 10.

Parker, R. L., Adams, J. W., and Hildebrand, F. A., 1962, A rare sodium niobate mineral from Colorado: *U.S. Geol. Surv.*, Prof. Paper 450–C, pp. C4–C6.

Parks, B., and Branner, G. C., 1932, A barite deposit in Hot Spring County, Arkansas: *Arkansas Geol. Surv.*, Inf. Circ. 1.

Parsons, G. E., 1957, Nemegosenda Lake–Columbium area: Canadian Mining Jour., v. **78**, p. 83.

Parsons, G. E., 1961, Niobium-bearing complexes east of Lake Superior: *Ontario Dept. Mines, Geol. Rept.* **3**.

Pazyuk, L. I., 1954, An example of alkaline metasomatism in carbonate rocks: Publications of the Geology- Geography faculty, Odessa Institute, v. **2** (in Russian).

Pecora, W. T., 1942, Nepheline syenite pegmatites, Rocky Bay Stock, Bearpaw Mountains, Montana: *Am. Mineralogist*, v. **27**, pp. 397–424.

Pecora, W. T., 1956, Carbonatites: A review: *Geol. Soc. America Bull.*, v. **67**, pp. 1537–1556.

Pecora, W. T., 1962, Carbonatite problem in the Bearpaw Mountains: *Geol. Soc. America, Petrologic studies*, Buddington Volume, pp. 83–104.

Pecora, W. T., and Fisher, B., 1946, Drusy vugs in a monzonite dike, Bearpaw Mountains, Montana: *Am. Mineralogist*, v. **31**, pp. 370–385.

Pecora, W. T., and Kerr, J. H., 1953, Burbankite and calkinsite, two new carbonate minerals from Montana: *Am. Mineralogist*, v. **38**, pp. 1169–1183.

Pecora, W. T., *et al.*, 1957, Preliminary geologic map of the Warrick quadrangle, Bearpaw Mountains: *U.S. Geol. Survey Misc. Geol. Inv.*, Map I–237.

Penfield, S. L., 1894, Anatase von Magnet Cove, Arkansas: *Zeitschr. f. Kristallog.*, v. **23**, p. 261.

Perrault, G., 1959, Determination de la composition chimique de pyrochlore d'Oka par spectrofluorescence des rayons X: *L'Ingénieur*, summer 1959, pp. 40–46.

Pfannenstiel, M., 1933, Die geologie des Kaiserstuhls. In: *Der Kaiserstuhl*, pubd. by Bad. Landesver. Naturkunde u. Naturschutz, pp. 18–127.

Phillips, K. A., 1955, Some notes on the carbonatite at Nkumbwa Hill, Isoka District: *Northern Rhodesia Geol. Surv.*, Rec. for 1953, pp. 20–23.

Pickering, R., 1962, Brief explanation of the geology—Quarter degree sheet 52, Endulen: *Tanganyika Geol. Surv.*, unpubd. rept, RP/26

Pinto Coelho, A. V., 1961, Notas sobre a petrografia da região do Monte Muambe: *Serv. de Geol. e Minas Moçambique, Bol.* **27**, pp. 66–68.

Poole, J. H. J., 1963, Radioactivity of sodium carbonate lava from Oldoinyo Lengai, Tanganyika: *Nature*, v. **198**, p. 1291.

Powell, J. L., 1962, The strontium isotopic composition and origin of carbonatites: Ph.D. thesis Massachusetts Institute of Technology, Cambridge, Mass., U.S.A.

Powell, J. L., 1965a, Isotopic composition of strontium in carbonate rocks from Keshya and Mkwisi, Zambia: *Nature*, v. **206**, pp. 288–289.

Powell, J. L., 1965b, Low abundance of Sr[87] in Ontario carbonatites: *Am. Mineralogist*, v. **50**, pp. 1075–1079.

Powell, J. L., 1965c, Isotopic composition of strontium in four carbonate vein-dikes: *Am. Mineralogist*, v. **50**, pp. 1921–1928.

Powell, J. L. (in press), Isotopic composition of strontium in whole-rock carbonatite and Kimberlite samples: *Int. Mineral Assoc.*, 1964 meeting, India.

Powell, J. L., Hurley, P. M., and Fairbairn, H. W., 1962, Isotopic composition of strontium in carbonatites: *Nature*, v. **196**, p. 1085.

Pozharitskaya, L. K., 1960, Carbonatites of Eastern Siberian ultrabasic alkaline complexes: *Sci. Res. Inst. Mineral Raw Materials*, No. 1 (in Russian).

Pozharitskaya, L. K., 1962, Geochemical properties of the processes of carbonatite formation: in the symposium, *Geology of Rare Element Deposits*, issue 17 (in Russian).

Pozharitskaya, L. K., and Epshtein, E. M., 1962, The problem of carbonatite genesis: in the symposium, *Geology of Rare Element Deposits*, issue 17 (in Russian).

Pozharitskaya, L. K., Frolov, A. A., and Epshtein, E. M., 1961, Prospecting criteria of rare-metal carbonatites: in the symposium, *Geology of Rare Element Deposits*, issue 14 (in Russian).

T

Pulfrey, W., 1936, Preliminary report on the geology of the No. 1 area, North and Central Kavirondo: *Kenya Geol. Surv., Rept.* 5.

Pulfrey, W., 1944, Note on the Homa Bay area, Kavirondo, Kenya: *Geol. Soc. London Proc.*, No. 1406, p. 101.

Pulfrey, W., 1950, Ijolitic rocks near Homa Bay, Western Kenya: *Geol. Soc. London Quart. Jour.*, v. **105**, pp. 425–460.

Pulfrey, W., 1953, A Kenya alnöite and associated skarns: *Jour. East African Uganda Nat. Hist. Soc.*, v. **22**, pp. 23–34.

Pulfrey, W., 1954, Alkaline syenites at Ruri, Kenya: *Geol. Mag.*, v. **91**, pp. 209–219.

Purdue, A. H., and Miser, H. D., 1923, Description of the Hot Springs quadrangle, Arkansas: *U.S. Geol. Surv.*, Geol. Atlas, Folio 215.

Quon, S. H., and Heinrich, E. W. (in press), Abundance and significance of some minor elements in carbonatitic calcites and dolomites: *Int. Mineral. Assoc.*, 1964 meeting, India.

Ramberg, I. B., 1964, Preliminary results of gravimetric investigations in the Fen area: *Norsk. Geol. Tiddsskr.*, v. **44**, pp. 431–434.

Ramsay, W., 1921, En melilitförande djupbergart fran Turja pa sydsidan av Kolahalvön: *Geol. Fören. Förh.*, v. **43**, p. 488.

Rapson, June E. (in press), Carbonatite in the alkaline complex of the Ice River area, Southern Canadian Rocky Mountains: *Int. Mineral. Assoc. Proc.*, 1964 meeting, India.

Rath, G. von, 1876, Brookit–(Arkansit–) krystalle von Magnet Cove, Arkansas: *Niederrhein Ges. Bonn. Sub.* v. **33**, p. 38.

Rebolo, J. D. R. F., and Ferro, B. P. A., 1962, Relatorio da actividade da l^a brigada geologia de campo no ano de 1961: *Serv. de Geol. e Minas Moçambique*, unpubd. rept.

Reck, H., 1914, Oldoinyo Lengai, ein Tatiger Vulkan in Gebiete der Deutsch Ostafrikanischen Bruchstufe: *Branca Festschrift*, v. **12**, pp. 373–409.

Reed, D. F., 1949a, Investigation of Christy titanium deposit, Hot Spring County Arkansas: *U.S. Bur. Mines Rept. Inv.* 4592.

Reed, D. F., 1949b, Investigation of Magnet Cove Rutile deposit, Hot Spring County, Arkansas: *U.S. Bur. Mines Rept. Inv.* 4593.

Reeve, W. H., 1963, The geology and mineral resources of Northern Rhodesia: *Northern Rhodesia Geol. Surv., Bull.* **3**.

Reeve, W. H., and Deans, T., 1954, An occurrence of carbonatite in the Isoka district of Northern Rhodesia: *Colon. Geol. Mineral Resources*, v. **4**, pp. 271–281.

Rein, G., 1950, Über essexite und tephrite des zentralen Kaiserstuhls und deren unwandlungs-produkte: *Fortschr. Miner.*, v. **28**, pp. 70–72.

Richard, J. J., 1942, Volcanological observations in East Africa. I. Oldonyo L'engai, The 1940–41 eruption: *Jour. East Africa Uganda Nat. Hist. Soc.*, v. **16**, pp. 89–108.

Richard, J. J., and van Padang, N., 1957, Catalogue of the active volcanoes of the world. Pt. 4, *Africa and the Red Sea*: Naples.

Ronenson, B. M., 1959, Basic features of the geological structure of the northern part of the Vishnev Mountains: *Geology and Prospecting*, No. 1, pp. 40–51, Inst. Higher Education (in Russian).

Ronenson, B. M., 1963, The petrology of the alkaline complex in the Vishnev Mountains: *Proc. First Ural Petrographic Conference*, Moscow Geological–Prospecting Inst., Moscow, pp. 109–120 (in Russian).

Rose, H. J., Blade, L. V., and Ross, M., 1958, Earthy monazite at Magnet Cove, Arkansas: *Am. Mineralogist*, v. **43**, pp. 935–997.

Rose, C. K., and Shannon, S. S., Jr., 1960, Cebolla Creek titaniferous iron deposits, Gunnison County, Colorado: *U.S. Bur. Mines, Rept. Inv.* 5679, pp. 1–30.

Ross, C. S., 1938, Volcanic activity at Magnet Cove, Arkansas: *Am. Geophys. Union Trans.*, 19th Ann. Meeting, Pt. 1, Nat. Res. Council, pp. 263–264.

Rowe, R. B., 1954, Notes on geology and mineralogy of the Newman columbium–uranium deposit, Lake Nipissing, Ontario: *Canada, Geol. Surv.*, Paper 54–55.

Rowe, R. B., 1955, Notes on columbium mineralization, Oka district, Two Mountains County, Quebec: *Canada Geol. Surv.*, Paper 54–22.

Rowe, R. B., 1956, Columbium (niobium) deposits of Canada: *Canadian Inst. Mining Metall. Bull.*, Sept., pp. 644–647.

Rowe, R. B., 1958, Niobium (columbium) deposits of Canada: *Canada Geol. Surv.*, Econ. Geol. Ser., No. 18.

Rub, M. G., 1960, Alkalic intrusives in the Maritime Province: *Izvest. Akad. Nauk SSSR*, v. **12**, pp. 56–71 (English transl.).

Russell, H. D., Hiemstra, S. A., and Groeneveld, D., 1954, The mineralogy and petrology of the carbonatite at Loolekop, Eastern Transvaal: *Geol. Soc. S. Africa Trans.*, v. **57**, pp. 197–208.

Saether, E., 1948a, On the genesis of peralkaline rock provinces: *Int. Geol. Congr., 18th sess.*, Pt. 2, pp. 123–130.

Saether, E., 1948b, Foreløpig meddelelse om resultat av undersøkelser i Fensfeltet: *Norsk. Geol. Tidsskr.*, v. **27**, pp. 66–73.

Saether, E., 1957, The alkaline rock province of the Fen area in southern Norway: *Det. Kgl. Norske. Vid. Selsk. Skr.*, No. 1.

Safiannikoff, A., 1959, Un nouveau minéral de niobium: *Bull. séances Acad. Roy. Sci. Outre-Mer*, v. **5**, pp. 1251–1255.

Saggerson, E. P., 1952, Geology of the Kisumu District. Degree sheet 41, N.E. quadrant: *Kenya Geol. Surv., Rept.* 21.

Saggerson, E. P., and Williams, L. A. J., 1963, Ngurumanite, a new hypabyssal rock from Kenya: *Nature*, v. **192**, p. 479.

Saggerson, E. P., and Williams, L. A. J., 1964, Ngurumanite from southern Kenya and its bearing on the origin of rocks in the Northern Tanganyika Alkaline District: *Jour. Petrology*, v. **5**, pp. 40–81.

Sahama, Th. G., 1953, Mineralogy and Petrology of a lava flow from Mt. Nyiragongo, Belgian Congo: *Ann. Acad. Scient. Fenn.*, ser. A. III, No. 35, pp. 1–25.

Sahama, Th. G., 1957, Complex nepheline-kalsilite phenocrysts in Kabfumu lava, Nyiragongo area, North Kivu in Belgian Congo: *Jour. Geol.*, v. **65**, pp. 515–526.

Sahama, Th. G., 1960, Kalsilite in the lavas of Mt. Nyiragongo (Belgian Congo): *Jour. Petrology*, v. **1**, pp. 146–171

Sahama, Th. G., 1961, Thermal metamorphism of the volcanic rocks of Mt. Nyiragongo (Eastern Congo): *Bull. Comm. Geol. Finlande*, v. **196**, pp. 151–175. Centre National de Volcanologie, No. 16.

Sahama, Th. G., 1962, Petrology of Mt. Nyiragongo: a review: *Edinburgh Geol. Soc., Trans.*, v. **19**, pp. 1–28.

Sahama, Th. G., and Meyer, A., 1958, Study of the volcano Nyiragongo. A progress report: *Exploration du Parc National Albert.* Mission d'études vulcanologuques, fasc. 2., Inst. des Parcs Nationaux du Congo Belge, Bruxelles.

Sahlböm, N., 1897, Analysen einiger gesteine aus dem nephelinsyenitgebiete der Insel Alnö: *Neues Jb. f. Min.*, v. **2**, pp. 97–101.

Samoilova, N. V., 1962, Petrochemical properties of the association of ijolite-melteigite rocks with nepheline syenites as illustrated by the alkaline intrusions of the Eniseiski Ridge: *Inst. Geol. Ore Deposits, Petrog., Mineralog.* and *Geochem., Akad. Nauk SSSR*, No. 76, pp. 143–169 (in Russian).

Sampson, D. N., 1956, The volcanic hills at Igwisi: *Tanganyika Geol. Surv.*, Rec. for 1953, v. **3**, pp. 48–53.

Sampson, D. N., 1958, The Uluguru Mountains. (A summary of progress to 1955): *Tanganyika Geol. Surv.*, Rec. for 1955, v. **5**, pp. 21–35.

Schneiderhohn, H., 1948, Neue beobachtungen und hypothesen im Kaiserstuhl: *Mitteil. der Bad. Geol. Landesanstalt*, pp. 30–36.

Schofield, A., and Haskin, L., 1964, Rare-earth distribution patterns in eight terrestrial materials: *Geochim. et Cosmochim. Acta*, v. **28**, pp. 437–446.

Schröcke, H., 1955, Über Alkaligesteine und deren Lagerstätten: *Neues Jb. f. Miner., Mh.*, pp. 169–189.

564 *References*

Schuling, R. D., 1961, Formation of pegmatitic carbonatite in a syenite-marble contact: *Nature*, v. **192**, p. 1280.

Searle, D. L., 1952, Geology of the area north-west of Kitale Township (Trans Nzoia, Elgon and West Suk): *Kenya Geol. Surv., Rept.* **19**.

Serba, B. I., 1959, A few notes on L. S. Borodin's article 'On the types of carbonatite deposits and their relation to massifs of ultrabasic alkaline rocks', *Akad. Nauk SSSR*, Geol. Ser., v. **3**, pp. 113–114 (in Russian).

Serba, B. I., 1962, Cobalt content in carbonatites: *Geokhimiya*, v. **9**, pp. 839–840 (in Russian). English transl., *Geochemistry*, v. **9**, pp. 967–968.

Serba, B. I., 1963, Carbonatites in the Sallanlatvinsk massif: *Soviet Geology*, v. **6**, pp. 125–131 (English transl.).

Sergeev, A. S., 1959, Fenites and fenitization in the contact aureole of alkaline and ultrabasic intrusions of the Khabosersky group: *Zapiski Vses. Mineralog.*, v. **88**, pp. 430–443 (in Russian).

Sergeev, A. S., 1962, Fenitized rocks of the Kovdorskii massif: *Sci. notes Leningrad State University*, No. 312, Geol. Ser. issue No. 13 (in Russian).

Shackleton, R. M., 1951, A contribution to the geology of the Kavirondo Rift Valley: *Geol. Soc. London Quart. Jour.*, v. **106**, pp. 345–389.

Shand, S. J., 1950, *Eruptive Rocks*: London, Thomas Murby, 4th ed.

Sharp, W. N., and Pray, L. C., 1952, Geologic map of the bastnaesite deposits of the Birthday claims, San Bernadino County, California: *U.S. Geol. Surv.*, Min. Inv., Field Studies, MF–4.

Sheinman, Yu. M., 1947, On a new petrographical province in the North Siberian Platform: *Izvest. Akad. Nauk SSSR, Geol. Ser.* No. 1 (in Russian).

Sheinman, Yu. H., 1955, Certain geological peculiarities of the ultrabasic and ultra-alkalic magmatic formations on platforms: *Zapiski Vses. Mineralog.*, v. **84**, pp. 143–158 (in Russian).

Sinclair, W. E., 1955, The Sukulu mineral deposits: *Mining Mag.*, v. **92**, pp. 216–218.

Sleight, V. G., 1941, Molybdenite at Magnet Cove, Arkansas: *Am. Mineralogist*, v. **26**, pp. 132–133.

Smith, W. C., 1938, Alkali rocks associated with limestone of apparently intrusive nature: *British Assoc. Adv. Sci.*, sec. C, pp. 416–417 (abstract only).

Smith, W. C., 1953, Carbonatites of the Chilwa Series of southern Nyasaland: *Bull. Brit. Mus. (Nat. Hist.) Mineralogy*, v. **1**, No. 4, pp. 95–120.

Smith, W. C., 1956, A review of some problems of African carbonatites: *Geol. Soc. London Quart. Jour.*, v. **112**, pp. 189–220.

Smyth, C. H., Jr., 1913, The chemical composition of the alkaline rocks and its significance as to their origin: *Am. Jour. Sci.*, ser. 4, v. **36**, pp. 33–46.

Smyth, F. H., and Adams, L. H., 1923, The system calcium oxide-carbon dioxide: *American Chem. Soc. Jour.*, v. **45**, pp. 1169–1184.

Snelling, N. J., 1965, Age determinations on three African carbonatites: *Nature*, v. **205**, p. 491.

Sobolev, N. D., 1959, The petrochemistry of ultrabasic rocks. Part I. Petrochemical properties of ultrabasic rocks and diagrams of their chemical composition: *Geochemistry*, v. **8**, pp. 839–864 (English transl.).

Soellner, J., 1912a, Die optischen Eigenschaften des dysanalytes von Vogtsburg und von Schelingen in Kaiserstuhl: *Zbl. Miner.*, pp. 310–317.

Soellner, J., 1912b, Über ein neues Vorkommen von Leucitophyr und Leucitophyrbreccie im Kaiserstuhl: *Zbl. Miner.*, pp. 571–574.

Soellner, J., 1912c, Über den geologischen Aufbau des Limberges bei Sasbach am Kaiserstuhl und über das Auftreten tertiärer Sedimente daselbst: *Mitteil. d. Bad. Geol. Landesanst.*, v. **7**, pp. 313–358.

Soellner, J., 1913a, Über Bergalith, ein neues melithreiches Ganggestein aus dem Kaiserstuhl: *Mitteil. d. Bad. Geol. Landesanst.*, v. **7**, pp. 415–466.

Soellner, J., 1913b, Über Leucitnephelintinguaitporphyr aus dem Kaiserstuhl: *Zbl. Miner.*, p. 367.

Soellner, J., 1913c, Über das auftreten von Essexit im Kaiserstuhl: *Zbl. Miner.*, pp. 230–234.

Soellner, J., 1913d, Bericht über die Exkursion nach dem Kaiserstuhl am 6 August 1913: *Zeitschr. d. Deutsch. Geol. Gesellsch.*, v. **65**, p. 516.

Soellner, J., 1915a, Über Olivinmonchiquit aus dem Kaiserstuhl: *Mitteil. d. Bad. Geol. Landesanst.*, v. **8**, p. 196.

Soellner, J., 1915b, Über das Auftreten aplitischer Ganggesteine im Essexit des Kaiserstuhls: *Mitteil. d. Bad. Geol. Landesanst.*, v. **8**, p. 202.

Soellner, J., 1927a, Über Edelopal und Milchopal aus dem Kaiserstuhl: *Zbl. Miner.*, p. 81.

Soellner, J., 1927b, Zur petrographie und Geologie des Kaiserstuhl-gebirges im Breisgau: *Neues Jb. f. Min.*, v. **55**, A, pp. 299–318.

Soellner, J., 1928, Über essexitisch–theralitisch–monzonitisch Tiefengesteine aus dem Kaiserstuhl: *Mitteil. d. Bad. Geol. Landesanst.*, v. **10**, pp. 1–93.

Soellner, J., 1939, Über den vermeintlichen Schlot vom gewann nonnensohl auf der Gemarkung Oberschaffhausen, Kaiserstuhl: *Zbl. Miner.*, v. **393**, pp. 433–442.

Sørum, H., 1955, Contribution to the mineralogy of the Søve Deposit I–II: *Det. kg. Norske. Vidensk., Selskr.*, v. **28**, Nos. 22–23.

Sousa Machado, F. J. de, 1958, The volcanic belt of Angola and its carbonatites: *Serv. Geol. e Minas, Companhia Mineira do Lobito*, Angola, mineographed publication.

Spence, J., 1957, The geology of part of the Eastern Province of Tanganyika: *Tanganyika Geol. Surv., Bull.* 28.

Spencer, R. V., 1946, Exploration of the Magnet Cove Rutile Co. property, Magnet Cove area, Hot Spring County, Arkansas: *U.S. Bur. Mines, Rept. Inv.* 3900.

Stahl, A., 1930, Eisenerze im nördlichen Sudwestafrikas: *Neues Jb. f. Min.*, v. **64**, B, pp. 165–200.

Stansfield, J., 1923, Extensions of the Monteregian petrographical province to the west and north-west: *Geol. Mag.*, v. **60**, pp. 433–453.

Stockley, G. M., 1943, The geology of the Rufiji District including a small portion of northern Kilwa District (Marumbi Hills): *Tanganyika Notes*, No. 16.

Strand, T., 1952, Blotittsövit på Stjernoy. Vest Finnmark: *Norsk. geol. Undersök.*, v. **183**, pp. 10–21.

Strauss, E. A., and Truter, F. C., 1951a, The alkali complex at Spitskop, Sekukuniland, Eastern Transvaal: *Geol. Soc. S. Africa Trans.*, v. **53**, pp. 81–125.

Strauss, E. A., and Truter, F. C., 1951b, Post-Bushveld ultrabasic, alkalic and carbonatitic eruptives at Magnet Heights, Sekukuniland, Eastern Transvaal: *Geol. Soc. S. Africa Trans.*, v. **53**, pp. 169–190.

Stringer, K. V., Holt, D. N., and Groves, A. W., 1956, The Chambe Plateau ring complex of Nyasaland: *Colon. Geol. and Min. Resources*, v. **61**, pp. 3–18.

Sturdy, D., Calton, W. E., and Milne, G., 1933, A chemical survey of the waters of Mount Meru, Tanganyika: *Jour. E. Africa Uganda Nat. Hist. Soc.*, v. **45**, p. 46.

Subramaniam, A. P., and Parimoo, M. L., 1964, The Amba Dongar fluorspar deposit—a unique example of mineralization related to Deccan volcanism. Advancing frontiers in geology and geophysics: *Hyderabad (Indian Geophys. Union)*, (Krishnan volume), pp. 441–450.

Sukheswala, R. N., and Udas, G. R., 1963, Note on the carbonatite of Amba Dongar (Gujarat State) and its economic potentialities: *Science and Culture*, v. **29**, No. 11, pp. 563–568.

Sukheswala, R. N., Udas, G. R., and Heinrich, E. Wm., 1965, Geology of the newly discovered carbonatite of India: *Canadian Mineralogist*, v. **8**, 397 (abstract only).

Sutherland, D. S., 1965, Potash-trachytes and ultra-potassic rocks associated with the carbonatite complex of the Toror Hills, Uganda: *Mineralog. Mag.*, v. **35**, pp. 363–378.

Swift, W. H., 1952, The geology of Chishanya, Buhera District, Southern Rhodesia: *Edinburgh Geol. Soc. Trans.*, v. **15**, pp. 346–359.

Swift, W. H., 1959, The geology of the Dorowa ring complex: *Rhodesian Min. Engng.*, v. **24**, pp. 45–46.

Taylor, R., 1955, The magnetite-vermiculite occurrences of Bukusu, Mbale district: *Uganda Geol. Surv., Rec. for 1953*, pp. 59–64.

Teale, E. O., 1924, The geology of Portuguese East Africa between the Zambesi and Sabi Rivers: *Geol. Soc. S. Africa Trans.*, v. **26**, pp. 103–129.

Temple, A. K., and Grogan, R. M., 1965, Carbonatite and related alkalic rocks at Powderhorn, Colorado: *Econ. Geol.*, v. **60**, pp. 672–692.

Teschamacher, J. E., 1849, On the identity of Arkansit with Brookite, and the measurement of the angles of the minerals: *Boston Soc. Nat. Hist., Proc.*, v. **3**, pp. 131–132.

Thoreau, J., Aderca, B., and Van Wambeke, L., 1958, Le gisement de terres rares de la Karonge (Urundi): *Bull. Acad. Roy. Sci. Colon.*, v. **4**, (new ser.) pp. 684–715.

Tilloy, R., and Tournoud, H., 1946, Rapport sur le massif du jebel Bou. Agrao: *Arch. Serv. et. gîtes minér.*, Rabat.

Tomkeieff, S. I., 1961, Alkalic ultrabasic rocks and carbonatites in the U.S.S.R.: *Int. Geol. Rev.*, v. **3**, pp. 739–758.

Törnebohm, A. E., 1882, Mikrosopische bergartsstudier XVII melilitbasalt från Alnö: *Geol. Fören. Förh.*, v. **6**, pp. 240–251.

Törnebohm, A. E., 1883, Mikroskopiska bergartsstudier XVIII Nefelin-syenit från Alnö: *Geol. Fören. Förh.*, v. **6**, pp. 547–549.

Trendall, A. F., 1961, Explanation of the geology of sheet 45 (Kadam): *Uganda Geol. Surv., Rept.* **6**.

Trendall, A. F., 1962, Kokipie and Lolekek: two minor volcanoes of eastern Uganda: *Uganda Geol. Surv., Rec. for 1957–1958*, pp. 46–63.

Tyndale-Biscoe, R., 1959, Alkali ring complexes in Southern Rhodesia: *Int. Geol. Congr., 20th sess., Assoc. de serv. Geol. Africains*, pp. 335–338.

Tyrrell, G. W., and Neilson, A. J., 1938, Igneous rocks from the neighbourhood of Mount Jombo and the Sabaki River. In McKinnon Wood, M., On a second collection of fossils and rocks from Kenya: *Monograph Hunterian Museum*, Glasgow, v. **6**, pp. 108–116.

Uhlig, C., 1907, Der sogennante gross Ostafrikanische Graben zwischen Magad (Natron See) und Lawa ya Mueri (Manyara See): *Geogr. Zeit.*, v. **13**, pp. 478–505.

Vail, J. R., 1962, Mount Xiluvo Vent, Mozambique: *Univ. of Leeds Res. Inst. African Geol.*, 6th Ann. Rept., 1960–1961, pp. 16–17.

Vail, J. R. (in press), Mesozoic igneous activity in Central Africa: *Int. Geol. Congr., 22nd sess.*, Pt. 16.

Vail, J. R., and Mallick, D. I. J., 1965, The nepheline syenite ring complex of the Mongolowe Hills, southern Nyasaland: *Malawi Geol. Surv., Rec. for 1961*, v. **3**.

Vainshtein, E. E., Pozharitskaya, L. K., and Turanskaya, H. W., 1961, Behaviour of the rare earths in the process of formation of carbonatites: *Geochemistry*, v. **11**, pp. 1151–1154 (English transl.).

Van Zijl, P., 1959, *The Geology, Structure and Petrology of the Alkaline Intrusions of Kalkfeld and Okorusu and the Invaded Damara Rocks*: Ph.D. dissertation, Univ. Stellenbosch, Rep. S. Africa.

Van Zijl, P. J., 1962, The geology, structure and petrology of the alkaline intrusions of Kalkfeld and Okorusu and the invaded Damara rocks: *Ann. Univ. Stellenbosch*, v. **37**, ser. A., No. 4, pp. 237–346.

Varne, R., 1966, The petrology of Mount Moroto: *Geol. Soc. London, Proc.* No. 1629, pp. 23–24. (abstract).

Veen, A. H., van der, 1960, The alteration of pyrochlore to fersmite in the Mbeya carbonatite: *Geol. en Mijnbouw*, new ser. 22, Billiton issue, pp. 512–515.

Veen, A. H., van der, 1963, A study of pyrochlore: *Verh. kon. Ned. Geol. Mijn. Genootsch.*, Geol. Ser., v. **22**, pp. 1–188.

Verfaillie, G., 1964, *Léve magnétique en composante verticale du Badberg au Kaiserstuhl*: EURATOM publication EUR, 1827, d, f, e, pp. 211–222.

Verhaeghe, M., 1963, Inventaire des gisements de calcaires, dolomies et travertins du Kivu du Rwanda et du Burundi: *Rép. du Congo Serv. Géol., Mem.* **3**.

Verwoerd, W. J. 1963, Rare-earth minerals in South African carbonatites: *S. Africa Geol. Surv. Ann.*, v. **2** for 1963.

Verwoerd, W. J. (in press a), The carbonatites of South Africa and South West Africa: *S. Africa Geol. Surv., Handbook* No. 6.

Verwoerd, W. J. (in press b), *South African Carbonatites and Their Probable Mode of Origin*: Ph.D. thesis, Univ. Stellenbosch, Rep. S. Africa.

Verwoerd, W. J. (in press c), Die Transvaalse vulkane en hul verwantskap met karbonatit: *Tydskrif. ver Naturwetenskap.*

Verwoerd, W. J. (in press d), The significance of fenitized granite pegmatites in the Spitskop Complex: *Geol. Soc. S. Africa Trans.*

Verwoerd, W. J., and Fosberry, Y. S. (in press), Occurrence of pumpellyite in South Africa: *S. Africa Geol. Surv. Ann.*, v. **2** for 1963, pp. 137–144.

Volotovskaya, N. A., 1958, Magmatic complex of ultrabasic, alkaline and carbonate rocks of the Vuori-Yarvi massif: *Zapiski Wses. Mineralog.*, v. **87**, pp. 290–303 (in Russian).

Volotovskaya, N. A., and Fizhenko, V. V., 1960, The Vuori-Yarvi massif: *Geology of The Union*, v. **37** (in Russian).

Volotovskaya, N. A., and Kukharenko, A. A., 1959, Types of carbonatite deposits and their relationship to massifs of ultrabasic alkaline rocks: *Izvest. Akad. Nauk SSSR., Geol. Ser.*, No. **3**, pp. 110–112 (in Russian).

Vorobyeva, O. A., 1947, Basic structural features of the alkaline intrusion in the Vishnev Mountains: *Izvest. Akad. Nauk SSSR.*, v. **6** (in Russian).

Vorobyeva, O. A., 1960, Alkali rocks of the USSR: *Int. Geol. Congr., 20th sess.*, Pt. **13**, pp. 7–17 (in English).

Wagner, P. A., 1922a, A remarkable rock from the Pretoria Salt Pan: *Geol. Soc. S. Africa Trans.*, v. **25**, pp. 101–106.

Wagner, P. A., 1922b, The Pretoria Salt Pan: a soda caldera: *S. Africa Geol. Surv., Mem.* **20**.

Walter, L. S., Wyllie, P. J., and Tuttle, O. F., 1962, The system $MgO–CO_2–H_2O$ at high pressures and temperatures: *Jour. Petrology*, v. **3**, pp. 49–64.

Wambeke, L. van, 1960, Geochemical prospecting and appraisal of niobium-bearing carbonatites by X-ray methods: *Econ. Geol.*, v. **55**, pp. 732–758.

Wambeke, L. van, *et al.*, 1964, *Les roches alcalines et les carbonatites du Kaiserstuhl*: EURATOM publication EUR, 1827, d, f, e.

Wambeke, L. van, 1964a, *Géochimie Minérale Des Carbonatites du Kaiserstuhl*: EURATOM publication EUR, 1827, d, f, e, pp. 65–91.

Wambeke, L. van, 1964b, *La géochimie des roches du Kaiserstuhl*: EURATOM publication EUR, 1827, d, f, e, pp. 93–192.

Wambeke, L. van, 1965, *A Study of Some Niobium-bearing minerals of the Lueshe carbonatite: deposit*: EURATOM publication EUR, 2110, e.

Wambeke, L. van (in press a), A study of some niobium-bearing minerals of the Lueshe carbonatite deposit: *Int. Min. Assoc.*, 1964 meeting, India.

Wambeke, L. van (in press b), Mineralogical and geochemical evolution of the carbonatites of the Kaiserstuhl, Germany: *Int. Min. Assoc.*, 1964 meeting, India.

Wambeke, L. van, and Wimmenauer, W., 1964, *Conclusions Générales*: EURATOM publication EUR, 1827, d, f, e, pp. 223–232.

Warren, C. H., Allen, J. A., and Connor, M. F., 1917, A titaniferous augite from Ice River, British Columbia: *Am. Jour. Sci.*, ser. 4, v. **43**, pp. 75–78.

Washington, H. S., 1900, Igneous complex of Magnet Cove, Arkansas: *Geol. Soc. America Bull.*, v. **11**, pp. 389–416.

Washington, H. S., 1901, The foyaite-ijolite series of Magnet Cove. A chemical study in differentiation: *Jour. Geol.*, v. **9**, pp. 607–622, 645–670.

Waters, A. C., 1955, Volcanic rocks and the tectonic cycle, in Crust of the Earth: *Geol. Soc. America, Spec. Paper*, v. **62**, pp. 703–722.

Watkinson, D. H., 1965, *Melting Relations in Parts of The System* $Na_2O–K_2O–Al_2O_3–SiO_2–CO_2–H_2O$ *With Applications To Carbonate and Alkalic Rocks*: Ph.D. thesis, Pennsylvania State Univ., U.S.A.

Watkinson, D. H., and Wyllie, P. J., 1964, The limestone assimilation hypothesis: *Nature*, v. **204**, pp. 1053–1054.

Watts, J. T., Tooms, J. S., and Webb, J. S., 1963, Geochemical dispersion of niobium from pyrochlore-bearing carbonatites in Northern Rhodesia: *Inst. Min. Metall. Trans.*, v. **72**, pp. 729–747.

Wayland, E. J., 1920, In *Uganda Geol. Surv. Ann. Rept.*, p. 37.

Williams, C. E., 1950, A preliminary account of the geology of the Sukulu carbonatite complex: *Uganda Geol. Surv. Rec.*, pp. 12–13.

Williams, C. E., 1952, Carbonatite structure: Tororo Hills, Eastern Uganda: *Geol. Mag.*, v. **89**, pp. 286–292.

Williams, C. E., 1956, The origin of carbonatites and related alkaline rocks: *Uganda Geol. Surv., Rec. for 1955*.

Williams, C. E., 1959, *The Sukulu Complex and the Origin of African Carbonatites*: Ph.D. thesis, Univ. of Cape Town, Rep. S. Africa.

Williams, J. F., 1891, The igneous rocks of Arkansas: *Arkansas Geol. Surv., Ann. Rept. for 1890*, v. **2**.

Wimmenauer, W., 1957, *Beiträge zur petrographie des Kaiserstuhls Einführung und Teil I. Neues Jb. f. Min., Abh.*, v. **91**, pp. 131–150.

Wimmenauer, W., 1959a, Abschnitte über petrographie und petrogenese In: *Erläuterungen geologischen exkursionskarte des Kaiserstuhls* 1 : 25,000. Pubd. by Geol. Landesamt Baden–Württemberg.

Wimmenauer, W., 1959b, Beiträge zur petrographie des Kaiserstuhls, Schluss von Teil I, Teile II, un Teile III: *Neues Jb. f. Min., Abh.*, v. **93**, pp. 133–173.

Wimmenauer, W., 1959c, Karbonatite im Kaiserstuhl: *Fortschr. Miner*, v. **37**, pp. 67–69.

Wimmenauer, W., 1962a, Zur petrogenese der eruptivgesteine und karbonatite der Kaiserstuhls: *Neues Jb. f. Miner., Mh.* 1, pp. 1–11.

Wimmenauer, W., 1962b, Beiträge zur petrographie des Kaiserstuhls, Teile IV und V: *Neues Jb. f. Miner., Abh.*, v. **98**, pp. 367–415.

Wimmenauer, W., 1963a, Beiträge zur petrographie des Kaiserstuhls; Teile VI und VII: *Neues Jb. f. Miner., Abh.*, v. **99**, pp. 231–276.

Wimmenauer, W., 1963b, Die stellung der olivin-nephelinite und melilithankaratrite im tertiären vulkanismus Mitteleuropas: *Neues Jahrb. f. Miner., Mh.*, pp. 278–282.

Wimmenauer, W., 1964, *Geologisch–petrographischer Überblick*: EURATOM publication EUR, 1827, d, f, e, pp. 17–30.

Wimmenauer, W. (in press), Carbonatites of the Kaiserstuhl (W–Germany) and their magmatic environment: *Int. Min. Assoc. Proc.*, 1964 meeting, India.

Workman, R., 1911, Calcite as a primary constituent of igneous rocks: *Geol. Mag.*, v. **8**, pp. 193–201.

Wright, J. B., 1963, A note on possible differentiation trends in Tertiary to Recent lavas of Kenya: *Geol. Mag.*, v. **100**, pp. 164–180.

Wyllie, P. J., 1965, Melting relationships in the system $CaO–MgO–CO_2–H_2O$, with petrological applications: *Jour. Petrology.*, v. **6**, pp. 101–123.

Wyllie, P. J., (in press a), Fractional crystallization in synthetic carbonatite magmas: *Int. Min. Assoc.*, 1964 meeting, India.

Wyllie, P. J. (in press b), Experimental data bearing on the petrogenetic links between kimberlites and carbonatites: *Int. Min. Assoc.*, 1964 meeting, India.

Wyllie, P. J., Cox, K. G., and Biggar, G. M. 1962, The habit of apatite in synthetic systems and igneous rocks: *Jour. Petrology.*, v. **3**, pp. 238–243.

Wyllie, P. J., and Biggar, G. M. (in press), Fractional crystalization in the "carbonatite systems" $CaO–MgO–CO_2–H_2O$ and $CaO–CaF_2–P_2O_5–CO_2–H_2O$: *Int. Min. Assoc.*, 1964 meeting, India.

Wyllie, P. J., and Haas, J. L., 1965, The system $CaO–SiO_2–CO_2–H_2O$: 1. Melting relationships with excess vapor at 1 kilobar pressure: *Geochim. et Cosmochim. Acta*, v. **29**, pp. 871–892.

Wyllie, P. J., and Haas, J. L. (in press), The system CaO–SiO$_2$–CO$_2$–H$_2$O: 2. The petrogenetic model: *Geochim. et Cosmochim. Acta.*

Wyllie, P. J., and Raynor, E. J. (in press), D.T.A. and quenching methods in the system CaO–CO$_2$–H$_2$O: *Am. Mineralogist.*

Wyllie, P. J., and Tuttle, O. F., 1959a, Synthetic carbonatite magma: *Nature*, v. **183**, p. 770.

Wyllie, P. J., and Tuttle, O. F., 1959b, Melting of calcite in the presence of water: *Am Mineralogist*, v. **44**, pp. 453–459.

Wyllie, P. J., and Tuttle, O. F., 1960a, The system CaO–CO$_2$–H$_2$O and the origin of carbonatites: *Jour. Petrology.*, v. **1**, pp. 1–46.

Wyllie, P. J., and Tuttle, O. F., 1960b, Experimental verification for the magmatic origin of carbonatites: *Int. Geol. Congr., 21st sess.*, Pt. 13, pp. 310–318.

Wyllie, P. J., and Tuttle, O. F., 1962b, Carbonatitic lavas: *Nature*, v. **194**, p. 1269.

Wyllie, P. J., and Tuttle, O. F., 1963, The quenching technique in non-quenchable systems: a discussion concerning the alleged thermal decomposition of portlandite at high pressures: *Am. Jour. Sci.*, v. **261**, pp. 983–988.

Yashina, R. M., 1953, A new province of alkaline rocks to the south-west of Tuva: *Doklady Akad. Nauk SSSR, Geol. Ser.*, v. **105**, No. 6. (in Russian).

Yashina, R. M., 1957, Alkaline rocks of south-west Tuva: *Izvest. Akad. Nauk SSSR, Geol. Ser.*, No. 5, pp. 17–36 (in Russian).

Zdorik, T. B., and Runov, B. E., 1961, New massif of alkaline rocks and carbonatites to the east of the Aldan Shield: *VAGT*, No. **7** (in Russian).

Zhabin, A. G., 1959, The new type of carbonatite manifestations in connection with the alkaline complex of the Vishnev-Ilmen Mountains: *Doklady Akad. Nauk SSSR*, v. **128** (in Russian).

Zhabin A. G., *et al.*, 1960, Paragenetic associations of accessory rare element minerals in the exomorphic, fenitized rocks of the miascite intrusion in the Vishnev Mountains: *Inst. Min. Geochim. Crystal Chemistry Rare Elements*, No. **4** (in Russian).

Zlatkind, Tz. G., 1945, Olivine turjaites (Kovdorites)—new deep-seated melilite rocks from the Kola Peninsula: *Soviet Geology*, No. **7** (in Russian).

Zlatkind, Tz. G., 1948, The Kovdoro Lake pluton of alkalic and ultrabasic rocks: *Doklady Akad. Nauk SSSR*, v. **117**, pp. 659–661 (in Russian).

Zlatkind, Tz. G., and Shailov, A. J., 1946, Eno-Kovdozero pluton of alkalic and ultrabasic rocks: *Soviet Geology*, v. **12** (in Russian).

Zlenko, N. D., 1961, Late Siniiski intrusions of the central type at the eastern outskirts of the Aldon Shield: *VAGT*, No. **7** (in Russian).

REFERENCES ADDED IN PROOF

Bouwer, R. F., 1957, *The Carbonate Member of The Palabora Igneous Complex:* Cape Town Univ., unpub. dissert.

Broughton, H. J., Chadwick, L. C., and Deans, T., 1950, Iron and titanium ores form the Bukusu Hill alkaline complex, Uganda: *Colon. Geol. Mineral Resources*, v. **1**, pp. 262–266.

Clarke, C. G., and Flegg, A. F., 1966, The Homa volcanic centre: *Geol. Soc. London Proc.*, No. 1629, pp. 26–27 (abstract).

Collins, B., 1966, The igneous centre of the Ruri Hills, Kenya: *Geol. Soc. London Proc.*, No. 1629, p. 24 (abstract).

Dixon, J. A., 1966, The North Ruri carbonatite complex: *Geol. Soc. London Proc.*, No. 1629, pp. 24–25 (abstract).

Findlay, A. L., 1966, The Rangwa centre and the Kisingiri volcano: *Geol. Soc. London Proc.*, No. 1629, pp. 27–28 (abstract).

King, B. C., 1966, Volcanism in eastern Africa and its structural setting: *Geol. Soc. London Proc.*, No. 1926, pp. 16–19 (abstract).

Kirchheimer, F., 1957, Bericht über das vorkommen von Uran in Baden—Württemberg: *Abh. Geol. Landesamt Baden—Württemberg*, v. **2**, pp. 1–127.

Kirchheimer, F., 1959, Über radioaktive und uranhaltige Thermal-sedimente, inbesondere von Baden—Baden: *Abh. Geol. Landesamt Baden—Württemberg*, v. **3**, pp. 1–67.

Le Bas, M. J., 1966, The intrusive and volcanic centres of the Wasaki area, West Kenya: *Geol. Soc. London Proc.*, pp. 25–26 (abstract).

McKie, D., 1962, Goyazite and Florencite from two African carbonatites: *Mineralog. Mag.*, v. **33**, pp. 281–297.

Macgregor, A. M., 1947, An outline of the geological history of Southern Rhodesia: *S. Rhodesia Geol. Surv., Bull.* **38.**

Moore, E. S., 1932, Goudreau and Michipicoten gold areas, District of Algoma: *Ontario Dept. Mines, Ann. Rept.* v. **40**, pt. 4.

Shand, S. J., 1931, The granite-syenite-limestone complex of Palabora, Eastern Transvaal and the associated apatite deposits: *Geol. Soc. S. Africa Trans.*, v. **34**, pp. 81–105.

Sturt, B. A., and Ramsay, 1965, The alkaline complex of the Breivikbotn area, Sørøy, Northern Norway: *Norges geol. Undersök.*, No. 231.

Sutherland, D. S., 1966, Intrusive complexes and volcanism in eastern Uganda: *Geol. Soc. London Proc.*, No. 1629, pp. 20–23 (abstract).

Whitworth, T., 1953, A contribution to the geology of Rusinga Island, Kenya: *Geol. Soc. London Quart. Jour.*, v. **109**, pp. 75–96 (abstract).

Whitworth, T., 1961, The geology of Mfanganu Island and western Kenya: *Overseas Geol. Min. Resources*, v. **8**, pp. 150–190.

Wilkinson, P., 1966, The Kilimanjaro—Meru Region: *Geol. Soc. London Proc.*, No. 1629, pp. 28–30 (abstract).